GREAT EVENTS
FROM
HISTORY II

GREAT EVENTS FROM HISTORY II

Science
and
Technology
Series

Volume 4
1952-1969

Edited by

FRANK N. MAGILL

SALEM PRESS

Pasadena, California   Englewood Cliffs, New Jersey

Library of Congress Cataloging-in-Publication Data
Great events from history II. Science and technology
series / edited by Frank N. Magill.
    p.   cm.
Includes bibliographical references and index.
    1. Science—History—20th century. 2. Technology—
History—20th century. I. Magill, Frank Northen, 1907-

Q125.G825 1991
509'.04—dc20
ISBN 0-89356-637-3 (set)   91-23313
ISBN 0-89356-641-1 (volume 4)   CIP

PRINTED IN THE UNITED STATES OF AMERICA

92-0370

LIST OF EVENTS IN VOLUME IV

1952   Wilkins Introduces Reserpine for the Treatment of
High Blood Pressure 1429

1952-1956   Müller Develops the Field Ion Microscope 1434

1952   Bevis Describes Amniocentesis as a Method for Disclosing
Fetal Genetic Traits 1439

1952   Salk Develops a Polio Vaccine 1444

1952   Baade Corrects an Error in the Cepheid Luminosity
Scale 1449

1953   De Vaucouleurs Identifies the Local Supercluster
of Galaxies 1454

1953   Du Vigneaud Synthesizes Oxytocin, the First
Peptide Hormone 1459

1953   Miller Reports the Synthesis of Amino Acids 1465

1953-1959   Liquid Bubble Chamber Is Developed, The 1470

1954-1957   Backus' IBM Team Develops the FORTRAN Computer
Language 1475

1954   Barghoorn and Tyler Discover 2-Billion-Year-Old
Microfossils 1481

1954   Bell Telephone Scientists Develop the Photovoltaic Cell 1487

1955   Franklin and Burke Discover Radio Emissions from
Jupiter 1492

1955   Ryle Constructs the First Radio Interferometer 1496

1956   First Transatlantic Telephone Cable Is Put Into
Operation, The 1502

1956   Heezen and Ewing Discover the Midoceanic Ridge 1508

1956   Birth Control Pills Are Tested in Puerto Rico 1512

1957   Isaacs and Lindenmann Discover Interferons 1517

1957   Sabin Develops an Oral Polio Vaccine 1522

1957   Sony Develops the Pocket-Sized Transistor Radio 1528

1957   Bardeen, Cooper, and Schrieffer Explain
Superconductivity 1533

1957   Jodrell Bank Radio Telescope Is Completed, The 1539

1957   Sputnik 1, the First Artificial Satellite, Is Launched 1545

1957   Esaki Demonstrates Electron Tunneling in
Semiconductors 1551

1957   United States Opens the First Commercial Nuclear
Power Plant, The 1557

1958   Donald Is the First to Use Ultrasound to Examine
Unborn Children 1562

1958   Sanger Wins the Nobel Prize for the Discovery of the
Structure of Insulin 1567

1958   Van Allen Discovers the Earth's Radiation Belts 1572

1958   Parker Predicts the Existence of the Solar Wind 1577

1958   United States Launches Its First Orbiting Satellite,
Explorer 1, The 1583

1959   Corroded Mechanism Is Recognized as an Ancient
Astronomical Computer, A 1588

1959   Hopper Invents the Computer Language COBOL 1593

1959   Radio Astronomy Team Sends and Receives Radar Signals
to and from the Sun, A 1598

1959   Leakey Finds a 1.75-Million-Year-Old Fossil Hominid 1603

1959   St. Lawrence Seaway Is Opened, The 1608

1959   Luna 2 Becomes the First Man-Made Object to Impact
on the Moon 1614

1959   Luna 3 Provides the First Views of the Far Side of
the Moon 1619

1960's   Anthropologists Claim That Ecuadorian Pottery Shows
Transpacific Contact in 3000 b.c. 1624

1960's   Plastic IUD Is Introduced for Birth Control, The 1629

1960's   Sperry Discovers That Each Side of the Brain Can
Function Independently 1635

1960   Mössbauer Effect Is Used in the Detection of
Gravitational Redshifting, The 1640

1960   Scientists Develop a Technique to Date Ancient Obsidian 1645

1960-1962 Hess Concludes the Debate on Continental Drift 1650

1960-1969 Vaccine Is Developed for German Measles, A 1655

1960   Oró Detects the Formation of Adenine from
Cyanide Solution 1662

1960   Tiros 1 Becomes the First Experimental Weather
Reconnaissance Satellite 1667

1960   First Laser Is Developed in the United States, The 1672

1960   Echo, the First Passive Communications Satellite, Is
Launched 1677

1961   Horsfall Announces That Cancer Results from
Alterations in the DNA of Cells 1682

1961   Nirenberg Invents an Experimental Technique That
Cracks the Genetic Code 1687

1961   Gagarin Becomes the First Human to Orbit Earth 1693

1961   Shepard Is the First United States Astronaut in Space 1698

1961	Calvin Wins the Nobel Prize for His Work on Photosynthesis	1703
1962	Giacconi and Associates Discover the First Known X-Ray Source Outside the Solar System	1708
1962	Lasers Are Used in Eye Surgery for the First Time	1714
1962-1967	Renfrew, Dixon, and Cann Reconstruct Ancient Near Eastern Trade Routes	1718
1962	Glenn Is the First American to Orbit Earth	1723
1962	Telstar, the First Commercial Communications Satellite, Relays Live Transatlantic Television Pictures	1728
1962-1963	Mariner 2 Becomes the First Spacecraft to Study Venus	1734
1962	Carson Publishes *Silent Spring*	1740
1963	Cassette for Recording and Playing Back Sound Is Introduced, The	1746
1963	Cohen Shows That Cantor's Continuum Hypothesis Is Independent of the Axioms of Set Theory	1751
1963	Schmidt Makes What Constitutes the First Recognition of a Quasar	1757
1963-1965	Penzias and Wilson Discover Cosmic Microwave Background Radiation	1762
1964	Quarks Are Postulated by Gell-Mann and Zweig	1767
1964-1965	Kemeny and Kurtz Develop the BASIC Computer Language	1772
1964-1965	Doell and Dalrymple Discover the Magnetic Reversals of Earth's Poles	1777
1964	Verrazano Bridge Opens, The	1782
1965	First Space Walk Is Conducted from Voskhod 2, The	1787
1965	Sealab 2 Expedition Concludes, The	1792
1965-1966	Venera 3 Is the First Spacecraft to Impact on Another Planet	1797
1965	Orbital Rendezvous of Gemini 6 and 7 Succeeds, The	1803
1966	Ardrey's *The Territorial Imperative* Argues That Humans Are Naturally Territorial	1808
1966	Simons Identifies a 30-Million-Year-Old Primate Skull	1814
1966	Soviet Luna 9 Makes the First Successful Lunar Soft Landing, The	1819
1966	Lunar Orbiter 1 Sends Back Photographs of the Moon's Surface, The	1825
1967	Davis Constructs a Solar Neutrino Detector	1830
1967	Favaloro Develops the Coronary Artery Bypass Operation	1835
1967	Manabe and Wetherald Warn of the Greenhouse Effect and Global Warming	1840
1967	Mandelbrot Develops Non-Euclidean Fractal Measures	1845

1967-1968 Barghoorn and Coworkers Find Amino Acids in
3-Billion-Year-Old Rocks 1851
1967 Kornberg and Coworkers Synthesize Biologically
Active DNA 1857
1967-1968 Bell Discovers Pulsars, the Key to Neutron Stars 1862
1967 Barnard Performs the First Human Heart Transplant 1866
1968 Friedman, Kendell, and Taylor Discover Quarks 1871
1968 *Glomar Challenger* Obtains Thousands of Ocean Floor
Samples, The 1876
1968 Wheeler Names the Phenomenon "Black Holes," 1881
1969 Bubble Memory Devices Are Created for Use in
Computers 1886
1969 Soyuz 4 and 5 Spacecraft Dock in Orbit, The 1891

1969-1970 First Jumbo Jet Service Is Introduced, The 1897
1969-1974 Very Long Baseline Interferometry (VLBI) Is Developed
for High-Resolution Astronomy and Geodesy 1902

CHRONOLOGICAL LIST OF EVENTS LXIII

GREAT EVENTS
FROM
HISTORY II

WILKINS INTRODUCES RESERPINE FOR THE TREATMENT OF HIGH BLOOD PRESSURE

Category of event: Medicine
Time: 1952
Locale: Boston, Massachusetts

Wilkins studied reserpine's unique blood pressure lowering effects, providing clinical medicine with a versatile and effective tool

Principal personages:
ROBERT WALLACE WILKINS (1906-   ), an American physician and clinical researcher who pioneered drug therapies for vascular and mental disorders
WALTER E. JUDSON (1916-   ) a colleague of Wilkins at Boston University who collaborated in the reserpine research

Summary of Event

Excessively elevated blood pressure, clinically known as hypertension, has long been recognized as a pervasive and serious human malady. In a few cases, hypertension is recognized as an effect brought about by discrete pathologies. Often, however, elevated blood pressure, or essential hypertension, occurs as the result of yet unknown specific causes. Despite this etiologic uncertainty, unattended hypertension leads to potentially dramatic health problems, including increased risk to kidney and heart disease and stroke. Risk is clearly related to the intensity of blood pressure elevation.

Recognizing the need to treat hypertension in a relatively straightforward and effective way, Robert Wallace Wilkins, a clinical researcher at Boston University's School of Medicine and the head of Massachusetts Memorial Hospital's Hypertension Clinic, began to experiment with reserpine in the early 1950's. Initially, samples made available to Wilkins were crude and unpurified. Eventually, the purified drug, reserpine, was used without exceptional changes relative to those observed with crude preparations. Reserpine has a long and fascinating history from use, both clinically and in folk medicine, in India. The source of reserpine is the root of the shrub *Rauwolfia serpentina*, first mentioned in Western medical literature in the 1500's but virtually unknown or at least unaccepted outside India until the mid-twentieth century. Crude preparation of *Rauwolfia serpentina* had been used for a variety of ailments in India for centuries prior to its first mention in the West. Not until the purification of reserpine in 1952 and the serious clinical consideration of Wilkins and his associate Walter E. Judson did *Rauwolfia serpentina* become a meaningful adjunct in modern medical practice.

Wilkins' work with the drug did not begin on an encouraging note because reserpine's actions do not take hold rapidly. This slowness of action had been known from the Indian literature. The standard observation in Western pharmacotherapy, however, was that most drugs work rapidly, within a few hours or days; if, for example, a week has elapsed without positive effects being shown by a drug, chances are not high that it will work at all. Additionally, physicians and patients alike, shouldered with the fear and uncertainty that accompanies difficult health problems, are looking for rapid improvement or at least indications that a turn for the better is nearing. Reserpine is deceptive in this temporal context. Wilkins and his coworkers nearly fell into the trap of time. First, in working with crude preparations of *Rauwolfia serpentina*, they were becoming quite pessimistic until a patient who had been treated for many consecutive days began to show symptomatic relief. Nevertheless, only after months of treatment did Wilkins become a strong believer in the drug's beneficial effects. The tendency to expect quick breakthroughs is so powerful that a parallel series of events ensued when pure preparations of reserpine became available in 1952. At first, reserpine did not appear to be the active agent of crude preparations; doubts began to grow among the clinical staff. Yet, when heart rate and blood pressure began to drop after a few weeks, the investigators could see that reserpine was producing results that generally could not be distinguished from crude preparations. It is interesting to note that reserpine is not the only drug to act slowly; the tricyclic antidepressants are notoriously slow in action, and the same uncertainties on the part of patients, investigators, and clinicians have been observed with these drugs too.

Once reserpine's activity began, Wilkins observed a number of important and unique consequences. Whether using the crude drug preparation or pure reserpine, the two most meaningful measures of blood pressure were significantly reduced in trial patients at the Hypertension Clinic at the Massachusetts Memorial Hospital. These two parameters are known as systolic blood pressure and diastolic blood pressure. Systolic pressure represents the peak of produced pressure in the arteries following a contraction of the heart. Diastolic pressure is the low point determined while the heart is resting. To lower the mean blood pressure in the system effectively, both of these contributory pressures must be reduced. Administration of low doses of reserpine produced an average drop in pressure of about 15 percent, a figure considered less than dramatic but still highly significant. A complex phenomenon such as blood pressure is determined by a multitude of factors, including the resistance of the arteries, the force of contraction of the heart, and the rate of the heart's beating. Coincident with the overt lowering of blood pressure, reserpine also reduced heart rate by about 15 percent, providing an important auxiliary action.

In the early 1950's, when reserpine was undergoing intense study by Wilkins, other therapeutic drugs were in use for hypertension. Noted examples included hexamethonium and the compound veratrum. Wilkins recognized almost immediately that reserpine's major contribution was likely to be as a drug to add to this therapeutic cast as opposed to an agent that would be used alone. His studies established that reserpine, plus at least one of the drugs already in use, produced an additive effect in lowering blood pressure. Indeed, at times the drug combinations produced more than an additive effect, or synergism. This type of effect occurs when the combination of drugs produces an effect that exceeds the simple arithmetic addition of the expected results of the individual drugs when administered alone. Wilkins also discovered that reserpine's particular value as an adjunct with other agents was caused by its particular dose responsiveness in the therapeutic realm. Although the drug is rather potent (producing wanted effects at a low dose), as the dose is increased further, reductions in blood pressure are difficult to achieve. Yet, as the dose is moved upward, the probability of side effects does tend to increase in a predictable fashion. Remarkable among these adverse effects are weight gain, diarrhea, nasal congestion, occasional reports of impaired sexual activity in males, and infrequent cases of unusual mental effects. Thus, the best use of reserpine was when it could be used in a low dose to avoid its toxicity, but in combination with other drugs to produce additive therapeutic effects.

Wilkins believed that reserpine's most unique effects were not those found directly in the cardiovascular system but those produced indirectly by the brain. Hypertension is often accompanied by neurotic anxiety, which is both a consequence of the justifiable fears of future negative health changes brought on by prolonged high blood pressure and contributory to the high blood pressure itself. Wilkins' patients invariably felt better mentally, were less anxious, and were sedated, but in an unusual sense. Reserpine made patients drowsy, but typically would not produce sleep, or if sleep occurred, it was reversed easily. These multiple mental effects are recognized now as characteristic of tranquilizing drugs, or antipsychotics; Wilkins attempted to control for these mental effects by using a traditional sedative-hypnotic drug, phenobarbital, in some of the patient groups under study. Phenobarbital, however, produced no observable antihypertensive effects versus placebo, while reserpine did. Although both drugs gave a type of sedation, the sedation was qualitatively different in the two cases. In effect, Wilkins had discovered, serendipitously, a new and important category of drugs, the tranquilizers.

Impact of Event

Reserpine holds a vital position in the historical development of antihypertensive drugs for two main reasons: First, it was the initial drug discovered to have wide-ranging effects in blocking the consequences in nerves, both in the brain and in the peripheral nervous system, which utilize norepinephrine or its close relative dopamine as transmitter substances. Drugs that interfere with this part of nervous system activity include one of the four major categories of modern antihypertensive drugs; reserpine remains an important member of this drug group. Second, reserpine was the first drug of any type to achieve broadly based clinical acceptance, use, and success. By 1950, many different drugs, some of them quite effective, were being used to treat hypertension. None, however, received massive support by physicians. Reserpine's introduction provided the first central theme for therapeutic use because it gave at least some effectiveness in most patients. This near universal effectiveness is caused by the drug's ability to act centrally and peripherally and to the central role the biogenic amines, especially norepinephrine, play in hypertension.

Research that followed Wilkins' seminal discoveries has uncovered reserpine's mechanism of action. Biogenic amines such as norepinephrine are stored in nerve terminals by being safely packaged into membranous sacs known as vesicles. Reserpine has high affinity for these storage sites, displacing the stored amines and, because of persistent binding, preventing the storage of newly synthesized amines. Thus, reserpine depletes the system of biogenic amines. Since the nerves using biogenic amines as transmitters critically control such parameters as blood vessel resistance, heart rate, force of heart contraction, and the brain's input to these peripheral actions, transmitter depletion lowers blood pressure by collectively reducing these factors. Concomitantly, reserpine's clinical efficacy led to a deeper understanding of both the way that nerves work and the means of controlling cardiovascular function. Thus, an important therapeutic drug becomes important also as a pharmacological tool. The drug's ability to deplete biogenic amine terminals of transmitter in a dose-responsive way has become an indispensable means of testing for biogenic amine involvement by neuroscientists.

Since the 1950's, medical science has rigorously explored the nature of cardiovascular function and diseases of the cardiovascular system such as hypertension. Many new factors have been identified in the genesis of hypertension. The role of salt balance, involvement of fatty substances such as cholesterol, hormonal action such as in the case of angiotensin, and the role of stress have all been recognized as vital components of a sophisticated physiological network. Nevertheless, despite all the new complications, cardiovascular activity is regulated at a basic level by the nervous system. Control of diet and life-style help tremendously in dealing with hypertension. Yet, without control of the nervous system, many cases of high blood pressure will remain problematic. Reserpine, a refined drug from a bushy Indian plant, has become one of the world's best-known drugs. This transition from crude natural product to the forefront of medical technology is grand testimony to the power of nature's synthetic machinery that produces molecules of vast utility and intrigue.

Bibliography

Comroe, Julius H., Jr. *Exploring the Heart: Discoveries in Heart Disease and High Blood Pressure.* New York: W. W. Norton, 1983. Comroe, one of the twentieth century's greatest cardiopulmonary physicians and researchers, is the director of the National Pulmonary Faculty Training Center at the University of California, San Francisco. He has produced a philosophically sensitive, beautifully illustrated, and conceptually brilliant history of medicine's attempts to understand better the heart and to bring its various diseases under control.

Gilman, Alfred G., et al., eds. *Goodman and Gilman's The Pharmacological Basis of Therapeutics.* 8th ed. New York: Macmillan, 1990. No book in the history of pharmacological study has made the impact of this tome, written for years by Gilman's father and the renowned Louis Goodman. Reserpine's basic actions, its clinical use in cardiovascular disease and psychiatry, in addition to parallel coverage of all other well-known drugs, are presented in exemplary fashion.

Lynch, James J. *The Language of the Heart: The Body's Response to Human Dialogue.* New York: Basic Books, 1985. Lynch, a professor of psychology at the University of Maryland School of Medicine, has written a book of unusual importance in a way that is extremely accessible to the nontechnical reader. He postulates how events in the psychosocial realm impact cardiovascular health and disease.

Trease, George Edward, and William Charles Evans. *Pharmacognosy.* 12th ed. London: Bailliere Tindall, 1983. The first edition of this classic book was published more than fifty years ago. It contains not only the standard characterization of a natural product such as reserpine and related alkaloids but also the broadest spectrum available of drugs derived from nonsynthetic sources.

Wilkins, Robert W., et al. "Reserpine in the Treatment of Hypertension." *The New England Journal of Medicine* 250 (1954): 477-478. This short article specifically compares the effects of crude *Rauwolfia serpentina* with pure reserpine. This movement from crude natural product to pure drug occurs virtually without exception in the development of drugs from natural sources in the context of modern Western medicine.

Wilkins, Robert W., and Walter E. Judson. "The Use of *Rauwolfia Serpentina* in Hypertensive Patients." *The New England Journal of Medicine* 248 (1953): 48-53. Extensive results of clinical testing and comparison with drugs in use at the time and history are presented.

Keith Krom Parker

Cross-References

Wilkins Discovers Reserpine, the First Tranquilizer (1950's), p. 1353; Favaloro Develops the Coronary Artery Bypass Operation (1967), p. 1835; Barnard Performs the First Human Heart Transplant (1967), p. 1866.

MÜLLER DEVELOPS THE FIELD ION MICROSCOPE

Category of event: Physics
Time: 1952-1956
Locale: University Park, Pennsylvania

Müller achieved atomic resolution with the field ion microscope, an improved version of his field emission microscope

Principal personages:
ERWIN WILHELM MÜLLER (1911-1977), a physicist, engineer, and research professor who was a recipient of many awards
J. ROBERT OPPENHEIMER (1904-1967), an American physicist who suggested that hydrogen atoms could be ionized in an electric field

Summary of Event

In the early twentieth century, developments in physics, especially quantum mechanics, paved the way for the application of new theoretical and experimental knowledge to the problem of viewing the atomic structure of metal surfaces. Of primary importance were George Gamow's 1928 theoretical explanation of the field emission of electrons by quantum mechanical means, and J. Robert Oppenheimer's 1928 prediction of the quantum mechanical ionization of hydrogen in a strong electric field.

In 1936, Erwin Wilhelm Müller developed his field emission microscope, the first in a series of instruments which would exploit these developments. It was to be the first instrument to view directly atomic structures, although not the individual atoms themselves. Müller's 1951 field ion microscope utilized the same basic concepts used in the field emission microscope, yet proved to be a much more powerful and versatile instrument. By 1956, Müller's invention allowed him to view the crystal lattice structure of metals in atomic detail by actually showing the constituent atoms.

The field emission and field ion microscopes examine the atomic surface structures of metals by viewing their projections on fluorescent screens. Since the field ion microscope is the direct descendant of the field emission microscope, it is essential to gain a basic understanding of the field emission microscope in order to understand the field ion microscope. In the case of the field emission microscope, the images are projected by electrons emitted directly from the tip of a metal needle, which constitutes the specimen under investigation. These electrons produce an image of the atomic lattice structure of the needle's surface. The needle serves as the electron donating electrode in a vacuum tube, also known as the cathode. A fluorescent screen serves as the electron receiving electrode, or the anode, and is placed opposite the needle. When a sufficient electrical voltage is applied across the cathode and anode, the needle tip emits electrons, which strike the screen. The image produced on the screen is a projection of the electron source—the needle surface's atomic lattice structure.

Two of the most important parameters in assessing the power of any microscope are magnification and resolution. While the former is a measure of the size of the smallest objects which the microscope can make visible, the latter measures the accuracy of the instrument. A microscope that has a magnification of one hundred times will make objects appear one hundred times larger than they are in reality. A microscope with a resolution of 2 millimeters can distinguish objects that are separated by a distance of 2 millimeters. Objects separated by less than 2 millimeters will not be seen as distinct objects. The electron emission process influences both of these parameters and would ultimately preclude the field emission microscope from depicting the images of individual metal atoms within the lattice.

Müller studied the effect of needle shape on the performance of the microscope throughout much of 1937. He discovered that the magnification of a field emission microscope depends upon the ratio of the fluorescent screen radius to the metal emitter radius. The more precise the tip of a needle is, the smaller its radius will be. The smaller this measure becomes, the larger the ratio of the screen radius to emitter radius becomes, and hence, the higher the magnification becomes.

When the needles had been properly shaped, Müller was able to realize magnifications of up to 1 million times. This magnification allowed Müller to view what he called "maps" of the atomic crystal structure of metals, since the needles were so small that they were often composed of only one simple crystal of the material. While the magnification may have been great, however, the resolution of the instrument was severely limited by the physics of emitted electrons, which caused the images Müller obtained to be continually blurred.

In 1943, while working in Berlin, Müller realized that the resolution of the field emission microscope was limited by two factors: the velocity of the electrons and their associated de Broglie wavelengths, a development of contemporary quantum mechanics which noted that entities, such as electrons, behave both as particles and as waves.

The electron velocity, a particle property, was extremely high and uncontrollably random, causing the micrographic images to be blurred. In addition, the electrons had an unsatisfactorily high wavelength. When Müller combined these two factors, he was able to determine that, theoretically, the resolution of the field emission microscope would never reach below 20 angstroms. This may seem quite small. In fact, a resolution of 20 angstroms is equal to a resolution of 0.000000002 meter. Müller noted, however, that the atoms in an atomic crystal lattice are separated by only 4 to 5 angstroms. Thus, the field emission microscope could never depict single atoms, for it was a physical impossibility for it to distinguish one atom from another.

By 1951, this limitation led him to develop the technology behind the field ion microscope. In 1952, Müller moved to the United States and founded the Pennsylvania State University Field Emission Laboratory. He perfected the field ion microscope from 1952 to 1956.

The field ion microscope utilized positive ions instead of electrons to create the atomic surface images on the fluorescent screen. By introducing an easily ionized gas, at first hydrogen, but usually helium, neon, or argon, into the evacuated tube, the emitted electrons ionized the gas atoms, creating a stream of positively charged particles, much like Oppenheimer had predicted in 1928. Müller has admitted that the use of positive ions (as opposed to electrons) to produce the image of the emitter lattice seemed to be unconventional. It involved more than switching the polarity of the field emission microscope by making the emitter cathode the anode, and the screen anode the cathode to produce a stream of positive particles. Given the limitations imposed by the quantum mechanical properties of electrons, it seemed that the larger and more massive ions would only compound the electron's inherent resolution problems. Yet, larger and more massive objects have much smaller wavelengths than less massive ones. Therefore, Müller's use of positive ions circumvented one of the resolution problems inherent in the use of imaging electrons. Like the electrons, however, the positive ions traversed the tube with unpredictably random velocities. Müller eliminated this problem by the cryogenic cooling of the needle tip with a supercooled liquefied gas such as nitrogen or hydrogen.

An essential difference between the field emission microscope and other microscopes is that the imaging medium—the electrons—actually comes from the specimen under examination: the metal needle. Positive ions will not travel through a metal crystal like the negatively charged electrons, because in the presence of an electric field, electrons are the conductors of electricity. Thus, the problem that presented itself to Müller was how to utilize the superior imaging properties of positive ions which, unlike the electrons of the field emission microscope, did not emit directly from the metal sample.

By 1956, Müller had perfected the means of supplying imaging positive ions by filling the vacuum tube with an extremely small quantity of an inert gas such as helium, neon, or argon. By using such a gas, Müller was assured that no chemical reaction would occur between the needle tip and the gas, for any reaction would alter the surface atomic structure of the needle and thus alter the resulting microscopic image.

The imaging process works largely because of the extremely high positive electrical potential present at the needle tip. Whereas the field emission microscope generated negative potentials at the emitter tip of approximately 40 million volts per centimeter, the field ion microscope generated positive potentials exceeding ten times that amount, approaching 500 million volts per centimeter. At this field strength, the atoms of the inert gas transfer one of their electrons to the needle. When this occurs, the atoms giving up an electron become positive ions and are accelerated by the electrical field toward the screen, where they create images of their place of origin on the emitter tip. The imaging ions allowed the field ion microscope to image the emitter surface to a resolution of between two and three angstroms, making it ten times more accurate than its close relative, the field emission microscope.

Impact of Event

The immediate impact of the field ion microscope was its influence on the study of metallic surfaces. It is a well-known fact of materials science that the physical properties of metals are influenced by the imperfections in their constituent lattice structures. In the early twentieth century, Max von Laue had demonstrated the existence of this structure by a process known as X-ray diffraction, actually altering the path of X rays in the presence of the lattice. The ability of actually viewing the atomic structure of the lattice, and thus the finest detail of any imperfection, evaded scientists until the field ion microscope. The field ion microscope is the only instrument powerful enough to view the structural flaws of metal specimens in atomic detail.

While the instrument may be extremely powerful, therefore, the extremely large electrical fields required in the imaging process preclude the instrument's application to all but the heartiest of metallic specimens. The field strength of 500 million volts per centimeter exerts an average stress on metal specimens in the range of almost 1 ton per square millimeter. Metals such as iron and platinum can withstand this strain because of the shape of the needles into which they are formed. Yet, this limitation of the instrument made it extremely difficult for the examination of biological materials, which cannot withstand the amount of stress that metals can. A practical by-product in the study of field ionization—field evaporation—eventually permitted scientists to view large biological molecules.

Müller's study of field ionization led to a useful by-product in the discovery of field evaporation. When the electrical field is increased beyond the limit required for the ionization of the imaging gas, individual atoms begin to shed, or "field evaporate," from the needle tip. When metal specimens are induced to field evaporate, the needle sheds the constituent atoms which are nearest the surface and, consequently, often combined with other materials. In the absence of these impurities, a field evaporated specimen remains, offering the scientist the best opportunity to view the pure metal's crystal structure.

In addition to the ability to view uncontaminated crystal structures, field evaporation also allowed surface scientists to view the atomic structures of biological molecules. By embedding molecules such as phthalocyanine within the metal needle, scientists have been able to view the atomic structures of large biological molecules by field evaporating much of the surrounding metal until the biological material remained at the needle surface.

Bibliography

Müller, Erwin W. "The Field Ion Microscope." *American Scientist* 49 (March, 1961): 88-98. This article is the most easily accessible of Müller's writings on the field ion microscope. It presents some introductory material on the physical limitations of the field emission microscope which eventually led to the field ion microscope's development. In addition, the lay reader should have no difficulty with the details of the field ion imaging process. The article is amply illustrated and contains a concise description of the uses and achievements of the instrument.

_____. "Field Ion Microscopy." *Science* 149 (August, 1965): 591-600. This article presents the technical details of the technology and the physics behind the field ion microscope. For the reader interested in a more technical introduction to the subject, this article contains much information on the theoretical and practical limitations and abilities of the field ion microscope. It also contains an important section on artifacts created by the imaging process.

_____. "The Imaging Process in Field Ion Microscopy from the FEM to the Atom Probe." In *Chemistry and Physics of Solid Surfaces,* edited by Ralf Vanselow and S. Y. Tong. Cleveland: CRC Press, 1977. Müller traces the history of the field emission and field ion microscopes and includes illustrations and micrographs from his original German publications. For those interested in the technical details of the applications of the field ion microscope, this is undoubtedly the finest source available.

Müller, Erwin W., and Tien Tzou Tsong. "Fundamentals of Field Ion Microscopy." In *Field Ion Microscopy: Principles and Applications.* New York: Elsevier, 1969. Müller's most comprehensive account of the application of his inventions in the field of surface science. The introductory chapter gives a concise account of the historical events leading to the development of both instruments. The bibliography at the end of this chapter is especially useful to those interested in the original German papers on the field emission and field ion microscopes.

Oudar, Jacques. "Recent Methods in the Study of Adsorption." In *Physics and Chemistry of Surfaces.* Glasgow: Blackie and Son, 1975. Devoted exclusively to the study of adsorption, Oudar details the use of both the field emission and the field ion microscopes in surface studies. Adequately illustrated, although sparse in technical content. This is a text devoted primarily to the theories of surface science and their subsequent testing, not the technology used in the laboratory.

William J. McKinney

Cross-References

Zsigmondy Invents the Ultramicroscope (1902), p. 159; Thomson Wins the Nobel Prize for the Discovery of the Electron (1906), 356; Bohr Writes a Trilogy on Atomic and Molecular Structure (1912), p. 507; Rutherford Presents His Theory of the Atom (1912), p. 527; Ruska Creates the First Electron Microscope (1931), p. 958; Müller Invents the Field Emission Microscope (1936), p. 1070.

BEVIS DESCRIBES AMNIOCENTESIS AS A METHOD FOR DISCLOSING FETAL GENETIC TRAITS

Category of event: Medicine
Time: February 23, 1952
Locale: Saint Mary's Hospital, Manchester, England

Bevis described amniocentesis, removal of amniotic fluid from the expectant mother; this endeavor contributed to its use as a tool for diagnosis of fetal maturity, health, and genetic defects

Principal personages:
> DOUGLAS BEVIS, an English physician who described amniocentesis, while assessing the risk factors in fetuses of Rh-negative women impregnated by Rh-positive men
> AUBREY MILUNSKY, an American pediatrician who specialized in current examination of the prenatal diagnosis of hereditary disorders

Summary of Event

At the beginning of a human pregnancy—conception—an egg and a sperm unite to produce the fertilized egg that will become a new human being. After conception, the fertilized egg passes from the oviduct into the uterus, while dividing and becoming an organized cluster of cells capable of carrying out different tasks in the nine-month-long group of events that will convert it to a newborn baby.

About a week after conception, the cluster of cells, now a vesicle containing the future human embryo, attaches to the uterine lining, penetrates it, and becomes intimately intertwined with uterine tissues. In time, the merger between the vesicle and the uterus results in formation of a placenta that connects the mother and the baby-to-be, the embryo, and an amniotic sac filled with the amniotic fluid in which the embryo floats.

Eight weeks after conception, the embryo (now a fetus) is about 2.5 centimeters long and possesses all the anatomic elements that will be present in the newborn baby. Next, it must grow and all the details that are expected in a baby will be perfected. At this time, about two and one-half months after her last menstruation, the expecting mother visits a physician and finds out that she is pregnant. At this time, expecting mothers begin to worry about possible birth defects in the babies they carry. Diabetic mothers and mothers over thirty-five years of age have higher than usual chances of delivering babies who have birth defects.

Many other factors inferred from the medical history an expecting mother provides to her physician can indicate the possible appearance of birth defects. In some cases, these birth defects may be so serious that the termination of the pregnancy may need to be considered. Disorders that produce extreme mental damage or fatal genetic disease can cause great havoc in affected families. In cases such as these, tragedy can be averted sometimes via therapeutic abortion where the data clearly support it.

In other cases, knowledge of possible physical problems in a fetus may allow their treatment—in the uterus—and save the newborn from problems that could persist throughout life or lead to death in early childhood. Information is obtained through the examination of the amniotic fluid in which the fetus is suspended throughout pregnancy. The process for obtaining this fluid is called amniocentesis. Amniocentesis, then, is a technique that may be used to allow physicians to examine the health and the presence or absence of genetic defects in human fetuses before they are born. Whenever a genetic defect is suspected, amniocentesis is performed. Usually, sixteen-week-old fetuses are used because it is a generally safe time to carry out the procedure, samples of amniotic fluid large enough for detailed analysis can be obtained without harming the fetus, and an adequate time period is available for completion of necessary genetic and biochemical studies soon enough for elective abortion, if necessary.

Amniocentesis also is utilized as a method for assessing the well-being and maturity of a fetus. In such cases, the procedure is carried out later in the pregnancy and may be repeated at appropriate intervals, when needed. For example, amniocentesis is required to assess fetal lung maturity when fetal respiratory distress syndrome is suspected. Modern amniocentesis, even where repeated, is relatively simple and is reported to result in a risk factor of less than 1 percent for mother and fetus.

Amniocentesis is carried out in several steps. First, the placenta is located by the use of ultrasound techniques. Then, the participating physician locates the fetus by abdominal palpation. Next, the expecting mother is given a local anesthetic and a 20-gauge needle is inserted carefully into the amniotic sac. As soon as amniotic fluid is seen, a 20 milliliter sample (about four teaspoons) is drawn into a hypodermic syringe and the syringe is removed. Amniocentesis is reported to be painless, and most patients feel only a little abdominal pressure during the procedure.

The amniotic fluid of early pregnancy resembles blood serum. As pregnancy continues, its content of substances from fetal urine and other fetal secretions increases. The fluid also contains fetal cells from skin, gastrointestinal, reproductive, and respiratory tracts. Therefore, it is of great diagnostic use. Immediately after the fluid is removed from the fetus, the fetal cells are separated out. Then, the cells are used for genetic analysis, and the amniotic fluid is examined by various biochemical techniques.

One important positive use of the amniotic fluid from amniocentesis is determination of its lecithin and sphingomyelin content. Lecithins and sphingomyelins are two types of body lipids (fatlike molecules) that are useful diagnostic tools. Lecithins are important because they are essential components of the so-called pulmonary surfactant of mature lungs. The pulmonary surfactant acts at lung surfaces to prevent the collapse of the lung air sacs (alveoli), when a person exhales. Subnormal lecithin production in a fetus indicates that it most likely will exhibit respiratory distress syndrome or a disease called hyaline membrane disease after birth. Both diseases can be fatal, so it is very valuable to determine whether fetal lecithin levels are adequate for appropriate lung function in the newborn baby. This is particularly important in fetuses being carried by diabetic mothers, who frequently produce newborns with such problems. The important measurement made in such at-risk infants is the ratio of the amounts of lecithin and sphingomyelin.

Fetuses unlikely to suffer respiratory distress syndrome have ratios around 2.0. Fetuses with ratios of 1.5 or less are likely candidates for the problem. Often, when amniocentesis identifies the risk of respiratory distress syndrome, the fetus in question is injected with hormones that help it to produce a mature lung. This effect is then confirmed by repeated use of amniocentesis. Many other problems caused by abnormal biochemical events can be assessed by the use of amniocentesis.

Advanced maternal age—pregnancy in women over thirty-five—is viewed by many as a leading basis for prenatal analysis by amniocentesis. The primary fears are chromosomal disorders; it has been reported that 0.5 percent of all liveborn children possess a major chromosomal abnormality. These diseases can be diagnosed by examination of fetal cells cultured from samples taken by amniocentesis. A particular fear is Down's syndrome (mongolism) and its resultant severe mental retardation. The incidence of this disease is about 0.004 percent in the children of twenty-year-old mothers and 3 percent in children of mothers who are more than forty-five years old. Other diseases that can be identified by similar chromosomal analysis include spina bifida, ancephaly, and Klinefelter's syndrome. Several of these disorders can be corrected while the fetus is still in the uterus, if diagnosed early enough. Where such treatment is not possible, the diagnosis makes it possible to identify the need for therapeutic abortion on the basis of the genetic data. Therefore, amniocentesis can be a very useful tool.

While some practitioners report that amniocentesis has been used since the 1920's, Douglas Bevis is credited widely as doing landmark research in the area. This endeavor was reported in February, 1952. Bevis described the technique and showed that it could be used to identify the risk of hemolytic disease in fetuses carried by Rh-negative women impregnated by Rh-positive men. The diagnostic tools used were the iron and urobilinogen content of the amniotic fluid. These chemicals arise from breakdown of blood in the at-risk fetus.

Impact of Event

For thousands of years, the inability to see or touch a fetus in the uterus was a staggering problem in obstetric care and in the diagnosis of the future mental and physical health of human offspring. A beginning to the solution of this problem occurred on February 23, 1952, when *Lancet* published a study called "The Antenatal Prediction of Hemolytic Disease of the Newborn." This study, carried out by Bevis, described use of amniocentesis for the assessment of the risk factors found in fetuses of Rh-negative women impregnated by Rh-positive men. The article is viewed by many as a landmark in medicine that led to the development of the wide use of amniocentesis as a tool for diagnosing fetal maturity, fetal health, and fetal genetic defects.

In the years that have followed Bevis' original observation, many improvements in the methodology of amniocentesis and the techniques used in the genetic and biochemical information obtained have led to refinement of outcomes of its use. Presently, hundreds of debilitating hereditary diseases can be diagnosed—and some can be ameliorated—by the examination of amniotic fluid and fetal cells isolated by amniocentesis. For many parents who have had a child afflicted by some hereditary disease, the use of the technique has become a major consideration in family planning. Furthermore, many physicians recommend strongly that all mothers over the age of thirty-four be tested by amniocentesis.

According to many researchers in the field, the basis for use of amniocentesis and prenatal analysis by "older" mothers is the larger number of at-risk children that are born. For example, more than 50 percent of babies afflicted by Down's syndrome are born of women who become pregnant at age thirty-five or older. The cost to society in both parental anguish and in dollars is staggering. The emotional cost is clear. It is estimated that about eight thousand seriously defective children are born to about 0.5 million mothers over the age of thirty-five each year in the United States. Aubrey Milunsky, a pediatrician, calculated that the yearly cost of institutional care for defective children would exceed $2 billion. In contrast, intervention in their birth, including prenatal diagnosis in older mothers, would cost $63 million.

There remains the question of whether such solutions are morally appropriate, but parents—and society—now have a choice resulting from the techniques that have developed since Bevis' 1952 observation. It is also hoped that these techniques will lead to means for correcting and preventing the diseases and preclude the need for considering the therapeutic termination of any pregnancy. It should be stressed that procedures that enable biochemical and surgical correction of hereditary diseases diagnosed in the fetus occur already (for example, respiratory distress syndrome).

Bibliography

Bevis, Douglas C. A. "The Antenatal Prediction of Hemolytic Disease of the Newborn." *Lancet* 1 (February 23, 1952): 395-398. The article describes Bevis' original work on amniocentesis and shows its utility to identify the risk of hemolytic disease of fetuses in Rh-negative women impregnated by Rh-positive men. Diagnosis is via iron and urobilinogen in amniotic fluid, noted as arising from breakdown of blood in the at-risk fetus. Implications of the work are discussed.

Filkins, Karen, and Joseph F. Russo. *Human Prenatal Diagnosis*. New York: Marcel Dekker, 1985. This text is written in an attempt to "clarify and rationalize aspects of diagnosis, genetic counseling, and intervention," and can be used as a guide to health professionals who care for pregnant women. Fourteen chapters by experts in the field cover topics absent in other texts available, such as the use of DNA analysis.

Milunsky, Aubrey. *The Prenatal Diagnosis of Hereditary Disorders*. Springfield, Ill.:

Charles C Thomas, 1973. This book details the practice and use of amniocentesis; the chromosomal/sex-linked and biochemical hereditary disorders, congenital malformations, genetic counseling, and the implications of genetics to society. Detailed listings of the basis for many hereditary diseases are included. In addition, almost nine hundred references are cited.

Reed, George B., Albert E. Claireaux, and Murray D. Bain, eds. *Diseases of the Fetus and Newborn: Pathology, Radiology, and Genetics*. St. Louis: C. V. Mosby, 1989. This authoritative and detailed text is aimed primarily at physicians. Nevertheless, it contains many topics of use to other qualified readers, including exposition of many related disease processes, description of the pathology of the main body systems, radiologic methods, and many topics in medical genetics and prenatal diagnosis.

Tucker, Susan M., and Sandra Bryant. *Fetal Monitoring and Fetal Assessment in High-Risk Pregnancy*. St. Louis: C. V. Mosby, 1978. This book highlights many important aspects of fetal monitoring. Its chapters on biophysical monitoring, biochemical monitoring, electronic monitoring, and nursing care/selected pattern interpretation provide much information to the interested reader. Descriptions of equipment, methodology, and data are included.

Verp, Marion S., and Albert B. Gerbie. "Amniocentesis for Pre-Natal Diagnosis." *Clinical Obstetrics and Gynecology* 24 (1981): 1007-1021. This brief technical review of amniocentesis covers a wide area in a concise manner. Topics discussed include counseling, composition of amniotic fluid, use of ultrasound, amniocentesis procedure, technical problems, risks of amniocentesis, and Rh sensitization. Seventy-five useful references are included for readers who need detailed information.

Sanford S. Singer

Cross-References

Sutton States That Chromosomes Are Paired and Could Be Carriers of Hereditary Traits (1902), p. 153; Sturtevant Produces the First Chromosome Map (1911), p. 486; Donald Is the First to Use Ultrasound to Examine Unborn Children (1958), p. 1562; Clewell Corrects Hydrocephalus by Surgery on a Fetus (1981), p. 2174; Daffos Uses Blood Taken Through the Umbilical Cord to Diagnose Fetal Disease (1982), p. 2205.

SALK DEVELOPS A POLIO VACCINE

Category of event: Medicine
Time: July 2, 1952
Locale: University of Pittsburgh, Pennsylvania

Salk developed the first vaccine that could prevent paralytic poliomyelitis (polio),
contributing invaluably to the virtual eradication of polio epidemics

> *Principal personages:*
> JONAS EDWARD SALK (1914-   ), an American physician, immunolo-
> gist, and virologist whose polio vaccine was the first effective preven-
> tative for polio
> THOMAS FRANCIS, JR. (1900-1969), an American microbiologist who
> was Salk's mentor in the study of the influenza virus; in charge of
> evaluation of the field trials of the Salk vaccine

Summary of Event

Poliomyelitis (polio) is an infectious disease that can adversely affect the central nervous system, causing paralysis and great muscle wasting in serious cases. It is caused by the destruction of motor neurons (nerve cells) in the spinal cord. Epidemiologists believe that polio has existed since ancient times, and evidence of its presence in Egypt, circa 1400 B.C., has been presented. Fortunately, the Salk vaccine and the later Sabin vaccine prevent the disease. Consequently, except in underdeveloped nations, polio is rare nowadays. Yet, once a person develops polio, there is still no cure for it. Fortunately, a large number of polio cases end without paralysis or any observable effect.

Polio is often called infantile paralysis. This results from the fact that it is most often seen in children. It is caused by a virus and begins with body aches, a stiff neck, and other symptoms that are very similar to those of a severe case of influenza. In some cases, within two weeks after its onset, the course of polio begins to lead to muscle wasting and paralysis. Even though other communicable diseases strike more people each year than polio, very few of them are viewed with more fear, because almost none produce such drastic, long-lasting consequences.

On April 12, 1955, the world was thrilled with the announcement that Jonas Edward Salk's poliomyelitis vaccine could prevent the disease. It was reported that schools were closed in celebration of this event, many universities awarded Salk honorary degrees, he was given a Congressional Medal, and France made him a member of the Legion of Honor. Salk, the son of a New York City garment worker, had become one of the most well known and publicly venerated medical scientists in the world.

Vaccination is a method of disease prevention whereby a small amount of a virus is injected into the body to prevent a viral disease by immunization. The process depends on the production of antibodies (body proteins that prevent the disease) in response to the vaccination. Vaccines are made of weakened or killed virus preparations. The technique of vaccination was pioneered, in 1796, by Edward Jenner, an English physician who prepared a vaccine for smallpox. Jenner used the weak, cowpox virus in his vaccine and made smallpox, which had killed 60 million people in the eighteenth century, rare in civilized countries.

Salk's work, leading to the development of the polio vaccine, began in 1938. At that time he was a senior medical student at New York University Medical School. There, he came into contact with the famous microbiologist Thomas Francis, Jr., who was studying methods for developing a "flu vaccine" by killing influenza viruses without loss of their ability to stimulate antibody production. Salk worked with him for several months, learning many of the important techniques of immunology and virology. Salk received a National Research Council fellowship to work with Francis, and their collaboration led to production of an effective flu vaccine used during World War II.

In 1947, Salk became the head of the Virus Research Laboratory at the University of Pittsburgh School of Medicine. He continued his efforts to produce much better influenza vaccine and began to study polio. Salk's first work on polio involved participation in identification of the number of distinct types of polio virus that existed among the 125 strains that had been observed by the scientific community. This endeavor was part of a multicenter study carried out at the University of Pittsburgh (by Salk), the University of Kansas (by Herbert A. Wenner), the University of Utah (by Louis P. Gebhardt), and the University of Southern California (by John F. Kessel). This information was required before a polio vaccine could be attempted, because it would tell researchers how many different types of virus the public needed to be protected against. After a long, arduous effort, Salk and his associates found that all of the known strains of polio virus belonged to three distinct groups (Types I, II, and III). Therefore, production of a totipotent polio vaccine required immunization against three viral types.

Actualization of the Salk vaccine was aided tremendously by the earlier work of the Harvard University microbiologists, John F. Enders, Frederick Chapman Robbins, and Thomas H. Weller. These scientists developed the first practical means to grow large quantities of polio virus outside the body, by the use of monkey kidney tissue cultures. Before their discovery, it had been possible to prepare only small quantities of the virus. The Salk vaccine was produced in two steps: First, polio viruses were grown in monkey kidney tissue cultures, similar to those of Enders and his coworkers. Then, these polio viruses were killed by treatment with just the right amount of formaldehyde to produce an effective vaccine. The killed-virus polio vaccine was found to be safe and to cause the production of antibodies against the disease, a sign that proved it should prevent polio.

In early 1952, Salk tested a prototype vaccine against Type I polio virus on children who were afflicted with the disease and were thus deemed safe from reinfection. This test showed that the vaccination greatly elevated the concentration of polio antibodies in these children. On July 2, 1952, encouraged by these results, Salk vaccinated forty-three children who had never had polio with vaccines against each of the three virus types. Vaccines against Type I, Type II, and Type III virus were given to thirty, two, and eleven children, respectively. All inoculated children produced high levels of polio antibodies and none of them developed the disease. Consequently, the vaccine appeared to be both safe in humans and likely to become an effective public health tool.

In 1953, Salk reported these findings in the *Journal of the American Medical Association*. In April, 1954, nationwide testing of the Salk vaccine began, via the mass vaccination of American schoolchildren. This effort was directed and evaluated by Salk's former mentor, Thomas Francis. It involved three test groups of six- to nine-year-old children. The first group was composed of nearly 423,000 children, who each received three, spaced-out vaccine innoculations. The 1.3 million doses of Salk vaccine used were produced by five pharmaceutical companies. Another, similar-sized group of children was given placebo injections (placebo is a treatment that contains no medication, given for comparison with a drug treatment being tested). Finally, a third, large group of children was observed but not injected. The results of the trial were electrifying. The vaccine was safe, and it greatly reduced the incidence of the disease. In fact, it was estimated that Salk's vaccine gave the schoolchildren 60 to 90 percent protection against polio.

Salk was instantly praised. Then, several cases of polio occurred as a consequence of the vaccine. Its use was immediately suspended by the Surgeon General, pending a complete examination. Soon, it was evident that all the cases of vaccine-derived polio were attributable to faulty batches of vaccine made by one pharmaceutical company. Salk and his associates were in no way responsible for the problem. Appropriate steps were taken to ensure that such an error would not be repeated and the Salk vaccine was again released for use by the public.

Impact of Event

The first reports on the polio epidemic occurred on June 27, 1916, when one hundred residents of Brooklyn, New York, were afflicted. Soon, the disease had spread. By August, 27,000 people had developed polio. Nearly seven thousand afflicted people died, and many survivors of the epidemic were permanently paralyzed to varying extents. In New York City alone, nine thousand people developed polio and two thousand died. Chaos reigned as large numbers of terrified people attempted to leave and were turned back by the police. Smaller polio epidemics occurred throughout the nation in the years that followed (for example, the Catawba County, North Carolina, epidemic of 1944). A particularly horrible aspect of polio was the fact that more than 70 percent of polio victims were small children. The summer months became a dreaded time for children likely to catch polio. Adults caught it too; the most famous of these adult polio victims was Franklin D. Roosevelt. There was no cure for the disease. The best available treatment was physical therapy.

As of August, 1955, more than 4 million polio vaccines had been given. The Salk vaccine appeared to work very well. This can be shown by comparison of the number of cases reported in 1955 and 1956, 28,985 and 14,647, respectively. It appeared that polio was being conquered. By 1957, the number of cases reported nationwide had fallen to 5,894. Thus, in two years, its incidence had dropped by about 80 percent.

This was very exciting, and soon other countries clamored for the vaccine. By 1959, ninety other countries had been supplied with the Salk vaccine. Worldwide, the disease was being eradicated, and nowadays it is quite rare.

Salk received many honors, including honorary degrees from American and foreign universities, the Lasker Award, a Congressional Medal for Distinguished Civilian Service, and membership in the French Legion of Honor. Yet, he received neither the Nobel Prize nor membership in the American National Academy of Sciences. It is believed by many that this neglect was a result of the personal antagonism of some of the members of the scientific community who strongly disagreed with his theories of viral inactivation.

Bibliography

Berg, Roland H. *Polio and Its Problems.* Philadelphia: J. B. Lippincott, 1948. The book gives a pre-Salk vaccine view of polio, including frightening national polio epidemics, the antipolio campaign by the National Foundation for Infantile Paralysis, and false starts toward chemical cures and polio vaccines. Useful physical therapy for polio victims, including that used at the Warm Springs Foundation and Sister Kenney's work are also explored.

Carter, Richard. *Breakthrough: The Saga of Jonas Salk.* New York: Trident Press, 1965. This biography carefully describes Salk's life and the saga of development of the polio vaccine. It is realistic and includes both Salk's triumphs and tribulations. It also outlines the stages of development of victory against polio.

Cohn, Victor. *Sister Kenney: The Woman Who Challenged the Doctors.* Minneapolis: University of Minnesota Press, 1975. This biography describes the life work of nurse Sister Elizabeth Kenney, whose treatment of polio victims revolutionized polio physical therapy, the only avenue of treatment until the Salk vaccine. It emphasizes her ability and describes her battle to win support for a therapeutic procedure that was superior to that used by physicians of the time.

Kovacs, Ernest. *The Biochemistry of Poliomyelitis Viruses.* New York: Pergamon Press, 1964. This book describes various aspects of the purification, biochemistry, and epidemiology of polio viruses. It also deals with the state of cells infected with polio viruses and the role of heredity in polio. The book is most useful to readers who desire detailed information on the viruses. It contains more than one thousand references.

Melnick, Joseph L. "Poliomyelitis." In *McGraw-Hill Encyclopedia of Science and Technology.* 6th ed. New York: McGraw-Hill, 1987. This brief summary of poliomyelitis presents a description of polio virus and its host range, the pathology of polio, the methodology for its diagnosis, and brief descriptions of the Salk and

Sabin vaccines. References are given for additional information on tissue culture, animal viruses, and the polio vaccines.

Rowland, John. *The Polio Man: The Story of Dr. Jonas Salk*. New York: Roy, 1960. This brief, chatty biography of Jonas Salk is best suited for young readers. Yet, it contains interesting information about Salk and the development of the Salk vaccine. One of its strongest points is the development of Salk's career.

Sanford S. Singer

Cross-References

Rous Discovers That Some Cancers Are Caused by Viruses (1910), p. 459; Calmette and Guérin Develop the Tuberculosis Vaccine BCG (1921), p. 705; Zinsser Develops an Immunization Against Typhus (1930), p. 921; Theiler Introduces a Vaccine Against Yellow Fever (1937), p. 1091; Isaacs and Lindenmann Discover Interferons (1957), p. 1517; Sabin Develops an Oral Polio Vaccine (1957), p. 1522; A Vaccine Is Developed for German Measles (1960), p. 1655; A Genetically Engineered Vaccine for Hepatitis B Is Approved for Use (1986), p. 2326; A Gene That Can Suppress the Cancer Retinoblastoma Is Discovered (1986), p. 2331.

BAADE CORRECTS AN ERROR IN
THE CEPHEID LUMINOSITY SCALE

Category of event: Astronomy
Time: August, 1952
Locale: Rome, Italy

Baade reconciled the several puzzling discrepancies in the distance determinations to nearby galaxies by proposing that the Cepheid luminosity scale was in error

Principal personages:
WALTER BAADE (1893-1960), an astronomer at the Mount Wilson and Palomar observatories who was a pioneer in the determination of the distances to the nearest galaxies, the evolution of stars and galaxies, and the nature of the populations of stars
EDWIN POWELL HUBBLE (1889-1953), an American astronomer who is best known as the discoverer of separate galaxies and of the expansion of the universe
ALLAN REX SANDAGE (1926-   ), a successor to Hubble and explorer of the extragalactic distance scale, galaxy evolution, and stellar ages
HARLOW SHAPLEY (1885-1972), an astronomer who pioneered the study of star clusters and galaxies

Summary of Event

The meeting of the International Astronomical Union held in Rome, Italy, in August, 1952, was rocked by a remarkable announcement by an attendee from California, Walter Baade of the Mount Wilson and Palomar observatories. Baade revealed, to the great surprise of many in attendance, that the universe must be twice as big as had been thought previously. This important discovery resulted from Baade's many years of painstaking work on the famous Andromeda galaxy, and other nearby members of the local group of galaxies, in which he found (and eventually solved) several very puzzling discrepancies.

The first of these discrepancies had been noted by Edwin Powell Hubble in the 1930's. He had discovered that the Andromeda galaxy seemed to contain more than a hundred fuzzy objects that he identified as most likely star clusters similar to the globular star clusters of Earth's Milky Way galaxy. These objects have hundreds of thousands of stars as members and occupy a volume of space that is approximately 50 light-years in diameter (a light-year is the distance that light travels in one year, approximately 10 billion kilometers). Hubble noticed, however, that the globular clusters of the Andromeda galaxy appeared to be, on the average, only a quarter as luminous as those of our galaxy. He also noticed that the explosive stars called novas that existed in the Andromeda galaxy never reached the high intrinsic brightnesses that Earth's Milky Way galaxy local novas exhibited. (Novas are double stars, one member of which is a collapsed, high-density object, which periodically erupt brilliantly when gas from the normal star falls onto the surface of the collapsed star, causing a nuclear detonation.)

In the early 1940's, Hubble, as well as most of the other astronomers at the Mount Wilson Observatory, left to do defense work. Baade, however, being a German citizen, was not allowed to do such work, so he stayed at the observatory as almost the only scientist. This provided him with a rare opportunity to use the largest telescope in the world, the Mount Wilson 254-centimeter reflector, for unlimited amounts of time. Furthermore, the frequent "black outs" of Los Angeles that occurred during World War II meant that the skies of Mount Wilson were often much darker than usual because the bright light interference that the city caused was not present. A consequence of these two circumstances was that Baade was able to take exquisite photographs of the Andromeda galaxy, far better than had been taken before. To Baade's consternation, these photographs did not show what he was trying to find: the central population of red stars of the Andromeda galaxy. According to all that is known about stellar populations in our galaxy, he should have seen easily some of these objects on his Andromeda plates, but they were not there. The white pulsating stars called RR Lyrae stars should have been visible, as should have the old, red giant stars that populate the old globular clusters of Earth's Milky Way. Baade, however, had one more trick to try. Reasoning that the red giant stars should be easier to detect on red light-sensitive photographic emulsions than the usual blue-sensitive ones, he tried these in the telescope, finding that they offered also the advantage of allowing longer exposures, up to eight hours in length. Success was at hand; the red plates showed the long-sought-after red giant stars, which were scattered throughout the images of the Andromeda galaxy, though concentrated mostly toward the central areas.

Baade's detection of the red giant stars in Andromeda did not solve any puzzles, however; it merely added to them, because the stars were four times fainter than they should have been. The reason for this strange discrepancy became, therefore, a puzzle. It was not known if the stars in different galaxies were all fundamentally different; as a result, knowledge gained about nearby stars could not be reliably extended to those in other galaxies. The other reason was that the method of measuring the distance to other galaxies, including the Andromeda galaxy, was in serious error. These reasons were attacked by Baade; he realized gradually that the various types of stellar populations must be understood first.

Until Baade's work on the Andromeda galaxy and its small companion galaxies, astronomers recognized no clear distinctions between populations of stars. It was known that stars with different characteristics seemed to exist in different star clusters, but it was a mystery as to why, and no real order to the chaos was evident. Astronomers hoped that, in general, stars did not differ too much from place to place, so that a reasonable amount of uniformity could be assumed when exploring various parts of the universe.

From 1943, when Baade first saw the red giant stars in Andromeda, to 1952, when he announced the solution to the puzzle, Baade concentrated on the problem of understanding the differences between stars in different environments. The final clue came from an unexpected source: two dwarf galaxies discovered in the southern skies by the Harvard astronomer Harlow Shapley. Named the Sculptor and Fornax dwarfs, these strange, low-luminosity objects seemed to have only red stars similar to those of the globular clusters and none of the bright blue stars found in the Milky Way and Andromeda galaxies. Thus, they represented a particular stellar population that was very different from the population of normal stars near the sun. Baade realized that this separation of stellar populations might be the key to the puzzle of the Andromeda galaxy: If there are two different populations of stars, then the principle of uniformity may not work, and the distance to Andromeda may be incorrect.

The distance to Andromeda had been established many years before by Hubble, who used what is called the "Cepheid period-luminosity scale." This important correlation had been discovered in 1914 by the Harvard astronomer Henrietta Swan Leavitt, who was studying periodically varying stars called Cepheids, which, because of their pulsations in size, vary in brightness every few days. Leavitt found that the Cepheids in a nearby galaxy named the Small Magellanic Cloud showed a remarkable correlation between their apparent brightnesses and their periods, such that the longest-period stars were the brightest. Because all the stars in the Small Magellanic Cloud are at about the same distance from Earth's Milky Way, then the true luminosities of Cepheid variables must be related to their periods. Furthermore, if the distance to even one Cepheid can be measured somehow, then the distances to all the other Cepheids can be determined simply by applying Leavitt's scale. Also, if a Cepheid in another galaxy can be discovered, then the distance to that galaxy can be found. The problem that faced astronomers who wanted to use the period-luminosity scale was the difficulty of measuring the distance to any Cepheid. All were found to be too distant (even the nearest ones in our galaxy). Shapley, however, found a way to overcome the difficulty. He showed that the globular clusters contain both Cepheid variables and RR Lyrae stars, so that the comparative luminosities of these two kinds of stars could be established. Fortunately, there were enough RR Lyrae stars near Earth's Milky Way that it was possible to measure their distances using accurate, geometrical methods. Therefore, they provided the bridge that calibrated the Cepheids' period-luminosity scale, and this relationship became an extremely important tool for measuring distances to galaxies. It was this method that Hubble had used to measure Andromeda's distance, which he found to be 900,000 light-years.

Baade realized in 1952 that his division of stellar types into two populations meant that there must be two types of Cepheids: those that existed in "normal" sunlike populations, which he called population I, and those that existed in globular clusters (and in the Sculptor and Fornax galaxies), which he called population II. If the population II Cepheids were intrinsically four times fainter than the population I Cepheids, then all the discrepancies and puzzles about the Andromeda galaxy would disappear. Baade concluded that the most reasonable explanation was that the Cepheid period-luminosity scale was incorrect and that all distances based on it must be underestimated by a factor of two. Thus, by announcing this discovery, Baade doubled the distance to the Andromeda galaxy and doubled the size of the universe.

Impact of Event

Baade's 1952 revision of the extragalactic luminosity scale was more than a simple correction of an error of the past. In addition to the direct impact that it had on cosmological problems of distances and sizes, it also signaled the beginning of the understanding of the physical differences between stars of different types. Astronomers began to understand better the life histories of stars that make up the different populations; with this understanding came a more reliable and sophisticated use of the principle of uniformity. It became clear that astronomers must understand the physical reasons for stellar differences before they can use the principle in other environments, because these reasons may show where the principle must be either modified or abandoned.

The doubling of the size of the universe was important. At the time of Baade's announcement, cosmology was in a fairly primitive stage, involving many assumptions and very little data. The size scale was one of these data, and it was a very essential part of the question of the nature of the cosmos. Also doubled were the sizes of the galaxies. Until 1952, it appeared that the Milky Way galaxy was an unusually large object, almost unique in its size. After Baade corrected the distances, however, it was seen that other galaxies were often as large and luminous as the Milky Way, and thus we were not seen to be in a special place, which was a situation that, since the time of Copernicus, was always a source of discomfort to astronomers.

The understanding of stellar populations and their differences was also important. Allan Rex Sandage, Baade's student and a disciple of Hubble, carried on the task of making stellar evolution an integral part of the study of galaxies. This led to a much better understanding of galaxies, their distances, their different types, and their evolution. With this understanding, astronomers now can use the Cepheid period-luminosity law reliably, after adjusting it for the known effects of different elemental abundances, different ages, and different galaxies' histories. Furthermore, other types of distance criteria can be used to plumb the depths of the universe, ones that could not have been considered if Baade had not introduced the importance of different population types and the importance of understanding the physical reasons for their differences.

Bibliography

Abell, George O. *Exploration of the Universe.* 4th ed. Philadephia: Saunders College Publishing, 1982. This elementary textbook has the best coverage of historical events up to the 1980's of any of the many astronomy texts. Abell knew and worked with Baade at Mount Wilson and Palomar observatories and writes about the topic of this essay with authority.

Baade, Walter. *Evolution of Stars and Galaxies.* Cambridge, Mass.: Harvard University Press, 1963. Baade published very little during his lifetime, but after his retirement from the Mount Wilson and Palomar observatories, he gave a series of lectures at the Harvard College Observatory, which were tape-recorded and transcribed. He died before editing the text, but Cecilia Payne-Gaposchkin, who had attended the lectures and who was a masterful writer, rewrote the transcriptions into one of the most interesting and readable books on galaxies.

Hodge, Paul. *Galaxies.* Cambridge, Mass.: Harvard University Press, 1986. A book for the interested layperson, this volume covers the distance scale, the population types, the nature of galaxies, and cosmology. It is fully illustrated.

Hubble, Edwin. *The Realm of the Nebulae.* New York: Dover, 1958. Based on a series of lectures given in 1936 at Yale University, this is Hubble's only book-length manuscript and his only attempt to put the entirety of his many fundamental discoveries about galaxies and the universe before the public. It is still a readable and fascinating book, one that can put the importance of Baade's later work in perspective.

Rowan-Robinson, Michael. *The Cosmological Distance Ladder.* New York: W. H. Freeman, 1985. Although this book is intended primarily for readers familiar with the technical details of modern astronomy, there are several sections that can be read with facility by nonscientists, especially chapter 1, which covers the history of the extragalactic luminosity scale.

Whitney, Charles A. *The Discovery of Our Galaxy.* New York: Alfred A. Knopf, 1971. This masterpiece of popular science is one of the best examples of astronomical history ever published. It discusses the entire subject of the recognition of our galaxy and its relationship with other galaxies, covering the Baade distance scale revision particularly deftly.

Paul Hodge

Cross-References

Leavitt's Study of Variable Stars Unlocks Galactic Distances (1912), p. 496; Hertzsprung Uses Cepheid Variables to Calculate the Distances to Stars (1913), p. 557; Shapley Proves the Sun Is Distant from the Center of Our Galaxy (1918), p. 655; Eddington Formulates the Mass-Luminosity Law for Stars (1924), p. 785; Hubble Demonstrates That Other Galaxies Are Independent Systems (1924), p. 790; Hubble Confirms the Expanding Universe (1929), p. 878.

DE VAUCOULEURS IDENTIFIES THE
LOCAL SUPERCLUSTER OF GALAXIES

Category of event: Astronomy
Time: 1953
Locale: Mount Stromlo Observatory, Australia

De Vaucouleurs observed the local supercluster of galaxies, sparking the study of the large-scale structure of the universe

Principal personages:

GÉRARD HENRI DE VAUCOULEURS (1918-), a French-born American astronomer who was the first to identify the local supercluster of galaxies

GEORGE OGDEN ABELL (1927-1983), an American astronomer who compiled a catalog of 2,712 clusters of galaxies

CHARLES DONALD SHANE (1895-1983), an American astronomer and director of Lick Observatory

CARL ALVAN WIRTANEN (1910-), an American astronomer whose photography and galaxy counts provided the basis for a map of the distribution of galaxies

JERZY NEYMAN (1894-1981), an American statistician and educator who worked on many applications of statistics to the distribution of galaxies in space

ELIZABETH LEONARD SCOTT (1917-), an American astronomer and statistician who worked on the distribution of galaxies in space

Summary of Event

Astronomers were able to observe dim patches of light, or nebulas, in the sky long before they discovered the nature of these nebulas, which today are known to be galaxies. Several early observers made lists or catalogs of these objects; for example, in 1888, Johann Louis Emil Dreyer's *New General Catalogue of Nebulae and Clusters of Stars.*

In the early 1920's, a debate over the nature of the so-called spiral nebulas came to a head and was resolved. (These nebulas received their name from their spiral shape.) One school of thought was that these spiral nebulas were pieces of the earth's star system, the Milky Way—relatively nearby, small objects. Another theory held that they were distant, very large, independent star systems. In 1924, Edwin Powell Hubble was able to settle the debate by determining the distance to one of the spiral nebulas, the Andromeda nebula. The distance he found was a large one, which indicated that the nebula was, in fact, a huge system, independent of the Milky Way. Harlow Shapley, in the 1920's, discovered the dimensions and rough structure of the Milky Way galaxy, and the work of Hubble and Shapley brought about the beginnings of the present picture of the universe: The Milky Way is a spiral galaxy in a universe that contains other galaxies of various shapes and sizes.

Astronomers began to study how galaxies are distributed in the sky. They did this by examining plates of the sky taken with large telescopes over long exposure times, which revealed many galaxies. They then counted the galaxies and noted their positions. Some of this work was done with photographs taken using traditional methods. The sky surveying process was changed in 1930 when the Schmidt camera was developed by Bernhard Schmidt. Large areas of sky could be photographed relatively quickly using this new camera, and it became easier for astronomers to make detailed surveys of the entire sky. Whether done with the Schmidt camera or with traditional methods, surveys of the night sky were a useful piece of work done by the new large telescopes in the first half of the twentieth century.

The sky surveys revealed interesting information about the way that galaxies appear to be distributed in space. Even before the nature of the spiral nebulas was known, astronomers had noted that spiral nebulas appear in clusters. The positions given in Dreyer's catalog reveal this information, and in 1922, a band of nebulas stretching nearly 40 degrees across the northern sky was observed by the English astronomer J. H. Reynolds. Knut Lundmark also noted this feature. (These may be considered the first observations of the local supercluster, although the observers did not identify or study what they observed.) In addition to identifying the local group (a group of nearby galaxies, of which the Milky Way is a part), astronomers identified other groupings of galaxies. The Coma cluster and the Virgo cluster of galaxies were defined and named for the constellations in which they appear. Hubble photographed faint galaxies, so faint that he thought he was seeing as far into the universe as he could and that he was witnessing a limit to the phenomenon of clustering. An earlier scheme proposed by C. V. L. Charlier suggested that there was a hierarchy of structure to the universe, with clusters of galaxies, making up clusters of clusters, which in turn made up still larger structures. Hubble's observations seemed to indicate that this hierarchy was not likely to exist.

By 1950, astronomers had gathered enough information about clusters of galaxies that they could arrive at a consensus on the general features of the clusters, such as the types of galaxies they contained and the sizes of the clusters. The largest cluster known was the Coma cluster, which contained more than one thousand individual galaxies. The galaxies in clusters were mostly elliptical galaxies (rounded or oval in shape, with no distinguishing structural features), and spirals without much spiral arm structure. Astronomers had also identified so-called field objects: isolated galaxies, mostly spirals, that did not appear to belong to any cluster. It had been suggested that perhaps the group of galaxies in the Virgo area of the sky might contain more than one cluster, but Hubble's work with faint galaxies seemed to rule out any hierarchical scheme of clustering of clusters.

It was on the basis of a sky survey, completed at Lick Observatory between 1947 and 1954 by Charles Donald Shane and Carl Alvan Wirtanen, that Elizabeth Leonard Scott and Jerzy Neyman applied the techniques of statistics to the question of the large-scale structure of the universe. Between 1952 and 1954, they published several papers regarding the probabilistic laws that describe clustering, posited that all galaxies belong to clusters, and mentioned the existence of "clouds" of galaxies, which was their term for superclusters. George Ogden Abell, at the University of California, Los Angeles, used plates taken with a Schmidt camera on Mount Palomar to make a catalog of 2,712 clusters of galaxies, and his work indicated that many of the clusters seemed to be members of superclusters. Fritz Zwicky, using the plates from the same sky survey, arrived at a different conclusion, similar to Hubble's: that the clusters do not form still larger clusters. Yet, Zwicky's clusters were, in general, larger than Abell's, and a single cluster could contain several centers of concentration, so perhaps he defined as a cluster what Abell would have called a supercluster.

In the early 1950's, Gérard Henri de Vaucouleurs first defined and described what is called the local supercluster. De Vaucouleurs went to work at the Mount Stromlo Observatory in Australia to update the Shapley-Ames catalog of bright galaxies, a standard tool for astronomers. While doing this work, he observed that the local group was located at the edge of a much larger grouping of clusters of galaxies. He referred to this larger grouping as a supergalaxy, and further estimated that other supergalaxies or "clouds," as he also referred to them, might exist as well. De Vaucouleurs estimated the local supercluster to be approximately 50 million light-years across and to be roughly disk shaped. The supercluster is centered on the Virgo cluster of galaxies, about 50 million light-years distant, and the local group of galaxies is a relatively remote outrider of the supercluster. De Vaucouleurs also identified what appeared to be another supercluster, which he called the southern supergalaxy; he posited that the local supercluster is neither unique nor unusual. De Vaucouleurs has gone on to conduct many studies of the superclustering phenomenon and of cosmology. Astronomers estimate the local supercluster to be about 100 million light-years across and to have a total mass of about 1,000 trillion times that of the sun. Astronomers also have discovered fine detail in the local supercluster and other superclusters. At first, de Vaucouleurs' work on the local supercluster was largely ignored by the astronomy community; his persistence in this work eventually gained recognition. The study of the large-scale structure of the universe is an exciting field in astronomy.

Impact of Event

More sky surveys and analysis of existing surveys have been done since the early work in the 1950's. Shane and Wirtanen at Lick Observatory made painstaking counts of galaxies in their survey, which measured out to a distance of about 1 billion light-years. These data were used by Phillip James Edwin Peebles to make a map of more than 1 million galaxies. This map reveals structure in the distribution of galaxies.

This map, however, is only a two-dimensional distribution; it does not differentiate between near galaxies and far ones, and it takes into account only a galaxy's coordinates on the sky. Astronomers also make three-dimensional surveys that take into account the distances of galaxies by using the redshifts of galaxies. Hubble and Milton Lasell Humason found, in the late 1920's, that light from galaxies is Doppler-shifted toward the red because of the motion of galaxies outward from the big bang, which appears to carry each galaxy away from all the others. The magnitude of red-shift is related to the speed of recession, which, in turn, is related to the distance of the galaxy. Astronomers use redshifts to determine the distances of galaxies, and then map out a three-dimensional plot of the galaxies' distribution in space. New technology such as CCDs (charge-coupled devices) enables astronomers to complete three-dimensional surveys of the sky, which have revealed some fascinating results.

Several groups of people have worked on superclusters of galaxies: a team from the Center for Astrophysics, led by Marc Davis and John Huchra, worked at Mount Hopkins; Stephen Gregory, Laird Thompson, and William Tifft worked at Kitt Peak; Brent Tully and Richard Fisher mapped the local supercluster. In addition to the local supercluster, others have been identified: the Hercules, Coma, and Perseus-Pisces superclusters. Common features of these superclusters have been identified. The hypothesis of de Vaucouleurs—that superclusters exist as organized structures—has been confirmed. Fine structure has been discovered, such as filaments and stream-ers, or strings of galaxies that link the various parts of the superclusters. In addition, astronomers have discovered voids, or spaces, in which no bright galaxies appear. Gregory's group was the first to identify a void, in the Coma supercluster, and at first they thought it was a fluke. Nevertheless, others soon identified more small voids. The first really large gap in space was found by people who were not mapping superclustering structures, but instead were trying to find an average density of gal-axies in the universe. Robert Kirshner, Augustus Oemler, and Paul Schechter chose a portion of sky near the constellation Boötes and set out to count galaxies per unit volume of space. They found a huge cavity in space that contained no bright galaxies at all. The study of these voids is a major puzzle for cosmologists.

The structure of superclusters may have much to teach astronomers about how the universe cooled and formed after the big bang. This field is at the forefront of cos-mological research, and may reveal even more startling information about the large-scale structure of the universe and how it came to be.

Bibliography

Bartusiak, Marcia. *Thursday's Universe*. New York: Times Books, 1986. Chapter 7, "Celestial Tapestry," gives an excellent overview of the current picture of the large-scale structure of the universe. Discusses superclustering, voids, and the observa-tional methods used to study them; gives information on the properties of some superclusters. Written for the layperson, it takes the reader into the world of as-tronomers and the work they are doing. Includes a bibliography, some photo-graphs.

Gregory, Stephen A. "The Structure of the Visible Universe." *Astronomy* 16 (April, 1988): 42-47. Written by an astronomer who has conducted important research in large-scale structure of the universe. Gives a good overview of the history of research into the distribution of galaxies, the current methods being used, and current results. Includes photographs and a map of the Perseus supercluster.

Gregory, Stephen A., and Laird A. Thompson. "Superclusters and Voids in the Distribution of Galaxies." *Scientific American* 246 (March, 1982): 106-114. Co-written by two astronomers who have done research on superclusters. Gives the history of the discovery of clustering and superclustering of galaxies, and an overview of current work in the field, including cosmological implications. In-cludes maps illustrating the superclusters, and drawings.

Melott, Adrian L. "Recreating the Universe." *Astronomy* 16 (May, 1988): 42-47. Discusses the cosmological and theoretical implications of current knowledge of the large-scale structure of the universe. Gives information on how astronomers use computer models to simulate processes suggested by various theories of how the universe formed and changed over time, and compares the results with the universe as it is observed. Illustrated with computer graphics.

Vaucouleurs, Gérard Henri de. *Discovery of the Universe: An Outline of the History of Astronomy from the Origins to 1956*. London: Faber & Faber, 1956. Written immediately after de Vaucouleurs' research that indicated the existence of the local supercluster; contains his views of his work. Although astronomers' knowl-edge has expanded greatly and in some cases changed since this was written, it is valuable for de Vaucouleurs' own writings on his discovery. Contains a drawing of the postulated structure of the local supercluster.

Zeilik, Michael. *Astronomy: The Evolving Universe*. 4th ed. New York: Harper & Row, 1985. An introductory textbook that contains a brief, but excellent, discus-sion of superclusters, complete with drawings and maps, including a photograph of the map done by Peebles. Discusses redshift measurements, intergalactic mat-ter, and related topics of interest. Intended for nonscience majors. Includes photo-graphs and drawings, study exercises, further readings, and a glossary.

Mary Hrovat

Cross-References

Slipher Presents Evidence of Redshifts in Galactic Spectra (1920's), p. 689; Hub-ble Determines the Distance to the Andromeda Nebula (1924), p. 766; Hubble Dem-onstrates That Other Galaxies Are Independent Systems (1924), p. 790; Hubble Confirms the Expanding Universe (1929), p. 878; Schmidt Invents the Corrector for the Schmidt Camera and Telescope (1929), p. 884; Tully Discovers the Pisces-Cetus Supercluster Complex (1986), p. 2306.

DU VIGNEAUD SYNTHESIZES OXYTOCIN, THE FIRST PEPTIDE HORMONE

Categories of event: Chemistry, medicine, and biology
Time: 1953
Locale: Cornell University Medical College, New York

Du Vigneaud's synthesis of oxytocin, a small polypeptide hormone from the pituitary gland, gave hope that the more complex polypeptides and proteins could be synthesized and used in medicine

Principal personages:

VINCENT DU VIGNEAUD (1901-1978), an American biochemist and winner of the 1955 Nobel Prize in Chemistry

FREDERICK SANGER (1918-   ), an English biochemist at the University of Cambridge who determined the structure of insulin

OLIVER KAMM (1888-1965), an American biochemist at Parke, Davis and Company who developed a method for preparing posterior pituitary preparations with high activity

LYMAN C. CRAIG (1906-1974), an American chemist at the Rockefeller Institute who developed a countercurrent distribution apparatus

WILLIAM H. STEIN (1911-1980), an American biochemist who, with Stanford Moore, developed a quantitative amino acid analysis method and was awarded the 1972 Nobel Prize in Chemistry

STANFORD MOORE (1913-1982), an American biochemist and cowinner of the 1972 Nobel Prize in Chemistry

WILLIAM H. HOWELL (1860-1945), an American physiologist at The Johns Hopkins University and pioneer in the study of blood coagulation

SIR EDWARD ALBERT SHARPEY-SCHAFER (1850-1935), an English physiologist who demonstrated in 1894 that an extract of the adrenal glands caused a rise in blood pressure

SIR HENRY HALLETT DALE (1875-1968), an English physiologist who first noted that extracts of the posterior pituitary caused contraction of uterine muscle; winner of the 1936 Nobel Prize in Physiology or Medicine

JOHN JACOB ABEL (1857-1938), an American pharmacologist and biochemist who was the first to isolate adrenaline and gave it the name "epinephrine"

Summary of Event

In England in 1895, physician George Oliver and Edward Albert Sharpey-Schafer, a physiologist, reported that an extract of bovine pituitary gland produced a rise in blood pressure when it was injected into animals. Three years later, William H. Howell at The Johns Hopkins University demonstrated that the increase in blood pressure (pressor effect) was derived only from the posterior lobe of the gland (also known as the neurohypophysis). In 1901, Rudolph Magnus and Sharpey-Schafer discovered that these extracts of the posterior lobe also could exert an antidiuretic effect. This observation was related to the fact that when the posterior lobe of the pituitary was removed surgically from an animal, it excreted an abnormally large amount of urine.

In addition to the pressor and antidiuretic activities in the posterior pituitary, two additional effects were found in 1909. Sir Henry Hallett Dale, an English physiologist, was able to show that the extracts could cause the uterine muscle to contract (oxytocic effect), and Isaac Ott and John C. Scott found that when lactating animals were injected with the extracts, milk was released from the mammary gland.

Following the discovery of these various effects, attempts were made to concentrate and isolate the substance or substances that were responsible. John Jacob Abel was able to concentrate the pressor activity at The Johns Hopkins University, using heavy metal salts and extraction with organic solvents. The results of the early work, however, were varied, primarily because most investigators used only one biological assay method to study the progress of the purification. Some investigators came to the conclusion that only one substance was responsible for all of the activities, while others concluded that two or more substances were likely to be involved.

In 1928, Oliver Kamm and his coworkers, at the drug firm of Parke, Davis and Company in Detroit, reported a method for the separation of the four activities into two fractions with high potency. One portion contained most of the pressor and antidiuretic activities, while the other contained the oxytocic and milk-releasing activities. Over the years, several names have been used for the two substances responsible for the effects, the generic name vasopressin generally has become the accepted one for the substance causing the pressor and antidiuretic effects, while the name oxytocin has been used for the substance possessing the oxytocic and milk-releasing activities. The two fractions that Kamm and his group had prepared were pure enough so that the pharmaceutical firm made them available for medical research related to obstetrics, surgical shock, and diabetes insipidus.

The problem of these hormones and their nature interested Vincent du Vigneaud at the George Washington University School of Medicine. Du Vigneaud became interested in hormones and their chemistry in 1923 after hearing a lecture on insulin given by his biochemistry teacher William Rose, who had just returned from Toronto, Canada, where Sir Frederick Grant Banting and Charles H. Best had reported success in the treatment of diabetes mellitus with preparations of the hormone.

While pursuing his Ph.D. studies at the University of Rochester School of Medicine, du Vigneaud worked with John R. Murlin, who was interested in insulin. Du Vigneaud was able to improve the method Abel had devised for crystallizing insulin and was able to show that all the sulfur content of insulin was a result of the amino acid cystine. Following his graduate work, du Vigneaud had a fellowship that allowed him to do research on insulin at The Johns Hopkins University with Abel. He spent the next year in Germany at the Kaiser-Wilhelm Institute working in Max Bergmann's laboratory on peptide synthesis.

Shortly after arriving at George Washington University, du Vigneaud collaborated with Kamm on the investigation of the latter's posterior pituitary fractions. He was able to show that the sulfur content of both the oxytocin and vasopressin fractions was a result of, as with insulin, the amino acid cystine. This helped to strengthen the concept that they were polypeptide or proteinlike substances. Du Vigneaud and his coworkers next tried to find a way of purifying oxytocin and vasopressin. This required not only the separation of the hormones themselves but also the separation from other impurities present in the preparations. Electrophoresis, a method used to separate proteins from one another, based on the differences in their charges, served to resolve them and give some additional purification.

In 1938, du Vigneaud and several of his coworkers left to work at Cornell University Medical College in New York. At about this time, du Vigneaud had to put aside the hormone studies to participate with other scientists in work related to World War II. Du Vigneaud was part of the team of English and American scientists who were asked to work on the chemistry of penicillin. The goal was to determine the structure of the antibiotic so that, if possible, it could be produced more efficiently through synthesis rather than fermentation.

During the war years and shortly thereafter, other techniques were developed that would give du Vigneaud the tools he needed to complete the job of purifying and characterizing the two hormonal factors. One of the most important was the countercurrent distribution method of Lyman C. Craig at the Rockefeller Institute. Craig had developed an apparatus that could do multiple extractions, making separations of substances with similar properties possible. Du Vigneaud had used this technique in purifying his synthetic penicillin, and as he returned to the study of oxytocin and vasopressin in 1946, he used it on his purest preparations. The procedure worked well, and milligram quantities of pure oxytocin were available in 1949 for chemical characterization.

Du Vigneaud and his group next used a new chromatographic method developed by William H. Stein and Stanford Moore at the Rockefeller Institute. This method not only separated amino acids but also determined them quantitatively. The procedure involved adding the amino acids derived from a protein to the top of a column of starch held in a glass tube. The amino acids were washed down the column with a solvent and came off the end separated from one another. Each of the amino acids was then determined quantitatively. Thus, the Stein and Moore analysis identified the amino acids in a mixture and also determined the amount of each. Du Vigneaud was able to break the pure oxytocin down into the component amino acids by heating it with acid. The mixture was analyzed by the Stein and Moore method. The analysis showed that the oxytocin was made up of one unit of eight different amino acids. In addition to the cystine detected earlier, du Vigneaud found aspartic acid, glutamic acid, glycine, isoleucine, leucine, proline, and tyrosine. Also released from the oxytocin on breakdown were three units of ammonia. This seemed to indicate that oxytocin was an octapeptide with an amide group, rather than a free carboxylic acid group, and that the aspartic acid and glutamic acid were derived from their respective amides, asparagine and glutamine.

The next task was to find out in what sequence the amino acids were joined together. The eight amino acids of oxytocin could be connected together in 181,440 different sequences, assuming that the hormone was a peptide with a structure similar to a small protein. It should be noted that the structure of cystine is such that it acts as two amino acids would in forming peptides. The two halves are connected together by two sulfur atoms. Oxytocin actually could be considered a nonapeptide (a peptide with nine amino acids), but historically it has been referred to as an octapeptide.

The approach that du Vigneaud used for structure determination was similar to that being used by Frederick Sanger in England, who was working on the structure of the larger insulin molecule. This involved breaking down the oxytocin molecule by different methods so as to obtain fragments of smaller peptides. By determining the structures of the smaller peptides, the structure of the oxytocin could be deduced. This approach was successful and completed the first stage of the chemical work. It was du Vigneaud's goal (having been interested in peptide synthesis for many years) to make synthetic oxytocin by duplicating the structure his group had worked out. Peptide synthesis is a very complicated procedure because of the chemical nature of the amino acids. Amino acids have two reactive ends. One is referred to as the amino group and the other as the carboxylic acid group. In a peptide, each amino acid can be attached through its two groups to two other amino acids. To synthesize a peptide, it is necessary to carry out the steps in such a manner that only one reaction occurs in any given step. This requires that the first amino acid used in the synthesis be protected on one of its reactive ends so that the second amino acid can react in only one of two possible ways. Also, the product formed in each step of the synthesis must be quite pure before adding the next amino acid. After all the amino acids have been linked, any protective groups must be removed without affecting the rest of the structure. Du Vigneaud's synthetic oxytocin was obtained and the method published in the *Journal of the American Chemical Society* in 1953.

Du Vigneaud wanted to prove that the synthetic and natural forms were identical in every physical, chemical, and biological property. The two forms were tested and found to act identically in every respect. In the final test, the synthetic form was found to induce labor when given intravenously to women about to give birth. Also, when microgram quantities of oxytocin were given intravenously to women who had recently given birth, milk was released from the mammary gland in less than a minute.

Thus, the task of synthesizing a natural, biologically active peptide hormone was completed for the first time. The structure and synthesis of beef vasopressin followed shortly thereafter. Vasopressin also was shown to be a cystine-containing octapeptide amide and differed from oxytocin by only two amino acids, with the rest of the sequence identical. Another interesting fact that du Vigneaud's group found was that vasopressin from hogs differed from beef vasopressin in that it had the amino acid lysine rather than the amino acid arginine. The synthetic forms of oxytocin and both types of vasopressin have replaced the natural forms for use in medicine.

Du Vigneaud received the Nobel Prize in Chemistry in 1955. His citation read: "For his work on biologically important sulfur compounds and particularly for the first synthesis of a polypeptidic hormone."

Impact of Event

The work of du Vigneaud and his associates demonstrated for the first time that it was possible to synthesize peptides that have properties identical to the natural ones and that these can be useful in certain medical conditions. Oxytocin has been used in the last stages of labor during childbirth, and vasopressin has been used in the treatment of diabetes insipidus when an individual has an insufficiency of the natural hormone, much as insulin is used by persons having diabetes mellitus.

After receiving the Nobel Prize, du Vigneaud continued his work on synthesizing chemical variations on the two hormones. By making peptides that differed from the oxytocin and vasopressin by one or more amino acids, it was possible to study how the structure of the peptide was related to its physiological activity. It was thought that analogs of the two peptides might be made that possessed only one of the activities associated with the natural peptides. Several other groups participated in this approach. The vasopressin analog desmopressin, which was first synthesized in 1966, has antidiuretic activity but little pressor activity; it is used in medicine.

After the structures of insulin and some of the smaller proteins were worked out, they, too, were synthesized, although with greater difficulty. Other methods of carrying out the synthesis of peptides and proteins have been developed and are used today. The production of biologically active proteins, such as insulin and growth hormone, has been made by the more efficient methods of biotechnology. The genes for these proteins can be put inside microorganisms, which then make them in addition to their own proteins. The microorganisms are then harvested and the useful protein hormones isolated and purified.

Bibliography

Bricas, E., and P. Fromageot. "Naturally Occurring Peptides." *Advances in Protein Chemistry* 8 (1953): 1-125. Covers the naturally occurring peptides of plants and animal origin. Sections on oxytocin and vasopressin cover the literature up to 1952. A good source of early references.

Dorsa, Daniel M. "Neurohypophyseal Hormones." In *Textbook of Physiology*, edited by Harry D. Patton. 21st ed. 2 vols. Philadelphia: W. B. Saunders, 1989. Covers the physiology and biochemistry of the neurohypophyseal hormones up to 1988. A good source of information for those interested in the physiological aspects of these hormones. Discusses their genesis in the hypothalamus and transport to the posterior pituitary gland.

Du Vigneaud, Vincent. "Hormones of the Posterior Pituitary Gland: Oxytocin and

Vasopressin." In *The Harvey Lectures, 1954-1955.* New York: Academic Press, 1956. A lecture given after the structure and synthesis of oxytocin had been accomplished; covers the experimental work in some detail. The vasopressin work discussed includes the proposed structures for beef and hog vasopressin and progress on the vasopressin synthesis. One of the best reviews on the subject.

_____. *A Trail of Research in Sulfur Chemistry and Metabolism and Related Fields.* Ithaca, N.Y.: Cornell University Press, 1952. Du Vigneaud's personal account of his chemical work from insulin to the posterior pituitary hormones. Ends shortly before the structure work is completed. One of the few autobiographical accounts by a chemist.

Farber, Eduard. *Nobel Prize Winners in Chemistry, 1901-1961.* Rev. ed. New York: Abelard-Schuman, 1963. Contains brief excerpts of the Nobel Prize lectures given by the recipients of these prestigious scientific awards, plus biographical information and comments made by the author.

Richard A. Hendry

Cross-References

Abel and Takamine Independently Isolate Adrenaline (1897), p. 16; Hopkins Discovers Tryptophan, an Essential Amino Acid (1900), p. 46; Banting and Macleod Win the Nobel Prize for the Discovery of Insulin (1921), p. 720; Li Isolates the Human Growth Hormone (1950's), p. 1358; Sanger Wins the Nobel Prize for the Discovery of the Structure of Insulin (1958), p. 1567; The First Commercial Genetic Engineering Product, Humulin, Is Marketed by Eli Lilly (1982), p. 2221.

MILLER REPORTS THE SYNTHESIS OF AMINO ACIDS

Category of event: Biology
Time: 1953
Locale: University of Chicago, Chicago, Illinois

Miller synthesized amino acids by combining a mixture of water, hydrogen, methane, and ammonia and exposing it to an electrical spark

Principal personages:
STANLEY LLOYD MILLER (1930-   ), a professor of chemistry who performed the first experiments that produced amino acids from gases presumed to be present in the primordial atmosphere of the earth
HAROLD CLAYTON UREY (1893-1981), a recipient of the 1934 Nobel Prize in Chemistry who developed a theory of the origin of the earth from a cold stellar dust cloud
ALEKSANDR IVANOVICH OPARIN (1894-1980), a Russian biochemist who proposed an origin of life by the assembly of organic compounds in a reducing atmosphere
JOHN BURDON SANDERSON HALDANE (1892-1964), a British scientist who hypothesized that organic compounds would have accumulated in the oceans if the earth had an early reducing environment

Summary of Event

The origin of life on Earth has long been an intractable problem for scientists. While most scientists can envision the development of life through geologic time from simple single-cell bacteria to complex mammals by the processes of mutation and natural selection, they have found it most difficult to develop a theory to define how organic materials were first formed and organized into life. This stage in the development of life—before biologic systems arose—is called chemical evolution and occurred between 4.5 and 3.5 billion years ago. Although great advances in genetics and biochemistry have shown the intricate workings of the cell, relatively little light has been shed on the origins of this intricate machinery of the cell. Some experiments, however, have provided important data from which to build a scientific theory of the origin of life. The first of these experiments was the classic work of Stanley Lloyd Miller.

Miller worked with Harold Clayton Urey, a Nobel laureate, on the environments of the early earth. John Burdon Sanderson Haldane, a British biochemist, had suggested in 1929 that the earth's early atmosphere was a reducing one—that it contained no free oxygen. In 1952, Urey published a seminal work in planetology, *The Planets*, in which he elaborated on Haldane's suggestion, and he postulated that the earth had formed from a cold stellar dust cloud. Urey thought that the earth's primordial atmosphere probably contained elements in the approximate relative abundances found in the solar system and the universe. It had been discovered in 1929 that the sun is approximately 87 percent hydrogen and by 1935 it was known that hydrogen encompassed the vast majority (92.8 percent) of atoms in the universe. In addition, the ratio of hydrogen to oxygen, nitrogen, or carbon is more than 1500:1. Urey reasoned that the earth's early atmosphere contained mostly hydrogen, with the oxygen, nitrogen, and carbon atoms chemically bonded to hydrogen to form water, ammonia, and methane. Most important, free oxygen could not exist in the presence of such an abundance of hydrogen. In contrast, today's atmosphere contains about 21 percent free oxygen because many of the light hydrogen atoms have escaped Earth's gravitational field into outer space. As a result, there are not enough hydrogen atoms to bond chemically to all the oxygen, and oxygen has slowly accumulated in the atmosphere.

As early as the mid-1920's, Aleksandr Ivanovich Oparin, a Russian biochemist, had argued that the organic compounds necessary for life had been built up on the early earth by chemical combinations in a reducing atmosphere. The energy from the sun would have been sufficient to drive the reactions to produce life. Haldane later proposed that the organic compounds would accumulate in the oceans to produce a "dilute organic soup" and that life might have arisen by some unknown process from that mixture of organic compounds.

Miller combined the ideas of Oparin and Urey and designed a simple, but elegant, experiment. He decided to take the gases presumed to exist in the early atmosphere (water, hydrogen, ammonia, and methane) and expose them to an electrical spark and determine which, if any, organic compounds were formed. To do this, he constructed a relatively simple system, essentially consisting of two Pyrex flasks connected by tubing in a roughly circular pattern. The water and gases in the smaller flask were boiled and the resulting fluid forced through the tubing into a larger flask that contained tungsten electrodes. As the gases passed the electrodes, an electrical spark was generated and from this larger flask the gases and any other compounds were condensed. The gases were recycled through the system, whereas the organic compounds were trapped in the bottom of the system.

Miller was trying to simulate conditions that prevailed on early Earth. He had to design the system so that results could be attained in only a few weeks. Therefore, he boiled the water to speed up the reactions, even though Urey had suggested the oceans probably did not boil at that period of the earth's history. Miller chose to use electrical discharge as the energy source, even though it was known that ultraviolet radiation would have provided the most abundant usable energy for the reactions that he sought. Technical difficulties in designing the experimental system to use ultraviolet radiation, however, required that he opt for electrical discharge. Nevertheless, his experimental design essentially reproduced possible conditions near the earth's origin. During the one week of operation, Miller extracted and analyzed the residue of compounds at the bottom of the system. The results were truly astounding. He found that numerous organic compounds had, indeed, been formed in only that one week. As much as 15 percent of the carbon (originally in the gas methane) had been combined into organic compounds, and at least 5 percent of the carbon was incorporated into biochemically important compounds. The most important compounds produced were some of the twenty amino acids essential to life on Earth. Miller's experiment had produced the amino acids glycine, alanine, aspartic acid, glutamic acid, and others.

The formation of amino acids is significant because they are the building blocks of proteins. Proteins consist of a specific sequence of amino acids assembled into a well-defined pattern. Proteins are necessary for life for two reasons: First, they are important structural materials used to build the cells of the body. Second, the enzymes that increase the rate of the multitude of biochemical reaction of life are also proteins. Miller not only had produced proteins in the laboratory but also had shown clearly that the precursors of proteins—the amino acids—were easily formed in a reducing environment with the appropriate energy.

Perhaps the most important aspect of the experiment was the ease with which the amino acids were formed. Of all the thousands of organic compounds that are known to chemists, amino acids were among those that were formed in this simple experiment. This strongly implied that one of the first steps in chemical evolution was not only possible but also highly probable. All that was necessary for the synthesis of amino acids were the common gases of the solar system, a reducing environment, and an appropriate energy source, and all were present on early Earth.

Impact of Event

Miller opened an entirely new field of research with his pioneering experiments. His results showed that much about chemical evolution could be learned by experimentation in the laboratory. As a result, Miller and many others soon tried variations on his original experiment by altering the combination of gases, using other gases, and trying other types of energy sources. Almost all the essential amino acids have been produced in the laboratory experiments as long as the gas mixture was a reducing one. Amino acids cannot be formed in these experiments if free oxygen is present. This clearly implies that free oxygen was not present on the early earth, a conclusion that has been supported by much recent geologic evidence.

At the time of Miller's first experiments, it was known that amino acids and proteins were key compounds in the biochemistry of life, but the exact role and nature of the nucleic acids was not entirely understood. The work of James D. Watson and Francis Crick elucidated the structure of deoxyribonucleic acid (DNA); later its central role in genetics became clear. Biologists now know that DNA is composed of three components: organic bases (adenine, guanine, cytosine, and thymine), a sugar (deoxyribose), and phosphate. Miller's work with amino acid synthesis led others to consider a similar approach to the synthesis of nucleic acids. In 1960, Juan Oro was able to synthesize adenine, one of the basic components of DNA, from a concentrated solution of hydrogen cyanide and ammonia, both thought to be present on early Earth. Adenine is not only one of the organic bases of DNA but also a component of adenosine triphosphate (ATP), the major energy carrier in the cell. It was also known that the sugar component of DNA—deoxyribose—could be formed from a concentrated solution of formaldehyde, and that the third component of DNA—phosphate—is naturally present on Earth through the weathering of rocks. Thus, Oro and others, using the Miller approach to the study of chemical evolution, had shown that many of the components of DNA could be synthesized from compounds presumed to be present in the primordial atmosphere.

These studies present a starting point from which to build a coherent theory of the origin of life. It is now clear that the precursors of proteins and DNA could have been synthesized on early Earth. One of the great questions about the origin of life is: Which came first, proteins or DNA?

In living systems today, proteins and DNA are intimately linked. The sequence of amino acids in a protein is specified by the sequence of bases in DNA. On the other hand, DNA cannot operate efficiently without enzymes (proteins). This could not have been the case in the beginning. Miller's classic experiment showed that amino acids were formed quite easily and that a "dilute, organic soup" as envisioned by Haldane could form. Carl Sagan calculated that the earth's oceans would have developed a 1 percent solution of organic compounds in approximately 300 million years, a time interval that is within the almost 1 billion years estimated for chemical evolution. Although the initial assembly of amino acids into proteins is not understood, Miller's experiments demonstrated that amino acids were probably much easier to form than the precursors of DNA. Adenine could be formed only from highly concentrated solutions of ammonium cyanide, concentrations not likely to be found in the oceans. Thus, Miller's experiments suggest that proteins may have formed before DNA.

Miller's work was based upon the presumed composition of the primordial atmosphere of the earth. The composition of this atmosphere was calculated on the basis of the abundance of elements in the universe. If this reasoning is correct, then it is highly likely that there are many other bodies in the universe that have similar atmospheres and are near energy sources similar to the sun. Miller's experiment strongly suggests that amino acids should have formed on other planets, and perhaps, life as well.

Bibliography

Dickerson, Richard E. "Chemical Evolution and the Origin of Life." *Scientific American* 239 (September, 1978): 70-86. The author presents clearly the origin of organic compounds and early life as understood by scientists. A detailed summary of chemical evolution gives the layperson an excellent introduction to the subject. Recommended to students with some background in chemistry and biology.

Dyson, Freeman. *Origins of Life.* New York: Cambridge University Press, 1985. An excellent book on the origins of life that outlines clearly the major advances in the study of chemical evolution. The question of whether proteins or DNA arose first is dealt with in some detail.

Oparin, A. I. *Origin of Life.* 2d ed. New York: Dover, 1953. The classic work on the origin of life by the father of the study of chemical evolution. Recommended for all serious students of the origin of life and for those interested in the history of science.

Orgel, L. E. *The Origins of Life.* New York: John Wiley & Sons, 1973. A well-written overview of the nature and origin of life. Chapter 8 discusses the work of Miller and describes the significance of his results.

Ponnamperuma, Cyril. *The Origins of Life.* New York: E. P. Dutton, 1972. A well-illustrated book written specifically for the layperson. Ponnamperuma is one of the major researchers into chemical evolution and he outlines clearly in chapter 5 the basic work done on the origin of organic compounds.

Jay R. Yett

Cross-References

Hopkins Discovers Tryptophan, an Essential Amino Acid (1900), p. 46; Ochoa Creates Synthetic RNA (1950's), p. 1363; Watson and Crick Develop the Double-Helix Model for DNA (1951), p. 1406; Calvin Wins the Nobel Prize for His Work on Photosynthesis (1961), p. 1703.

THE LIQUID BUBBLE CHAMBER IS DEVELOPED

Category of event: Physics
Time: 1953-1959
Locale: Berkeley, California

Liquid hydrogen was employed as the visualizing medium in the bubble chamber, making it sensitive enough to detect high-energy subatomic particles while providing nuclear collision targets

Principal personages:
DONALD A. GLASER (1926-   ), an American physicist and molecular biologist who invented the bubble chamber in 1952 and was awarded the 1960 Nobel Prize in Physics
LUIS W. ALVAREZ (1911-1988), an American physicist who was the first to exploit the liquid hydrogen bubble chamber to investigate elementary subatomic particles
CARL DAVID ANDERSON (1905-   ), an American physicist who first suggested that Glaser look for an alternative to the cloud chamber

Summary of Event

One of the most difficult problems in experimental nuclear physics is the detection of atomic and subatomic particles. One of the earliest techniques to examine the properties of these particles was to use an apparatus known as the cloud chamber. The cloud chamber consisted of a chamber filled with a supersaturated vapor in a state of expansion. In other words, the gas in the chamber is very near the point of condensing into a liquid. When placed near a source of radioactivity, the charged particles constituting the radiation would travel through the chamber, leaving a trail of condensed droplets in their wake, much like the condensation trail from a jet airplane. The cloud chamber enabled scientists to ascertain the energy distribution of charged particles by measuring the curvature of the droplet paths in the presence of a magnetic field. The cloud chamber had limited applicability, however, and it was largely because of deficiencies in the cloud chamber that the bubble chamber was developed.

While studying the properties of cosmic rays and their constituent muon particles in the late 1940's, Carl David Anderson set one of his graduate students, Donald A. Glaser, to the task of developing a better method of applying the cloud chamber to cosmic-ray physics. Although Glaser did improve on the cloud chamber by employing two chambers in tandem separated by a powerful electromagnet in order to study high-energy muons, his work eventually led him to invent the bubble chamber.

By 1950, Glaser had completed his graduate work and was free to work on a project of his own—the bubble chamber. It not only was a marked departure from the cloud chamber but also was an instrument the use of which marked a turning point in the physics community. With the growing use of particle accelerators during and after World War II, physics was in a transition from a discipline in which a relatively small number of scientists could run experiments with relatively small and inexpensive apparatus. Cosmic-ray physics was one such enterprise. Particle accelerators ushered in the age of high-energy physics, however, so called because of the tremendous energies at which these machines could accelerate atomic and subatomic particles. The bubble chamber became the most powerful detection device for high-energy physics in the 1960's. Resulting largely from the expense and engineering complexity of both accelerators and bubble chambers, high-energy physics demanded large investments of both money and labor. Therefore, although the bubble chamber was conceived as a solution to the problems of small-scale cosmic ray physics experiments, it became ultimately the tool of large-scale, high-energy physics experiments.

Given that the cloud chamber exploited the instability of a supersaturated vapor, Glaser reasoned that other instabilities in nature could be exploited also in order to visualize atomic and subatomic particles. Glaser and his research assistant, David Rahm, wondered if instead of gas they could employ a liquid, which, near its boiling point, would boil in the presence of accelerated charged particles. After a thorough study of droplet formation, Glaser determined that charged particles would induce a trail of bubbles, essentially localized boiling, in an enclosed vat of superheated liquid (a liquid that is heated above its boiling point but kept from boiling by storing it under high pressure).

Glaser's first experimental confirmation of his idea came when he induced boiling in a glass bulb filled with superheated ether. Ether normally boils at 135 degrees Celsius, but Glaser kept the bulb under pressure, and was able to maintain the liquid in a superheated state of about 150 degrees Celsius. When he achieved the superheated state, he brought a piece of radioactive cobalt, cobalt-60, near the bulb. Cobalt-60 is a source of gamma radiation, and when brought near the bulb, the source induced violent boiling.

Physically speaking, it is easy to show why this primitive bubble chamber worked. A pure liquid can be brought to a temperature above its boiling point in a very clean container for short periods. The length of time depends on the pressure under which the liquid is kept. If an impurity, such as a piece of broken glass, is introduced into the liquid, boiling begins spontaneously around the impurity. In other words, the impurity disrupts the balance between the liquid and gas phases of the liquid, causing the spontaneous release of the gas, also known as boiling.

With this new experimental knowledge, Glaser embarked on a project to develop a "clean" bubble chamber applicable to particle physics. He believed that the chamber would have to be as clean as possible so that the only boiling observed in the liquid was the result of test particles in the chamber, not stray impurities and imperfections of no experimental interest. From 1950 to 1953, Glaser and Rahm worked on the technical details of the bubble chamber until they had completed a 1.9-centimeter-diameter ether chamber that controlled liquid pressure with a hand-turned piston.

After bubble tracks were examined, the piston could be lowered, pressurizing the chamber and thus returning the liquid to its superheated state.

In May of 1953, Glaser presented preliminary results of his bubble chamber experiments at the Washington, D.C., meeting of the American Physical Society. Glaser was more concerned with the use of the apparatus in cosmic ray physics, but there were those in the audience who saw the device as the perfect tool for accelerator-driven, high-energy physics. One of those in attendance was Luis W. Alvarez, a physicist at Ernest Orlando Lawrence's Radiation Laboratory at the University of California at Berkeley. Alvarez was intrigued by the potential utility of the Glaser invention, and particularly by Glaser's suggestion that ether be replaced by liquid hydrogen as an imaging medium.

It was important to observe the tracks made by particles entering the chamber; however, another important aspect of bubble chamber physics was the ability to observe the interactions of the entering particles with the particles making up the imaging medium. Particle physicists were studying the constituents of matter, and the particles they investigated constituted the bubble chamber liquid as well. Therefore, there was much to be learned from the collisions between the energetic entering particles and the particles making up the liquid. Any electrically charged particle, such as a muon, proton, or electron, made a track in the bubble chamber. Neutral particles such as neutrons and neutrinos left no tracks, but their collisions with the particles of the liquid often created charged particles, leaving evidence of their presence. For experiments in which a large variety of collisions was essential, it was important to use a visualizing medium that was also a good target for collisions. Liquid hydrogen was the answer—it was the simplest of all elements, with a nucleus consisting of only one proton. In 1953, Glaser began a collaboration with the Darragh Nagle team from the University of Chicago, which he hoped would lead to the liquid hydrogen chamber. At the same time, Alvarez and his team at Berkeley began the same pursuit. Both projects marked the first time that the instrument was used in tandem with a particle accelerator.

The Alvarez group was the first to observe particle tracks in a chamber filled with liquid hydrogen. This accomplishment marked the end of a collaboration of physicists and engineers who made some important modifications of Glaser's original work. Liquid hydrogen poses some unique difficulties because it boils at such a low temperature (−246 degrees Celsius) and because it burns violently in air. When the hydrogen is forced into an unstable superheated state at high pressure, the sudden release of that pressure could result in accidental fires. Therefore, Alvarez had to add experts in cryogenics, the science of extremely low temperatures, to his team. The most important modification of the Glaser apparatus was the development of the "dirty" chamber. A large glass chamber to hold liquid hydrogen under extremes of both temperature and pressure was an engineering impossibility. Yet, the only way to keep the inner walls of a chamber perfectly clean and smooth was to construct them of glass. The Alvarez team discovered accidentally that boiling near the imperfections in the chamber's walls had no adverse effect on the all-important bubble tracks in the center of the chamber. Therefore, they abandoned the quest for the perfectly clean glass chamber and set out to develop a metal chamber with glass viewing ports. This allowed the construction of larger chambers, giving physicists more freedom in the types of collisions they could observe.

From 1954 forward, the Berkeley team dominated bubble chamber research, and by 1955, Alvarez was reporting the results of pion research with his 10-centimeter chamber. In that same year, he planned the design for a 25-centimeter liquid hydrogen chamber. This proposal eventually led to the development of the 183-centimeter chamber at Berkeley to be used in tandem with its large particle accelerator, the Bevatron. Operation of this apparatus began in 1959.

Impact of Event

The most important impact of the liquid hydrogen bubble chamber came in the field of high-energy particle physics. The bubble chamber allowed physicists to examine a greater number of collisions between high-energy particles than ever before. Cameras attached to the chambers permitted scientists to examine hundreds of photographs of each experimental run. The tracks shown in these pictures offered evidence of the energy and charge of the particles under investigation. The liquid hydrogen bubble chamber allowed physicists to discover more than three times as many elementary particles than were known prior to 1950.

Alvarez and his team at Berkeley led the discipline in the teaming of bubble chambers and particle accelerators. One problem in the study of high-energy particles is that most of the very interesting particles do not last long after a collision. Alvarez used high-speed cameras triggered by computerized data analysis in order to photograph the tracks of particles. The complex data-gathering apparatus for this task was dubbed "Franckenstein," after James Franck, one of the scientists who took on the task of developing the computerized data analyzer. By 1960, it was becoming clear that the role of the human observer had to be minimized in order to gather and analyze all of the data potentially gathered by a bubble chamber. Interesting events were too numerous and happened far too quickly.

With the use of Franckenstein-type data analysis, Alvarez exploited the bubble chamber to make such discoveries as the ability of a muon (a negatively charged particle more than two hundred times heavier than the electron) to catalyze the fusion of two hydrogen nuclei, producing huge amounts of energy. Fusion is the process that produces energy in stars, and research to tap this form of energy continues.

By the mid-1960's, every research center with a particle accelerator either had a bubble chamber or was in the process of building one. Heavy liquid chambers filled with fluids such as Freon, a fluorinated hydrocarbon, began to be used during this time; they offered physicists the opportunity to observe many more collisions than the hydrogen chamber, as Freon has a more complex structure than hydrogen. Freon was also safer to work with than hydrogen and could be contained at a temperature of 50 degrees Celsius, as opposed to the cryogenic temperatures of liquid hydrogen.

Bibliography

Aleksandrov, Yuri A., et al. *Bubble Chambers.* Translated by Scripta Technica. Bloomington: Indiana University Press, 1967. This is a technical introduction to the physics and engineering of bubble chambers, yet offers a concise introductory chapter on the history and significance of the bubble chamber. The prose is awkward at times, owing to the fact that the text was translated into English from its original Russian.

Galison, Peter. "Bubble Chambers and the Experimental Workplace." In *Observation, Experiment, and Hypothesis in Modern Physical Science*, edited by Peter Achinstein and Owen Hannaway. Cambridge, Mass.: MIT Press, 1985. This article details the entire history of the bubble chamber and discusses its effect on the physics community, in terms of both new discoveries and how the practice of physics changed. The best historical account of this invention and should be read by anyone deeply interested in the subject.

_____. *How Experiments End.* Chicago: University of Chicago Press, 1987. This book is primarily an account of three historical events in twentieth century physics: the discovery of the muon, the determination of the gyromagnetic ratio, and the discovery of weak neutral currents. Galison discusses the role of all experimental apparatus, including the bubble chamber, in the context of the latter two events. He discusses how physics theory and experiment come into agreement, and how the results given by an apparatus such as the bubble chamber are never completely certain.

Glaser, Donald. "The Bubble Chamber." *Scientific American* 192 (February, 1955): 46-50. Written by the inventor, this article is the best possible introduction to the bubble chamber for the layperson. It is amply illustrated, and Glaser spares the highly technical details, opting instead for a discussion of how he developed the apparatus and its uses.

Pickering, Andrew. *Constructing Quarks.* Chicago: University of Chicago Press, 1984. This book is not devoted exclusively to the bubble chamber but instead to the sociological development of particle physics. Pickering discusses the role of apparatus, including the bubble chamber.

William J. McKinney

Cross-References

Lawrence Develops the Cyclotron (1931), p. 953; Cockcroft and Walton Split the Atom with a Particle Accelerator (1932), p. 978; University of California Physicists Develop the First Synchrocyclotron (1946), p. 1282; The Tevatron Particle Accelerator Begins Operation at Fermilab (1985), p. 2301; The Superconducting Supercollider Is Under Construction in Texas (1988), p. 2372.

BACKUS' IBM TEAM DEVELOPS THE FORTRAN COMPUTER LANGUAGE

Category of event: Applied science
Time: 1954-1957
Locale: New York City

Backus led the design and development of FORTRAN, the first major computer programming language

Principal personages:

JOHN BACKUS (1924-   ), a software engineer and manager at IBM, coinventor of ALGOL and Backus-Naur Form and inventor of Speed-coding and FORTRAN

JOHN W. MAUCHLY (1907-1980), a physicist, engineer, and a principal designer of the ENIAC who invented Short Code, the first "high level" computer language

PETER NAUR (1928-   ), a Danish astronomer and computer scientist who refined Backus' method of language specification and produced Backus-Naur Form

HERMAN HEINE GOLDSTINE (1913-   ), a mathematician and computer scientist who was the coinventor of software design using flow charts

JOHN VON NEUMANN (1903-1957), a Hungarian-American mathematician and physicist who was a coinventor of software design using flow charts

MAURICE VINCENT WILKES (1913-   ), an English computer scientist and principal designer of the EDSAC who coauthored the first programming text

Summary of Event

FORTRAN (FORmula TRANslating system)—the first widely accepted, high-level computer language—was delivered by John Backus and coworkers at IBM in April, 1957. It was designed to support programming in a mathematical language natural to scientists and engineers and has achieved unsurpassed success in scientific computation.

Computer languages are means of specifying what instructions a computer should execute and in what order. They can be divided into categories of progressively higher degrees of abstraction. At the lowest level is binary or machine code: Binary digits (or another base, such as octal or hexadecimal) specify in complete detail every instruction that the machine will execute. This was the only "language" available in the early days of the first computers, such as the ENIAC, and required manually setting switches and plugboard connections. All higher levels of language are implemented by having a program process instructions written in the higher language into binary (also called object code).

Assembly language replaces numbers with names: Instead of having to write numeric instructions, say "14" for "clear accumulator register and add," one can write the mnemonic instruction "CLA"; likewise, instead of writing numeric addresses, one can assign an arbitrary name to a memory location. The first rudimentary assembler was developed in the late 1940's by Maurice Vincent Wilkes' team for the EDSAC computer at the University of Cambridge. High-level languages, or simply programming languages, are largely or entirely independent of the underlying machine structure. The assembler instruction CLA is therefore excluded, since it refers to a specific register, the accumulator. Rather than naming registers, a high-level language will exclusively use programmer-specified variable names to hold and process data. FORTRAN was the first language of this type to win widespread acceptance.

The emergence of machine-independent programming languages was a gradual process, spanning the initial decade of electronic computation. One of the earliest developments was the invention of flowcharts ("flow diagrams") by Herman Heine Goldstine and John von Neumann in 1947. Flowcharting became the most influential software methodology during the first twenty years of computing.

Short Code was the first language to be implemented that contained some high-level features, such as the ability to use mathematical equations. The idea came from John W. Mauchly, and it was implemented on the BINAC in 1949 with an interpreter; later, it was carried over to the UNIVAC I. Interpreters do not translate a source statement into a series of binary machine instructions; instead, they directly execute (interpret) the source statement. Thus, every time the interpreter reencounters a statement, it must be interpreted again. Compilers, on the other hand, convert the entire program into object code before it is executed. Although interpreters have some advantages, a major disadvantage is that an interpreted program normally will run more slowly than the same program compiled.

Much early effort went into building up libraries of subroutines for handling commonly encountered problems, especially scientific calculations requiring floating-point arithmetic and array indexing. A number of interpretive languages arose to support these features. Among the most influential was Speedcoding, defined in 1953 by John Backus for the IBM 701. As long as floating-point and indexing operations had to be performed in software, however, scientific computation would remain relatively slow. Therefore, Backus lobbied successfully for a direct hardware implementation of these operations on IBM's new scientific computer, the 704. Backus then started the Programming Research Group at IBM in order to develop a translator (compiler) to allow programs to be written in a more mathematical language, rather than a machine-oriented language. In November, 1954, they defined an initial version of FORTRAN.

To perform the mathematical calculation of doubling a number and multiplying by a further number requires, in machine or assembler language, the following steps: loading two registers, shifting one, multiplying them, checking for overflow, and finally storing the result back in memory. The obscurity and awkwardness of this process guaranteed that it would not generally be used by nonprofessional programmers. In FORTRAN, on the other hand, the same operation is expressed simply by A = (2 * B) * C. In general, FORTRAN supported constructs with which scientists were already acquainted, such as functions and multidimensional arrays. It also provided control mechanisms for iteration (repeated calculations in the DO loop), conditional branching (IF and GOTO), and sophisticated input-output (FORMAT). In defining a powerful notation accessible to scientists and engineers, FORTRAN opened up programming to a much wider community.

Backus' success in getting the IBM 704's hardware to support scientific computation directly, however, posed a major challenge: Since such computation would then be much faster, the object code produced by FORTRAN could ill afford to be slow— it would not be able to hide its inefficiencies behind the normal inefficiencies of scientific computation, since those were gone. The lower-level interpreters and compilers preceding FORTRAN produced programs that were usually five to ten times slower than their hand-coded counterparts; therefore, efficiency became the primary design objective for Backus. The highly publicized claims for FORTRAN met with widespread skepticism among programmers. In Backus' terms, in those days programmers formed a "priesthood" used to coding around the highly obscure oddities of early hardware and to fitting code into incredibly small memories. Efficient programming was thought of as a "black art" that could hardly be automated.

Much of the team's efforts, therefore, went into discovering ways to produce the most efficient object code, and, in fact, the degree of efficiency achieved with FORTRAN was not equaled again until the optimizing compilers of the late 1960's. The FORTRAN compiler used an algorithm for assigning data to the IBM 704 registers that was nearly optimal, actually simulating the operation of the potential object code. It also performed a variety of global optimizations—for example, moving calculations outside repeated loops, when possible.

The compiler's efficiency, combined with the language's clarity and ease of use, guaranteed its success. By 1959, many 704 installations programmed exclusively in FORTRAN. By 1963, virtually every computer manufacturer either had delivered or promised a version of FORTRAN; by 1964, there were forty-three different FORTRAN compilers. Most of these compilers differed slightly from one another in how they implemented the language, but they all supported the same basic set of instructions. They also supported the major piece missing from FORTRAN I, but supplied one year later (1958) in FORTRAN II, which was the SUBROUTINE—a piece of code that could be compiled once and shared by different programs thereafter.

Incompatibilities among manufacturers were minimized by the popularity of IBM's version of FORTRAN; everyone wanted to be able to support IBM programs on their own equipment ("porting" the program to the new equipment). Nevertheless, there was sufficient interest in obtaining a standard for FORTRAN that the American National Standards Institute adopted a formal standard for it in 1966. A revised standard was adopted in 1978, yielding FORTRAN 77.

Impact of Event

In demonstrating the feasibility of efficient high-level languages, FORTRAN inaugurated a period of great proliferation of programming languages, including ALGOL, LISP, COBOL, BASIC, PL/I, PASCAL, and the other "third-generation" languages. Most of these languages attempted to provide similar or better high-level programming constructs but oriented toward a different, nonscientific programming environment. COBOL, for example, is a business-oriented language.

Backus, meanwhile, sat on the international committee that designed ALGOL-58. There, he invented a specification language in order to provide a precise definition of the syntax of ALGOL. Peter Naur enhanced the language for ALGOL-60, and it is now known as Backus-Naur Form (BNF) and is widely employed in defining language and data communications standards.

FORTRAN, while remaining the dominant language for scientific programming, has not found general acceptance outside that domain. Despite some new programming constructs introduced with FORTRAN 77, it still lacks sophisticated string manipulation, list handling, and other facilities. An IBM project established in 1963 to extend FORTRAN found the task too unwieldy and instead ended up producing an entirely different language, PL/I (delivered in 1966). In the beginning, Backus and his coworkers actually believed their revolutionary language would virtually eliminate the burdens of coding and debugging. Far from that, it launched software as a field of study and as an industry. Beyond stimulating the introduction of new languages, FORTRAN encouraged the development, for example, of operating systems. Assembler systems had already grown into simple operating systems, called monitors. Another early, and very primitive, operating system was the FORTRAN Monitor System for the IBM 709 (a followup to the 704), which was introduced in the late 1950's. This monitor system handled many of the operational tasks on the computer for the FORTRAN programmer, such as supporting the compilation, loading, and execution of FORTRAN programs as a single procedure, as well as aiding in their debugging. Operating systems since then have been greatly extended to support, for example, simultaneously active programs (multiprogramming) and the networking together of multiple computers.

A further important development in programming languages was the introduction of functional languages, with APL, LISP, and Backus' Formal Functional Programming (FFP). In the now traditional languages such as FORTRAN—which Backus calls "von Neumann languages"—the flow of control is explicitly specified, for example, via the DO loops of FORTRAN. In functional programming, control is specified implicitly in the patterns of nested function calls. Functional programming is a further step in abstraction from specific machine architectures and, in particular, away from reliance on von Neumann architecture. Backus has been an especially vocal proponent of the functional approach: "We have come to regard the DO, FOR, WHILE statements and the like as powerful tools, whereas they are in fact weak palliatives that are necessary to make the von Neumann style of programming viable at all." Whatever the limitations and future of Backus' constructs, their implementation in FORTRAN was clearly a vital step in the continuing evolution of computer software.

Bibliography

Calingaert, Peter. *Assemblers, Compilers, and Program Translation*. Potomac, Md.: Computer Science Press, 1979. A readable, standard computer science text covering assemblers, macros, loaders, and compiler theory and techniques.

Meissner, Loren P., and Elliot I. Organick. *FORTRAN 77: Featuring Structured Programming*. 3d ed. Reading, Mass.: Addison-Wesley, 1980. A standard textbook on FORTRAN, introducing basic programming concepts. Includes exercises and examples.

Metropolis, N., J. Howlett, and Gian-Carlo Rota, eds. *A History of Computing in the Twentieth Century*. New York: Academic Press, 1980. A collection of papers originally presented at a conference on computing history at the Los Alamos Scientific Laboratory in 1976. The authors, from both sides of the Atlantic, include many of the principals involved in the early development of computers and computer software. Of special interest is Donald Knuth and Luis Trabb Pardo's eighty-page "The Early Development of Programming Languages."

Rosen, Saul, ed. *Programming Systems and Languages*. New York: McGraw-Hill, 1967. An anthology of papers records early efforts to develop and understand programming languages such as FORTRAN, ALGOL, COBOL, LISP, PL/I (known then as NPL). Introduced by a historical survey by Rosen.

Sammet, Jean E. *Programming Languages: History and Fundamentals*. Englewood Cliffs, N.J.: Prentice-Hall, 1969. A massive description of 120 computer languages and their histories. Introduces the basic concepts of computer languages and their compilers.

Wexelblat, Richard L., ed. *History of Programming Languages*. New York: Academic Press, 1981. An excellent collection of papers and transcripts of discussion from the ACM History of Programming Languages conference in 1978. Sessions on the histories of thirteen major languages, including FORTRAN, ALGOL, LISP, COBOL, BASIC, and PL/I. Includes John Backus' paper "The History of FORTRAN I, II, and III."

Wilkes, Maurice V., David J. Wheeler, and Stanley Gill. *The Preparation of Programs for an Electronic Digital Computer*. Reading, Mass.: Addison-Wesley, 1951. The first general text on programming methods, written by the EDSAC design team. Describes the rudimentary assembler for the EDSAC and the use of subroutine libraries, with examples. Of historical interest only.

Kevin B. Korb

Cross-References

Eckert and Mauchly Develop the ENIAC (1943), p. 1213; The First Electronic

Stored-Program Computer (BINAC) Is Completed (1949), p. 1347; UNIVAC I Becomes the First Commercial Electronic Computer and the First to Use Magnetic Tape (1951), p. 1396; Hopper Invents the Computer Language COBOL (1959), p. 1593; Kemeny and Kurtz Develop the BASIC Computer Language (1964), p. 1772.

BARGHOORN AND TYLER DISCOVER
2-BILLION-YEAR-OLD MICROFOSSILS

Categories of event: Earth science and biology
Time: April 30, 1954
Locale: Madison, Wisconsin; Cambridge, Massachusetts

Barghoorn and Tyler's photographs of a number of microorganisms ushered in a new era of Precambrian paleontology, and the fossil discoveries were the first in a series crucial to understanding the origin and early development of life on Earth

Principal personages:

ELSO BARGHOORN (1915-1984), an American paleontologist and member of the United States National Academy of Sciences

STANLEY ALLEN TYLER (1906-1963), an American geologist who was a specialist in Precambrian geology and ore deposits

CHARLES DOLITTLE WALCOTT (1850-1927), the head of the United States Geological Survey, a specialist in Cambrian paleontology, and the first person to document Precambrian fossils

Summary of Event

On April 30, 1954, the American journal *Science* published a brief article by Elso Barghoorn and Stanley Allen Tyler entitled "Occurrence of Structurally Preserved Plants in Pre-Cambrian Rocks of the Canadian Shield," which had been submitted for publication on February 11. The article figured and described five morphologically distinct types of microorganisms, including slender, unbranched filaments and spherical colonies made up of filaments, which were judged to resemble living blue-green algae, and branched filaments and spherical bodies, which were compared with living aquatic fungi.

These fossils had first come to the attention of Tyler, a geologist working with banded iron deposits of Precambrian age on the shores of Lake Superior. A puzzling circumstance was the association of coal with the iron ore deposits, since the iron ore was known to be approximately 2 billion years old, and no convincing evidence of co-occurring life-forms that could have produced coal was known at the time. Examination of the coal revealed what appeared to be microscopic plants. Tyler showed them to William Schrock of the Massachusetts Institute of Technology, who thought they resembled living fungi and suggested that Tyler consult with Barghoorn in the Harvard University botany department.

Barghoorn agreed that the material appeared to be microbial. As a biologist, he recognized that convincing proof of life-forms so early in geologic time would be immensely significant. He suggested returning to the site and conducting a systematic search for life-forms in the coal-bearing rocks. Following the coal seams into

Canada, they collected samples of black gunflint chert, which was cut into thin sections with a diamond saw for microscopic observation. The choice of rock type was deliberate. The formation contained visible structures known as stromatolites, of a type earlier workers had tentatively identified as beings remains of algal reefs. Moreover, chert is a sedimentary rock that has been infiltrated by fine-grained quartz; its stability, impermeability, and fine grain lead to excellent preservation of organic remains. For example, the Devonian Rhynie chert, one of the classic Paleozoic fossil formations, has yielded beautifully preserved specimens, including structurally intact shrubby plants, plant spores, cuticle, wood, and pieces of primitive insects. The Rhynie specimens are less than a quarter as old as the gunflint assemblage. Even in the gunflint chert, however, organic cell walls remain intact, preserving cellular structure and traces of surface ornamentation.

When examined under the microscope, the thin sections revealed spheres and filaments. Both clearly were hollow and bounded by a sturdy wall of organic material; there was doubt that these were microorganisms. In the 1954 publication, some specimens were identified as blue-green algae, with a bacterial level of cellular organization, and others as relatively more advanced aquatic fungi. Nevertheless, subsequent detailed investigations have cast doubt on the identification of fungi in this or any other assemblage more than 1.5 billion years old. In papers published in 1965 and 1971, Barghoorn attributed a bacterial or blue-green algal origin to all of the gunflint organisms.

Tyler and Barghoorn were not the first to report microorganisms from Precambrian rocks of the Canadian shield; John W. Gruner had described and illustrated filaments of presumed algal affinities of comparable age between 1922 and 1925. Gruner's papers attracted less attention than Tyler and Barghoorn's for several reasons. First, the material was not as well preserved or illustrated and was not completely convincing. Second, prior to the routine use of radioactive decay as a means of dating rocks, the extreme antiquity of the specimens was not appreciated. Finally, although students of evolution and the geologic history of life are aware now that about five-sixths of biological evolution on Earth took place in the Precambrian era (this has been an area of intense speculative and investigative interest since World War II), few people were actively interested in the Precambrian in the 1920's.

Tyler and Barghoorn continued to collaborate on their investigations of gunflint organisms. After an interval of ten years, they published in *Science* a more detailed paper on their findings entitled "Microorganisms from the Gunflint Chert." Meanwhile, a concerted effort was under way at Harvard University and elsewhere to identify and investigate from a paleontological perspective other Precambrian sedimentary formations. J. William Schopf, who worked with Barghoorn as a graduate student at Harvard from 1963 to 1968 and subsequently joined the faculty of the University of California at Los Angeles, was active particularly in expanding knowledge of the scope of the Precambrian fossil record and in integrating the evidence with theories about the origin of life and Earth's earliest biosphere. He jokingly refers to the latter speculative activities as "biogeopoetry."

Impact of Event

The impact of Tyler and Barghoorn's paper is appreciated best in the context of the historical development of Precambrian paleobiology. Since the beginning of systematic paleontological investigation in the early nineteenth century, it has been recognized that the fossil record of readily visible plants and animals begins abruptly with the Cambrian period, originally defined by its stratigraphic position and characteristic fossils and now known to have begun approximately 580 million years ago. Cambrian sedimentary rocks contain abundant fossils of corals, sponges, and shellfish. The abrupt appearance of diverse, relatively advanced animals and the absence of fossils in Precambrian sediments were remarked upon by Charles Darwin, who could find no explanation for this phenomenon. Charles Dolittle Walcott, an American geologist who has been called the founder of Precambrian geology, made a systematic search for fossils in Precambrian rocks at the beginning of the twentieth century. He found a colonial alga, a few primitive shells, and worm trails in late Precambrian formations in the Grand Canyon, but confirmed the lack of macrofossils in most Precambrian sedimentary rocks. He also compared Precambrian specimens of characteristic laminated pillow-shaped objects with a Cambrian "organism," which had been named Cryptozoon, and concluded that both were elements from an algal reef. This important observation was not widely accepted. Such objects, which are called stromatolites now, are widespread in Precambrian sedimentary rocks as much as 3 billion years old. Accompanying microfossils and comparison with living forms indicate that stromatolites are formed by blue-green algae and possibly by other bacteria. Similar formations occur today in certain shallow tropical waters. The early work of Walcott and Gruner stands out among other Precambrian papers of very dubious quality. By 1950, there was a small body of evidence for Precambrian life, none of it universally accepted or completely convincing. Radiometric dating had confirmed what had already been suspected from stratigraphic evidence: that the Precambrian encompassed a far longer time span than the Phanerozoic (literally, the age of evident life—everything since the Precambrian). Estimates suggest that the earth was created 4.5 billion years ago.

In the absence of a fossil record, scientists turned to the laboratory and to comparison of living forms in an effort to formulate hypotheses about the origins and early evolution of life on Earth. Harold C. Urey and Stanley Miller postulated in the early 1950's that nonbiological processes early in the earth's history had created an "organic soup" in which electrical discharge produced complex molecules capable of replicating themselves and in which the precursors of the earliest cells developed. It was recognized that there was a fundamental distinction among living organisms between those that lack nuclei (prokaryotes), including bacteria and blue-green algae, and those having nuclei (eukaryotes), including plants, animals, fungi, and most algae, and that the transition from prokaryote to eukaryote was a major evolutionary hurdle. Assuming that life as it is known today evolved on Earth (a debatable assumption as long as there was no convincing Precambrian fossil record), then the most fundamental milestones in biological history, the evolution of cells and the evolution of eukaryotes, must have taken place in the enigmatic Precambrian.

In the years since Tyler and Barghoorn's paper, no direct fossil evidence for chemical evolution has emerged. The oldest sedimentary rocks that have not been subject to extensive deformation that would obliterate or distort organic traces—the 3.2-billion-year-old Fig Tree group in South Africa and the 3.5-billion-year-old Warrawoona group in Australia—contain rods and spheroids of presumed bacterial or blue-green algal origin, and stromatolites 3 billion years old have been found in Africa. This implies that the structure, mechanisms of heredity, and mechanisms of photosynthesis in prokaryotic cells evolved more than 3 billion years ago.

The time of emergence of eukaryotic cells and complex multicellular organisms is more apparent in the fossil record, although there is some debate about what constitutes sufficient evidence for the eukaryotic condition in a fossil microorganism. Approximately 1.5 billion years ago, there was an increase in size in fossil microbial cells, with forms corresponding to the size range for living eukaryotic algae predominating; true branching appears in filamentous organisms, and spores in tetrads are found. The 680-million-year-old Australian Ediacara fauna, from the very late Precambrian, contains a wide variety of soft-bodied multicellular animals, including jellyfish, soft corals, and worms. As had long been suspected, the explosion of macroscopic fossils at the onset of the Cambrian corresponds to the evolution of shells and was preceded by a period when soft-bodied animals predominated. That period was, however, brief compared with the 2.5-billion-plus years of microbial dominance and microbial evolution that preceded it.

It has been recognized for some time that living organisms have transformed the face of the earth in the Phanerozoic; the importance of their role in geological processes in the Precambrian was evident only when a usable fossil record became available. The fossil record provides information about the types and in some cases the abundance of microorganisms that were present at various stages in geologic time; the inorganic geologic record provides evidence for atmospheric and climatic changes, and comparison of the biochemistry of living forms provides clues as to probable conditions at the time various metabolic processes evolved.

The fossil record has been helpful in developing hypotheses about the role of oxygen in the early biosphere. The iron formations that were the subject of Tyler's investigation are the remains of a massive global geochemical event that took place approximately 2 billion years ago and that is the ultimate source of most of the world's high-grade iron ore. Fossil assemblages corresponding in age to these "red beds" contain numerous simple microbial forms whose size and level of organization correspond well to modern blue-green algae. Like more advanced algae and higher plants, blue-green algae produce oxygen as a by-product of their manufacture of starch and other carbohydrates from carbon dioxide and water. According to hypothesis, the beginning of the red beds in the geologic column marks the point in time when oxygen-producing photosynthesis evolved. This released free oxygen into water, which held quantities of soluble iron. Over a period of millions of years, oxygen released by blue-green algae oxidized iron in ocean water; the precipitated iron formed the red beds. When soluble iron was depleted, the oxygen content of the atmosphere began to rise.

Indirect fossil evidence for rising oxygen levels exists in the form of specialized nitrogen-fixing cells in blue-green algae and the appearance of eukaryotes, whose metabolism depends on free oxygen. Free oxygen made possible creation of the ozone layer, which was crucial to colonization of the land by plants and animals.

Large-scale geologic changes made by living organisms and the global interaction of the living and nonliving components of the planet are of more than academic interest. Human industrial processes that alter the composition of the earth's atmosphere may have precedent in the remote geologic past, and an understanding of the dynamics of the system throughout geologic time is crucial to preventing disastrous mistakes in the present.

Bibliography

Barghoorn, E. S. "The Oldest Fossils." *Scientific American* 224 (May, 1971): 12, 30-42. Includes electron micrographs of microorganisms from the 3-billion-year-old Fig Tree formation in South Africa and excellent color photographs of organisms from the gunflint chert.

Barghoorn, E. S., and S. A. Tyler. "Microorganisms from the Gunflint Chert." *Science* 147 (February 5, 1965): 563-577. Review article in a journal aimed at professional scientists in all disciplines: slightly more technical than articles appearing in the journal *Scientific American*. Includes illustrations and formal descriptions of a large number of diverse gunflint microorganisms and a detailed discussion of the geology of the region where the fossils were found. Published after Tyler's death; summarizes their joint work between 1954 and 1963.

Day, William. *Genesis on Planet Earth*. 2d ed. New Haven, Conn.: Yale University Press, 1984. A clear, well-presented account of current theory about the origin and nature of life on Earth. The first five chapters describe the origin of the earth and the early geologic history of life and include a historical narrative of key paleontological discoveries. Focuses on the chemistry of life processes and possible evolutionary pathways; includes a discussion of the evidence for organic matter elsewhere in the universe. Presupposes familiarity with scientific terminology and organic chemistry.

Schopf, J. William, ed. *The Earth's Earliest Biosphere*. Princeton, N.J.: Princeton University Press, 1983. A collection of papers from a symposium on early life. The chapter by Preston Cloud, "Early Biologic History: The Emergence of a Paradigm," divides Precambrian studies into four eras: the gestational century, 1850 to 1950; the emergent decade, the 1950's; the breakthrough decade, the 1960's; and the takeoff decade, the 1970's. Provides a clear account of research prior to 1954 and places the significance of Tyler and Barghoorn's research in a larger context.

_____. "The Evolution of the Earliest Cells." *Scientific American* 239 (September, 1978): 16, 110-112. Written for the well-informed layperson. Illustrated with color micrographs of a variety of Precambrian microorganisms that give a good impression of the nature of the fossil evidence. Includes a discussion of the role of oxygen in key metabolic pathways of prokaryotes and eukaryotes and a clear explanation of the relevance of this analysis to timing events in the evolution of cells and of the earth's atmosphere.

Martha Sherwood-Pike

Cross-References

Elster and Geitel Demonstrate Radioactivity in Rocks, Springs, and Air (1901), p. 93; Boltwood Uses Radioactivity to Obtain the Age of Rocks (1905), p. 285; Nirenberg Invents an Experimental Technique That Cracks the Genetic Code (1961), p. 1687; Barghoorn and Coworkers Find Amino Acids in 3-Billion-Year-Old Rocks (1967), p. 1851.

BELL TELEPHONE SCIENTISTS
DEVELOP THE PHOTOVOLTAIC CELL

Categories of event: Applied science and physics
Time: May, 1954
Locale: Bell Telephone Laboratories, Murray Hill, New Jersey

Pearson, Fuller, and Chapin, of Bell Telephone Laboratories, developed the photovoltaic cell, which produces electrical power from sunlight

Principal personages:

GERALD LEONDUS PEARSON (1905-1987), a research physicist at Bell Laboratories who was concerned with the development of silicon rectifiers, which led to the invention of the solar cell

CALVIN S. FULLER (1902-   ), a chemist at Bell Laboratories whose work on diffusing impurities into the surface of semiconductors was basic to the development of high-efficiency solar cells

DARYL M. CHAPIN (1906-   ), a physicist at Bell Laboratories who investigated direct conversion of solar into electrical energy

Summary of Event

Sunlight was first converted into electrical power in 1839 when French physicist Alexandre-Edmond Becquerel immersed two metal plates into a conducting fluid and exposed the apparatus to the sun. A small but observable voltage was generated. In 1873, Willoughby Smith discovered that selenium, a semiconductor, was sensitive to light. Further investigations proved that an electrical current was generated. Charles Fritts, in the 1880's, developed the first selenium solar cell. In spite of his optimism as to their future, his solar cells never attained much acceptance as a potential power source because of a low conversion efficiency, about 1 percent, for converting sunlight into electrical power.

In the early 1930's, scientists "rediscovered" Fritts's selenium cells. The new selenium cells, though useful for producing very small electrical currents, were still limited in their conversion efficiency. The search was on again for more efficient devices to convert sunlight to energy.

If a crystal is viewed as a periodic array of atoms, symmetry and proximity can be envisioned as causing the discrete electron energy levels to spread out and form bands in the solid. Two kinds of energy bands are formed: valence bands and conduction bands. In a pure semiconductor, at 0 Kelvins, the valence band is filled with electrons, and the conduction band is empty. At higher temperatures, thermal energies are sufficient to activate a small percentage of the electrons from the valence band to the conduction band. When an electron moves from the valence to the conduction band, it leaves behind a vacant electron site, or hole. This hole can act as a charge carrier, as can the electrons in the conduction band, in that a valence electron from a nearby chemical bond can transfer into the hole. The hole, hence, effectively migrates throughout the crystal. In a pure semiconductor, there are an equal number of conduction electrons and holes. When impurities are added to semiconductors, the band structure is altered, modifying the conducting properties of the material. An extrinsic semiconductor is formed. If an atom such as arsenic, with five valence electrons, is added to a semiconductor like silicon, four of the valence electrons participate in the covalent bonding; one electron remains unbonded. This excess electron is only weakly bonded to the arsenic atom; thus, its energy level is only slightly below the conduction band. Very little energy is necessary to raise this electron to the conduction band. Atoms with five valence electrons are called donor atoms, and semiconductors doped with donor atoms are called n-type semiconductors.

If a semiconductor is doped, instead, with an atom such as aluminum, with three valence electrons, bonds can be formed with only three of the neighboring atoms. An electron deficiency, or hole, remains in the fourth bond. The energy levels of such impurity atoms lie slightly above the valence band; hence, the levels are easily accessible to electrons in the valence band. When an electron jumps to this higher level, a hole is left behind in the valence band. Since such impurity atoms effectively accept electrons from the valence band, they are called acceptor atoms, and semiconductors doped with acceptor atoms are called p-type semiconductors. When p- and n-type semiconductors are intimately contacted, the boundary region between the two materials is called a p-n junction. Within this junction region, electrons from the n-region can migrate into the p-region, and holes from the p-region migrate into the n-region until a steady-state condition is reached. The electric field set up by this boundary layer prevents further motion of electrons and holes across the boundary. A p-n junction is critical to the operation of all semiconductor devices.

In the early 1950's, three Bell Telephone Laboratories research scientists, Calvin S. Fuller, Daryl M. Chapin, and Gerald Leondus Pearson, were working on three independent research projects. A set of fortuitous circumstances brought them, and their research, together to develop a much more efficient photovoltaic cell.

The photogeneration of a voltage across p-n junctions had been known since R. S. Ohl, also of Bell Laboratories, made the first solar cell in 1941. Nevertheless, like its predecessors, this cell was very inefficient. No real improvement in conversion efficiency was attained until the discovery of extrinsic semiconductors.

In 1950, Fuller began investigating the surface properties of germanium. Two particular effects interested him: the surface properties of germanium as they affected the electrical behavior of the very pure crystals that were being grown, and a curious property called "thermal conversion." The latter was, at this time, not understood. By this time, many advances had been made in solid state devices. The transistor and the p-n junction transistor had been developed. The band theory of metals was well established and also was being adapted to semiconductors. It was a puzzle, however, how a semiconducting crystal of, for example, germanium could change from a n-type conductor, which conducts negative charges (electrons), to a p-type conductor, which conducts positive charges, or vice versa. Fuller recognized that thermal conversion was related to the way people were handling the crystals when they etched and washed them. As Fuller recollected, "If one took very great pains to make very pure water, better than conductivity type, and then looked for this thermal effect in the germanium crystal, it did not happen. . . . The crystal was so sensitive that if you went into a laboratory and grabbed the doorknob and then happened to lightly touch the crystal, it would convert; that is it would change type from n to p on subsequent heating above about 500°C." It appeared that something in the ordinary water supply, later identified as copper, was responsible for this effect. The copper rapidly diffused into the crystal above about 500 degrees Celsius, creating acceptor sites, and hence, converting an n-type to p-type crystal. Subsequent work by Fuller and his colleagues identified group three elements as acceptors and group four elements as donors in silicon and germanium.

Meanwhile, another research group at Bell Laboratories, headed by Chapin, was seeking a dependable alternative energy source to power communication systems in isolated areas. Chapin was convinced that a solar-powered device would be the ideal solution, but his attempts to develop a more efficient selenium cell were unsuccessful.

Pearson (director of the rectifier program at Bell Laboratories), was aware of Fuller's investigations regarding diffusion in semiconductors. He was attempting to make surface junctions using lithium in silicon. Unfortunately, the diffusion rate of lithium was too high to produce useful diffusion junctions. In discussions with Fuller, it was suggested that Pearson try phosphorus and boron, which Fuller knew formed permanent junctions for room temperature use. The result was an efficient power rectifier 0.75 square centimeter in size, yielding 20 amps through a resistance of 0.08 ohm.

By chance, Pearson exposed one of Fuller's doped semiconductor crystals to light. Pearson recalled that to his surprise, "I noticed that it was very light-sensitive." He soon brought this information to the attention of Chapin, and the three scientists joined forces to develop an improved, more efficient photocell. According to Pearson, "Although at the start we weren't going after a solar cell at all, upon this discovery, we turned it into a solar cell project." The result was a permanent cell with an efficiency of nearly an order of magnitude better than the best selenium or copper oxide photocells in popular use.

The first of their new solar cells, with an efficiency of about 6 percent, was presented at the National Academy of Sciences meeting in Washington in May, 1954. Subsequent solar cells attained 12 to 15 percent efficiency on cells of almost a 2.5-centimeter-squared area, a respectable efficiency even today.

Impact of Event

Though the new Bell Laboratories solar cell was greeted with a storm of enthusiasm, its inventors chose to emphasize small-scale applications. They recognized that the solar cells were still limited in their application, primarily because of their high cost.

The first application of the silicon solar cell, in 1957, was to power a telephone repeater in Americus, Georgia. An array of cells delivered 9 watts of power, which was used to charge a nickel-cadmium storage battery. Though the process worked very well, it was not cost-effective compared to conventional energy sources.

Commercial use of silicon solar cells began when they became the preferred source of electrical power for space satellites. Solar cells were used in the first orbiting satellite, Vanguard 1, launched on March 17, 1958. Its radio transmitter, powered by solar cells, operated for eight years before failing because of radiation damage. Solar cells were also used in the 1960's, as a power source in the Telstar satellites; they continue today on all satellites for electrical power generation.

For many years, terrestrial applications of solar cells remained largely unexplored. With the increased concern regarding energy supplies and energy prices following the 1973 Organization of Petroleum Exporting Countries (OPEC) oil embargo, however, interest again focused on converting the sun's energy to electrical power. Many people, including officials within the U.S. Department of Energy, hoped that solar electrical energy would compete with electrical power from coal and nuclear generation. The early estimates of a capital cost of one thousand dollars per kilowatt, about that for coal-fired plants, however, were much too optimistic, perhaps by a factor of ten or fifteen. As remarked by Fuller in 1986, "We never believed or intended the cells would compete with coal or nuclear plants at the present stage of development."

Smaller-scale uses of photovoltaics are, nevertheless, increasing dramatically. Thousands of homes are powered by solar cell arrays. The majority of these installations are small and on remote dwellings by homeowners who wish to power some lights, a radio or television, but who are located in an isolated area. Some have more sophisticated systems and have connected their systems to the utility grid and engage in buy/sell arrangements with a power company.

The most noticeable boom in solar cell use, however, is undoubtedly in small devices such as hand-held calculators and watches. These have been made possible to a large extent by the development of amorphous (noncrystalline) silicon solar cells. Compared to crystalline silicon, amorphous silicon absorbs light more strongly in the visible spectrum, and it has a greater energy gap between the valence and the conduction band. This results in a higher theoretical efficiency than for single-crystal silicon cells. These efficiencies, however, have not been realized. In spite of this, the simple fabrication steps and the thin films that can be utilized mean that they can be a practical and relatively inexpensive solar cell if the 7 percent efficiency observed in the laboratory can be attained commercially.

Bibliography

Komp, Richard J. *Practical Photovoltaics.* Ann Arbor, Mich.: Aatec, 1984. In spite of the title, which leads one to expect only a set of "how-to" instructions, this book has almost a five-page foreword describing the history of photovoltaics and chapters devoted to the manufacture of solar cells, new technological developments, the photovoltaics industry, and the future of photovoltaics. Illustrated, with bibliography, glossary, and index.

Merrigan, Joseph A. *Sunlight to Electricity: Prospects for Solar Energy Conversion of Photovoltaics.* Cambridge, Mass.: MIT Press, 1975. Somewhat dated as to "state-of-the-art" technology and demand, but useful and interesting from a historical perspective, especially since it was published at the peak of energy concern following the 1973 OPEC oil embargo. Summarizes the mid-1970's perspective on economic considerations and business opportunities regarding photovoltaics. Extensive bibliography, indexed.

Millman, S., ed. *A History of Engineering and Science in the Bell System: Physical Sciences (1925-1980).* Murray Hill, N.J.: AT&T Bell Laboratories, 1980. A summary of the various developments at Bell Laboratories, providing a very brief description of the technological advances and the individuals involved at each stage. Fairly abbreviated (solar cells are discussed explicitly). More instructive for those with some previous understanding of semiconductors.

Raisbeck, Gordon. "The Solar Battery." *Scientific American* 193 (December, 1955): 102-110. One of the first scientifically oriented articles for the nonscientist regarding the Bell Laboratories solar cells. Interesting from a technical as well as historical perspective.

Swan, Christopher C. *Suncell: Energy, Economy, and Photovoltaics.* San Francisco: Sierra Club Books, 1986. Describes a variety of photovoltaic-related issues, including an extremely simplified description of what they are, recent innovations in photovoltaics, the photovoltaic industry, and the marketplace. Appropriate for the nonscientist, who is concerned not with the operation of solar cells, but only with their potential use and markets. Very optimistic approach as to their potential. Bibliography, indexed.

Nancy J. Sell

Cross-References

Elster and Geitel Devise the First Practical Photoelectric Cell (1904), p. 208; Einstein Develops His Theory of the Photoelectric Effect (1905), p. 260; Shockley, Bardeen, and Brattain Discover the Transistor (1947), p. 1304; Esaki Demonstrates Electron Tunneling in Semiconductors (1957), p. 1551; The United States Launches Its First Orbiting Satellite, Explorer 1 (1958), p. 1583; Telstar, the First Commercial Communications Satellite, Relays Live Transatlantic Television Pictures (1962), p. 1728; Bell Laboratories Scientists Announce a Liquid-Junction Solar Cell of 11.5 Percent Efficiency (1981), p. 2159.

FRANKLIN AND BURKE DISCOVER RADIO EMISSIONS FROM JUPITER

Category of event: Astronomy
Time: 1955
Locale: Carnegie Institute, Washington, D.C.

While testing antenna arrays for mapping galactic radio noise, Burke and Franklin discovered unexpected radio bursts in the 17-meter band from the planet Jupiter, the first detection of natural radio signals from a planet

Principal personages:
   BERNARD BURKE (1928-   ), an American physicist and astrophysicist
   KENNETH FRANKLIN (1923-   ), an American astrophysicist

Summary of Event

Although radio telescopes had been developed and employed in studies of galactic radiation since the mid-1930's, specific radio investigations of the solar system began only after World War II. In 1945, Robert H. Dicke first detected radio emissions from the moon at a wavelength of 1.25 centimeters, shortly after the U.S. Army Signal Corps sent and received the first radar echoes from the moon. Despite technical advances in receiver electronics and antenna array design, however, as radio astronomy historians A. G. Smith and T. D. Carr noted in 1964, there was no science of planetary astronomy prior to 1955, since theoretical as well as technical concerns focused most astronomical efforts at stellar and galactic objects. Perhaps the chief driving force behind the development of radio astronomy for the solar system was the entirely accidental and serendipitous discovery by American astronomer Kenneth Franklin and physicist Bernard Burke of natural radio emissions from the planet Jupiter.

In mid-January, 1955, the two scientists were actively engaged in carrying out a variety of calibration and reception tests for a large ("Mills cross") radio interferometer, which the Carnegie Institution's Laboratory of Space and Terrestrial Sciences had installed near Washington, D.C. This array had been funded and designed specifically for mapping the general cosmic background of ambient and discrete radio sources at a frequency (wavelength) of 22.2 megacycles per second. The Mills cross design, in particular, is a symmetric square array with four equal arms centered on a fixed axis. Previous radio astronomers had shown that this aperture configuration could be configured to yield a narrow search beam of about 2.5 degrees, which, then, could be optimally directed and focused to receive and track specific galactic regions. In a well-known account of these events ("An Account of the Discovery of Jupiter as a Radio Source," 1959), Franklin specifically recalled that during these calibration tests "at times the records exhibited a feature characteristic of (irregular) interference (similar to those from lightning discharges). . . . I recall saying once that we would have to investigate the origin of that interference some day. We joked that it was probably due to the faulty ignition of some farm hand returning from a date."

Notwithstanding their initial attitudes, when Burke subsequently compared a number of test recordings from their array, he and Franklin were surprised to find that the "interference" always occurred as short, or transient, bursts at about the same sidereal time (time measured with respect to stellar and not solar positions). Although this suggested initially that their radio noise was likely celestial and not terrestrial in origin, a quick search through a star atlas failed to reveal any established or possible radio-star that would have been present in the antenna's beam at the correct time. Somewhat later, the seismologist Howard Tatel suggested rather facetiously to Burke and Franklin that the noise might very well be from the planet Jupiter. "We were amused at the preposterous nature of this remark, and for an argument against it, I [Franklin] looked up Jupiter's position in the *American Ephemeris & Nautical Almanac*. I was surprised to find that Jupiter was just about in the place." Shortly thereafter, Franklin hand-plotted on a graph of celestial time versus celestial coordinate (right ascension) the positions of all the anomalous radio interference events for a two-month period. He then plotted the celestial positions of Jupiter, Uranus, and two galactic nebula, NGC 2420 and 2392, which all were close to the apparent position of the radio bursts at the above observation times. As each point was plotted, they appeared right between the boundary lines representing the beginning and end of each radio interference event. This meant that these events were recorded only when the planet Jupiter was in the confines of the narrow principal beam of the Mills cross. The source of the intermittent radiation was determined to be associated with Jupiter.

After their initial publication, Burke and Franklin reviewed earlier array test records from 1956 and found that they had unknowingly missed a previous strong burst from Jupiter. Nevertheless, almost immediately after Burke and Franklin's publication, an Australian radio astronomer C. H. Shain, long active in lunar radar and galactic radiotelescope studies, reexamined an extensive collection of radio records from 1950 and 1951 recorded at a somewhat lower frequency of 18.3 megahertz per second. Shain independently confirmed and extended the results of Burke and Franklin, finding no less than sixty-one records having signals that could be attributed to Jupiter using their same tracking method. Although missing the acolades of "discoverer," Shain was able to demonstrate that the radio bursts came from a very localized area on Jupiter's disk and not from the planet as a whole. Shain further showed that this localized radio source could be received only when it was near the center of the Jovian disk. He found that the burst occurrences encompassed one major intensity peak and two lesser flanking bursts, which although not associatable with any visible features such as Jupiter's "red spot," were highly directional in nature.

Impact of Event

The discoveries of Burke and Franklin in 1955 and Shain in 1955 and 1956 quickly gave tremendous technical and competitive impetus to further radio studies of Jupiter and the other planets. In 1956, the first reported reception of what appeared to be similar sporadic radio signals from Venus at a somewhat shorter wavelength (11 meters) was found, although these were not confirmed by other researchers, and refocused many efforts to even shorter wavelengths. The first microwave (centimeter wavelength) radio emissions from Jupiter, Mars, and Venus were detected in 1956 by researchers at the U.S. Naval Research Laboratory in Washington, D.C. In contrast to recordings of Burke and Franklin, these decimetric radio emissions occurred as continuous radio noise. Although from 1956 to 1958 microwave observations of Jupiter at 3-4 centimeters revealed no new findings about the planet, during the summer of 1958, radio measurements determined at 10.3 centimeters indicated a Jovian disk temperature of 640 Kelvins, unexpected in comparison to the ~140 Kelvins at 3.15 centimeters. It was then recognized that if, like Earth, the temperature of Jupiter's atmosphere varied with depth, higher temperatures should be observed at longer radio wavelengths. Soon many observations at 21, 22, 31, and 68 centimeters, respectively, indicated temperatures on Jupiter's disk of ~2,500 Kelvins, ~3,000 Kelvins, ~5,500 Kelvins, and more than 20,000 Kelvins. Limits on the Jovian atmosphere had been set previously only by observing pressure broadening of specific elemental lines in Jupiter's visual spectra. Although the radiometric temperature of Jupiter's outer layers agreed well with that estimated from assuming ice crystals of solidified ammonia, the longer-wavelength data caused notable rethinking of theories explaining planetary atmosphere formation and dynamics.

In June, 1959, Field submitted a paper to the *Journal of Geophysical Research*, first proposing that synchrotron radiation was responsible for the enhanced temperatures of Jupiter's atmosphere. Synchrotron radiation is composed of electromagnetic waves emitted by charged particles moving in regular orbits in a magnetic field at relativistic speeds. The large magnetic fields of extended size and their associated strong polarization were confirmed subsequently by observations in 1961. Another important and resistant discovery in 1964 demonstrated that the probability of receiving decimetric emissions from Jupiter was closely associated with the orbital position of the Jovian satellite Io. The satellite flybys of Pioneer 10 and 11 consequently showed that Jupiter's numerous cloud belts consist of different gases of differing temperatures at different heights. Additional irregular radio noise also has been observed, thought to arise from what are essentially lightning storms on Jupiter's dark side. Both Saturn and Venus were discovered to be radiating in the microwave band, also.

Although intrinsically feeble in terms of absolute power, next to the sun, Jupiter has the solar system's strongest natural radio source. Greater numbers of observations having improved accuracy, resolution, and spectral bandwidth have further refined, but not essentially altered, the findings fortuitously recognized by Franklin and Burke.

Bibliography

Bracewell, R. N., ed. *Paris Symposium on Radio Astronomy*. Palo Alto, Calif.: Stanford University Press, 1959. Gives a good collection of radio telescope designs and capabilities during the 1950's.

Franklin, K. L. "An Account of the Discovery of Jupiter as Radio Source." *Astronomical Journal* 64 (1959): 37-39. The principal source for the historical sequence of events of the radio source. Fascinating.

Krüger, Albrecht, ed. *Introduction to Solar Radio Astronomy and Radio Physics.* Dordrecht, The Netherlands: Kluwer Academic Press, 1979. Presents an account of technology and methods in planetary radio astronomy.

Rohlfs, Kristen. *Tools of Radio Astronomy.* New York: Springer-Verlag, 1986. A semitechnical account of radio telescope array, receiver, and signal processor principles.

Smith, A. G., and T. D. Carr. *Radio Exploration of the Planetary System.* Princeton, N.J.: D. Van Nostrand, 1964. The first detailed, nontechnical account of the rapid growth of solar system radio astronomy following Franklin and Burke's discovery.

Wall, J. V., and A. Boksenberg, eds. *Modern Technology and Its Influence on Astronomy.* New York: Cambridge University Press, 1990. A collection of papers by historians of science examining the limits and opportunities on prior radio astronomy caused by hardware and software constraints.

Washburn, Mark. *Distant Encounters: The Exploration of Jupiter and Saturn.* San Diego: Harcourt Brace Jovanovich, 1983. A popular account of Pioneer flyby results for the middle planets.

Gerardo G. Tango

Cross-References

Jansky's Experiments Lead to the Founding of Radio Astronomy (1930), p. 934; Reber Builds the First Intentional Radio Telescope (1937), p. 1113; Reber Makes the First Radio Maps of the Universe (1942), p. 1193; Ryle's Radio Telescope Locates the First Known Radio Galaxy (1946), p. 1271; Ryle Constructs the First Radio Interferometer (1955), p. 1496; The Jodrell Bank Radio Telescope Is Developed (1957), p. 1539; A Radio Astronomy Team Sends and Receives Radar Signals to and from the Sun (1959), p. 1598; The First Ring Around Jupiter Is Discovered (1979), p. 2104.

RYLE CONSTRUCTS THE
FIRST RADIO INTERFEROMETER

Category of event: Astronomy
Time: 1955
Locale: Cambridge, England

Ryle developed the first radio interferometer, an astronomical instrument involving several radio telescopes coordinated by computer

Principal personages:

SIR MARTIN RYLE (1918-1984), an English astronomer who applied radar technology to the construction of radio telescopes, including high-resolution multiple radio telescope interferometers

KARL JANSKY (1905-1950), an American radio engineer who invented radio astronomy and first detected extraterrestrial radio sources

HENDRIK CHRISTOFFEL VAN DE HULST (1918-   ), a Dutch radio astronomer who proposed that hydrogen atoms emit radio waves with a 21-centimeter wavelength

HAROLD IRVING EWEN (1922-   ), an American astrophysicist at Harvard University who verified van de Hulst's proposal

EDWARD MILLS PURCELL (1912-   ), an American physicist who received the 1952 Nobel Prize in Physics for his radio astronomy and astrophysics research

Summary of Event

Electromagnetic radiation consists of packets of energy called photons, which behave both as particles and waves and travel at the speed of light (approximately 300 million meters per second). The electromagnetic radiation spectrum ranges from long-wavelength, low-frequency radiations to progressively shorter-wavelength, higher-frequency radiations (from radio to television to microwave to infrared to visible light to ultraviolet to X rays to gamma rays to cosmic rays). All of these radiations are emitted by various objects in the universe, most notably stars such as Earth's sun.

Since the early 1600's, astronomy has relied on optical telescopes (glass lenses) for resolving stellar objects unviewable with the naked eye. The Italian scientist Galileo pioneered the use of telescopes, while verifying Nicolaus Copernicus' heliocentric (sun-centered) theory of the solar system. Optical telescopes detect the visible light emission from stars, galaxies, quasars, and other astronomical objects. Through the late twentieth century, astronomers developed more powerful optical telescopes for peering deeper into the cosmos and viewing objects located hundreds of millions of light-years away from the earth.

In 1933, Karl Jansky, an American radio engineer with Bell Telephone Laboratories, constructed a radio antenna receiver for locating sources of telephone interference. Jansky discovered that an intense radio burst occurred at approximately the same time every day. The radio burst occurred every twenty-three hours and fifty-six minutes, the time required for one complete Earth rotation about its axis relative to the stars. He mapped the radio source as emanating from outside the solar system in the direction of the constellation Sagittarius. He had detected radio waves from the center of the Milky Way galaxy, a discovery that confirmed astronomer Harlow Shapley's 1918 mapping of the Milky Way's center to Sagittarius. Jansky's radio telescope was a horizontal antenna that detected radio emissions from the earth's horizon. Except for detecting radio emissions from the center of the galaxy, the instrument had few other uses. Jansky's pioneering work was discovered by Grote Reber, an Illinois radio amateur.

In 1935, Reber constructed the first dish-shaped radio telescope, the forerunner of today's instruments. Reber used his 9-meter diameter radio telescope to repeat Jansky's experiments and to locate other radio sources in space. He confirmed Jansky's conclusion that the Milky Way's galactic center emits radio waves. He also precisely mapped the locations of various radio sources in space, some of which later were identified as galaxies and quasars.

Following World War II, radio astronomy blossomed with the help of surplus radar equipment. Radar operators had discovered that the sun produced radio interference in radar signals, which is not surprising considering that radar uses slightly higher-frequency microwaves. Radar equipment was used to demonstrate that the sun is a strong radio source. The work of Jansky and Reber further strengthened the drive to understand the nature of extraterrestrial radio sources.

In 1944, the Dutch astronomer Hendrik Christoffel van de Hulst had proposed that hydrogen atoms emit radio waves with a 21-centimeter wavelength. According to his theory, a hydrogen atom undergoes a phase transition once every 10 million years and emits 21-centimeter radio waves in the process. Because hydrogen is the most abundant element in the universe (approximately 60-80 percent by weight) and because hydrogen is the primary elemental component of most stars, van de Hulst had explained the nature of extraterrestrial radio waves. His theory later was confirmed by the American radio astronomers Harold Irving Ewen and Edward Mills Purcell of Harvard University. Eventually, astrophysicists demonstrated that atoms of each element emit radio waves at characteristic wavelengths and therefore that stars emit radio waves as they emit visible light waves. By coupling the newly invented computer technology with radio telescopes, astronomers were able to generate a radio image of a star almost identical to the star's optical image. A major advantage of radio telescopes over optical telescopes is the ability of radio telescopes to detect extraterrestrial radio emissions day or night, while optical telescopes are limited to nighttime viewing.

Following World War II, major research groups were formed in England, Australia, and The Netherlands. English radio astronomy efforts were headed by Sir Bernard Lovell at the Nuffield Radio Astronomy Laboratories in Jodrell Bank, J. S. Hey at the Royal Radar Establishment in Malvern, and Sir Martin Ryle at the Mullard Radio Astronomy Observatory of the Cavendish Laboratory, University of Cambridge. Australian efforts were led by J. L. Pawsey and John G. Bolton.

Ryle had worked with radar for the Telecommunications Research Establishment during World War II. Following the war, he received a fellowship to study astronomy at the Cavendish Laboratory in Cambridge. He concentrated on the development of radio telescopes and applied these instruments to the analysis of radio emissions from the sun and nearby stars. He helped to establish the Cavendish Laboratory's Mullard Radio Astronomy Observatory, where he became director in 1957.

The radio telescopes developed by Ryle and other astronomers operate on the same basic principles as satellite television receivers. A constant stream of radio waves from a star or galaxy penetrates the earth's atmosphere and strikes the parabolic-shaped reflector (dish) of the radio telescope. The radio waves bounce off the reflector, the parabolic shape of the dish aiming the radio waves at a focusing point above the dish. The focusing point is another reflector, which bounces the concentrated radio beam to the center of the dish, where it is funneled down a feed horn to electronic cables. The electronic cables transmit the radio signal to a radio receiver, then an amplifier, and finally to a chart recorder, or computer. A radio telescope, therefore, captures a radio beam, concentrates it, amplifies it, and records it for analysis.

With large-diameter radio telescopes, astronomers can locate stars and galaxies unviewable with the naked eye and unviewable with optical telescopes. This ability to detect more distant objects is called resolution. Like optical telescopes, large-diameter radio telescopes have better resolution than smaller ones. Very large radio telescopes were constructed in the late 1950's and early 1960's (Jodrell Bank, England; Green Bank, West Virginia; Arecibo, Puerto Rico). Instead of building larger radio telescopes to achieve greater resolution, however, Ryle developed a method using smaller radio telescopes to reach the same goal. The result was interferometry, a technique that uses a computer to combine the incoming radio waves of two or more movable radio telescopes pointed at the same stellar object.

Suppose that one had a 30-meter-diameter radio telescope. Its radio wave collecting area would be limited to its diameter. If a second identical 30-meter-diameter radio telescope was linked with the first in synchrony, then one would have an interferometer. The two radio telescopes would point exactly at the same stellar object, and the radio emissions from this object captured by the two telescopes would be combined by computer to produce a higher-resolution image. If the two radio telescopes were located 1.6 kilometers apart, then their combined resolution no longer would be limited to the area of a single 30-meter-diameter receiving dish. Instead, the combined interferometer resolution would be equivalent to that of a single radio telescope dish 1.6 kilometers in diameter.

Ryle constructed the first true radio telescope interferometer at the Mullard Radio Astronomy Observatory in 1955. He used combinations of radio telescopes to produce interferometers containing about twelve receivers. Ryle's interferometer greatly improved radio telescope resolution for detecting stellar radio sources, mapping the locations of stars and galaxies, assisting in the discovery of quasars (quasi-stellar radio sources), measuring the earth's rotation about the sun, and measuring the motion of the solar system through space.

Impact of Event

Ryle's development of radio interferometry greatly expanded the power of radio telescopes and significantly helped radio astronomy to emerge as the leading facet of late twentieth century astronomy. Interferometry has enabled astronomers to see further and further into the past, to observe objects which existed as long ago as 10 billion years. Interferometry also stimulated the development of innovative telescope designs and arrays for improved resolution.

Following Ryle's discovery, interferometers were constructed at radio astronomy observatories throughout the world. The United States established the National Radio Astronomy Observatory (NRAO) in rural Green Bank, West Virginia. NRAO is operated by a consortium of nine eastern universities and is funded by the National Science Foundation. At Green Bank, a three-telescope interferometer was constructed, with each radio telescope having a 26-meter-diameter dish. With an additional 91-meter-diameter radio telescope and a 43-meter fully steerable radio telescope, NRAO became a world leader in radio astronomy research. The United States Naval Observatory would eventually operate the NRAO interferometer for precision navigation and timekeeping.

During the late 1970's, NRAO constructed the largest radio interferometer in the world, the Very Large Array (VLA). The VLA, located approximately 80 kilometers west of Socorro, New Mexico, consists of twenty-seven 25-meter-diameter radio telescopes linked by a supercomputer. The radio telescopes are arranged in a Y-shape covering an area 32 kilometers by 32 kilometers across the flat New Mexico desert. Each telescope is mounted on a transport vehicle on a railroad track. Nine telescopes are located on each of three 21-kilometer railroad tracks that together form the Y-shape interferometer. The VLA has a resolution equivalent to that of a single radio telescope 32 kilometers in diameter.

Even larger radio telescope interferometers can be synthesized. A technique known as very long baseline interferometry (VLBI) has been used to construct artificially a radio telescope having an effective diameter of several thousand kilometers. Such an arrangement involves the precise synchronization of radio telescopes located in several different parts of the world, followed by analysis of the data (stored on magnetic tape) at a central processing laboratory. For example, Supernova 1987A in the Large Magellanic Cloud was studied using a VLBI arrangement between observatories located in Australia, South America, and South Africa.

Future radio telescope interferometers include even larger VLBI arrangements. The launching of radio telescopes into orbit and linking them with ground-based radio telescopes could synthesize a radio telescope whose effective diameter would be larger than the earth. Such a powerful radio telescope could be produced by the late 1990's, according to George A. Seielstad, assistant director of Green Bank operations for NRAO. An orbiting Soviet radio telescope called Radioastron, scheduled for launch in 1993, could be linked with a new 100-meter-diameter radio telescope in Green Bank and with orbiting radio telescopes operated by Japan and the European Space Agency. Such powerful instruments will enable astronomers to map the distribution of galaxies, quasars, and other cosmic objects, to understand the origin and evolution of the universe, and possibly to detect meaningful radio signals from extraterrestrial civilizations.

Bibliography

Associated Universities, Inc. *The National Radio Astronomy Observatory.* Charlottesville, Va.: National Radio Astronomy Observatory, 1981. This small book is a simple presentation of astronomy and radio astronomy. It uses clear illustrations and outstanding photographs to describe basic radio astronomical principles. The VLA and other NRAO radio telescopes are described.

Kellermann, Kenneth I., and A. Richard Thompson. "The Very-Long-Baseline Array." *Scientific American* 258 (January, 1988): 54-63. This survey article, written by two radio astronomers, is a discussion of the principles behind VLBI. A proposed linkage of ten American radio telescopes is described, along with the VLA and future orbiting radio telescope interferometers.

Kippenhahn, Rudolf. *Light from the Depths of Time.* Translated by Storm Dunlop. New York: Springer-Verlag, 1987. This book is an outstanding introduction to astronomy and cosmology for the average reader. Kippenhahn simplifies many complex astronomical concepts in a very entertaining fashion. Chapter 10, "The Radio Sky," describes the history of radio astronomy, including the work of Jansky, Reber, Ryle, and other astronomers.

Lovell, Sir Bernard. *The Story of Jodrell Bank.* London: Oxford University Press, 1968. This historical chronicle is Lovell's personal account of the construction of the 76-meter-diameter Jodrell Bank radio telescope, one of the largest radio telescopes in the world. He describes the history of radio astronomy, including the work of Ryle and other astronomers.

McDonough, Thomas R. *The Search for Extraterrestrial Intelligence: Listening for Life in the Cosmos.* New York: John Wiley & Sons, 1987. This entertaining book is a discussion of serious scientific efforts to detect the existence of intelligent life elsewhere in the universe. Chapter 16, "The Final Frontier," discusses the history of radio astronomy and the current use of some radio telescopes to detect potentially intelligent radio signals from outer space.

Rubin, Vera, and George V. Coyne, eds. *Large-Scale Motions in the Universe: A Vatican Study Week.* Princeton, N.J.: Princeton University Press, 1988. This book is a collection of scientific papers presented by leading astronomers and radio astronomers at an annual Vatican astronomy conference. The various research papers describe the applications of radio astronomy to the mapping of galaxies in space, thereby giving scientists some idea of the organization of the universe.

Seielstad, George A. *At the Heart of the Web: The Inevitable Genesis of Intelligent Life*. Boston: Harcourt Brace Jovanovich, 1989. This book, written by a leading NRAO astronomer, is a lively discussion of cosmology and Earth's place in the universe. The book links biology and other major scientific disciplines to astronomy. It also presents radio astronomical methods and data.

Silk, Joseph. *The Big Bang*. Rev. ed. New York: W. H. Freeman, 1989. This book is a comprehensive, yet very readable, discussion of current views of the origin and evolution of the universe. It discusses cosmology, galaxies, quasars, and radio astronomy, including radio telescope interferometers.

Verschuur, Gerrit L. *The Invisible Universe: The Story of Radio Astronomy*. New York: Springer-Verlag, 1974. This book is an outstanding discussion of radio astronomy and its history. All aspects of radio astronomy are clearly described and illustrated. Chapter 2, "The Birth of Radio Astronomy," describes the early work of Jansky, Reber, Lovell, Ryle, and other radio astronomers.

David Wason Hollar, Jr.

Cross-References

Jansky's Experiments Lead to the Founding of Radio Astronomy (1930), p. 934; Ryle's Radio Telescope Locates the First Known Radio Galaxy (1946), p. 1271; De Vaucouleurs Identifies the Local Supercluster of Galaxies (1953), p. 1454; Franklin and Burke Discover Radio Emissions from Jupiter (1955), p. 1492; The Jodrell Bank Radio Telescope Is Completed (1957), p. 1539; Giacconi and Associates Discover the First Known X-Ray Source Outside the Solar System (1962), p. 1708; Schmidt Makes What Constitutes the First Recognition of a Quasar (1963), p. 1757; Very Long Baseline Interferometry (VLBI) Is Developed for High-Resolution Astronomy and Geodesy (1969), p. 1902; The Oldest Known Galaxy Is Discovered (1988), p. 2367.

THE FIRST TRANSATLANTIC TELEPHONE CABLE IS PUT INTO OPERATION

Category of event: Applied science
Time: 1956
Locale: Continental United States to Europe

The first transatlantic cable was designed to transmit telephone traffic between the United States and Europe

Principal personages:

SAMUEL F. B. MORSE (1791-1872), a telegraph inventor who laid the first telegraph cable

CYRUS WEST FIELD (1819-1892), an American financier who formed a company to lay the first telegraph cable

Summary of Event

The history of submarine cable design and development is largely a chronicle of repeated frustration and failure. From the time of the first telegraph communication, scientists had attempted to lay cable along the bottoms of waterways in order to connect distant points in as direct a route as possible at minimal cost for right-of-way access. Even before the first lines were constructed on land, telegraph inventor Samuel F. B. Morse had strung a telegraph cable across New York Harbor. In 1852, American financier Cyrus West Field organized a company to lay the first telegraph cable from the American continent to Europe. On August 5, 1858, the first cable was in place, and U.S. President James Buchanan communicated with Queen Victoria to inaugurate the first transoceanic electronic communication link. Unfortunately, the euphoria was short-lived. The cable failed a month later when its insulation was damaged by high-voltage transmission. In 1865, another company tried and failed to lay a new cable. Not until 1869 was the first truly successful effort completed and the first reliable transatlantic cable in place.

The time interval from the invention of the telegraph to the first reliable transoceanic telegraph cable transmissions was relatively short compared to the time it took to deploy a transoceanic telephone cable. The first transatlantic telephone cable was put into service in 1956, approximately one hundred years after the first telegraph cable. The physical character of telephony requires much more of cable than does the relatively simple transmission mode used in telegraphy. Voice communication requires that a broad range of vocal character be transmitted successfully over wire, requiring that cable be designed to achieve a high degree of frequency response. As in land-line transmission, submarine cable must carry signals over long distances without significantly distorting them, a challenge whose solution proved elusive to researchers for almost three-quarters of a century.

In fairness, it must be pointed out that early interest in radiotelephony diverted the attention of researchers away from cable for much of the first half of the twentieth century. It was not until after World War II that research on submarine cable design began in earnest. Radiotelephony proved somewhat unreliable for transoceanic communication, as shortwave broadcasts were highly susceptible to interference and noise caused by changes in weather patterns.

A key scientific discovery in the late 1940's, that of the transistor, made the problem of telephone circuit amplification appear solvable. Just as amplifiers, or repeaters, were needed in long-distance land-line transmission to maintain signal strength and quality, so were they necessary in submarine cable for the same reasons. In land lines, however, maintenance of amplifiers was a much simpler task than in submarine cable. Early telephone repeaters were designed to incorporate vacuum tubes, devices used in early broadcasting to amplify and transmit radio waves. While research into their use in submarine cable actually occurred during the 1920's, the effort was regarded as futile even then.

Transistors held great promise in that they were compact, inexpensive, stable, long-lived, and energy-efficient. The first few years following their discovery, however, proved frustrating to telephone engineers, who were unable to incorporate them successfully in facility designs. Eventually, refinements in the transistor concept led to the breakthrough that resulted in their ultimately successful application in submarine cable design.

Submarine cable had to be designed to withstand the unusual, often hostile environments found at the bottom of the ocean. Pressure, moisture, and cold were formidable opponents, and a variety of cable sheathing and insulating materials used in experiments that simulated such conditions had proved unreliable over the long haul. In addition, over the years, various materials had been used that varied in terms of their elasticity and their ability to withstand heat or cold without cracking or otherwise disintegrating. Following World War II, polyethylene emerged as a primary material for encapsulating wire because of its nonpolarity and relative lack of impurities. After much experimentation, a formula of polyethylene and 5 percent Butyl rubber was used in the manufacture of the SB submarine cable system, the design that would be used ultimately in the construction of the first transatlantic telephone cable.

It was important to submarine cable designers that the transatlantic cable have multicircuit capacity. The first cable included sixty-four voice channels, each of which could be used simultaneously with the others. Each channel was able to transmit a high-quality voice conversation in two directions simultaneously. This represented a significant advantage over radiotelephony, which required the use of two frequencies to accomplish the same task. The cable also had the advantage of a relative lack of interference by atmospheric or human-made electromagnetic conditions.

The 1956 cable deployment and operation was a success. The cable sheathing and insulation proved reliable, and the quality of the circuits was acceptable. Soon, a new system called SD was deployed. It carried 128 two-way circuits and utilized an improved polyethylene resin formula for improved quality and uniformity. Over the next decade, additional cables were laid, each an improvement over the last. By the early 1970's, yet another system, SG, was put into service with forty-two hundred circuits.

Undersea telephone cable technology was challenged by another emergent technology almost from the time it was first deployed. By 1962, merely six years after the first submarine telephone cable was put into operation, AT&T began to supplement underwater cable with satellite transmission of telephone conversations. The company launched Telstar, a satellite that received signals from ground stations, amplified them, then relayed them back to down links around the globe. Telstar contained the equivalent of six hundred voice circuits. Over the years, many more satellites were launched by a number of governmental, military, and commercial interests, expanding the number of satellite voice circuits into the hundreds of thousands. As capacity increased, the cost of using satellites for international voice communication decreased substantially, and the transatlantic telephone cables, although they were still kept in service, became secondary transmission facilities.

As satellites were increasingly employed for long-distance telephone transmission, technology continued to improve. In the early 1990's, a new kind of submarine cable was under development using fiber optics as the primary conductor. Proponents believed that light fiber submarine cable would be able to transmit a virtually unlimited number of voice, data, and video information exchanges at very low cost.

Light fiber was an improvement on other fronts as well. Despite the convenience and relative low cost of satellite transmission, there were significant problems with it that were of concern to many telephone customers. Satellite signals were often subject to electromagnetic interference, a major hindrance to acceptably high-quality transmission. During the 1980's, the amount of data traffic versus voice traffic as a percentage of total traffic over the global telecommunications network was growing, and improvements in digital transmission technology were pushing the speed of data transmission upward. Electromagnetic interference made high-speed transmission of that data difficult to accomplish. Fiber-optic technology answered the challenge by providing a virtually interference-free transmission capability.

Another problem was security. Satellite signals could be intercepted easily, making satellite transmission inappropriate for some communications. Fiber optics, on the other hand, offered secure transmission by virtue of the fact that there was no radiation of signal transmission. Interception of light fiber transmissions was much more difficult. By the early 1990's, undersea cable using fiber optics in place of metallic transmission media was on the forefront of telephony, an emerging technology with great promise for the future.

Impact of Event

Submarine cables were not new in 1956. In fact, the first transoceanic cable had been deployed a century earlier to carry telegraph signals between the United States and continental Europe. The first submarine cable was only a first step in the evolution of underwater transmission facilities. The quality of signals transmitted over it was poor, and signal strength was so weak that it could communicate only a few words per minute. After the invention of the telephone two decades later, attempts to use telegraph cables to transmit telephone conversations were unsuccessful. The distance was too great for the relatively unsophisticated amplification techniques available, and the nature of the steel conductor at the core of the cable made it unacceptable for voice traffic because it was technically incapable of achieving the range of frequency response necessary for voice transmission.

Another factor that influenced the evolution of submarine cable technology was the political situation in Europe during the first half of the twentieth century. Two world wars that polarized much of the European community disrupted the economic and political landscape on that continent, and laying a transatlantic telephone cable during that time would have been a risky proposition at best, an enterprise fraught with uncertainty. In a real sense, the laying of a transatlantic telephone cable was a technical achievement that would have to wait until the mid-1950's, after the telecommunications infrastructure of that war-torn continent had been rebuilt and the Allied economies stabilized. Also, it was necessary for operators of the U.S. telecommunications network to demobilize and to adjust to the newly emerging opportunities in Europe.

The first transatlantic telephone cable was a significant achievement in telephony, but it also represented the first step in the establishment of a truly global, instantaneous electronic voice communication network. Its deployment two years before Sputnik, the first human-made satellite to circle the earth, meant that virtually every home with a telephone was connected to the transoceanic network. It was a significant achievement in the design of long-distance conductors, amplifiers, and submarine cable insulation and sheathing. For the first time, the reliability of submarine telephone circuitry had been demonstrated successfully, and efforts to increase the number of circuits to accommodate growing demand for overseas voice communication were under way.

As has often been the case throughout history, the superiority of one innovative technology over others can evaporate suddenly with the appearance of yet another that promises greater return for one reason or another. Such was the case with the submarine cable. It was designed to provide multiple voice circuits to expedite instantaneous person-to-person communication among continents utilizing the national telephone networks in countries that would be reached via that cable. While it provided that service reliably for many years, soon geosynchronous satellites high above the equator were able to offer the same service, but with much greater circuit capacity. Another advantage was the satellite's unique ability to relay voice conversations to even the most remote locations on the face of the earth. In theory, an elaborate telephone network was not required for two parties—each located in some remote corner of the world—to communicate with each other. As long as each had a transmitter and receiver capable of supporting a relay via a communications satellite, telecommunications infrastructure was not required. Such a relay could span oceans as well as continents quite easily. This capability made the satellite extremely attractive to many countries that lacked adequate telecommunications infrastructure, and it was only a matter of time before it would be used extensively to relay transoceanic telephone conversations.

Once the new fiber-optic transoceanic cables are in operation, providing expanded capacity and improved security characteristics beyond those available from satellites, it is probable that these advantages will result in a strong demand among users in need of secure high-speed data transmission facilities. Some observers believe the truly golden era of the undersea cable is yet to come.

Bibliography

Brooks, John. *Telephone: The First Hundred Years.* New York: Harper & Row, 1976. This excellent corporate history of the Bell system includes many anecdotes and colorful stories about the early years of telephony, giving life and context to what could otherwise be described as a highly technical description of the birth and development of one of the world's most remarkable companies. Includes a discussion of the evolution of transoceanic cable in the Bell Laboratories.

Danielian, Noorbar R. *AT&T: The Story of Industrial Conquest.* New York: Vanguard Press, 1939. A good look at some of the personalities involved in the development of the world's largest telephone network. Provides a strong backdrop for gaining an understanding of how and why decisions were made regarding the adoption of technical innovations at AT&T through the years.

Millman, S., ed. *A History of Engineering and Science in the Bell System: Communications Sciences (1925-1980).* Short Hills, N.J.: AT&T Bell Laboratories, 1984. This book discusses the various foundations of applied physics in communications technology, including television, radio, lightwave transmission, and digital communications. Index.

_____, ed. *A History of Engineering and Science in the Bell System: Physical Sciences (1925-1980).* Murray Hill, N.J.: AT&T Bell Laboratories, 1983. This book contains a very good overview of the problems (and solutions) encountered in the construction of the first cables designed for transoceanic service. Prepared by the Bell Laboratories, it discusses such arcane subjects as the physics of polymers, dielectrics, and crystal growth. Index.

Ress, Etta Schneider. *Signals to Satellites in Today's World.* Mankato, Minn.: Creative Educational Society, 1965. This heavily illustrated book is a layperson's overview of the evolution of communication technology over the centuries up to the mid-1960's. Includes a good discussion of the history of transoceanic cable from the middle of the nineteenth century to the deployment of the first telephone cable in 1956. Illustrated.

Smits, F. M., ed. *A History of Engineering and Science in the Bell System: Electronics Technology (1925-1975).* Indianapolis: AT&T Bell Laboratories, 1985. Reviews developments in electronics that have been incorporated into the design of long-distance cable and related equipment, including the transistor, integrated circuits, and optical devices. Index.

Michael S. Ameigh

Cross-References

Marconi Receives the First Transatlantic Telegraphic Radio Transmission (1901), p. 128; Fleming Files a Patent for the First Vacuum Tube (1904), p. 255; The First Transcontinental Telephone Call Is Made (1915), p. 595; Transatlantic Radiotelephony Is First Demonstrated (1915), p. 615; The Principles of Shortwave Radio Communication Are Discovered (1919), p. 669; Shockley, Bardeen, and Brattain Discover the Transistor (1947), p. 1304; Direct Transoceanic Dialing Begins (1971), p. 1934; The First Commercial Test of Fiber Optic Telecommunications Is Conducted (1977), p. 2078.

HEEZEN AND EWING DISCOVER
THE MIDOCEANIC RIDGE

Category of event: Earth science
Time: 1956
Locale: Atlantic Ocean

After leading the expedition to gather echograms of the ocean's floor, Ewing discovered the existence of the Midoceanic Ridge and postulated, with Heezen, the existence of a midoceanic rift

> *Principal personages:*
> MAURICE EWING (1906-1974), an American geophysicist who led the expedition that resulted in the discovery of the Midoceanic Ridge
> BRUCE CHARLES HEEZEN (1924-1977), an American oceanographer and geologist who developed the theory of the Midoceanic Rift with Maurice Ewing
> REGINALD AUBREY FESSENDEN (1866-1932), a Canadian physicist and engineer who was responsible for inventing the earliest sonar in 1914
> HARRY HAMMOND HESS (1906-1969), an American geologist who postulated the idea of seafloor spreading
> ALFRED LOTHAR WEGENER (1880-1930), a German meteorologist and geophysicist who first proposed the theory of continental drift

Summary of Event

From the blind vision creatures of sea, land, and air to the development of sonar and from a war that encompassed the world to seafloor mapping, modern science received the research necessary to prove the theory of continental drift and in the process to make great strides in filling in gaps and adding new information to the world of ideas. Alfred Lothar Wegener, the multifaceted scientist responsible for proposing the theory of continental drift, first began formulating his notion when he noticed that the coastlines of Africa and South America fit together as if they had once been parts of one huge continent. Preceded by at least five others, including Francis Bacon, in his observations on the jigsawlike quality of continents, Wegener was the first to investigate the possibility fully. His research spanned the sciences and culminated in the publication *Die Entstehung der Kontinente und Ozeane* (1912; *The Origin of Continents and Oceans,* 1924). His hypothesis explained the mysteries of similar fossils found on opposite sides of the earth and the similarity of geographic detail in parts of the world. Unfortunately, his hypothesis neglected to explain how the continents could be in motion, constantly breaking and rejoining.

The explanation Wegener omitted was found several years later during World War II. In 1912, spurred by the *Titanic* disaster, Reginald Aubrey Fessenden completed an off- and on-again project aimed at creating an echo-detection device for seagoing vessels to be alerted to the presence of icebergs. About 1914, the former assistant to Thomas Edison produced his invention that created sound-waves under water. By listening to the echoes picked up by the underwater microphone, Fessenden could detect objects by changes in the echo in the same way many ocean creatures, and even some land creatures, had used blind vision for millennia. Fessenden's early device became known later as the sonar when Paul Langevin improved on his concept and introduced it to the seafaring public for general use.

Following the example of creatures known for their ability to navigate in the darkness, such as the bat and certain aquatic animals, the sonar was created. Sonar is an abbreviation for sound navigation ranging; it was used by ships to seek, hunt, or guard against the new terror of the seas, the German submarines. Sonar operates by the emission of high-pitched signals, followed by the interpretation of the echoes to indicate the presence of submarines, sea life, or anything else noteworthy below the surface. During the war, the Navy used a device similar in working principal to the sonar, called the Fathometer, to map the ocean's floor around Iwo Jima. Aboard the USS *Cape Johnson* was Harry Hammond Hess, a geologist from Princeton University. He realized that with the technology of echo sounding, the seafloor could be mapped at last. While Hess's eventual contribution to the exploration of the seafloor was more along the lines of data interpretation rather than actual physical data gathering, the task he made possible was carried out by a colleague and friend from Columbia University, Maurice "Doc" Ewing.

Leading a group of scientists from the Lamont Geological Observatory in Palisades, New York, Ewing began his journey with the intent to map a string of undersea mountains called the Midatlantic Ridge. He found in the process, however, that simple mapping was next to impossible in lieu of the discoveries made by his team. Sounding by echo with sonar and the Fathometer and utilizing data from oceanic earthquakes, they charted their progress, noting with interest that the underwater earthquakes reported by the seismologists Beno Gutenberg and Charles Richter occurred with increasing frequency along the ridge. Another exciting and inexplicable discovery was made during the process of dredging rock from the seafloor in hopes of finding ancient crustal rock from the formation of the earth. Instead of churning up progressively chronological layers of rock with the newest at the top, the oldest among the rocks found was approximately 150 million years old, and the others were even younger. Perhaps the greatest discovery of all—that of the Midoceanic Ridge—occurred after the actual data collection and during the interpretation of the echograms.

Columbia University graduate student Bruce Charles Heezen, in collaboration with Marie Tharp, also from Columbia University, began mapping the ocean floor based on data from previous expeditions. Working in Columbia University's Lamont-Doherty Geological Observatory, their examination of the echo-sounding passes revealed more topography. Much of the topography was very rugged terrain pierced by land jutting upward in the form of cliffs, crags, and more important, mountains. The increasing detail of their mapping soon revealed that the ridge was not a regular mountain range or system. The ridge was 1,829 to 3,048 meters high, 74,028 kilometers long, with a continuous V-shaped, groovelike valley, later known as a rift valley. Often compared to the laces of a baseball, the superlative mountain range crisscrossed the world. Heezen expanded on Tharp's suggestion that the groove-shaped valley recorded by the echograms was a rift when it was compared to the median rift and the similar earthquake pattern found there. Although the then-current echograms—records of echo soundings—did not reveal the presence of a rift along the crest of the ridge, Heezen remained certain of his theory. He and Ewing developed a hypothesis on the existence of the rift and later made predictions on where the research team of the International Geophysical Year might look. By 1958, the Heezen-Ewing theory that the ridge contained a rift was proven correct. The work of Ewing and Heezen, which officially proposed the existence of the rift, sparked interest in further study of midoceanic ridges.

Impact of Event

Beginning in 1872, HMS *Challenger* began an expedition of discovery across the oceans. The first large-scale attempt to learn more about the earth's waters resulted in massive amounts of research collected; it led to the precedent of large team efforts, combining the knowledge of several sciences to work toward one end. Because of various reasons, further group expeditions to the sea were put on hold for roughly half a century until, facilitated by war and technology, another group set out to discover the secrets beneath the sea. What had been previously impossible to HMS *Challenger* was readily accessible to the newest seagoing scientists—the actual mapping of the seafloor. Where the expedition of 1872 used a man-operated dredge and specimen containers, the 1956 expedition led by Maurice Ewing used the latest in sonar and dredging equipment to complete a goal first visualized by Hess.

Leading a group of scientists from the Lamont Geological Observatory, Ewing began his journey with the intent to map a string of undersea mountains called the Midatlantic Ridge. He found in the process, however, that simple mapping was next to impossible in view of the discoveries made by his team. Hess tackled the strange information they gathered in a piece he called "an essay in geopoetry," so named because of the extraordinary lack of supporting data for his proposition. Using the same information from which Ewing and Heezen developed and eventually proved their theory of the existence and location of a midoceanic rift, Hess went a step further in his speculations.

He proposed that hot rock rose from the earth's interior through the frequently recorded earthquakes surrounding the midoceanic ridges. The continuous upwelling of hot rock continually forces the rift to part and the seafloor to spread as the material from each eruption cools and is pushed away at a rapid pace of a few centimeters per year. When the spreading seafloor encounters an obstruction such as a continent base, it moves under the obstruction, or *subducts*. Dubbed "seafloor spreading" by Robert Dietz, Hess's theory helped validate Wegener's idea of continents in drift. In addition to the validation of a decades-old theory, the work of Heezen and Ewing opened a new venue of research to scientists as the world entered the 1957-1958 International Geophysical Year.

Bibliography

Cox, Allan, and Robert Brian Hart. *Plate Tectonics: How It Works.* Palo Alto, Calif.: Blackwell Scientific Publications, 1986. While only partially related to the topic of the Midoceanic Ridge, Cox and Hart's work is a good follow-up on the interweaving of sciences used to create the total picture of the ocean's floor.

Hill, M. N., ed. *The Seas: Ideas and Observations on the Progress of Study of the Seas.* Vol. 3. New York: Interscience, 1963. Written for the researcher; well illustrated. Discusses geophysical exploration, topography and structure, and sedimentation. Includes reference sources at the end of each chapter.

Idyll, C. P. *Exploring the Ocean World: A History of Oceanography.* New York: Thomas Y. Crowell, 1969. Geared for high school and college students. Contains photographs, charts, and graphs. A chronology of oceanographic developments is included.

Menard, H. W. *The Ocean of Truth: A Personal History of Global Tectonics.* Princeton, N.J.: Princeton University Press, 1986. For the nontechnical reader. Menard's writing style is very informative and his presentation is entertaining. Includes personal recollections and excerpts from letters.

Packard, George L. *Descriptive Physical Oceanography: An Introduction.* 3d ed. Elmsford, N.Y.: Pergamon Press, 1979. This is a nontechnical introduction for undergraduates in the sciences and advanced high school students.

Sears, M., and D. Merriman, eds. *Oceanography: The Past.* New York: Springer-Verlag, 1980. Written for the researcher and graduate student of oceanography. Most chapters contain numerous notes and references. It is an excellent reference source, but with few illustrations.

Thurman, Harold V. *Introductory Oceanography.* 4th ed. Westerville, Ohio: Charles E. Merrill, 1975. General survey for students; good introductory text. Includes a glossary and references after each chapter. Well illustrated.

Weiner, Johnathan. *Planet Earth.* New York: Bantam Books, 1986. This is a companion volume to the PBS television series which is an introductory-level discussion of earth sciences in general. In addition to basic information on the work of Heezen and Ewing, there is a general background of the history of sea exploration and the projects that resulted from their work.

Earl G. Hoover

Cross-References

Wegener Proposes the Theory of Continental Drift (1912), p. 522; Langevin Develops Active Sonar for Submarine Detection and Fathometry (1915), p. 620; The German *Meteor* Expedition Discovers the Midatlantic Ridge (1925), p. 805; Hess Concludes the Debate on Continental Drift (1960), p. 1650.

BIRTH CONTROL PILLS ARE TESTED IN PUERTO RICO

Category of event: Medicine
Time: April-December, 1956
Locale: Río Piedras, Puerto Rico

Pincus directed the first large-scale test of the birth control pill in Puerto Rico, paving the way for worldwide use of a safe, effective contraceptive

Principal personages:

GREGORY PINCUS (1903-1967), a biologist who directed the laboratory and clinical studies of the first birth control pill

MIN-CHUEH CHANG (1908-   ), a reproductive biologist who tested the first birth control pill on laboratory animals

JOHN ROCK (1890-1984), a gynecologist who directed the first study of the birth control pill in an infertility clinic

CELSO-RAMON GARCIA (1921-   ), a physician who was in charge of the large-scale test of the pill in Puerto Rico and Haiti

EDRIS RICE-WRAY (1904-   ), a physician who was responsible for the day-to-day test of the birth control pill in Puerto Rico

KATHERINE DEXTER MCCORMICK (1875-1967), a millionaire who provided the financial funding for the development of the first birth control pill

MARGARET SANGER (1879-1966), an activist for the right of women to birth control who was the driving force that convinced scientists to develop the birth control pill

Summary of Event

Margaret Sanger was an ardent crusader for birth control and family planning. For decades, she traveled throughout the United States, campaigning for the legalization of contraception. Although she lectured on the use of the condom, diaphragm, and rhythm methods of birth control, she knew that these methods were cumbersome and often ineffective. Deciding that a foolproof contraceptive was necessary, Sanger met with her friend, the wealthy socialite Katherine Dexter McCormick. A 1904 graduate in biology from the Massachusetts Institute of Technology, McCormick had the knowledge and the vision to invest in biological research. Sanger persuaded her to invest in research to prevent pregnancy. Sanger arranged a meeting between McCormick and Gregory Pincus, head of the Worcester Institutes of Experimental Biology. Pincus had been directing laboratory studies on several aspects of reproductive physiology. After listening to Sanger's pleas for an effective contraceptive and McCormick's offer of financial backing, Pincus agreed to focus his energies on finding a pill that would prevent pregnancy.

Pincus organized a team to conduct research on both laboratory animals and humans. The laboratory studies were conducted under the direction of Min-Chueh Chang, a Chinese-born scientist who had been studying sperm biology, artificial insemination, and in vitro fertilization. The goal of his research was to see whether pregnancy might be prevented by manipulation of the hormones usually found in a woman. It was already known that there was one time when a woman could not become pregnant—when she already was pregnant. In 1921, Ludwig Haberlandt, an Austrian physiologist, had transplanted the ovaries from a pregnant rabbit into a nonpregnant one. The latter failed to produce ripe eggs, showing that some substance from the ovaries of a pregnant female prevents ovulation. This substance was later identified as the hormone progesterone by George W. Corner, Jr., and Willard M. Allen in 1928. If progesterone could inhibit ovulation during pregnancy, maybe progesterone treatment could prevent ovulation in nonpregnant females as well. In 1937, this was shown to be the case by scientists from the University of Pennsylvania, who prevented ovulation in rabbits by injections of progesterone. The high cost of progesterone prevented medical exploitation of this finding for humans. Not until 1951, when Carl Djerassi and other chemists devised inexpensive ways of producing progesterone in the laboratory, was serious consideration given to the medical use of progesterone. The synthetic progesterone, known as a progestin, had a chemical structure with even greater clinical activity than the natural hormone.

In the laboratory, Chang tried more than two hundred different progesterone and progestin compounds, searching for one that would inhibit ovulation in rabbits and rats when given to them in their food. Finally, two compounds were chosen, progestins derived from the root of a wild Mexican yam. Pincus arranged for clinical tests to be carried out by Celso-Ramon Garcia, a physician, and John Rock, a gynecologist. Rock was a devout Catholic who, in 1936, had opened the first clinic to teach the rhythm method of birth control to Catholic women. Before meeting with Pincus, Rock was experimenting already with natural progesterone as a treatment for infertility. It was thought that in some women infertility was caused by insufficient progesterone. Rock hypothesized that three months of progesterone treatment would strengthen these women's uteruses and oviducts, making pregnancy more likely when the treatment was discontinued. The treatment was effective in some women, but required that large doses of expensive progesterone be injected daily.

Rock was hopeful that the synthetic progestin that Chang had found effective in animals would be helpful in infertile women as well. With Garcia and Pincus, Rock treated another group of fifty infertile women with the synthetic progestin for three months. After treatment ended, seven of these previously infertile women became pregnant within half a year. In this group, however, Garcia, Pincus, and Rock made an additional observation. They took several physiological measurements of the women while they were taking the progestin and were able to conclude that ovulation did not occur while the women were taking the progestin pill. The reason for this somewhat indirect method of testing the ability of progestin to inhibit ovulation had its basis in one of Sanger's failures. In Massachusetts, it was still illegal to provide contraceptive aids. Garcia, who had a position at the University of Puerto Rico, tried a similar study on a group of twenty presumably fertile medical students. These women failed also to ovulate during treatment.

Having showed that the hormone could effectively prevent ovulation in both animals and humans, the investigators still had several problems to solve: the side effects that might occur in women using progestins for a long time; if women would find progestins an acceptable way to prevent conception; if it would be effective and reliable over the long term; and if women would remember to take the pill, day after day, for months or even years. To solve these problems, the birth control pill needed to be tested on a large scale, with many women taking it for several months. After considering the legal ramifications of testing it in Maryland, as well as considering several other countries, Pincus finally decided to conduct the first large-scale test in Puerto Rico. Through Garcia, he already had several contacts there. The social climate in Puerto Rico was more tolerant of contraception than on the mainland. The crowded island people knew the pressure of population growth, and about 20 percent of women resorted to legal sterilization as a way to limit their family size. In addition, testing progestin in Puerto Rico would keep it out of sight of the anti-birth-control activists in Massachusetts.

The test started in April of 1956. Edris Rice-Wray, a physician, was responsible for the day-to-day management of the project. As director of the Puerto Rico Family Planning Association, she had seen firsthand the need for a cheap, reliable contraceptive. The women she recruited for the study were married women from a low-income population living in a housing development in Río Piedras, a suburb of San Juan. Word spread quickly, and soon women were volunteering to take the pill that would prevent pregnancy. In the first study, there were 221 women who took a pill containing 10 milligrams of progestin and 0.15 milligram of estrogen. (The estrogen was added to help control breakthrough bleeding.) Results of the first large-scale test were reported in 1957. Overall, the pill proved highly effective in preventing conception. None of the women who took the pill according to directions became pregnant in that test, and most women who wanted to get pregnant after stopping the pill had no difficulty. Nevertheless, 17 percent of the women had some unpleasant reactions, such as nausea or dizziness. The scientists believed that these mild side effects, as well as the one death from congestive heart failure, were unrelated to the use of the pill.

Even before the final results were announced, additional field tests were begun by Garcia in Haiti, by Rice-Wray in Mexico, by Adeline Pendleton Satterthwaite in Humacao, Puerto Rico, and by Edward T. Taylor and Henry L. Olson in Los Angeles. In 1960, the Food and Drug Administration (FDA) approved use of the pill developed by Pincus and his collaborators as an oral contraceptive.

Impact of Event

The pill, as it was called, was not without its drawbacks. From the earliest trials, some doctors were concerned about the prolonged use of hormones by normal, healthy women. For the average woman, however, the advantages were more obvious. The pill was more effective and easier to use than other birth control methods. It did not interfere with sexual intercourse and did not influence subsequent pregnancies. Most important, the birth control pill was a contraceptive that a woman could control herself, without needing to rely on her partner to take precautions. Within two years of approval by the FDA, more than a million women in the United States were using the pill.

Within a few years, increasing numbers of problems were reported in pill users, particularly problems of the circulatory system. In general, however, these problems were discussed at medical conferences and the information was not made known to the women using the pill. The prevailing attitude of most doctors at the time was that people are not able to make informed decisions about medical matters. A growing consumer movement in the 1960's had repercussions in the field of women's health. Women began protesting their medical treatment, and Congress held hearings to determine whether women were being misinformed about possible side effects from taking the pill. In 1970, the FDA required drug companies to include information about possible adverse effects in the packages of the pill.

Under pressure from the public, pharmaceutical companies sponsored additional research into the circulatory disorders found in some women. When these were found to be related to the high estrogen content in the pill, these were reformulated to contain much lower amounts of hormone.

New contraceptives were developed in the 1960's and 1970's, but the birth control pill remains the most widely used method of preventing pregnancy. More than 60 million women use the pill worldwide, although women who smoke or who are more than thirty-five years old are dissuaded from using the birth control pill.

The greatest impact of the pill has been in the social and political world. Before Sanger began the push for the pill, birth control was regarded often as socially immoral and often illegal as well. Women in those post-World War II years were expected to have a lifelong career as a mother to their many children. With the advent of the pill, a radical change occurred in society's attitude toward women's work. Women had more freedom to work and enter careers previously closed to them because of fears that they might get pregnant. Women could control more precisely when they would get pregnant and how many children they would have. The Women's Movement of the 1960's—with its change to more liberal social and sexual values—gained much of its strength from the success of the birth control pill.

Within a few years, public opinion had been inalterably changed. In 1967, Massachusetts finally liberalized its anti-birth-control law. While the birth control pill developed by Pincus is not the best method of birth control for all couples, the success of the pill made birth control an accepted fact for the vast majority of people.

Bibliography

Djerassi, Carl. *The Politics of Contraception: The Present and the Future.* San Francisco: W. H. Freeman, 1981. Analysis of the advantages and disadvantages of the pill. Includes selections from Senate hearings on the safety of the pill. Future prospects in contraception for males and females are discussed. The final chapter, "The Chemical History of the Pill," provides valuable insights into Djerassi's work, including a clear explanation of the chemistry of the pill.

Douglas, Emily Taft. *Margaret Sanger: Pioneer of the Future.* Garrett Park, Md.: Garrett Park Press, 1975. A delightful biography of Margaret Sanger, from her earliest exposure to the problems of population growth as a young nurse, to her later success in encouraging Pincus to develop a birth control pill. Her friendships with the world's leaders make fascinating reading.

Hartmann, Betsy. *Reproductive Rights and Wrongs: The Global Politics of Population and Contraceptive Choice.* New York: Harper & Row, 1987. Argues that women's health has been sacrificed by those who make the pill, neglecting other methods of contraception. Especially critical of oral contraceptive use in Third World countries, where medical monitoring of side effects is limited. While not a universally accepted viewpoint, this is a well-researched summary of some criticisms of the oral contraceptive.

McLaughlin, Loretta. *The Pill, John Rock, and the Church.* Boston: Little, Brown, 1982. An exceptionally well-researched biography of John Rock by a journalist who does not disguise her adulation of the doctor. Includes biographical material on Miriam Menkin, whose work with Rock has been largely ignored. Rock's struggle with the Catholic Church is described vividly.

Pincus, Gregory. *The Control of Fertility.* New York: Academic Press, 1965. Dedicated to McCormick, Pincus summarizes his work on the pill. A somewhat technical compilation of research in early years of development of the oral contraceptive, including both animal and clinical work. Although fairly dated scientifically, it is a good source for understanding the research that Pincus conducted.

Seaman, Barbara, and Gideon Seaman. *Women and the Crisis in Sex Hormones.* New York: Rawson, 1977. As women's health activists, the authors believe strongly that women were insufficiently warned of the effects hormones have on the body. Includes history of oral contraceptive development. Somewhat strident in tone, but an earnest plea for less reliance on the pill by women.

Judith R. Gibber

Cross-References

Ivanov Develops Artificial Insemination (1901), p. 113; The Plastic IUD Is Introduced for Birth Control (1960's), p. 1629; Baulieu Develops RU-486, a Pill That Induces Abortion (1982), p. 2185.

ISAACS AND LINDENMANN DISCOVER INTERFERONS

Category of event: Medicine
Time: 1957
Locale: National Institute for Medical Research, Mill Hill, England

Isaacs and Lindenmann discovered interferons, proteins produced by body cells to fight viral diseases and currently viewed as potential tools to fight cancer

Principal personages:
ALICK ISAACS (1921-1967), a Scottish physician and microbiologist who discovered interferon while seeking to understand why people catch only one viral disease at a time
JEAN LINDENMANN, a Swiss researcher who, as a visiting scientist, participated in the discovery of interferon
SIR MACFARLANE BURNET (1899-1985), an Australian microbiologist with whom Isaacs worked during a Rockefeller fellowship that began his analysis of viral interference

Summary of Event

Over half of the communicable diseases that inconvenience, harm, and even kill humans are caused by viruses that contain ribonucleic acid (RNA) as their hereditary material. This RNA generates the ability of these "RNA viruses" to cause human disease, once a virus infects a human cell. The diseases caused by RNA viruses include the common cold, the measles, influenza, polio, and even some types of cancer. Viral diseases are unaffected by antibiotics, the therapeutic miracle drugs that cure infectious bacterial diseases. The only common, chemotherapeutic defense against viral diseases that the body cannot fight off (for example, crippling polio) is their prevention by the use of vaccines.

It has been known for many years that people do not catch more than one viral disease at a time. This is thought to be caused by the biological action of proteins, called interferons, secreted by virus-infected cells. There are three kinds of interferons: leukocytic, fibroepithelial, and immune types. The fibroepithelial and leukocytic interferons are believed to be most important in protection against viral infection. The interferon type produced in response to a viral invasion, however, depends on the kind of body cell that is infected and on the infecting virus involved.

Interferons are present in both plants and animals. In all the organisms that contain interferons, they are believed now to act as the primary cellular defense against viruses. Not only do interferons destroy the original infecting viruses, but also they protect organisms from many other viruses after a specific virus attack. The discovery of interferons is credited to Alick Isaacs and Jean Lindenmann. Isaacs, a physician-microbiologist, received his medical training at Glasgow University; however, he preferred basic research to clinical medicine. Therefore, he entered into graduate study of bacteriology. Isaacs did so well that he was granted a Medical Research Council Studentship (1947) and a Rockefeller Traveling Fellowship (1948); these awards allowed Isaacs to work with eminent microbiologists in England and Australia, such as Sir Macfarlane Burnet. He began study of viral influenzas (now known to be caused by an RNA virus). Understanding influenza remained Isaacs' primary research goal throughout his career.

Isaacs' discovery of interferon arose from his examination of the so-called viral interference phenomenon. That is, the observation that any RNA virus usually can prevent the growth, in a cell, of other RNA viruses added to it. Isaacs' first efforts— carried out in Australia—showed that the interference caused by influenza viruses had nothing to do with the penetration of cells by the viruses. Rather, it appeared to be caused by an event that occurred in the interior of the infected cell. In 1951, Isaacs returned to England, to work in the National Institute for Medical Research, at Mill Hill. He continued his study of viral interference and of influenza viruses. His collaboration with Lindenmann—a visiting Swiss scientist—produced the crucial experiments (in 1957) that led to their being credited with discovery of the interferons.

Two very important initial discoveries that Isaacs and Lindenmann made in in vitro experiments: The interfering agent was present in the culture fluid around the tissue samples being studied, and the infected tissues were stimulated to produce the interfering agent. They named the uncharacterized interfering agent, interferon. Subsequent study demonstrated that this interferon was a protein or a substance that required a protein for its action.

The discovery of interferon identified what appeared to be a new, important mechanism for defense against viral infection. It seemed likely that interferon would have exceptional therapeutic value because it worked against many different viruses, not only against the one that caused its production. In 1961, Isaacs was appointed to head the virus research division at Mill Hill. In ensuing years, he was awarded several honorary medical degrees in response to his work and was elected to the Royal Society of London. Soon, the crusade to understand interferon action was under way around the world. Isaacs participated also in the World Health Organization's efforts to understand influenza better. Regrettably, Isaacs did not live to see interferon research come to fuller fruition; he died of an intercranial hemorrhage on January 26, 1967.

Soon, however, the molecular basis for interferon action was identified. It was found that entry of an RNA virus (actually its RNA core) into a cell causes the cell to produce interferon, which is then secreted from the cell, or released from the cell if the RNA virus infection kills it. The interferon molecules released in these ways come into contact next with uninfected cells. They interact with these cells and confer upon them a great resistance to the original, infecting RNA virus and to a large number of other RNA viruses that would otherwise be infectious.

Interferons prevent viruses from killing protected cells by stopping the usual sequence of events that occurs when a virus infects a cell. That is, the virus interacts with the cell, penetrates its cell membrane, and releases its RNA core into the cell; the RNA core converts the cell to a virus factory that makes the viral RNA and the viral proteins that will become new viruses (viral progeny); these viral components are assembled and become hundreds of viral progeny; the viral progeny destroy the infected cell, enter other nearby cells, and start the process over again; and the steps are repeated over and over again.

Interferons act by stopping the synthesis of both viral proteins and viral RNA. This results from the fact that interferons cause cells to produce two proteins: an oligoadenylate synthetase (synthetase) and elF-2 kinase. The biological effects of these virus-thwarting proteins are as follows: First the kinase prevents the synthesis of viral proteins by inactivating one of the biomolecules (elF-2) required for protein production. Second, synthetase causes production of a small piece of RNA, called two-five-A. Two-five-A causes the destruction of viral RNA. The production of an interferon requires the presence of viral RNA in an infected cell. Therefore, soon after a viral infection is under control, interferon synthesis stops and consequently, oligoadenylate synthetase and elF-2 kinase are not produced any longer.

Impact of Event

Many years have passed since the work of Isaacs, Lindenmann, and their associates spotlighted the interferons. Examination of these potentially important chemicals has progressed slowly because of their scarcity and the difficulty involved in the manufacture of pure interferons. Nevertheless, the consequences of the discovery of the interferons and existing studies of their biological properties have been exciting in several ways. For example, it is widely believed now that interferons are the cell's first line of defense against viral infection and that production of the appropriate interferon will lead to the destruction of most infectious RNA viruses. Furthermore, a causal relationship between interferons and natural recovery from viral infections has developed from numerous experiments. In one case, *The Status of Interferon* (1977), interferons are reported to be useful in treatment of hepatitis. Furthermore, it has been demonstrated that interferon therapy can successfully ameliorate rabies, viral encephalitis, and eye infections.

A second exciting aspect of interferon action relates to cancer therapy. Interferon use evolved from the observation that many types of cancer cell tissue cultures are killed by the addition of interferons. One reported example of therapeutic use of interferon against cancer, in *Interferon: The New Hope for Cancer* (1981), is treatment of osteogenic sarcoma, a bone cancer that often attacks teenagers. This cancer, which usually kills 85 percent of those afflicted, is now treated successfully via interferons. Furthermore, reports of other valuable interferon-based cancer therapy fill the literature of cancer research.

Such success is not entirely unexpected, because many of the interferon-treatable cancers are those thought to be caused by RNA viruses. Researchers believe that the response of some cancers to interferon administration may be related to the fact that interferons affect the immune response (*Interferon*, 1987). Such a concept fits well with another cancer theory, which proposes that many cancers are immunologic phenomena.

Until the mid-1980's led to genetically engineered interferons, they were very rare (for example, 25 gallons of blood yielded 1 milligram of pure interferon). Many early studies of interferon action were less than ideal. Consequently, there was considerable controversy about the overall efficacy of the interferons in cancer therapy. The results with genetically engineered interferons, however, were encouraging; they promised to become part of the modern armamentarium of the therapy of cancer and serious viral diseases.

Bibliography

Andrewes, Christopher H. "Alick Isaacs." *Dictionary of National Biography*. Vol. 2. New York: Oxford University Press, 1982. This brief biographical essay on Isaacs describes some aspects of his family, his schooling, and development of his career. Some events leading to Isaacs' discovery of interferon, with Lindenmann as collaborator, are enumerated. Insight into Isaacs' personality is given, along with an evaluation of the importance of interferon.

Baron, Samuel. "Interferon." *McGraw-Hill Encyclopedia of Science and Technology*. 6th ed. New York: McGraw-Hill, 1987. This brief exposition of interferons presents a description of interferon production, interferon types, the mechanism of their action, their properties, and their possible role in cancer therapy. References to animal viruses, cancer, virus interference, and study of interferons are given also.

Burke, Derek C. "The Status of Interferon." *Scientific American* 236 (April, 1971): 42-50. This article describes the protein nature of interferon and explains some aspects of its purification, action mechanism, and attempted use in chemotherapy. Burke also points out some tribulations in proving its chemotherapeutic efficacy and its promise as a chemotherapeutic agent against serious viral diseases.

Edelhart, Mike, and Jean Lindenmann. *Interferon: The New Hope for Cancer*. Reading, Mass.: Addison-Wesley, 1981. This interesting book simplistically explains how interferons work, describes the discovery of interferon by Isaacs and Lindenmann, and traces the development of interferon research from basics to modern genetic engineering. It is a good interferon lesson for the less technical reader.

Stewart, William E., II, et al., eds. *Interferons and Their Actions*. Cleveland: CRC Press, 1977. This highly technical text is of most use to readers who wish detailed information. It contains nine chapters that deal with topics including the mechanism of interferon induction, regulation of the process, the purification of interferons, the genetics of human interferons, possible mechanisms of its antiviral activity, and interferon chemotherapy. Hundreds of references are cited.

Zubay, Geoffrey. *Biochemistry*. 2d ed. New York: Macmillan, 1988. This brief description of interferons and their actions identifies the three types of interferons, differentiates between them, describes the mechanism by which they operate, and explains elF-2 kinase and oligoacenylate synthetase. A brief diagrammatic representation of interferon action is included.

Sanford S. Singer

Cross-References

Rous Discovers That Some Cancers Are Caused by Viruses (1910), p. 459; Calmette and Guérin Develop the Tuberculosis Vaccine BCG (1921), p. 705; Papanicolaou Develops the Pap Test for Diagnosing Uterine Cancer (1928), p. 864; Zinsser Develops an Immunization Against Typhus (1930), p. 921; Theiler Introduces a Vaccine Against Yellow Fever (1937), p. 1091; Salk Develops a Polio Vaccine (1952), p. 1444; Sabin Develops an Oral Polio Vaccine (1957), p. 1522; A Vaccine Is Developed for German Measles (1960), p. 1655; A Genetically Engineered Vaccine for Hepatitis B Is Approved for Use (1986), p. 2326; A Gene That Can Suppress the Cancer Retinoblastoma Is Discovered (1986), p. 2331.

SABIN DEVELOPS AN ORAL POLIO VACCINE

Category of event: Medicine
Time: 1957
Locale: Children's Hospital Research Foundation, Cincinnati, Ohio

Sabin developed a polio vaccine consisting of weakened strains of poliovirus, which, when eaten, caused a harmless infection in the gut and stimulated long-lasting immunity but did not cause paralytic disease

Principal personages:

ALBERT BRUCE SABIN (1906-   ), a Soviet-born American virologist who devoted his career to the development of vaccines and is particularly known for the development of the oral polio vaccine

JOHN FRANKLIN ENDERS (1897-1985), an American microbiologist and scientist who was a cowinner of the 1954 Nobel Prize in Physiology or Medicine

RENATO DULBECCO (1914-   ), the virologist who developed the technique used by Sabin to isolate and purify his poliovirus vaccine strains and cowinner of the 1975 Nobel Prize in Physiology or Medicine

Summary of Event

Almost a century ago, the first major poliomyelitis (polio) epidemic was recorded. Thereafter, epidemics of increasing frequency and severity struck the industrialized world. By the 1950's, as many as sixteen thousand individuals, most of them children, were being paralyzed by the disease each year.

Within twenty years of the first epidemic, scientists had shown that polio was caused by a virus and had discovered that deliberate injection of this virus into monkeys caused them to develop paralytic polio. This important discovery raised hopes that a vaccine would be developed quickly to control the disease. Unfortunately, although a means was now available to test the safety and effectiveness of potential vaccines in animals prior to use in humans, the choice of the monkey species was unfortunate because it fostered the mistaken belief that the virus infected humans as it did monkeys, namely, by inhalation through the nose.

It is now known that, in humans, poliovirus enters the body through ingestion by the mouth. It replicates in the throat and the intestines and establishes an infection that normally is harmless. From there, the virus can enter the bloodstream. Only in rare individuals does it make its way to the nervous system, where it attacks and destroys nerve cells crucial for muscle movement. The presence of antibodies in the bloodstream will prevent the virus from reaching the nervous system and causing paralysis. Thus, the goal of vaccination is to administer poliovirus that has been altered so that it cannot cause disease, but nevertheless will stimulate the production of antibodies. There are three types of poliovirus; a vaccine must stimulate antibodies against all three types in order to protect against disease.

Albert Bruce Sabin received his medical degree from New York University College of Medicine in 1931. Polio was epidemic in 1931, and Sabin's experience with the disease stimulated a lifelong interest in polio research. No other man, according to eminent virologist John R. Paul, "contributed so much effective information—and so continuously over so many years—to so many aspects of poliomyelitis, as Sabin."

While working at the Rockefeller Institute, Sabin studied methods to grow the virus that did not depend on experimentally infected monkeys. In 1936, he and Peter Olinsky successfully grew poliovirus for the first time outside an animal using tissues cultured in vitro. They found that the virus would infect and replicate in brain tissue obtained from human fetuses but would not grow in tissues that were not of the nervous system. These results were promising because a method to provide a large amount of the virus was needed to produce a vaccine. The technique was limited, however, because it depended on the availability of human fetuses. Moreover, their results tended to strengthen the prevailing, but incorrect, idea that polioviruses attacked nerve cells only.

In 1949, Thomas Huckle Weller, John Franklin Enders, and Frederick Chapman Robbins provided the breakthrough that was so eagerly sought by successfully growing poliovirus in cultures of human and monkey nonnervous tissue. (For this feat, they received the 1954 Nobel Prize in Physiology or Medicine.) There is no ready explanation for why their experiments succeeded, whereas those of Sabin and Olinsky did not. Most likely, the discrepancy results from the use of different strains of poliovirus; Sabin and Olinsky used a strain that had been propagated repeatedly by injection directly into the brains of monkeys; this strain apparently lost its ability over time to infect other types of cells. In contrast, the Enders group used a strain that had been isolated directly from a human polio patient.

Tissue culture proved to be an excellent source of virus. Jonas Salk soon developed an inactive polio vaccine, consisting of virus grown from tissue culture that had been inactivated (killed) by chemical treatment. This vaccine became available for general use in 1955, almost fifty years after poliovirus had first been identified.

Sabin, however, was not convinced that an inactivated virus vaccine was adequate. He believed that such an inactive vaccine would provide only temporary protection and that individuals would have to be vaccinated repeatedly in order to maintain protective levels of antibodies. Knowing that natural infection with poliovirus induced lifelong immunity, Sabin believed that a vaccine consisting of a living virus was necessary to produce long-lasting immunity. Also, unlike the inactive vaccine, which is injected, a living virus (weakened so that it would not cause disease) could be taken orally and would invade the body and replicate of its own accord. It would, therefore, more closely mimic natural infection and naturally induced immunity without causing disease.

Sabin was not alone in his beliefs. Hilary Koprowski and Harold Cox also favored a living virus vaccine and had, in fact, begun searching for weakened strains of poliovirus as early as 1946 by repeatedly growing virus in rodents. When Sabin began his search for weakened virus strains in 1953, a fiercely competitive contest to achieve an acceptable live virus vaccine ensued. About this time, Sabin completed a series of extremely important experiments comparing how well poliovirus multiplies in various tissues of monkeys and humans. These results formed the basis for his strategy to produce a living vaccine: He would search for strains of poliovirus that would multiply extensively in the human intestine, but not in the human nervous system.

Sabin's approach was based on the principle that, as viruses acquire the ability to replicate in a foreign species or tissue (for example, in mice), they become less able to replicate in humans and thereby to cause disease. Sabin used Enders' tissue culture technique to isolate those polioviruses that grew most rapidly in monkey kidney cells. He then employed a technique developed by Renato Dulbecco that allowed him to propagate and study the progeny of individual virus particles. The recovered virus then was injected directly into the brain or spinal cord of monkeys to identify those that did not damage the nervous system. These meticulously performed experiments, which involved approximately nine thousand monkeys and more than one hundred chimpanzees, finally enabled Sabin to isolate rare mutant polioviruses that would replicate in the intestinal tract but not in the nervous system of chimpanzees, or, it was hoped, of humans. In addition, the weakened virus strains were shown to stimulate antibodies when they were fed to chimpanzees; this was a critical attribute for a vaccine strain.

By 1957, Sabin had identified three strains of attenuated viruses that were ready for small experimental trials in humans. A small group of volunteers, including Sabin's own wife and children, were fed the vaccine with promising results. Sabin then gave his vaccine to virologists in the Soviet Union, Eastern Europe, Mexico, and Holland for further testing. Combined with smaller studies in the United States, these trials established the effectiveness and safety of his oral vaccine.

During this period, the strains developed by Cox and by Koprowski were being tested also in millions of persons in field trials around the world. In 1958, two laboratories independently compared the vaccine strains and concluded that the Sabin strains were superior. Nevertheless, amid Cold War tensions, doubts were voiced about the reliability of the Soviet studies and the effectiveness of Sabin's "communist vaccine." In 1959, an American microbiologist who was sent to the Soviet Union to evaluate the program returned with a favorable report. In 1962, after four years of deliberation by the United States Public Health Service, all three of Sabin's vaccine strains were licensed for general use.

Impact of Event

The development of polio vaccines ranks as one of the triumphs of modern medicine. Rarely has a serious disease been controlled so quickly and dramatically as was poliomyelitis in the developed areas of the world. During the high prevaccine rates of the early 1950's, paralytic polio struck 13,500 out of every 100 million Americans. Use of the Salk vaccine greatly reduced the incidence of polio, but outbreaks of paralytic disease continued to occur: Fifty-seven hundred cases were reported in 1959 and twenty-five hundred cases in 1960. In 1962, the oral Sabin vaccine became the vaccine of choice in the United States. Since its widespread use, the number of paralytic cases in the United States has dropped precipitously, eventually averaging fewer than ten per year. Worldwide, the oral vaccine prevented an estimated 5 million cases of paralytic poliomyelitis between 1970 and 1990.

There were a number of reasons why the oral vaccine was favored over the inactive vaccine. The oral vaccine is cheaper and is easier to administer; therefore, it is more suitable for mass immunization campaigns. Another advantage is that the live viruses of the oral vaccine multiply in the intestines of the vaccinated individual; some of the vaccine viruses may then be excreted and passed on to nonvaccinated individuals, inducing a protective immunity in them as well. As these viruses multiply, they raise antibodies in the intestines as well as in the bloodsteam. These antibodies subsequently prevent wild (unweakened) viruses from infecting the intestines. Thus, wild viruses cannot spread through a population in which the majority of persons have received the oral vaccine. This form of "herd immunity" helps protect those individuals who have not been vaccinated.

The oral vaccine is not, however, without problems. Occasionally, the live virus mutates to a disease-causing (virulent) form as it multiplies in the vaccinated person. When this occurs, the person may develop paralytic poliomyelitis. Also, the mutated virus may be excreted and picked up by others, and cause disease in them. The inactive vaccine, in contrast, cannot mutate to a virulent form. The use of oral polio vaccine has reduced the incidence of polio in the United States to only a handful of cases each year. Ironically, nearly all of these cases are caused by the vaccine itself.

The issue of whether the United States should change from its predominant use of the oral vaccine to the safer inactive vaccine is being debated now. A new inactive vaccine that produces a good immunity with fewer injections has been developed. It is likely that a program using both inactive and oral vaccines will be adopted in the future.

In developing countries of the world, the vaccination issue is more pressing. Millions receive neither polio vaccine; as a result, at least 250,000 individuals are paralyzed or die each year. The World Health Organization has set a goal of eliminating polio by the year 2000. Political will and adequate funding as well as effective vaccines will be needed if the frightening images of crippled children are to become only a memory for everyone.

Bibliography

Berg, Roland H. *The Challenge of Polio: The Crusade Against Infantile Paralysis.* New York: Dial Press, 1946. A short book that accurately and impartially describes the history of polio research prior to the major breakthroughs leading to vaccine development. Outstanding for Berg's remarkable ability to present involved technical problems in simple, nontechnical terms and to convey a sense of the process of medical research.

Klein, Aaron E. *Trial by Fury: The Polio Vaccine Controversy.* New York: Charles Scribner's Sons, 1972. A highly readable, popularized account of the research leading to the licensing of the Salk and Sabin vaccines. Describes the important role of the National Foundation and March of Dimes. Despite reliance on sensationalism, the account conveys how public pressure can affect decisions made by scientific foundations and government. Glossary and chronology are particularly helpful for the layperson; includes photographs, bibliography, and index.

Paul, John R. *A History of Poliomyelitis.* New Haven, Conn.: Yale University Press, 1971. A comprehensive, gripping, and thoroughly documented account of the political, scientific, and personal struggles and developments that marked the history of the knowledge about polio. Written by a scholar who was deeply involved in polio research, who served on many key scientific committees, and who knew personally most of the scientists described. Includes numerous portrait photographs of polio researchers, and both subject and name indexes.

Plotkin, Stanley A., and Edward A. Mortimer, Jr. *Vaccines.* Philadelphia: W. B. Saunders, 1988. A textbook for advanced students with a good background in virology/immunology. The development, use, effectiveness, and possible side effects for various bacterial and viral vaccines are described by experts. Three chapters are devoted to poliovirus vaccines, focusing on the inactive vaccine, the oral vaccine, and on a brief but detailed history. Well referenced.

Scott, Andrew. *Pirates of the Cell: The Story of Viruses from Molecule to Microbe.* New York: Basil Blackwell, 1985. An up-to-date, clearly written, highly recommended introduction to viruses for those with minimal background in biology. Introductory chapters describe key aspects of viruses and virus infections; later chapters deal with more specialized topics including virus vaccines (traditional as well as new approaches) viral therapy, cancer, and AIDS (acquired immune deficiency syndrome). Well illustrated, with references and bibliography.

Waterson, A. P., and Lise Wilkinson. *An Introduction to the History of Virology.* London: Cambridge University Press, 1978. An accurate, readable account of the early development of the understanding of viruses as infectious agents of disease, written for those with some background in biology. Illustrated, with brief biographical notes about pioneering scientists who made important contributions to the emerging field of virology.

Robin S. Treichel

Cross-References

Harrison Observes the Development of Nerve Fibers in the Laboratory (1907), p. 380; Rous Discovers That Some Cancers Are Caused by Viruses (1910), p. 459; Calmette and Guérin Develop the Tuberculosis Vaccine BCG (1921), p. 705; Zinsser Develops an Immunization Against Typhus (1930), p. 921; Theiler Introduces a

Vaccine Against Yellow Fever (1937), p. 1091; Salk Develops a Polio Vaccine (1952), p. 1444; Isaacs and Lindenmann Discover Interferons (1957), p. 1517; A Vaccine Is Developed for German Measles (1960), p. 1655; A Genetically Engineered Vaccine for Hepatitis B Is Approved for Use (1986), p. 2326; A Gene That Can Suppress the Cancer Retinoblastoma Is Discovered (1986), p. 2331.

SONY DEVELOPS THE POCKET-SIZED TRANSISTOR RADIO

Category of event: Applied science
Time: 1957
Locale: Tokyo, Japan

Sony introduced a transistorized pocket radio and opened up a mass market for electronics

Principal personages:

JOHN BARDEEN (1908-1991), an American physicist who coinvented the first point-contact transistor

WALTER H. BRATTAIN (1902-   ), an American physicist who coinvented the first point-contact transistor

WILLIAM SHOCKLEY (1910-   ), an American physicist who led the Bell Laboratories team that produced the first transistors

AKIO MORITA (1921-   ), a Japanese physicist and engineer who was the cofounder of the Sony electronics company

MASARU IBUKA (1907-   ), a Japanese electrical engineer and industrialist who cofounded Sony with Morita

Summary of Event

The invention of the first transistor by William Shockley, John Bardeen, and Walter H. Brattain of Bell Laboratories in 1947 was a scientific event of great importance. Its commercial impact, however, was negligible. Although great predictions were made for the commercial future of the transistor when it was introduced, the years that followed did not mark a revolution in communications and electronics.

The commercial potential of the transistor lay in the possibility of using semiconductor materials to carry out the functions performed by vacuum tubes, the fragile and expensive tubes that were the electronic heart of radios, sound amplifiers, and telephone systems. Transistors were smaller, more rugged, and less power-hungry than vacuum tubes. They did not suffer from overheating. They offered an alternative to the unreliability and short life of vacuum tubes.

Further research at Bell Laboratories produced another major invention in 1951, the junction transistor produced by Shockley. This type of transistor was simpler and more efficient than the point-contact. It became the pioneer of the first generation of devices that went into production.

Bell Laboratories had begun the semiconductor research project in an effort to find a better means of electronic amplification. This was needed to increase the strength of telephone signals over long distances. Each new transistor produced by the Bell Laboratories team was tested as a speech amplifier. Therefore, the first commercial use of the transistor was sought in speech amplification, and the small size of the device made it a perfect component for hearing aids. Engineers from the Raytheon Company, the leading manufacturer of hearing aids, were invited to Bell Laboratories to view the new transistor and to help assess the commercial potential of the technology.

Yet, before the transistor could be incorporated into new products, the United States government had to approve the diffusion of this technology. Many applications of semiconductors were to be found in military equipment, where small size and rugged dependability were at a premium. The armed forces promised to be frequent customers for transistors, and their support was essential in the development of the technology. The removal of the secret classification for semiconductor research opened the door for its commercial application. After securing the necessary patent protection, Western Electric announced in 1951 that it would issue licenses for the manufacture of transistors. The license fee was twenty-five thousand dollars. About twenty-five companies purchased licenses and began to search for uses for semiconductors. The first transistorized consumer product, the hearing aid, was soon on the market. The early models built by Raytheon used three junction transistors and cost more than two hundred dollars. They were small enough to go directly into the ear or could be incorporated into eyeglasses.

The major direction of the commercial application of semiconductors was to replace the control and amplification functions carried out by vacuum tubes. The perfect opportunity for this substitution was the radio set, a consumer product that stood in millions of homes. Vaccum tubes were the most expensive part of a radio set and the most prone to break down. The technical barrier that had to be overcome before radios could be transistorized was the poor performance of transistors at the high frequencies required by radio. The early junction transistors operated best at low frequencies, and subsequently more research was required to produce a commercial high-frequency transistor. Several of the licensees embarked on this quest, including the Radio Corporation of America (RCA), the Texas Instruments Company, and the Tokyo Telecommunications Engineering Company of Japan.

The Tokyo Telecommunications Engineering Company of Japan, formed in 1946, had produced a line of instruments and consumer products based on vacuum tube technology. Its most successful product was a magnetic tape recorder. In 1952, one of the founders of the company, Masaru Ibuka, visited the United States to learn more about the use of tape recorders in schools and found out that Western Electric was preparing to license the transistor patent. With only the slightest understanding of the workings of semiconductors, the company purchased a license in 1954 with the intention of using transistors in a radio set.

The first task facing the Japanese was to increase the frequency response of the transistor to make it suitable for radio use. Then, a method had to be found to manufacture them cheaply. At this time, junction transistors were made from slices of germanium crystal. Growing the crystal was not an exact science, nor was the process of doping it with impurities to form the different layers of conductivity. The Japanese engineers found that failure rate for high-frequency transistors was extremely high. The yield of good transistors from one batch ran as low as 5 percent, which made them extremely expensive and put the whole project in doubt. The great advantage of using transistors was reliability and low cost. The junction transistors were simple devices that did not need the intricate interior wiring of vacuum tubes. Replacing vacuum tubes with solid state components made of semiconductors was motivated by cost rather than performance, and if transistors proved more expensive, then it was not worth using them.

Engineers from the Tokyo Telecommunications Engineering Company came to the United States to search for information about the production of transistors, visiting factories and laboratories to learn firsthand. In 1954, the first high-frequency transistor was produced in Japan. The success of Texas Instruments in producing the components for the first transistorized radio (introduced by the Regency Company in 1954) spurred the Japanese to greater efforts. Much of their engineering and research work was directed at the manufacture and quality control of transistors. In 1955, they introduced their transistor radio, the TR-55, which carried the brand name of Sony. The name was chosen because the executives of the company believed that this product had an international appeal and therefore required a brand name that could be recognized easily and remembered in many languages. One of the cofounders of the company, Akio Morita, was convinced that the future of the organization depended on a connection with the West, and the cumbersome title of Tokyo Telecommunications Engineering Company was changed to Sony in 1957. This company had acknowledged its roots in the technology of sound and revealed a global marketing strategy.

Although Sony's transistor radios were successful in the marketplace, Ibuka and Morita were committed to further development of their basic product. Continual efforts were made to reduce the cost of manufacturing transistors and increasing the range of frequencies with which they could operate. Ibuka was disappointed that the transistor radio was still comparatively large and cumbersome, despite the fact that the tiny transistors replaced the array of vacuum tubes. Ibuka decided to make full use of the advantages of transistors and develop a radio in which all elements should be miniaturized, including the loudspeaker, the capacitor, the transformer, and the batteries. This was certainly not the first attempt to reduce the size of a radio, for the United States Army had produced a specification for a hand-held radio set in the 1940's. What was different about Ibuka's strategy, and significant in the growth of the Japanese electronics industry, was that a technological path was determined by the expectations of the market for the product. Ibuka saw a consumer market for a miniature radio and gave his engineers the task of designing a radio small enough to fit into a shirt pocket.

Impact of Event

The pocket-sized transistor radio, the Type 63—given the trade name "Transistor Six" radio was introduced in 1957. It was an immediate success. Sony sold them by the millions, and millions of imitations were also purchased under brand names such as "Somy" and "Sonny." This product became an indispensable part of the youth-oriented popular culture of the late 1950's and 1960's, when transistor radios provided a cheap and convenient entrée into the crowded airwaves of commercial radio. This product could be taken anywhere and used at any time. Its very low cost enabled the masses to enjoy radio wherever there were broadcasts—from New York to Tokyo.

Ibuka's strategy of reducing the size of the radio was an important event in the relationship of technology to the user. The pocket-sized radio was the first of a line of electronic consumer products that brought the technology into personal contact with the user. Sony was convinced that miniaturization did more than make products more portable, it established a one-on-one relationship between people and machines. Sony produced the first all-transistor television in 1960. Two years later, it began to market a miniature television with a 13-centimeter screen in the United States. The continual reduction in the size of Sony's tape recorders reached a climax with the portable tape player introduced in the 1980's. The Sony "Walkman" was a marketing triumph and a further reminder that Japanese companies lead the way in the design and marketing of electronic products.

The successful development of the pocket radio was also an important event in the rise of Japanese manufacturing. Sony had to convince its suppliers to follow its lead and design its own components rather than copy them from American or European parts. Like many other Japanese manufacturers, Sony bought many of the component parts of its products from small subcontractors. The development of the "pocketable" transistor radio required exhaustive dialogue with the subcontractors to decrease the size of their components. In the case of the loudspeaker and batteries, smaller sizes lessened the performance of the component and was therefore resisted by the contractors. The successful introduction of the pocket-sized transistor radio in 1957 was as much a testament to the negotiating skills of Ibuka as it was to Japanese engineering.

The new consumer electronic products coming from Japan in the 1950's were indications of the growing self-reliance of an industrial base emerging from the ravages of World War II. American scientific research and American inventions were often the starting point for important new products, but the Japanese excellence in manufacturing and their skill in marketing was to give them the commercial benefits of new electronics technology.

Bibliography

Lyons, Nick. *The Sony Vision*. New York: Crown, 1976. A popular history of the Sony Company that follows its activities to the 1970's. Well illustrated and informative, this book gives a full account of the development of many of the company's most important products.

Morita, Akio, with Edwin Reingold and Mitsuko Shimomura. *Made in Japan: Akio Morita and Sony*. New York: E. P. Dutton, 1986. A personal account of the rise of Sony from the end of World War II to the late 1980's. Gives Morita's philosophy of business and provides insights into Sony's strategy, but often sinks into promotion of the company and Japanese culture.

Queisser, Hans J. *The Conquest of the Microchip*. Cambridge, Mass.: Harvard University Press, 1988. A clear and concise overview of the history of electronics from Edison to present. This technical history describes the technology in terms that the average reader can understand. Places the transistor in a broader context.

Reid, T. R. *The Chip: How Two Americans Invented the Microchip and Launched a Revolution*. New York: Simon & Schuster, 1984. This history of business and technology begins with the transistor and shows how the integrated circuit came about. Reid's acquaintance with the leading figures provides useful insights into the electronics industry.

Scott, Otto J. *The Creative Ordeal: The Story of Raytheon*. New York: Atheneum, 1974. This history of one of the leading companies in electronics gives the story of the application of the transistor from the American viewpoint.

Andre Millard

Cross-References

Fleming Files a Patent for the First Vacuum Tube (1904), p. 255; Shockley, Bardeen, and Brattain Discover the Transistor (1947), p. 1304; Bardeen, Cooper, and Schrieffer Explain Superconductivity (1957), p. 1533; Esaki Demonstrates Electron Tunneling in Semiconductors (1957), p. 1551; The Cassette for Recording and Playing Back Sound Is Introduced (1963), p. 1746; Compact Disc Players Are Introduced (1982), p. 2200.

BARDEEN, COOPER, AND SCHRIEFFER
EXPLAIN SUPERCONDUCTIVITY

Category of event: Physics
Time: February-July, 1957
Locale: Urbana-Champaign, Illinois

Bardeen, Cooper, and Schrieffer were the first physicists to explain how some metals, approaching absolute zero (−237.59 degrees Celsius), lose their resistance to electricity

Principal personages:

JOHN BARDEEN (1908-1991), a University of Illinois physicist who was the only person in the history of the Nobel Prize to receive it twice in the same field, once for his work on the transistor effect (1956) and again for his work on superconductivity (1972)

NIELS BOHR (1885-1962), a Danish Nobel laureate in physics who addressed the problem of superconductivity but always fell short of a valid explanation of the phenomenon

LEON N COOPER (1930-   ), a physicist who, in collaboration with John Bardeen and John Robert Schrieffer, articulated the first explanation of how metals, as they approach absolute zero (−237.59 degrees Celsius), lose their resistance to electricity, and for which he shared a Nobel Prize in Physics

RICHARD P. FEYNMAN (1918-1988), an American physicist who was on the brink of explaining superconductivity when the BCS theory was made public in February, 1957

FRITZ WOLFGANG LONDON (1900-1954), a physicist who, with his brother, HEINZ LONDON (1907-1970), also a physicist, identified superconductivity as a quantum phenomenon on a macroscopic scale

HEIKE KAMERLINGH ONNES (1853-1926), a Dutch physicist who was the first to observe superconductivity in his experiments

JOHN ROBERT SCHRIEFFER (1931-   ), a graduate student in physics under Bardeen, who, in collaboration with Bardeen and Leon N Cooper (with whom he shared a Nobel Prize in Physics), articulated the first plausible explanation of superconductivity

Summary of Event

In 1911, Dutch physicist Heike Kamerlingh Onnes, later a Nobel laureate in physics, observed in his study of the electrical resistance of mercury, as its temperature was lowered to the vicinity of absolute zero, that at −237.59 degrees Celsius, resistance decreased so markedly that it could not be measured with the instruments available. Onnes had discovered, and was soon to report on, superconductivity. For nearly half a century later, the phenomenon was tested extensively in the laboratory with various metals and was confirmed by far-ranging experiments, yet defied scientific explanation.

John Bardeen read David Shoenberg's *Superconductivity* upon its publication in 1938. Already aware of the breakthrough physicists Fritz London and Heinz London had made in 1935 when they reported to a meeting of the Royal Society in London that superconductivity is a quantum phenomenon on a macroscopic scale, Bardeen became intrigued by the physical puzzles that superconductivity posed. His interest was further piqued when he participated, during the summer of 1938, in a program at the University of Pittsburgh on the physics of metals.

By 1940, Bardeen had begun to formulate his own theory of superconductivity. His thinking, however, was diverted into other channels with the onset of World War II. His work at the Naval Ordnance Laboratory between 1941 and 1945 led him into the research on the transistor effect for which he was awarded his first Nobel Prize in 1956.

Bardeen's interest in superconductivity was rekindled in 1950 when he learned of the discovery of the isotope effect—as it turned out, one of the missing pieces in the intricate puzzle of superconductivity. The new research on the isotope effect demonstrated that even though superconductivity is an electronic event, it is dependent in a significant way upon the vibrations of the crystal lattice within which the electrons travel. With the shift in his research interests, Bardeen moved in 1951 to the University of Illinois at Urbana-Champaign, where he became professor of physics and electrical engineering.

Because research on superconductivity is so complex that a researcher working alone cannot carry it out, Bardeen sought a recommendation from the Institute for Advanced Study at Princeton for a field theorist to collaborate with him. Leon N Cooper, a recent Ph.D. in physics from Columbia University, joined Bardeen at Illinois. In 1956, they were joined in their research by one of Bardeen's graduate students, John Robert Schrieffer, who had chosen superconductivity as his area of doctoral investigation.

Bardeen's method—to segment complex, seemingly insoluble problems into smaller problems capable of solution—led to his dividing the collaboration into investigations of the constituent parts of the problem. He assigned to Schrieffer the task of working on the thermodynamic properties of superconduction and to Cooper the task of investigating its electrodynamic properties.

It was already known that twenty-six metallic elements, including lead and tin, are superconductors in their common forms, although each has a different transition temperature within a small range of degrees immediately above absolute zero. Another ten alloys share the same property. It was known that superconductors with relatively high transition temperatures are not good conductors in their usual state. The highest transition temperature, -214.44 degrees Celsius, was found in an alloy of aluminum, niobium, and germanium.

Bardeen and his colleagues knew that no convincing evidence had yet suggested that superconductivity takes place only at extremely low temperatures. Much of its practical potential is intimately connected to being able to achieve the phenomenon at higher temperatures, although temperatures close to absolute zero can be achieved inexpensively with liquid nitrogen.

The immediate task, however, was to understand and explain plausibly the dynamics of a phenomenon that had for a half century been known to exist and about which much was already known, although no convincing explanation for superconductivity had been forthcoming from the extensive experiments that physicists throughout the world were conducting.

As early as 1950, Bardeen had traced the relationship of the electron-phonon interaction to superconductivity. The first important clue to this interaction, which Bardeen had adjusted when the isotope effect was finally articulated, came in realizing that the superconducting transition temperature varies inversely as the square root of the isotopic mass. Bardeen conjectured that the energy gaps he had discovered in 1940 arose from dynamic interactions with phonons rather than from small lattice displacements. This theory presupposes that electrons have their own energy in a field of phonons.

The interaction of electrons brought about by the background crystal lattice occurs when a single electron causes the lattice, which has a degree of elasticity, to become slightly distorted as it moves. This was thought to occur because of the coulomb attraction of a negatively charged electron with the lattice, whose charge is positive. If another electron sensed this distortion, it seemed to be affected by it just enough to cause a weak interaction and a pairing.

In an article in the *Physical Review* of July 17, 1950, however, Bardeen observes that in variations in the temperature of mercury with isotopic mass, superconductivity results from the interaction of electrons with lattice vibrations, not from a period lattice distortion, as had previously been supposed. Bardeen also suggested ways of calculating the energy as the temperature approaches zero, an indispensable step that earlier measuring equipment was not sensitive enough to permit being carried out.

As early as 1956, Cooper had shown that when two electrons are in the presence of a high-density fluid of electrons, they interact and attract each other, even though their interaction may not be strong. In doing so, they bind, forming a pair, often designated as a Cooper pair, with opposite momentums. A year later, Bardeen and his colleagues discovered the means of constructing a wave function in which all the significant electrons formed into pairs. Then, by adjusting the wave function to minimize its free energy, they were able to use it as a means of developing a complete microscopic theory of superconductivity, the initial findings of which they published in February, followed by additional evidence during the next six months.

One can perhaps best visualize the electrons' actions by likening them to people in a crowded railway station. The people are squeezed together in close proximity, all moving in specific directions. They will predictably bump into anything in their paths, including each other. If something causes all of them to shift to one side of the space while they continue moving, the motion will be totally chaotic and unpredictable. At every contact with another person or object, energy will decrease substantially or disappear entirely, which is what happens to electrons in normal metals when they collide with each other or with anything anomalous in the crystal lattice, such as impurities.

If current is run into the electric field, each collision will dissipate energy, causing conductivity that will steadily diminish the energy. If, however, the people (electrons) are weakly paired, as the Cooper pairs are, separated by a distance that is precisely the length of coherence, the resistance of all the people (electrons) that are not part of the pair is reduced by about a hundred times. Among electrons, it is this state that approaches superconductivity.

It was also discovered that besides lacking resistance, superconductors can prevent external magnetic fields from entering their own interiors, making them perfectly diamagnetic. The quantum wave function in superconductivity differs in quality from normal state wave functions, as the Bardeen-Cooper-Schrieffer (BCS) theory purports.

Impact of Event

The search for perpetual motion antedates the discovery of superconductivity by hundreds of years. The two phenomena are closely related, however, in that each promises extremely efficient means of transmitting the energy that fuels developed societies and offers hope to underdeveloped ones. The articulation of the BCS theory solved a dilemma that had occupied scientists for more than half a century. It suggested ways to develop new, ultrasensitive, and highly accurate devices for measuring voltages, currents, and magnetic fields, as well as for improving heavy engineering equipment significantly and developing sophisticated, hypersensitive computer elements.

Because of the resistance it encounters in transmission, much of the energy that reaches its destination over conventional power lines is lost before it arrives where it will be put to use. Superconductive lines eliminate the resistance, thereby increasing exponentially the amount of energy that can be transmitted to a given destination.

The potential the theory unlocked for building superfast trains is impressive. Running in troughs, hovering above superconductive rails, such trains can achieve incredible speeds safely, efficiently, and economically, as is seen in some of the so-called bullet trains that serve Japan and parts of Europe. The electromagnets fundamental to the operation of such trains have been derived from the diamagnets that experiments in superconductivity revealed.

Although superconductivity is being achieved at higher temperatures, particularly when copper and oxygen atoms are present to form chains of atoms in the crystal, some problems relating to the process remain, such as brittleness, the dispersion of impurities at the surfaces of the crystals, and chemical instability under some situations, such as high humidity. Research in the field, however, is yielding promising results with such materials as compounds of bismuth.

Experiments are under way to find new superconductive materials whose transition temperature is high, possibly above room temperatures. Researchers are also considering the creation of environments in which the attractive interaction mechanism between electrons is stronger than the electron-lattice interaction that has been present in all superconductors to date.

It has been suggested that the interiors of neutron stars, and of at least one of the planets, could be superconductive. The BCS theory has, indeed, broad cosmic implications for those who are attempting to understand the beginnings of the universe. It is known that the time it takes for a supercurrent to decay exceeds 100,000 years. The building of great superconductors in both the United States and Europe will enable scientists to understand more fully and measure more accurately the persistence of superconducting loops. Some scientists have conjectured that the lifetime of some persistent currents is infinite.

Among the immediate advances the BCS theory made possible was research in such areas as elementary particle and electroweak theory. David Pines, for example, has applied the theory to the concept of the superfluidity of nuclear matter. The impact of the BCS theory is sufficiently broad and profound that one can only speculate on how many new worlds it has opened to scientists. Certainly, it marks a turning point in the way the scientific community has viewed many of the phenomena that have been central concerns to scientists for decades, even centuries.

Bibliography

Bogoliubov, Nikolai N., V. V. Tolmachev, and D. V. Shirkov. *A New Method in the Theory of Superconductivity.* New York: Consultants Bureau, 1959. The book is valuable for its explanations of the various unsuccessful attempts to explain superconductivity. A highly technical book, it makes one appreciative of the quantity of research worldwide that preceded the articulation of the BCS theory.

Hoddeson, Lillian. "John Bardeen and the Discoveries of the Transistor and the BCS Theory of Superconductivity." In *A Collection of John Bardeen's Publications on Semiconductors and Superconductivity.* Urbana: University of Illinois Press, 1988. Hoddeson's introduction to this book honoring John Bardeen on his eightieth birthday is informed, accurate, and readable. Hoddeson has perhaps the clearest understanding of any available writer of the significance of the BCS theory. Her own background in physics is strong and her writing style is appealing. Some technical language, but accessible to readers willing to put forth some effort.

London, Fritz. *Superfluids.* New York: John Wiley & Sons, 1950. This book was one of two major reasons that John Bardeen revived his research in superconductivity after a decade's lapse. London's new insights piqued Bardeen's curiosity and were the precipitating force for the major redirection in his career.

Schrieffer, John Robert. *The Theory of Superconductivity.* New York: Benjamin, 1964. One of the major researchers in the group that articulated the BCS theory, Schrieffer presents an accurate explanation, although it is extremely technical and may be inaccessible to those with insufficient backgrounds. Various summaries in the book are easier to understand than much of the supporting text.

Shoenberg, David. *Superconductivity*. Cambridge, England: Cambridge University Press, 1938. Shoenberg's explanation of superconductivity presents the problem in remarkable (and at times, diffuse) detail, although at the time of his writing, no solution to the problem had been forthcoming. This book was extremely influential to John Bardeen, who was led by it to an early (1940) statement of a theory of superconductivity, later to be supplanted by the BCS theory.

R. Baird Shuman

Cross-References

Einstein States His Theory of Special Relativity: $E = mc^2$ (1905), p. 297; Thomson Wins the Nobel Prize for the Discovery of the Electron (1906), p. 356; Einstein Completes His Theory of General Relativity (1915), p. 625; Noether Shows the Equivalence of Symmetry and Conservation (1918), p. 650; Lawrence Develops the Cyclotron (1931), p. 953; The World's First Breeder Reactor Produces Electricity While Generating New Fuel (1951), p. 1419; Esaki Demonstrates Electron Tunneling in Semiconductors (1957), p. 1551; The United States Opens the First Commercial Nuclear Power Plant (1957), p. 1557; Optical Pulses Shorter than One Trillionth of a Second Are Produced (1974), p. 2020; Von Klitzing Discovers the Quantized Hall Effect (1980), p. 2136; Bednorz and Müller Discover a High-Temperature Superconductor (1986), p. 2311; The Superconducting Supercollider Is Under Construction in Texas (1988), p. 2372.

THE JODRELL BANK RADIO TELESCOPE IS COMPLETED

Category of event: Astronomy
Time: August, 1957
Locale: Jodrell Bank, near Manchester, England

The Big Dish at Jodrell Bank, the world's largest fully steerable radio telescope dish for nearly twenty years, greatly advanced radio astronomy

Principal personages:

SIR BERNARD LOVELL (1913-   ), an English radio astronomer who led in the construction and utilization of several radio telescopes, including the 76-meter Big Dish at Jodrell Bank

KARL JANSKY (1905-1950), an American radio engineer who first detected radio signals from space

GROTE REBER (1911-   ), an American radio engineer who initiated the concept of mapping the sky at radio frequencies

Summary of Event

From prehistoric times to the 1930's, astronomy relied almost exclusively on information obtained with the human eye, even if this visible light had been funneled by a telescope or recorded photographically. Amid New Jersey potato fields, that changed. In 1931, while searching for the source of static in ship-to-shore radio communications, Karl Jansky, an engineer for Bell Laboratories, built a large radio aerial in the New Jersey countryside. Eliminating all possible terrestrial sources of the radio hiss, such as thunderstorms, Jansky realized that he was detecting radio waves from space. The region above the stinger of the Scorpion in the constellation Scorpius emitted the strongest waves. This was soon recognized as the direction of the center of the Milky Way galaxy.

Radio waves and visible light are members of a family, called electromagnetic waves, to which X rays, gamma rays, infrared waves, ultraviolet waves, and microwaves belong as well. Caused by accelerating electrons, all electromagnetic waves move with the same speed in a vacuum, but they differ in frequency, that is, in the number of oscillations of the wave per second. The frequencies of visible light range over a factor of about two; borrowing a musical term, astronomers sometimes refer to this spread as an octave. The problem which astronomers experienced with the myriad octaves of electromagnetic radiation may be compared to the life of someone in a house with fifty windows, each with a slightly different view of the surroundings. Until 1931, astronomers had been able to open only one of those windows: the window of visible light. Jansky's detection of these radio waves, however, opened many new windows for science, inaugurating what is now known as invisible astronomy. Invisible astronomy utilizes about 50 octaves of electromagnetic waves; the twentieth century's burgeoning of astronomical information was a direct result.

Astronomers recognized the potential of Jansky's discovery only after Grote Reber demonstrated the value of observing the heavens at radio frequencies. Reber, an amateur astronomer, read of Jansky's work and built a dish a little less than 10 meters in diameter in the garden of his home in Wheaton, Illinois. It was the first radio detector constructed in the shape of a paraboloid, a surface generated when a parabola is rotated about its axis. Reber's radio dish could be pointed toward any part of the sky. Reber completed the first survey of astronomical radio sources in his spare time and reported his findings to the scientific community during World War II.

The war stimulated research into radio transmission and detection, including work by Sir Bernard Lovell, the eventual creator of the Big Dish; many historians attribute the success of the Royal Air Force during the Battle of Britain to the invention and refinement of radar, an acronym for "radio detection and ranging." With radar, the reflection of a broadcast radio signal allows the location of an object. The English led the field in radar and radio astronomy because of their weather. Unlike optical signals, radio waves are unaffected by clouds; therefore, locations that are often overcast may serve for radar or radio astronomy. One of the premier English investigators of radar was Lovell, who, after completing his doctorate in physics at Bristol University in 1936, became assistant lecturer in physics at the University of Manchester. Applying his technical skills for the Air Ministry Research Establishment during World War II, he led the development of one form of airborne radar.

The end of the war in Europe made available radio and radar research for both war surplus equipment and veteran experimenters, including Lovell. Returning to the faculty of the University of Manchester with two trailers of radar equipment borrowed from the army, Lovell followed up on a question that had arisen during his wartime research and demonstrated in October, 1946, that meteor showers could be studied by radar. To avoid radio interference from the city of Manchester, Lovell conducted his research at the University's Jodrell Bank Experimental Station in Cheshire, 32 kilometers south of Manchester. At the time, Jodrell Bank was a botanical research station; no one suspected it would become a global center for a new branch of astronomical research.

Soon afterward, Lovell erected a stationary radio aerial almost 67 meters across. If all other factors, such as materials and specific design employed, are the same, then bigger is better—a fact just as true with radio telescopes as with optical telescopes. A larger telescope can detect fainter signals, a phenomenon analogous to cupping a hand behind one's ear to hear fainter sounds. In addition, more collecting area increases resolution, that is, the ability to see details and distinguish two adjacent sources (the ability, for example, to tell whether an approaching automobile is using one headlight or two).

Although this large dish soon afforded fascinating glimpses of the radio universe, its immobility frustrated Lovell and his colleagues. Carried by the rotation of the earth, it swept across only a paltry swath of the sky. To remedy this, Lovell proposed in 1949 the idea of a radio telescope which, though comparable to the fixed dish in diameter, was fully steerable. Although its scientific impact was inestimable, difficulties in obtaining the requisite funding impeded its construction. In lobbying for the Big Dish, Lovell displayed the tenacity and persuasiveness that served him and his research projects for many years. Named in 1951 as director of the Jodrell Bank Laboratory and the first person to hold a chair in radio astronomy, Lovell convinced the Nuffield Foundation and the English government in 1952 to share the cost of building the giant radio telescope, which spanned about as many octaves of radio waves as a piano keyboard spans in sound.

There were many technical hindrances facing Sir H. Charles Husband, the engineer in charge of the construction. To cover all sectors of the sky above England, Husband designed the telescope to move freely about two perpendicular angles called altitude and azimuth—altitude being the angle from the horizon to the object under observation, and azimuth being the measurement from North in the horizontal plane. The critical problem—how to align so delicately something so large—was solved, in part, by the ingenious suggestion of Patrick M. S. Blackett, the 1948 Nobel laureate in physics and University of Manchester faculty member with whom Lovell had studied cosmic-ray showers before the war. Blackett proposed that the telescope be oriented by gear-and-rack mechanisms obtained from the Royal Navy, which previously had turned the turrets for 38-centimeter guns on the now-dismantled battleships *Royal Sovereign* and *Revenge*.

A second and greater impediment confronting Husband was the integrity of the huge reflector: It must retain its precise paraboloidal shape to within a few centimeters either when moved by the gear-and-rack mechanisms or when subjected to wind. Wind can cause a structure to flutter or undergo large vibrations until the structure shakes to pieces. In the preceding decade, a suspension bridge over the Tocoma Narrows had met a similar fate from a mild wind; high-speed aircraft had lost their wings to similar effects. To avoid this, engineers at the National Physical Laboratory studied scale models of the Big Dish in wind tunnels under gale conditions and then refined its design. Eventually, Husband used nearly 2 million kilograms of steel in the entire telescope, some 300,000 kilograms in the 76-meter-wide bowl itself, which is more than two and one-half times the diameter of the dome of the Grand Rotunda in the United States Capitol Building. The rigidity of the dish is even more striking when one recognizes that, if inverted, it would have formed the largest domed roof in the world at that time.

Construction of the facility was authorized in 1952. Through the ensuing four and one-half years, Husband and Lovell met many obstacles, fiscal as well as technical. The Big Dish finally cost almost $2 million, a cost overrun of about $800,000. Lovell encountered controversy often during his career; at one point during the construction of the Big Dish, Lovell was threatened with imprisonment because he was unable to give a university official a writ for a million pounds. Nevertheless, the scientific return on this sizable investment began during the evening of August 2,

1957. That night, the Milky Way wrote its radio signature on the detectors of the Big Dish for the first time.

Impact of Event

Originally, the Big Dish had two primary scientific missions. Functioning as a giant ear, it could listen to the radio waves produced in various parts of the sky. Also, alternately transmitting a burst of radio energy and listening for the echo, it could be used for radar studies of objects within the solar system. During its long and distinguished lifetime, the Big Dish would hear many signals of great scientific interest. Few, if any, however, would create the public sensation occasioned by Lovell's announcement to the press on October 13, 1957, that he had tracked successfully the carrier rocket of Sputnik, the first artificial satellite, as it had flown over England the previous night. Two years later, on September 13, 1959, Lovell verified that Luna 2, the first spacecraft to reach the lunar surface, had crashed on the Moon. He also tracked the first lunar orbital mission by Luna 10 in 1966 and the epochal manned landing on the Moon by Apollo 11 on July 20, 1969. Although this score-keeping in the space race accounted for less than 2 percent of the total research at Jodrell Bank (now more properly called the Nuffield Radio Astronomy Laboratories), Lovell received much publicity.

Led by the Big Dish, the radio telescopes at Jodrell Bank scored many scientific breakthroughs, among them measuring the angular diameter of radio sources and detecting radio waves from nebulas completely outside the Milky Way. These nebulas—cool clouds of gas and dust—contain atoms of neutral hydrogen in their lowest energy states that emit a distinctive radio signal 21 centimeters in wavelength, which is the distance between crests of the wave. One expensive modification to the Big Dish during its construction enabled it to detect radio waves of that 21-centimeter wavelength.

The Big Dish is not the only instrument that Lovell contributed to astronomy; the Multi-Element Radio-Linked Interferometer (MERLIN), named for a famous English scholar, overcomes a major hindrance to radio astronomy: the deterioration of resolution as the wavelength forming the image increases. Even for a gargantuan radio telescope with a diameter of 305 meters, such as the one at Arecibo, Puerto Rico, the wavelength used is approximately one million times that of visible light. Consequently, radio astronomers soon generated a technique called interferometry, in which two separate receivers are linked to achieve the resolution that would be given by a single antenna as wide as their separation. Lovell's contribution to this arena was the MERLIN, which, with a resolution thousands of times finer than the unaided human eye, has disclosed the cores of radio galaxies and quasars in unexpected detail.

On September 30, 1980, Lovell retired as director of Jodrell Bank, his career marked by spectacular triumphs and swirling controversy. History will judge the significance of Jodrell Bank, as Lovell did in his 1968 book *The Story of Jodrell Bank*: "It is unlikely that a scientific project has ever survived so many crises to attain ultimate success."

Bibliography

Cornell, James, and John Carr, eds. *Infinite Vistas: New Tools for Astronomy.* New York: Charles Scribner's Sons, 1985. A compilation of eleven essays, published under the auspices of the Smithsonian Institution Astrophysical Observatory. Since the quality is uniformly high, the book would serve as a valuable resource for a reader interested in a slightly more technical overview of the frontiers of astronomy.

"He Keeps Score for the Space Race." *Business Week*, October 30, 1965, 96-100. Written in the middle of the race to the moon, this article provides more insight into the high-profile role Lovell assumed as international arbiter of space missions. He is shown as opinionated but unquestionably competent.

Henbest, Nigel, and Michael Marten. *The New Astronomy.* Cambridge, England: Cambridge University Press, 1983. A delightful work, combining the talents of the two authors, respectively, Astronomical Consultant for *New Scientist* and Director of the Science Photographic Library. Lavish color illustrations and lucid prose mark sections on each branch of astronomy, visible and invisible. For either browsing or serious study.

Lovell, Sir Bernard. *The Jodrell Bank Telescopes.* New York: Oxford University Press, 1985. Primarily discusses events from 1960 to 1982. MERLIN is described, as are many other ideas by Lovell, some of which were funded and some of which were not.

_____. *Out of the Zenith.* New York: Harper & Row, 1973. This book describes the actual astronomical research done with the Big Dish in more technical detail. Covers events up to 1970.

_____. *The Story of Jodrell Bank.* New York: Harper & Row, 1968. A first-person account of how Jodrell Bank Observatory began with two wooden huts and borrowed equipment. Lovell writes clearly of the years from World War II to the clearing of the debt on the Big Dish in 1960. It is anecdotal, thoroughly illustrated, and fascinating. A primary source.

_____. *Voice of the Universe.* Rev. ed. New York: Praeger, 1987. A revision and updating of *The Story of Jodrell Bank* (1968) in which three more chapters are added: "Thirty Years On," "The Mark IA Telescope," and "MERLIN and the Future." There are additional illustrations, and a broader perspective is given by the intervening years.

"Lovell Hits Back at Jodrell Bank Study." *New Scientist*, May 26, 1983, 523. A glimpse of the controversy in which Lovell found himself, even after his retirement as Director of Jodrell Bank. Allows the reader to see something of the clamor and pressures involved in conducting a major research facility.

Pfeiffer, John. "Big Dish—England's Radio Telescope." *Science Digest* 39 (January, 1956): 10-12. An interesting popular account of the construction of the 76-meter antenna, which focuses on the magnitude of the engineering finesse it required. Given the date of the article, the mention of computer control for the instrument seems almost anachronistic.

Shapley, Harlow, ed. *Source Book in Astronomy, 1900-1950.* Cambridge, Mass.: Harvard University Press, 1960. A selection of sixty-nine contributions to illustrate the explosion of astronomical research during the first half of the twentieth century. An article entitled "The Beginning of Radio Astronomy" by Grote Reber succinctly gives the reader the immediacy of his ground-breaking work.

Clyde Smith

Cross-References

Jansky's Experiments Lead to the Founding of Radio Astronomy (1930), p. 934; Reber Builds the First Intentional Radio Telescope (1937), p. 1113; Reber Makes the First Radio Maps of the Universe (1942), p. 1193; Ryle's Radio Telescope Locates the First Known Radio Galaxy (1946), p. 1271; Franklin and Burke Discover Radio Emissions from Jupiter (1955), p. 1492; Ryle Constructs the First Radio Interferometer (1955), p. 1496; A Radio Astronomy Team Sends and Receives Radar Signals to and from the Sun (1959), p. 1598.

SPUTNIK 1, THE FIRST
ARTIFICIAL SATELLITE, IS LAUNCHED

Category of event: Space and aviation
Time: October 4, 1957
Locale: Baikonur Cosmodrome in the Soviet Union

Launched by the Soviet Union in 1957, Sputnik 1 shocked people around the world and created a technological revolution that has not ended

Principal personages:

KONSTANTIN TSIOLKOVSKY (1857-1935), a Soviet schoolteacher and the acknowledged founder of rocketry in the Soviet Union

HERMANN OBERTH (1894-1989), a theoretician, with visions of space travel, who was another rocket pioneer

ROBERT H. GODDARD (1882-1945), an American scientist and the acknowledged founder of rocketry in the United States, who experimented with numerous rocket vehicles

SERGEI P. KOROLEV (1907-1966), a Soviet rocket scientist involved in spaceflight

WERNHER VON BRAUN (1912-1977), a German who worked on rocket projects for Nazi Germany during World War II

ARTHUR C. CLARKE (1917-   ), the author of more than fifty books and the acknowledged founder of telecommunications satellites

Summary of Event

Sputnik 1 ("Fellow Traveler" in Russian), humankind's first artificial satellite to orbit Earth, was placed into successful orbit on October 4, 1957, by the Soviet Union. The launch of this small aluminum sphere, 0.58 meter in diameter and weighing 83.6 kilograms, shocked people around the world and created a technological revolution that has yet to end.

Orbiting Earth every ninety-six minutes, at 28,962 kilometers per hour, Sputnik 1 came within 215 kilometers of the earth at its closest point (perigee) and 939 kilometers away at its farthest point (apogee). Humankind's first artificial satellite carried equipment to measure atmospheric density and to conduct experiments on the transmission of electromagnetic waves from space. Equipped with two radio transmitters (at different frequencies) that broadcast for twenty-one days, Sputnik 1 was in orbit for ninety-two days until January 4, 1958, when it disintegrated in the atmosphere.

The significance of the successful launch of Sputnik 1 came not from its size but from the implications of the philosophy and technology that lay behind the launch. The successful orbit of Sputnik 1 had been achieved by using a modified Soviet Intercontinental Ballistic Missile (ICBM), constructed under the guidance of Soviet rocket expert Sergei P. Korolev.

Within a month of Sputnik 1, Sputnik 2 was successfully placed into orbit by the Soviet Union, and this "fellow traveler" had an orbital payload of 508.3 kilograms. A single quotation sets the tone of the initial post-Sputnik period in the United States and, perhaps, around the world. Chester Bowles, a former United States Ambassador to India and Nepal from 1951 to 1953, wrote in "The New Challenge" in 1958 that "armed with a nuclear warhead, the rocket which launched Sputnik 1 could destroy New York, Chicago or Detroit 18 minutes after the button was pushed in Moscow."

Although the general public may have been shocked by the worldwide headlines that resulted from the launch of Sputnik 1, the achievement came as no surprise to individuals who followed rocketry issues. In June of 1957, the United States Air Force issued a nonclassified memorandum "stating that there was every reason to believe that the Russian satellite shot would be made on the hundredth anniversary" of Konstantin Tsiolkovsky's birth.

William E. Burrows pointed out in his publication *Deep Black: Space Espionage and National Security*: "Whatever else they were, however, Sputnik and its booster [rocket] were not surprises to [President] Eisenhower and the intelligence specialists who reported to the National Security Council." The June 2, 1957, edition of *The New York Times* even reported on a Soviet newspaper article that stated: "We have created the rockets and all the instruments and equipment necessary to solve the problem of the artificial earth satellite." On August 27, 1957, Telegraphnoye Agentstvo Sovyetskovo Soyuza, or the Telegraph Agency of the Soviet Union (TASS), announced the launch of an ICBM by the Soviet Union. Sputnik 1, which came a few months later, was no surprise, and the "race into space" was on in earnest.

Sputnik 1 was placed into orbit utilizing a modified ICBM as a booster rocket. Rockets, from the Italian word *rochetta* (lance cover), have been used by humans since at least the twelfth century, when sources reveal that Europeans and Chinese were using black powder devices. In 1659, the Polish engineer Kazimir Semenovich published his *Roketten für Luft und Wasser* (rockets for air and water), which had a drawing of a three-stage rocket, and in 1687, Sir Isaac Newton published his *Philosophiae Naturalis Principia Mathematica* (published in English in 1729, two years after his death, as *Mathematical Principles of Natural Philosophy*), wherein it was pointed out that for every action there is an equal and opposite reaction.

Rockets were used and perfected for warfare during the nineteenth and twentieth centuries. This perfection contributed eventually to the launch of Sputnik 1. Although Sputnik 1 was important for purely scientific reasons, military and commercial implications were not lost to individuals and governments around the world.

Nazi Germany's *Vergektungswaffe Zwei*, or V-2 rocket (thousands of which were launched by Germany against England in 1944 and 1945, during the closing years of World War II), was the prototype for American and Soviet rocket designers in the 1945 to 1957 period. In the Soviet Union, Tsiolkovsky had been thinking and writing about space flight since the last decade of the nineteenth century, and in 1934, Korolev published his own work entitled *Rocket Flight into the Stratosphere*. In the

United States, Robert H. Goddard had been thinking and experimenting with rockets since the first decade of the twentieth century, and in 1919, the Smithsonian Institution published his *A Method of Reaching Extreme Altitudes.*

In 1922, Hermann Oberth, a schoolmaster inspired at the age of twelve by the nineteenth century works of the French novelist Jules Verne, wrote to Goddard to obtain a copy of the Smithsonian publication. In 1923, Oberth published *Die Rakete zu den Planetenräumen* (the rocket into planetary space), and in 1925, Oberth and Tsiolkovsky began corresponding and exchanging ideas about rocketry plans. As Wernher von Braun and Frederick I. Ordway III wrote in their *History of Rocketry and Space Travel*: "As the writings of Tsiolkovsky, Goddard, and Oberth attained wider circulation, a growing number of rocket enthusiasts began the work that led directly to space flight," and, hence, to the launch of Sputnik 1 on October 4, 1957.

Von Braun had worked on various rocket projects for Nazi Germany during World War II and, as the war was ending in May, 1945, von Braun and several hundred other individuals involved in German rocket projects surrendered to Americans in Europe. Hundreds of other German rocket experts also ended up in the Soviet Union to continue with their research. Tom Bower pointed out in his *The Paperclip Conspiracy: The Hunt for the Nazi Scientists* (1987), so named because American "recruiting officers had identified [Nazi] scientists to be offered contracts by slipping an ordinary paperclip onto their files," that American rocketry research benefited tremendously because of Nazi scientists who switched their allegiances after World War II.

The successful launch of Sputnik 1 by the Soviet Union on October 4, 1957, convinced the experts, as well as the general public, that space activities were no longer in the realm of science fiction. The successful launch of Sputnik 2 on November 3, 1957, carrying humankind's first space traveler, a dog named Laika (who was mercifully poisoned in orbit because there were no plans to retrieve her), demonstrated that the technology of the Soviet Union was indeed formidable and the launch of Sputnik 1 was not an isolated phenomenon.

Impact of Event

With the launch of Sputnik 1, the plans of designers and dreamers, rocketry friends and foes, came to a focal point in a relatively small artificial satellite. After October 4, 1957, the Soviet Union and other nations launched additional experimental satellites, and the United States successfully orbited its first artificial satellite, Explorer 1, on January 31, 1958, after the first United States launch of a Vanguard satellite failed on December 6, 1957.

Sputnik 1 was the forerunner of numerous satellites orbiting Earth, which provide individuals not only with scientific data but also with various commercial applications from satellites at various altitudes. If one thinks of a satellite, equipped with the proper electronic equipment, as a tower in the sky, then something at the top of that tower can be used to view things and relay information from the earth below. Arthur C. Clarke published a technical paper in 1945 entitled "Extra-Terrestrial Relays: Can Rocket Stations Give World-wide Radio Coverage?" in which he pointed out that three satellites placed in equatorial orbit at the proper altitude would provide worldwide coverage.

If a satellite were placed in an orbit of 36,000 kilometers over the equator and traveled at 11,068 kilometers per hour (the time of the rotation of the earth at the equator), then that satellite would appear to be in a stationary position at an altitude of 36,000 kilometers. These communications satellites would abound at the end of the twentieth century, fewer than forty years after Sputnik 1.

The first communications satellite capable of relaying a communications signal from the ground was Echo 1, launched by the United States on August 12, 1960, into an Earth orbit, ranging from 1,524 kilometers (perigee) to 1,684 kilometers (apogee). This satellite was a 75.9-kilogram sphere, which was inflated to a 30-meter balloon once in orbit. This satellite had no capability to amplify or direct the electromagnetic waves reflected off its metallic surface, and it succumbed to meteorite action and decayed by May 24, 1968.

Seven years after the launch of Sputnik 1, on April 6, 1965, a satellite called "Early Bird" was launched into an Earth orbit of 35,003 to 36,606 kilometers by INTELSAT, the International Telecommunications Satellite organization, and commercial telecommunications service via satellite began on April 25, 1965. This was the first satellite that produced the television phrase "live via satellite" between North America and Europe. What was once clearly headline or banner news a few decades ago has become commonplace; multisatellite launches from a single rocket are now common occurrences, and it all began with Sputnik 1.

In the first twenty-five years after Sputnik 1 was launched, from 1957 to 1982, a total of 2,389 objects were placed into various Earth orbits by more than twenty-four nations. This figure of 2,389 means that, on the average, humankind was launching something into space every 3.82 days for this twenty-five-year period, all beginning with Sputnik 1.

Communications satellites, weather satellites, space stations, and trips to the moon all resulted from the successful launch of the first artificial satellite. Sputnik 1's impact was not only in space but also elsewhere, for as the Pulitzer Prize-winning author Walter McDougall stated in 1987: "Sputnik and the space race brought on massively increased government involvement in research and development—not just in military but even in civilian technology." Government influence had an impact in education and other areas as a result of Sputnik 1.

In the closing decade of the twentieth century, multikilogram satellites in geostationary orbit at 36,000 kilometers are receiving and transmitting electronic information all over the globe; one can only hazard intelligent guesses about the space and telecommunications technology that will be available in the twenty-first century.

Bibliography

Baker, David. *The Rocket: The History and Development of Rocket and Missile Technology.* New York: Crown, 1978. An excellent overview, from beginning firecrackers to strategic rocketry, this 276-page, well-illustrated and well-indexed volume cannot be surpassed.

Bower, Tom. *The Paperclip Conspiracy: The Hunt for the Nazi Scientists.* Boston: Little, Brown, 1987. Fascinating account of "Operation Paperclip" and how the United States worked with rocket scientists from Nazi Germany after World War II.

Bowles, Chester. "The New Challenge." In *Britannica Book of the Year: 1958*, edited by Walter Yust. Chicago: Encyclopædia Britannica, 1958. A valuable "jumping off" point for general research, the Book of the Year also helps to place events within the context of the times. Although telecommunications through satellites has developed tremendously, it does not have a single reference to the potential of satellites to be used as communication devices.

Bowser, Hal. "How the Space Race Changed America: An Interview with Walter A. McDougall." *American Heritage of Invention & Technology* 15 (Fall, 1987): 24-30. The key journal on invention and technology. Bowser's interview is an excellent companion piece to McDougall's book (cited below).

Clarke, Arthur C. *Ascent to Orbit: A Scientific Autobiography, the Technical Writings of Arthur C. Clarke.* New York: John Wiley & Sons, 1984. Clarke, now termed the "father" of satellite communications by many, is both a gifted science-fiction and science-fact author. This volume, by the author of *2001: A Space Odyssey* (1968), covers his technical writings from the early pioneering 1945 essay to comments on telecommunications and the "global village."

King-Hele, D. G., et al. *The R. A. E. Table of Earth Satellites, 1957-1982.* New York: John Wiley & Sons, 1983. Provides the readers with exceptionally detailed chronological information on the 2,389 launches of space vehicles and satellites between 1957 and 1982. An informative compendium.

Ley, Willy. *Rockets, Missiles, and Men in Space.* New York: Viking Press, 1968. An outstanding overview. Includes science fiction as well as mythological and historical interests in space.

McDougall, Walter A. . . . *The Heavens and the Earth: A Political History of the Space Age.* New York: Basic Books, 1985. An excellent overview into political activities before and after the launch of Sputnik 1.

Von Braun, Wernher, and Frederick I. Ordway III. *History of Rocketry and Space Travel.* Rev. ed. New York: Thomas Y. Crowell, 1969. A well-illustrated companion piece to the Baker publication (cited above). Unique because of the role von Braun played in both Nazi Germany and United States rocketry experiments.

Winter, Frank H. *Prelude to the Space Age: The Rocket Societies, 1924-1940.* Washington, D.C.: Smithsonian Institution Press, 1983. The key volume for information about the rocket societies of the time period. For a wide audience.

Charles F. Urbanowicz

Cross-References

Tsiolkovsky Proposes That Liquid Oxygen Be Used for Space Travel (1903), p. 189;

Goddard Launches the First Liquid Fuel Propelled Rocket (1926), p. 810; The Germans Use the V-1 Flying Bomb and the V-2 Goes into Production (1944), p. 1235; The First Rocket with More than One Stage Is Created (1949), p. 1342; The United States Launches Its First Orbiting Satellite, Explorer 1 (1958), p. 1583; Tiros 1 Becomes the First Experimental Weather Reconnaissance Satellite (1960), p. 1667; Echo, the First Passive Communications Satellite, Is Launched (1960), p. 1677; Telstar, the First Commercial Communications Satellite, Relays Live Transatlantic Television Pictures (1962), p. 1728; The First Permanently Manned Space Station I Is Launched (1986), p. 2316.

ESAKI DEMONSTRATES ELECTRON TUNNELING IN SEMICONDUCTORS

Category of event: Physics
Time: October 11, 1957
Locale: Tokyo, Japan

Esaki provided the first unequivocal experimental demonstration of electron tunneling in solids, stimulating research and development involving other tunneling phenomena

Principal personages:

> LEO ESAKI (1925-   ), a Japanese physicist, noted for research and development work in electronics who was a cowinner of the 1973 Nobel Prize in Physics
>
> IVAR GIAVER (1929-   ), a Norwegian physicist and pioneer in the development of superconductor tunnel junctions who was a cowinner of the 1973 Nobel Prize in Physics
>
> BRIAN D. JOSEPHSON (1940-   ), an English physicist and pioneer in the theory of tunneling between superconductors who was a cowinner of the 1973 Nobel Prize in Physics

Summary of Event

On October 11, 1957, the journal *Physical Review* received a brief article, submitted as a letter to the editor, entitled "New Phenomenon in Narrow Germanium p-n Junctions." The author was a Japanese graduate student enrolled in a doctoral program in physics at the University of Tokyo and working simultaneously in research and development at Sony Corporation, where he was studying the characteristics of semiconductor transistors. The article, which was published on January 15, 1958, described an "anomalous current voltage characteristic in the forward direction"—that is, a current that flowed across a p-n junction at voltages too low to surmount the potential barrier characteristic of the junction. A mathematical explanation was provided, with references indicating that the phenomenon had been predicted on theoretical grounds by A. H. Wilson, J. Frankel and A. Joffe, and L. Nordheim in separate papers in 1932. The expression "tunneling" was not used in the paper, and there was no discussion of applications of the device described.

Tunneling refers to the ability of a particle to pass through a region forbidden to it by a classical mechanical model. The theory of tunneling is a natural corollary to the models of Louis de Broglie and Erwin Schrödinger concerning the dual wave/particle nature of matter. A particle modeled as a wave has a finite probability of passing through a barrier. In macroscopic terms, a ball modeled as a wave has a finite but exceedingly small probability of passing through a brick wall. Although the probability of an electron's passing through a potential barrier a few nanometers thick is also small, it is sufficiently high that one could expect to be able to demonstrate the phenomenon experimentally. A tunneling model had been invoked correctly as an explanation for electron emission from cold metals in high external electrical fields in the 1920's, and had been used with less success to interpret current transfer characteristics in metal-semiconductor contacts.

Semiconductor tunnel diodes (sometimes called Esaki tunnel diodes after Leo Esaki) and transistors are similar in form and composition, and the development of the tunnel diode followed directly from the invention of the transistor by William Shockley, John Bardeen, and Walter H. Brattain in 1948 and its subsequent rapid incorporation into electronics technology. It was no accident that Esaki made his discoveries while working for the Sony Corporation, a pioneer in incorporating transistor technology into consumer goods for mass consumption. The rapid advances in transistor technology during the 1950's made possible the manufacture of semiconductor diodes precise enough in form and composition to demonstrate the effects Esaki was studying.

The operation of transistors and semiconductor tunnel diodes depends on the electrical properties of semiconductors that have been "doped" with impurities. The distribution of energy states of electrons within a crystalline solid is analogous to the distribution of energy states of electrons in an isolated atom; in the solid, the electron shells merge to form a continuous valence band. Conduction of electricity within a solid depends on the existence of unfilled electron valence bands. In a conductor (such as copper), the outer electron shell is unfilled and electrons move freely; in an insulator, the outer shell is filled. Pure (intrinsic) semiconductors such as silicon have a filled outer valence band, but they conduct electricity because the energy gap between the filled valence band and the next-higher empty band is low relative to the gap in good insulators, and some electrons are raised to the higher energy level by thermal excitation.

The conducting capacity of an intrinsic semiconductor can be increased by the addition of impurities in the form of an element that has either one fewer or one more outer valence electron than the parent semiconductor crystal. Crystalline silicon, an intrinsic semiconductor with a valence of +4, can be doped with a material with a +3 valence, giving rise to an unsatisfied bond with one of the valence electrons and producing what is known as a p[ositive]-type semiconductor, or with a material with a +5 valence, resulting in an extra electron and producing an n[egative]-type semiconductor. A p-n junction is formed where the two types abut.

When a p-type and an n-type semiconductor are joined, a potential barrier exists in a narrow region surrounding the junction because holes and electrons pair up; in the classic transistor, current flows across the junction only when the externally applied voltage increases to the point that it is sufficient to surmount the potential barrier. A transistor consists of three elements: a base, a collector, and an emitter. A weak current flowing into the base and out the emitter controls a much stronger current between the collector and emitter. The weak current acts as a switch, turning the semiconductor junction on and off, and thus controlling the flow of the stronger current across the junction. As a simple on/off switch, transistors control the flow of current in logic circuits in electronic computing devices. In a radio, the transistor serves as an amplifier, imparting the frequency of amplitude modulation of the incoming signal to a stronger current, which generates the audio output.

Esaki's 1957 contribution to transistor technology began with the development of techniques for improving the precision of impurity doping, in terms of both the concentration of impurities and the distance across the p-n contact. The experiments which Wilson, Frankel and Joffe, and Nordheim had performed in attempting to demonstrate tunneling in metal-semiconductor junctions had failed because the existing technology was inadequate to produce a sufficiently thin junction. Esaki observed that current flow as a function of voltage across a heavily doped germanium p-n junction did not follow the usual pattern of zero flow over the range below the potential barrier and abrupt rise at the potential barrier (the simple on/off switching property of the classic transistor). The flow did, however, show two maxima, one below the voltage of the potential barrier the other at the barrier. Esaki concluded that the lower peak could be ascribed to electrons "tunneling"—that is, crossing the barrier without reaching the higher energy level. This phenomenon of tunneling by electrons had been predicted on theoretical grounds based on the wave properties of particles. In the 1930's, C. Zener had invoked the tunneling principle to explain the dielectric breakdown of insulating materials, suggesting that high voltages caused electrons to tunnel from the full valence band to the empty conduction band, and a similar mechanism had been postulated for the breakdown of p-n junctions at high voltages. In both of these cases, theoretical calculations based on the tunneling model failed to predict the observed results, and a mechanism other than tunneling was shown ultimately to be operating. The mathematical tunneling models, on the other hand, accurately predicted the empirical results Esaki had obtained.

The Esaki tunnel diode exhibits some advantages and some disadvantages when compared with a nontunneling transistor. It is capable of operating at higher switching speeds and over a wider temperature range, it is more radiation resistant, it requires two rather than three terminals, it operates at microwave frequencies, it is hard to damage with overload current, and it is relatively insensitive to atmospheric gases. Its disadvantages include gain only in alternating current and a small usable voltage swing. In practical terms, the Esaki tunnel diode was most important as a first step in the discovery of electronic devices employing tunneling phenomena. Tunnel diodes are used together with transistors in computers and have been found to be particularly useful in sensitive microwave detectors, serving as an inexpensive alternative to masers in microwave amplifiers.

Demonstration of the tunneling phenomenon in p-n semiconductor junctions stimulated investigation in other areas, notably in the field of superconductivity. In 1960, Ivar Giaver applied tunneling theory to the curent-voltage curve between superconducting metals separated by a thin insulating oxidizing film. The results confirmed the microscopic theory of superconductivity postulated by Bardeeen, Leon N Cooper, and John Robert Schrieffer and were sensitive enough to measure the energy gap that forms when the electrons condense into correlated bond pairs in a super-conductor.

The work of Esaki and Giaver stimulated a blossoming of research into tunneling effects in solids. Brian D. Josephson, who in the early 1960's was a graduate student at the University of Cambridge, formulated a theory of tunnel junctions between superconductors that predicted a supercurrent associated with the tunneling of bonded electron pairs across the junction. Two effects were predicted: a D-C Josephson effect in which a supercurrent flows in the absence of a voltage drop across the junction, and an A-C Josephson effect in which current oscillates at a frequency that is dependent on the voltage drop across the junction. Both predictions were greeted initially with skepticism until demonstrated experimentally in the laboratory. The A-C and D-C Josephson effects gave rise to a whole new generation of instruments of unprecedented sensitivity. Esaki, Josephson, and Giaver shared the 1973 Nobel Prize in Physics for their work on tunneling effects in solids.

In 1960, Esaki left Sony Corporation to join the staff of International Business Machines (IBM) in the United States, where he has had a long and fruitful career in theoretical and practical solid-state research. His work for IBM on superlattices— devices composed of extremely thin alternating layers of p and n semiconductors— was especially noteworthy.

Although an American resident, Esaki retained his Japanese citizenship and con-tinued to be an active member of the Japanese scientific and business community, serving on the board of directors of IBM Japan and acting as a kind of unofficial diplomat in technological contacts between the two countries. He assumed a stance of polite neutrality when both countries claimed the honor of his Nobel Prize.

Impact of Event

The significance of the demonstration of tunneling in solids can be divided conve-niently into three areas: microelectronic engineering problems of broad applicability, specialized scientific instrumentation, and implications for theoretical physics.

Esaki tunnel diodes are a common component of the ubiquitous silicon chip, which revolutionized communications and information processing in the last quarter of the twentieth century. In practical engineering terms, the diode itself (or its cousin, the transistor) is a microscopic or near-microscopic region that has been selectively doped with impurities and isolated from the surrounding silicon crystal by a thin layer of insulating oxide. The entire chip (to paraphrase the introduction to *Micro-electronics and Society*) contains perhaps 100,000 of such elements photograph-ically stamped on a device the size of a cornflake and equivalent to a room full of the tubes and wire circuits that powered the earliest computers. The minuteness and low cost of the switching elements were critical to the development of accessible com-puter technology. Tunnel diodes, with their unique current-voltage response charac-teristics, introduced greater flexibility into the engineering process.

Discovery of the A-C and D-C Josephson effects provided physicists with the basis for powerful tools to study the superconducting state, in which substances cooled to near absolute zero behave as if they were enormous atoms. A superconducting interferometer based on the Josephson effect enabled physicists to verify earlier theories of the superconducting wave function and to demonstrate its long-range quantum phase coherence.

Supercurrents across Josephson junctions are orders of magnitude more sensitive to applied electrical and magnetic fields than the most sensitive transistors. The unprecedented sensitivity of these devices made possible previously impossible experiments in many fields. Superconducting quantum interference devices (SQUIDS), consisting of one or more Josephson junctions connected in a superconducting loop, form the building blocks of supersensitive magnetometers, power meters, voltameters, gradiometers, and low-temperature thermometers. As switches in digital applications, SQUIDS are used in memory and logic circuits requiring high switching speed and ultralow-power dissipation. In terms of computer technology, this translates into vastly increased speed of operation and greater memory accessibility, with an equivalent degree of miniaturization of components. Because of the low temperatures required to achieve the superconducting state, supercomputers and electronic instrumentation employing Josephson effects are the province of large research facilities and government and military installations.

The A-C Josephson effect is used to define the volt in standards laboratories, replacing the formerly used standard cell. There has been a general tendency in later years to define measurements in terms of quantum effects, which are both more precise and more reproducible than the physical objects formerly used as standards.

Bibliography

Braun, Ernest, and Stuart Macdonald. *Revolution in Miniature: The History and Impact of Semiconductor Electronics.* Cambridge, England: Cambridge University Press, 1978. A historical survey of the development and diffusion of transistor technology and the progress of integrated circuits from sophisticated military and scientific instrumentation to mass-produced applications. Esaki's research is not mentioned specifically, and the book as a whole downplays the contributions of the Japanese.

Esaki, Leo. "Long Journey into Tunneling." *Science* 183 (March 22, 1974): 1149-1155. This article is the text of Esaki's Nobel lecture, delivered on December 12, 1973. The theoretical and technical antecedents to Esaki's tunneling discoveries are explained, as well as the sequence of events that took place in his laboratory. The explanations of tunnel diodes, metal-oxide semiconductor junctions, and resonant transmission are highly technical.

Friedrichs, Günter, and Adam Schaff. *Microelectronics and Society: For Better or for Worse. A Report to the Club of Rome.* New York: Pergamon Press, 1982. Although the book as a whole is a collection of papers about the impact of the microelectronic revolution on many aspects of human society, including the workplace, the Third World, communications, information technology, and warfare, chapter 2 ("The Technology") and chapter 3 ("The Technology Applied") give clear, diagrammatic, nontechnical descriptions of how microelectronic semiconductor devices work. The reader is able to visualize transistors as isolated devices and as subunits in the complex circuitry of computers.

Gentile, Sylvester P. *Basic Theory and Application of Tunnel Diodes.* Princeton, N.J.: D. Van Nostrand, 1962. A general textbook and manual aimed at electronics engineers. The first two chapters contain clear explanations of the workings of transistors and tunnel diodes in diagrammatic, nonmathematical terms. The remainder of the book consists of descriptions of specific circuit types employing tunnel diodes.

Langenberg, D. N. "The 1973 Nobel Prize for Physics." *Science* 182 (November 16, 1973): 701-704. A relatively nontechnical overview of the subject of tunneling, describing the separate contributions of Esaki, Giaver, and Josephson and the way in which they complement one another. Assesses the significance of tunneling phenomena to the infrastructure of science and technology.

Scientific American Editors. *Microelectronics.* San Francisco: W. H. Freeman, 1977. A compendium of illustrated, semipopular articles that appeared in the September, 1977, issue of *Scientific American*, reissued in book form. Chapter 2, on microelectronic circuit elements, gives clear descriptions of the theory of p-n junctions and the structure and functions of semiconductor transistors, though without specific reference to tunneling diodes. Josephson's low-temperature superconductor tunneling phenomena are discussed later in the context of high-level memory storage systems.

Martha Sherwood-Pike

Cross-References

De Broglie Introduces the Theory of Wave-Particle Duality (1923), p. 741; Shockley, Bardeen, and Brattain Discover the Transistor (1947), p. 1304; Sony Develops the Pocket-Sized Transistor Radio (1957), p. 1528; Bardeen, Cooper, and Schrieffer Explain Superconductivity (1957), p. 1533; Bubble Memory Devices Are Created for Use in Computers (1969) p. 1886; Rohrer and Binnig Invent the Scanning Tunneling Microscope (1978), p. 2093; Von Klitzing Discovers the Quantized Hall Effect (1980), p. 2136.

THE UNITED STATES OPENS THE FIRST COMMERCIAL NUCLEAR POWER PLANT

Categories of event: Applied science and physics
Time: December 2, 1957
Locale: Shippingport, Pennsylvania

The Duquesne Light Company and the United States Atomic Energy Commission opened the first full-scale commercial nuclear power plant, giving birth to the nuclear power industry

Principal personages:

ENRICO FERMI (1901-1954), an Italian-American physicist who won the 1938 Nobel Prize in Physics for his neutron studies and headed the first controlled nuclear chain reaction

OTTO HAHN (1879-1968), a German physical chemist who won the 1944 Nobel Prize in Chemistry for his discovery of uranium fission

LISE MEITNER (1878-1968), an Austrian-Swedish physicist who first explained nuclear fission and its associated energy

HYMAN G. RICKOVER (1898-1986), a Polish-American naval officer who led the development of the first atomic submarine

LEWIS L. STRAUSS (1896-1974), an American naval officer and science adviser to President Dwight D. Eisenhower, who was chairman of the Atomic Energy Commission

Summary of Event

On December 2, 1957, the first full-scale commercial nuclear power plant in the United States was started up at Shippingport, Pennsylvania, on the fifteenth anniversary of the first controlled nuclear chain reaction directed by Enrico Fermi. Nuclear fission was discovered in Germany by Otto Hahn after he had bombarded uranium with neutrons in 1938 and observed traces of radioactive barium. When Hahn's former associate, Lise Meitner, received word of this result, she recognized the possibility that neutrons had split uranium nuclei (92 protons) into two smaller nuclei to produce barium (56 protons) and krypton (36 protons). Meitner and her nephew, Otto Robert Frisch, calculated the enormous energy that would be released in this type of reaction from the electrical repulsion of the fragments (such as barium, krypton, strontium, cesium, and so on), publishing their results early in 1939.

Nuclear fission was quickly verified in several laboratories, and the Danish physicist, Niels Bohr, soon developed a theory of fission showing that the rare uranium 235 (U-235) isotope (235 nucleons: 92 protons and 143 neutrons) is much more likely to fission, especially with slow neutrons, than the common uranium 238 (U-238) isotope that makes up 99.3 percent of natural uranium. It was also recognized that fission would produce additional neutrons that could cause new fissions with even more neutrons, producing a self-sustaining chain reaction. In this process, the fissioning of one gram of U-235 would release energy equivalent to burning about three million tons of coal.

The first controlled chain reaction was demonstrated on December 2, 1942, in a nuclear reactor at the University of Chicago under the leadership of Fermi. He used a graphite "moderator" to slow the neutrons by collisions with carbon atoms. A large enough lattice of graphite and uranium was assembled to achieve a "critical mass" in which the number of neutrons not escaping from the "pile" would be sufficient to sustain a U-235 chain reaction. Cadmium "control rods" could be inserted to slow the reaction by absorbing neutrons. It was also recognized that U-238 in the reactor would capture fast neutrons to produce the new element plutonium, which is also fissionable. During World War II, large reactors were built to "breed" plutonium since it was easier to separate than U-235. An experimental breeder reactor at Arco, Idaho, was the first to use the energy of nuclear fission to produce a small amount of electricity (about 100 watts) on December 20, 1951.

Power reactors designed to produce substantial amounts of electricity use the heat generated by fission to produce steam or hot gas to drive a turbine connected to an ordinary electric generator. The first power reactor design to be developed in the United States was the pressurized water reactor (PWR), in which water under high pressure (up to 150 atmospheres) was used as the moderator-coolant. This "light water" design uses fuel elements of enriched uranium (usually about 3 percent U-235) in the form of rods or plates at temperatures of about 300 degrees Celsius. After circulating through the reactor core, the hot pressurized water flows through a heat exchanger to produce steam. Reactors moderated by "heavy water" (containing deuterium atoms made of a proton and a neutron in place of hydrogen atoms) can operate with natural uranium.

The pressurized water system was used in the first reactor to produce substantial amounts of power, the experimental Mark I reactor. It was started up on May 31, 1953, at the Idaho National Engineering Laboratory, and was the prototype for the reactor used in the first nuclear-powered submarine. Under the leadership of Hyman G. Rickover, who was head of the Division of Naval Reactors of the Atomic Energy Commission (AEC), Westinghouse Electric Corporation was engaged to build a PWR system to power the submarine USS *Nautilus*. It began sea trials in January of 1955 and ran for two years before refueling.

On December 8, 1953, President Dwight D. Eisenhower gave his "Atoms for Peace" speech, emphasizing the need for an international program of civilian uses of atomic energy. In the same month, the AEC selected the Duquesne Light Company, a Pittsburgh utility, to construct the first full-scale nuclear power station at Shippingport, Pennsylvania, located on the south bank of the Ohio River about 40 kilometers northwest of Pittsburgh. Admiral Lewis L. Strauss, a science adviser to Eisenhower who would later chair the AEC, recommended Westinghouse to manufacture the reactor, adapting the Navy's PWR system and receiving continued assistance from Rickover. Duquesne Light Company, led by its president, Philip A.

Fleger, leased the land to the AEC, provided the turbine generator, plus $5 million for research and development, and became responsible for operation and maintenance.

In the meantime, the first experimental nuclear power plant for generating electricity was completed at Obninsk in the Kaluzhskaya region of the Soviet Union in June of 1954, under the direction of the Soviet physicist Igor Kurchatov. It used a graphite-moderated and water-cooled reactor with 550 kilograms of 5 percent enriched uranium and produced 5 megawatts of electric power. The first full-scale nuclear power plant was built in England at the Calder Hall station at Windscale (now Sellafield) in Cumbria under the direction of the British nuclear engineer Sir Christopher Hinton. It consisted of two gas-cooled, graphite-moderated reactors that began producing about 90 megawatts of electric power in October, 1956. At the same time, General Electric Corporation was developing the boiling water reactor (BWR) system, in which the "light water" moderator-coolant is boiled directly within the reactor core. They began operation of a 5-megawatt experimental nuclear power plant at Pleasanton, California, in 1957.

The Shippingport Atomic Power Station became the first full-scale nuclear-powered electric generating plant in the United States when it began producing electric power on December 18, 1957. Its pressurized water reactor cost about $50 million and employed a square annular array of highly enriched uranium fuel elements (52 kilograms of U-235) surrounded both inside and out with a "blanket" of normal uranium dioxide (12,000 kilograms). This arrangement provided a uniform release of fission energy throughout the 2×2 meter cylindrical core with twenty-four hafnium control rods. The pressure vessel was 10 meters tall and 3 meters in diameter with 22-centimeter steel walls. It produced about 60 megawatts of electric power for the Duquesne Light Company until 1964, when its reactor core was replaced, which increased its power to 100 megawatts with a maximum capacity of 150 megawatts.

The Shippingport plant operated until 1974 with its second core, after which the reactor core was again replaced with a breeder core to serve as a breeder demonstration program for the remainder of its twenty-five-year design lifetime. It was shut down and disconnected from the power grid on October 1, 1982, and was decommissioned by General Electric between 1984 and 1989. Its fuel was removed by the Department of Energy (successor to the AEC), and its pressure vessel was sent to Hanford, Washington, for burial. The Beaver Valley Power Station on an adjacent site continues to provide electric power for the Duquesne Light Company from two 1,000-megawatt PWRs.

Impact of Event

The opening of the Shippingport Atomic Power Station marked the beginning of the nuclear power industry in the United States, with all of its glowing promise and eventual problems. Strauss predicted that electrical energy would become too cheap to meter. The AEC hoped to encourage the participation of industry, with government support limited to research and development. They encouraged a variety of reactor types in the hope of extending technical knowledge. By 1955, four groups submitted proposals: Commonwealth Edison in Chicago proposed a BWR; Consumers Public Power District in Nebraska suggested a sodium-graphite reactor; Detroit Edison submitted plans for a fast-breeder reactor; and Yankee Atomic, a consortium of thirteen New England utilities, proposed a PWR based on the Shippingport design.

The Dresden Nuclear Power Station, completed by Commonwealth Edison in September, 1959, at Morris, Illinois, near Chicago, was the first full-scale privately financed nuclear power station in the United States. Its 185-megawatt BWR, containing 58 tons of uranium, was built by General Electric at a cost of $61 million. By the mid-1960's, experimentation over power reactor types ended and light water reactors (LWRs) became the industry standard, including PWRs built by Westinghouse and other companies, and BWRs built by General Electric. By 1973, forty-two plants were in operation producing 26,000 megawatts, fifty more were under construction, and about one hundred were on order. Industry spokesmen predicted that 50 percent of the nation's electric power would be nuclear by the end of the twentieth century.

The promise of nuclear energy has not been completely fulfilled. Growing concerns about safety and waste disposal have led to increased efforts to delay or block the construction of new plants. The cost of nuclear plants rose as legal delays and inflation pushed costs higher, so that many in the planning stage could no longer be competitive. The 1979 Three Mile Island accident in Pennsylvania, and the much more serious 1986 Chernobyl accident in the Soviet Union, provided new ammunition for opponents, in spite of the success of the containment system at Three Mile Island and the steady depletion of fossil fuels. By 1986, more than one hundred nuclear power plants were operating in the United States, including about seventy PWRs and about thirty BWRs, producing about 60,000 megawatts of power. This provided about 17 percent of electric power production in the United States, as compared with 25 percent in Japan and 70 percent in France. More than three hundred reactors in twenty-five countries provide about 200,000 megawatts of electric power worldwide.

Bibliography

Glasstone, Samuel. *Sourcebook on Atomic Energy.* Princeton, N.J.: D. Van Nostrand, 1967. An excellent source on all aspects of nuclear energy. A sixty-five-page chapter on nuclear reactors gives a good historical summary of the development of reactors of all types, with many photographs and diagrams and nearly forty references to further literature on the early development of nuclear reactors.
Inglis, David R. *Nuclear Energy: Its Physics and Its Social Challenge.* Reading, Mass.: Addison-Wesley, 1973. A good introduction for general readers at the college level. Includes a chapter on nuclear power reactors with several diagrams and photographs and sixteen references. A number of interesting appendices provide useful information and documents on nuclear energy.
Marion, Jerry B., and Marvin L. Roush. 2d ed. *Energy in Perspective.* New York:

Academic Press, 1982. A good college survey-course textbook with chapters on energy consumption, energy sources, and the effects of nuclear radiation. A chapter on nuclear power gives a good introduction to the nuclear industry with many photographs, tables, and diagrams.

Stobaugh, Robert, and Daniel Yergin, eds. *Energy Future: Report of the Energy Project at the Harvard Business School*. New York: Random House, 1979. A general discussion of the energy debate, including a chapter, "The Nuclear Stalemate" by I. C. Bupp, with a brief historical review of the nuclear industry and a critique of LWR technology in the United States.

Williams, Robert C., and Philip L. Cantelon, eds. *The American Atom*. Philadelphia: University of Pennsylvania Press, 1984. This book is subtitled "A Documentary History of Nuclear Policies from the Discovery of Fission to the Present 1939-1984." The chapter on nuclear power has a brief introduction on the history of the nuclear industry and excerpts from several documents, including the Atomic Energy Act of 1954 and a 1979 report on the Three Mile Island accident.

Joseph L. Spradley

Cross-References

Hahn Splits an Atom of Uranium (1938), p. 1135; Fermi Creates the First Controlled Nuclear Fission Chain Reaction (1942), p. 1198; The World's First Nuclear Reactor Is Activated (1943), p. 1230; The World's First Breeder Reactor Produces Electricity While Generating New Fuel (1951), p. 1419; The Chernobyl Nuclear Reactor Explodes (1986), p. 2321.

DONALD IS THE FIRST TO USE ULTRASOUND TO EXAMINE UNBORN CHILDREN

Categories of event: Medicine and physics
Time: 1958
Locale: Edinburgh, Scotland

The use of ultrasound for the detection of fetal inconsistencies has become a valuable tool in medicine

> *Principal personages:*
> IAN DONALD, an obstetrician who developed ultrasound use in medicine
> PAUL LANGEVIN (1872-1946), a colleague of the Curies, who conceived the initial principle on which the submarine sonar for Allied forces in World War I was based
> MARIE CURIE (1867-1934) and PIERRE CURIE (1859-1906), the husband and wife scientific team that researched and developed the field of radioactivity; their work was instrumental in the development of ultrasonics
> ALICE STEWART, the researcher who drew attention to the dangers of radiation on the developing fetus when X-ray procedures are performed on pregnant women

Summary of Event

In the early 1900's, two major events made it essential to develop an appropriate means for detecting unseen underwater objects. First, the *Titanic* disaster in 1912 involved a large submerged, unseen, and silent iceberg. This obstructive and destructive iceberg caused the sinking of the *Titanic* and resulted in the death of many lives and the loss of valuable treasure. The second event was the threat to the Allied powers by German U-boats during World War I. The threat of possible defeat at sea was sufficient impetus for the French and English Admiralties to form a joint committee in 1917. The Anti-Submarine Detection and Investigation Committee (ASDIC) found ways to counter the German naval developments. Paul Langevin, a former colleague of Pierre Curie and Marie Curie, applied techniques developed in their laboratories in 1880 to formulate a crude ultrasonic system to detect submarines. These techniques used beams of sound waves of very high frequency, which were nondivergent and under directional control.

The advent of World War II made it necessary for the development of faster electronic detection technology to improve the efforts of ultrasound researchers. Langevin's crude invention evolved into the sophisticated system termed sound navigation ranging (sonar), which was important in the success of the Allied forces. Sonar was based on the pulse echo principles and, like the radio detecting and ranging (radar) system, had military implications. This vital technology was classified as a military secret and kept hidden until after the war. Later, it was applied to engineering, metallurgy, and other industrial uses. At the same time, in medicine, concerns were being raised over the use of ion-producing X rays on pregnant women.

Ian Donald's interest in engineering and principles of sound waves began when he was a young schoolboy. While he was in the British Royal Air Force, he continued and maintained his enthusiasm by observing the development of the anti-U-boat warfare efforts. He went to medical school after World War II and began a career in obstetrics. By the early 1950's, Donald had embarked on a study of how to apply sonar technology in medicine. He moved to Glasgow, Scotland, a major engineering center in Europe that presented a fertile environment for collaboration and interdisciplinary research. Donald collaborated with engineers and technicians in his medical ultrasound research. They used inanimate and tissue materials in many trials. Donald was applying his ideas in clinical research to develop applicable and appropriate ultrasound technology in medicine, especially in gynecology, his specialty. Several of his early research efforts were destroyed by powerful generators, excessive heating of tissue, and other inappropriate experimental methodologies. His failures led to new pathways and new discoveries. He was interested in adapting the A-scan method of probing metal structures and welds for cracks and flaws to medicine. Kelvin Hughes, the engineering manufacturing company that produced the Flaw Detector Apparatus, gave advice, expertise, and equipment to Donald and his associates to continue their research. Based on the applicability of this equipment, Donald devised water tanks with flexible latex bottoms. These were coated with a film of grease and probed onto protuberant abdomen of women. In 1957, an unusual case made Donald realize the potential of ultrasonic use in medicine. A male patient with a large atrial mass, clinically diagnosed as a myxoma, needed a mitral valve repair. Donald made the correct diagnosis with his ultrasound equipment prior to surgery. The echo picture enabled him to determine that a dislodged thrombus produced the atrial mass, not a myxoma. The patient died before surgical intervention, but the autopsy confirmed the diagnosis.

The use of diagnostic radiography became controversial when it was evident that these examinations were the cause of potential leukemias and other injury to the fetus. It was realized from the earliest days of radiology that radiation may cause tumors, particularly of the skin. The aftereffects of radiological studies in obstetrics were recognized much later and confirmed by studies of atomic bomb survivors and of patients receiving therapeutic irradiation. The use of radiation in obstetrics posed several major threats to the developing fetus, most notably the production of neoplasm later in life, genetic damage, and the production of development anomalies in the unborn fetus.

In 1958, bolstered by earlier clinical reports and animal research findings, Alice Stewart and her colleagues presented a major case control study of 1,326 children in England and Wales who had died of cancer before the age of ten between 1953 and 1958. There was a 91 percent increase in leukemias in children who were exposed to intrauterine radiation, as well as a higher percentage of fetal death. Although controversial, this report led to reduction in the amount of exposure of pregnant women to X rays, with subsequent reduction in fetal abnormalities and death. These reports came out at a very opportune time for Donald to accomplish the development of a technique: ultrasonography that would provide useful perinatal information without the adverse effects of radiation. These findings gave impetus and credence to the use of ultrasonography in obstetrics.

The use of ultrasound gained ground. Obstetricians were able to visualize echoes from fetal heads, and this mechanism helped them in determining difficult cases before delivery. Donald was also able to measure accurately the biparietal diameter. The technology continued to improve from the limited unidimensional A-scan technique to the plan position indication (PPI) system, a two-dimensional system developed during the war. This PPI system produced a series of dots of light that coalesced to provide tissue outlines. This improvement led to the easier visualizations of the X and Y linear potentiometers and the determination of inclination by sine/cosine potentiometers. This resulted in the B-mode ultrasound technique that is used widely today.

During a meeting of the American College of Surgeons, held in Glasgow in 1958, Donald presented case reports of his work to demonstrate the results of their years of efforts in the application of ultrasound in obstetrics. They could differentiate with certainty several gynecological tumors, ascites, and gross obesity. Unfortunately, fetal echoes, especially the cranium, were demonstrable only when they were above the level of the pubis symphysis. Donald's research report on his work with ultrasound was published in 1958 with the renowned English medical journal, *Lancet*. This technology was still in its infancy, and it had many potentials. To eliminate the flaws, the Kelvin Hughes Center developed an automatic scanner for standardization. These developments are still in use today.

Ultrasound utilizes high-frequency sound waves produced by small pulse generators. These pulses usually range from 1 to 10 megahertz. A crystal that transmits the sound beam also can be used to receive the reflected signal. The signal (sound wave) varies, depending on the tissue density. The reflected sound is displayed on a scanning oscilloscope.

In medicine, low-power ultrasound is used in place of radiation-producing X rays to reproduce images of internal bodily organs. In one method, the A-mode measures tissues, which is then converted to distance. This is used in echoencephalography to measure midline deviation in procedures where needle aspiration is required. A second method is the B-mode scanning, which indicates enhanced brightness. The returning echoes are displayed as dots of varying brightness on a phosphorus-coated oscilloscope, with polaroid photography making a permanent record. The B-mode scan is widely used because of versatility. It can be applied in the scanning of the neck, abdomen, pelvis, and extremities. In combination with Gray-scale scanning, the B-mode technique is able to display internal structures of varying density as procedures are performed. It makes the identification of the correct fetal head diameter to be measured (the biparietal diameter) much easier. Another method is the

TM-mode, which is used primarily in echocardiography. The pulsating heart requires a fast technique that will permit the sound to enter the chest and return before the next sound pulse.

Impact of Event

With continued refinement and development, ultrasonography is now a highly specialized and technical field. Today, every area of medicine is affected by the use of ultrasound in some way. The usefulness of ultrasound in obstetrics is a result of its ability to visualize anatomical detail, detect time-dependent changes in structural organization, and characterize the three-dimensional geometry of intrauterine structures.

Diagnostic ultrasound first gained clinical acceptance in obstetrics, and its major contributions have been in the assessment of fetal size and growth. The use of ultrasound in obstetrics goes beyond diagnostic enhancement. In combination with amniocentesis, ultrasound is an invaluable tool in operative procedures necessary to improve the outcomes of pregnancy. Other uses in pregnancy include detecting multiple gestational sacs, diagnosing missed abortions, identifying blighted ova, diagnosing ectopic pregnancy, locating the placenta prior to amniocentesis, predicting fetal maturity and development, displaying retained products of conception, and detecting fibromyoma during pregnancy.

As can be expected, safety has been a concern especially for a developing vulnerable fetus that is exposed to high-frequency sound. The hazards are well documented in medical literature. It is understandable that some fear may be applicable to radiation-producing X rays in the use of sonar in obstetrics. Research has not been able to document any known ionizing effect of sonography on the developing fetus. It produces neither heat nor cold. It has no cantation effect. It has not been shown to produce any toxic or destructive effect on the auditory or balancing organs of the developing fetus. Teratogenesis and interference with normal development have not been evident in extensive research performed. Chromosomal abnormalities have not been reported in any of the studies conducted.

Ultrasonography, because it is safe and noninvasive, has become the principal means for obtaining morphological information about intrauterine structures. With this procedure, the contents of the uterus—as well as the internal structure of the placenta, fetus, and fetal organs—can be evaluated at any time during pregnancy. The use of ultrasonography remains a most valued tool in medicine, especially obstetrics, because of Donald's work.

Bibliography

Bartrum, Royal J., Jr., and Harte C. Crow. *Real-Time Ultrasound: A Manual for Physicians and Technical Personnel.* 2d ed. Philadelphia: W. B. Saunders, 1983. This is a how-to technical book that informs physicians and ultrasonographers of the applications of this medium in the diagnosis of various illnesses.

Callen, Peter W. *Ultrasonography in Obstetrics and Gynecology.* Philadelphia: W. B.

Saunders, 1983. This book discusses the various aspects and applications of ultrasound in obstetrics and gynecology. Contributors include radiologists, obstetricians, gynecologists, anatomists, surgeons, and perinatologists. Excellent source for the interested reader.

Donald, Ian. "Medical Sonar: The First Twenty-five Years." In *Recent Advances in Ultrasound Diagnosis 2*, edited by Asim Kurjak. New York: Elsevier North-Holland, 1980. Donald writes about his search and development of the ultrasound uses in medicine.

_____. "Ultrasonics in Obstetrics (Sonar)." In *Practical Obstetric Problems*. 4th ed. Philadelphia: J. B. Lippincott, 1969. Discusses the practical application of issues and problems that occur in obstetrics. The discussion on ultrasound is found in the last chapter. Covers the future of this diagnostic modality.

Stewart, A., J. Webb, and D. Hewitt. "A Survey of Childhood Malignancies." *British Medical Journal* 10 (1958): 1495-1508. For the interested reader.

Margaret I. Aguwa

Cross-References

Barkla Discovers the Characteristic X Rays of the Elements (1906), p. 309; Langevin Develops Active Sonar for Submarine Detection and Fathometry (1915), p. 620; Frédéric Joliot and Irène Joliot-Curie Develop the First Artificial Radioactive Element (1933), p. 987; X Rays from a Synchrotron Are First Used in Medical Diagnosis and Treatment (1949), p. 1336; Bevis Describes Amniocentesis as a Method for Disclosing Fetal Genetic Traits (1952), p. 1439; Hounsfield Introduces a CAT Scanner That Can See Clearly into the Body (1972), p. 1961; Optical Pulses Shorter than One Trillionth of a Second Are Produced (1974), p. 2020; Clewell Corrects Hydrocephalus by Surgery on a Fetus (1981), p. 2174.

SANGER WINS THE NOBEL PRIZE FOR THE DISCOVERY OF THE STRUCTURE OF INSULIN

Category of event: Chemistry
Time: 1958
Locale: Cambridge, England

Sanger pioneered the determination of the amino acid sequence and composition of protein

Principal personage:
FREDERICK SANGER (1918-   ), a chemist who pioneered the techniques that won for him the 1958 Nobel Prize in Chemistry

Summary of Event

The hormone insulin was the first protein molecule for which the complete structure was determined by chemical means. The primary structure of insulin (its amino acid composition and sequence) was the result of the study of primarily one individual, Frederick Sanger. The results of Sanger's ten years of study were so momentous that he was awarded the Nobel Prize.

Proteins are one of the four major compounds associated with living cells. Proteins serve a variety of functions in living cells. They can serve as hormones, antibodies, transporters, and the like. In living cells, proteins are being degraded and synthesized continuously. The ability to synthesize proteins at a rate faster than their degradation is usually an indication of the well-being of a cell, a tissue, an organ, a life-form. Without some of these proteins or their normal complement, a cell may well cease to function.

The building blocks of proteins are nitrogen-containing compounds referred to as amino acids. For the most part, only twenty amino acids are found in protein. A single type of protein, insulin, does not need to contain all twenty amino acids. The difference between one protein type and another, insulin from the oxygen transporter hemoglobin, is primarily which amino acids the protein contains and the order (sequence) they are in. The sequence and composition are collectively referred to as the primary structure. Therefore, the primary structure is the signature of an individual protein.

Insulin was chosen as the first protein whose primary structure was to be deciphered because insulin, bovine, ovine, or porcine in source, was available in pure form and was very abundant. The necessity of this protein for life was well documented in 1944 when Sanger began his monumental task. Sanger had the necessary tools to bring his dream to fruition. A technique, referred to as chromatography, was the main tool employed. This technique allows the separation and identification of compounds that are similar in chemical form. For example, even though the amino acids are similar in chemical form, there is sufficient difference between them to be separated and identified by chromatography. For this endeavor, paper was the support medium on which the physical separation was achieved. Another tool available was a method of separating the amino acids chemically in a protein. When a protein is synthesized, the amino acids are joined to one another by a chemical bond—a carbon atom, common to all amino acids. A carbon atom of one amino acid is joined to a nitrogen atom (again common to all amino acids) of the next amino acid, until the protein is assembled. This bond is called the peptide bond. It had been discovered that proteins could be digested (breaking the peptide bond and chemically separating the amino acids) if treated with hydrochloric acid. The longer the exposure to the acid, the more complete the digestion. The acid digestion was completely random in its beginning stages. Complete hydrolysis usually takes from 24 to 48 hours at 110 degrees Celsius in an evacuated system. This period usually will break all peptide bonds. A shorter period of time will yield free amino acids, as well as partially digested products, of varying lengths (differing in the number of amino acids still in the peptide bond).

Acid hydrolysis of insulin revealed the presence of fifty-one amino acids. Of the twenty possible amino acids found in proteins, seventeen were found in the protein. One amino acid—cysteine—was especially important, yet troublesome. Cysteine contains a sulfur atom that can link up with a sulfur atom of a neighboring cysteine forming a strong bond referred to as a disulfide bond. This can lead to cross-links in a protein. Fortunately, this bond could be broken specifically with performic acid, which did not break the peptide bonds.

Fifty-one amino acids were found in insulin (composition), but the order in which they occurred (sequence) had to be determined, for example, if the fifty-one amino acids were in one continuous chain or if they were in more than one chain. The presence of cysteine with the possibility of cross-links suggested more than one chain, but it was yet to be determined how many. Another instrumental tool that aided in the sequencing was the chemical 1-fluoro-2,4-dinitrobenzene (FDNB). This chemical reacts with nitrogen-containing groups of amino acids that are not in peptide bonding. The most important group with which it will react is the nitrogen-containing group at one end of a protein chain, referred to as the N-terminal amino acid. There is only one N-terminal amino acid for every protein chain. There are no circular proteins. Reaction of the reagent—now commonly referred to as Sanger's reagent—with the protein will lead to an interaction of the reagent with the N-terminal amino acids, among other types of reactions. If the protein is then acid hydrolyzed, the N-terminal amino acids can be identified by the fact that they have been labeled with DNP (dinitrophenol—a by-product of FDNB reacting with the nitrogen atom). Using this procedure, insulin was found to consist of two chains. One chain was found to have twenty-one amino acids, with the amino acid glycine as N-terminal; the other chain was found to consist of thirty amino acids, with the amino acid phenylalanine as its N-terminal. The two chains could be separated from each other by chromatography. What remained was the task of sequencing each chain separately and then determining how the two chains were joined. Insulin consists of six molecules of cysteine—four in the glycine chain (A chain) and two in the phenylalanine chain (B chain).

Sanger decided to hydrolyze a chain partially and deduce the sequence of the chain by the fragments produced. This is similar to putting together a jigsaw puzzle in the dark while wearing gloves. For example, if partial acid hydrolysis produced fragments such as A-B, A-B-C-D, C-D-E, and E-F and A, C, and E were determined to be the N-terminal amino acids in the fragments, then the sequence could be concluded logically to be A-B-C-D-E-F. Yet, if hydrolysis also produced a free amino acid, G, it was not known where it would be in the sequence. It could come before A as well as after F. Understanding this problem is the key to understanding the meticulous work that Sanger undertook. Hundreds of fragments had to be generated, separated, reacted with FDNB, and then analyzed. The sequences of both chains were attained by this procedure. This analysis was accomplished after about eight years.

What remained was to determine how the two chains were joined. When a protein, containing sulfurs of cysteines joined to one another is acid-hydrolyzed, these sulfurs can recombine in a variety of ways. By complex analysis of these products and the use of enzymes, Sanger was able to inhibit some of these reactions and then was able to determine the proper disulfide bonding involved in holding the chains together. The importance of this can be explained as follows. The A-chain has cysteines at positions 6, 7, 11, and 20. The B-chain has cysteines at positions 7 and 19. Only disulfide bonding between A-7 and B-7, A-20 and B-19, and A-6 and A-11 renders a biologically active protein. With the setting of the disulfide cross-links, Sanger had succeeded in putting it back together again.

Impact of Event

The scientific community was amazed by Sanger's ten-year effort. For the first time, the primary structure of a protein was known. Soon after Sanger's report, the primary structures of other proteins were forthcoming. From the point of technique, the pathway taken for insulin by Sanger now was employed for hemoglobin, myoglobin, lysozyme, and many other proteins. The technique of chromatography was refined by Sanger and others to a point of its being employed for the purification of other proteins, which is the first prerequisite for sequence determination. Additionally, as an off-shoot of chromatography, the technique of electrophoresis was employed in protein and nucleic acid research. This is a cornerstone technique for modern-day nucleic acid sequencing.

Differences in three amino acids in the A-chain of insulin have been the basis for discriminating one species source of insulin from another; more important, these three amino acids have been found to be the reason for the decreased efficacy of bovine and porcine insulins used in humans in the treatment of diabetes mellitus. After prolonged administration, a person may develop an immunological reaction to the hormone. If this occurs, the species of the administered insulin must be changed.

The knowledge of the primary structure of a protein also opened the door to the possibility of its now being synthesized chemically in the laboratory. This had, and still has, far-reaching importance, in both the scientific and medical arenas. It was no longer a dream to be able to synthesize a protein that could be administered clinically in the human form and in pure form. Today, growth hormone, interferon, factor VIII (missing in hemophiliacs), and many more proteins now are used routinely in a clinical setting in an attempt to save lives or to increase the quality of the lives of individuals for whom they are indicated. The synthesis of these proteins could be accomplished only if their primary structure were known.

As a further consequence, the studies of many protein chemists gave impetus to the studies of DNA (deoxyribonucleic acid). In simple terms, DNA contains the message for the primary structure of a protein. DNA molecules are sequences of nitrogenous bases, which are translated into the primary structure of a protein. The knowledge of the primary structure and the elucidation of the genetic code offered the medical world a two-fold attack. If the primary structure were known, the gene (a sequence of bases in DNA) for the protein could be synthesized and inserted possibly into the DNA of a host cell, such as bacteria, which would then synthesize the protein for humankind. This idea is the foundation of modern-day genetic engineering.

Today, proteins used in the treatment of humans originated either from chemical synthesis or from genetic engineering. Protein and nucleic acid chemistry complement each other. Sanger's work was so momentous because he pioneered the field.

Bibliography

Hunkapiller, M. W., J. E. Strickler, and K. J. Wilson. "Contemporary Methodology for Protein Structure." *Science* 226 (1984): 304-311. The authors present methods that were developed since 1959, which currently are involved in protein chemistry. It reveals how some of modern-day technology would have reduced Sanger's efforts drastically.

Lehninger, Albert L. "Proteins: Covalent Structure and Biological Functions." In *Principles of Biochemistry.* New York: Worth, 1982. In this chapter, the concept of sequence determination of proteins as well as its importance is presented in clear and concise fashion.

Rawn, J. David. "DNA Replication." In *Biochemistry.* New York: Harper & Row, 1983. This chapter shows how sequencing of DNA and proteins went hand-in-hand. It informs the reader that Sanger was awarded a second Nobel Prize for his pioneering efforts in the sequencing of nucleic acids. Chapter 30 presents information on the use of chemically synthesized proteins as well as the use of recombinant DNA.

Sanger, Frederick, and E. O. P. Thompson. "The Amino-Acid Sequence in the Glycyl Chain of Insulin." *Biochemical Journal* 15 (February, 1953): 353-374. This article, although lengthy and chemically presented, describes and elaborates on the difficulties encountered by Sanger in the sequence determination. For the specialist.

Stein, William H., and Stanford Moore. "Chromatography." In *Biophysical Chemis-*

try: Physical Chemistry in the Biological Sciences, Readings from Scientific American. San Francisco: W. H. Freeman, 1975. Chromatography was one of the major techniques that was employed by Sanger. This article presents this technique in a nontechnical manner.

Thompson, E. O. P. "The Insulin Molecule." In *The Chemical Basis of Life: An Introduction to Molecular and Cell Biology, Readings from Scientific American.* San Francisco: W. H. Freeman, 1973. This review article, written in 1955, is a concise review of the time frame during which the structure of insulin was elucidated. Thompson was instrumental in some of Sanger's findings; therefore, he presents the topic with firsthand knowledge.

Joseph M. Maturo III

Cross-References

Abel and Takamine Independently Isolate Adrenaline (1897), p. 16; Bayliss and Starling Discover Secretin and Establish the Role of Hormones (1902), p. 179; Banting and Macleod Win the Nobel Prize for the Discovery of Insulin (1921), p. 720; Li Isolates the Human Growth Hormone (1950's), p. 1358; The Artificial Sweetener Cyclamate Is Introduced (1950), p. 1368; Du Vigneaud Synthesizes Oxytocin, the First Peptide Hormone (1953), p. 1459; Berg, Gilbert, and Sanger Develop Techniques for Genetic Engineering (1980), p. 2115; The Artificial Sweetener Aspartame Is Approved for Use in Carbonated Beverages (1983), p. 2226.

VAN ALLEN DISCOVERS
THE EARTH'S RADIATION BELTS

Category of event: Earth science
Time: 1958
Locale: University of Iowa, Iowa City

Van Allen pioneered the use of artificial satellites for earth studies, which led to the discovery of electrically charged particles trapped within the earth's magnetic field

Principal personage:
 JAMES VAN ALLEN (1914-   ), an American physicist, naval officer, and veteran of World War II

Summary of Event

William Gilbert, English physician and physicist, wrote in 1600 that Earth has a magnetic field similar to a bar magnet. He reported that a compass points roughly north and south and that it is the magnetic poles of the earth's magnet that attract the compass needle. Because the magnetic field has two poles, it is a dipole field, as opposed to a monopole field, of an electrically charged particle.

Other research over the centuries has increased an understanding of the magnetic field. Roughly 95 percent of the field is the result of sources deep within the interior of the earth, while the remainder is attributable to electrical currents in the upper atmosphere and other sources in space. The poles are not stationary, but wander over the face of the earth. The poles are currently located in the islands north of Canada. It can be inferred, therefore, that the interior source is not a permanent bar magnet but rather a dynamo effect generated in the liquid, metallic outer core of the earth.

Until the late 1950's, the field and its changes could be charted only on the earth's surface. This hindered the understanding of the earth's magnetic field and inhibited the development of better field-generation theories and determination of the field's shape, strength, and volume of space that it occupied. This changed, however, with the development of artificial satellites. The idea of launching a payload into Earth orbit had fascinated scientists such as Robert H. Goddard for several decades.

As a result of the rocket and jet experimentation conducted during World War II, the dream of launching artificial satellites came closer to reality. The V-2 rockets designed by Wernher von Braun and others for the destruction of English cities in World War II could reach an altitude of 100 kilometers. Although they did not reach the speeds necessary to place a satellite in orbit, they were a step in the right direction. After the war, captured German scientists and rockets formed the basis for the United States' space efforts, such as Projects Mercury, Gemini, and Apollo.

James Van Allen started studying cosmic rays as an undergraduate. He received his Ph.D. in 1939. During the war, he served as a naval officer and worked on a proximity fuse for artillery shells. This device used a radar signal emanating from the shell that reflected back from the target to trigger the fuse that caused the shell to explode. Van Allen worked to miniaturize the electronic components needed for the small confines of the shell. After the war, Van Allen worked to reduce the instrument packages being sent aloft in the captured V-2 rockets. These rockets could go higher because they were now lifting smaller payloads, but they were still not capable of orbiting these payloads into permanent Earth orbit. By 1954, however, Van Allen and his colleagues began talking about the possibility of using larger, more powerful rockets which were then under development. In 1955, President Dwight D. Eisenhower announced that the United States would launch an artificial satellite within two years.

Scientists designated the time period from July 1, 1957, to December 31, 1958, as the International Geophysical Year. During this time period, the earth and its surrounding area were to be studied intensely by scientists around the world to learn more about the planet. The Soviets announced their intention to launch an artificial satellite as part of this study. They launched Sputnik 1 into Earth orbit on October 4, 1957.

In order to demilitarize the space effort, the United States had designed the rockets of the Vanguard program from the ground up. The Soviets, on the other hand, used a rocket designed for the delivery of nuclear weapons. The Vanguard rockets proved unreliable. The United States finally launched Explorer 1 on January 31, 1958, using a military missile.

As part of the design effort, Van Allen utilized his experience by reducing payload experiments into a package of smaller mass for launch by America's less powerful rockets. Although the payloads were smaller, they were more sophisticated because of the efforts of Van Allen and others.

Van Allen's interest in cosmic rays was also apparent when, on July 26, 1958, the United States included a Geiger counter in its launch of Explorer 4 to detect space radiation. When the counter's radio signal was transmitted to Earth for analysis, it did something strange: It increased to a maximum, decreased to zero, and then increased again to a maximum. Van Allen correctly interpreted this not as a result of an actual decrease in radiation but as a result of the instrument's inability to handle high levels of radiation. This is analogous to turning the volume of a radio too high when the sound becomes distorted as the electronics are driven beyond their design limits.

Further study revealed the nature of the radiation: The Earth's magnetic field temporarily traps electrons and other electrically charged particles emitted from the sun in the solar wind. Some of the particles also may come from Earth's upper atmosphere as its gases interact with the solar wind particles. When an electrically charged particle encounters a magnetic field, the particle may engage in one of three motions: One, if the particle moves parallel to the field, the field does not affect the particle's motion. Two, if the particle is moving perpendicular to the field, the particle will assume a circular motion perpendicular to the field. Finally, if the particle encounters the field at any other direction, the charged particle will move in a spiral motion around the magnetic field.

The earth's magnetic field fans out at the magnetic pole in the Southern Hemisphere, arcs over Earth's equator, and converges on the magnetic pole in the Northern Hemisphere. The field is strongest at the poles and weakest halfway between. The field reaches from Earth's surface into space, decreasing in strength the farther it is from Earth. Particles such as electrons enter the field and spiral along the field lines. As the field strength increases near the poles, the particles bounce off this area and spiral toward the opposite poles. The particles may perform this spiral-bounce motion many times before they finally escape from the field into outer space.

There are two regions in the field that have high radiation levels. Aligned with the center of Earth, they are both donut-shaped, with crescent-shaped cross sections. The inner surface begins at 3,000 kilometers above the earth's surface and is at its thickest portion at 5,000 kilometers. The outer region is 16,000 kilometers from the earth's surface and is 6,500 kilometers thick. Although the particles consist mostly of electrons, the inner belt does contain some protons and other particles.

In honor of Van Allen's discovery, these regions of high-level radiation were named the Van Allen radiation belts. The fact that the earth has these belts of trapped particles has far-reaching implications that will affect how space is utilized now and in the future.

Impact of Event

Before exploring near-Earth space with artificial satellites, scientists had a simplistic view of the earth's magnetic field. It was considered a simple dipole field having no spectacular features. Now, it is known that the solar wind distorts the shape of the magnetic field. The interactions between the wind and field push the field into the side closest to the sun and pull it into a tail on the opposite side.

The sun goes through an eleven-year cycle in which it is quiet, then becomes more active, and then returns to the quiescent stage. During its active phase, the sun's surface sends streamers of hot, ionized gases into space. Because these gases are electrically charged, they encounter the earth's magnetic field. This plays havoc with radio communication on Earth because the ionized layers within Earth's atmosphere that reflect radio waves interact with the solar wind. As the particles move along the magnetic-field lines, some interact with air molecules high in the atmosphere, thereby producing the northern lights, or aurora borealis.

The interaction between the magnetic field and the upper atmosphere also may relate to the ozone "holes" found in upper atmosphere. The ozone atmospheric layer provides protection against ultraviolet radiation in sunlight. Anything that affects the amount of ozone is of interest because its depletion will result in an increase of skin cancers.

It has been learned that orbiting satellites are a very convenient method for communication, navigation, and Earth monitoring. As more satellites are placed in orbit, however, convenient orbital paths are filling up, creating the need to expand space usage farther from Earth. The Van Allen radiation belts will complicate this goal because their high levels of radiation require the use of extra shielding for the satellite's instruments, thereby increasing the mass of the payload.

The Van Allen radiation belts also explain a mystery about Jupiter: For decades, scientists have detected radio signals that originate from that planet. It is now known that Jupiter has a strong magnetic field with associated Van Allen radiation belts. The trapped particles are producing the radio waves as they spiral along the magnetic-field lines.

The spiraling and bouncing behavior of the particles in the field leads to the energy crisis. Because convenient energy sources are becoming depleted, other methods must be found for generating the needed energy. One method is the fusion of hydrogen nuclei into helium with the release of energy. For fusion to occur, however, high temperatures of millions of degrees are needed, but no material can contain anything that hot. It is possible to produce a magnetic "bottle," where the high temperature hydrogen plasma spirals along the field and bounces at the ends of the "bottle" where the field increases in strength.

This article provides an example of how discoveries in one area of science can influence another area. It has happened many times in the past and will continue for as long as humanity is curious about the universe.

Bibliography

Frank, L. A., and James Van Allen. "A Survey of Magnetospheric Boundary Phenomena." In *Research in Geophysics*. Vol. 1, *Sun, Upper Atmosphere, and Space*, edited by Hugh Odishaw. Cambridge, Mass.: MIT Press, 1964. This chapter includes many figures of the earth's magnetic field and of the trapped particles moving along the field. Although it is somewhat dated, when studied with other articles in this bibliography, a historical perspective of the belts may be gained.

O'Brien, Brian. "Radiation Belts." *Scientific American* 208 (May, 1963): 84-96. Although written five years after the discovery of the Van Allen radiation belts, this article provides a wealth of information about them, including maps of the belts around the earth, and the shape of the earth's magnetic field.

Roederer, J. G. *Dynamics of Geomagnetically Trapped Radiation*. New York: Springer-Verlag, 1970. This is a highly technical text which contains calculus-level mathematics.

Van Allen, James. "Interplanetary Particles and Fields." *Scientific American* 233 (September, 1975): 160-173. This is a good update article about the Van Allen radiation belts and contains many figures.

Williams, Donald. "Charged Particles Trapped in the Earth's Magnetic Field." In *Advances in Geophysics*. Vol. 15, edited by H. E. Landsberg and J. Van Mieghen. New York: Academic Press, 1971. This technical article surveys the types of trapped particles, what their sources are, how they escape from the magnetic field, and how they are transported. Presents future directions for research. Contains 210 references.

Stephen J. Shulik

Cross-References

Kennelly and Heaviside Propose the Existence of the Ionosphere (1902), p. 174; Millikan Names Cosmic Rays and Investigates Their Absorption (1920), p. 694; Sputnik 1, the First Artificial Satellite, Is Launched (1957), p. 1545; The United States Launches Its First Orbiting Satellite, Explorer 1 (1958), p. 1583.

PARKER PREDICTS THE EXISTENCE OF THE SOLAR WIND

Category of event: Astronomy
Time: January 2, 1958
Locale: Chicago, Illinois

Parker predicted the existence of the solar wind, which was confirmed by a Soviet satellite in 1959

Principal personages:

EUGENE N. PARKER (1927-   ), a University of Chicago physicist who was awarded the Space Science Award of the American Institute of Aeronautics and Astronautics and the Sydney Chapman Medal of the Royal Astronomical Society

LUDWIG BIERMANN (1907-   ), a German astrophysicist whose work on comet tails inspired Parker

SYDNEY CHAPMAN (1889-1970), an English mathematician and physicist whose work on thermal diffusion in ionized gases influenced Parker

JOHN A. SIMPSON (1916-   ), a University of Chicago physicist and member of the Manhattan Project

SUBRAHMANYAN CHANDRASEKHAR (1910-   ), a 1983 Nobel laureate in physics for formulating the theory of the development of white dwarf stars

K. I. GRINGAUZ (1925-   ), the principal investigator for the Soviet satellite that first registered the existence of the solar wind

Summary of Event

The solar wind is one of the most fascinating interplanetary phenomena to be found in Earth's solar system. Its very name summons up visions of the kind of wild and primitive natural violence that characterizes the life of any star, including the sun. When it first was proposed, however, the notion of a steady stream of charged particles emanating from the sun at supersonic speeds was not universally accepted. Even when the solar wind was confirmed by satellite instrument packages, it continued to be dismissed by some as impossible.

Events that now are known to be caused by the solar wind were quite familiar by the 1950's. The auroras, for example, both at the North Pole (aurora borealis) and at the South Pole (aurora australis), had been observed for centuries. The fact that the tail of a comet always points away from the sun, no matter in which direction the comet is moving, was known. Magnetic storms, which cause fluctuations in Earth's magnetic field and induce voltages in telegraph and electrical transmission lines, had been observed. Scientists knew that the sun was responsible, or at least involved.

In 1957, Eugene N. Parker was an assistant professor at the Institute for Nuclear Studies and the Department of Physics at the University of Chicago. At that time, he had been working on the origin of Earth's magnetic field, thermal instability of the gas in the atmosphere of the sun, and cosmic-ray modulation. Ludwig Biermann, Director of the Max Planck Institute for Astrophysics in Munich, was visiting the University of Chicago that same year. Biermann told Parker of his studies of comet tails. Comets are essentially chunks of rock dust and ice, "dirty ice balls" that spend most of their time outside the solar system far beyond the orbit of Pluto. Occasionally, for reasons not fully understood, an individual comet is deflected (perhaps by the gravitational field of a passing star) so that it begins a round-trip journey to the sun and back. As it nears the sun, solar heat vaporizes the ice, which releases dust particles, and both vapor and dust create a tail. Solar radiation ionizes the atoms in the tail, making it visible as one of the most spectacular sights.

Biermann was interested in why comet tails always point away from the sun, even when that means that the tail is pointing in the direction in which the comet is moving. That behavior had been attributed to radiation pressure, which is the pressure exerted by any electromagnetic field, such as that from a light source, on whatever that field strikes. The pressure of sunlight, although very small, is substantial so far as the tenuous tail of a comet is concerned. Nevertheless, calculations by Biermann involving the absorption cross section of the atoms in a comet tail showed that they did not present sufficient surface area for solar radiation to have the effect that was observed: The dust and gas in the tail are not merely being carried away from the comet; they are being blown away with great force. Given that a single atom can be pushed only insofar as it casts a shadow, and that the shadow cast by an individual atom is inadequate, radiation pressure could not be the answer. The classical explanation simply did not work, Biermann believed, and there was only one other explanation: solar corpuscular radiation. Solar corpuscular radiation is the discharge of particles from the sun at the time of a solar flare. Such bursts were known to cause the auroras and magnetic storms. The rest of the time, however, interplanetary space was thought to be empty.

The idea was interesting, and although it was not taken seriously by most workers in the field, it appeared to be inescapable. The corpuscular radiation evidently was shot out from the sun with average velocities on the order of 500 kilometers per second.

Biermann's findings also fitted in well with work being done at the University of Chicago by John A. Simpson, a colleague of Parker. Simpson was one of the first to recognize the importance of the variations in cosmic-ray intensity. He made great strides in the study of cosmic-ray modulation and its implications for the active conditions in space.

Parker was influenced by Biermann's theories, because although they are obscured often by clouds, there are always auroras somewhere around the auroral zone of Earth. There are always small fluctuations in Earth's magnetic field. The tail of a comet always points away from the sun. Interplanetary space, therefore, always must be filled with solar corpuscular radiation. Parker needed to determine why it was always there and why it was moving so forcefully out from the sun even between the occurrences of solar flares. Shortly after a discussion with Biermann, Parker was in Boulder, Colorado, where he had been invited to give a lecture at the High Altitude Observatory. He had an opportunity to learn of the work of Sydney Chapman on the solar corona. The corona is an envelope of thin, hot gas that surrounds the sun. Chapman showed Parker some calculations indicating that the outer atmosphere of the sun, the corona, extended out into space, past the orbit of Earth, because of its high temperature. (At such high temperatures, even a very tenuous gas transmits a substantial amount of heat.) The high temperature of the corona was causing it to expand slowly upward against the gravitational field of the sun. It gradually increased in speed until at 2 to 5 solar radii, it reached supersonic velocity. The farther away from the sun it got, the thinner it became.

Chapman's conclusion not only was novel and interesting but also appeared to be inescapable. A little more thought, however, seemed to indicate a conflict with Biermann's equally inescapable conclusion that solar corpuscular radiation continually fills interplanetary space. Both Chapman's static corona and Biermann's solar corpuscular radiation must be composed of solar material, ionized hydrogen, that is, a plasma of protons and electrons. Both plasmas would be very tenuous so that the individual protons and electrons rarely would collide among themselves. It is not possible to have one tenuous plasma streaming at high velocity through another. The two would interact electrostatically with each other to produce ripples and electrostatic fields that would stop the streaming, locking the two plasmas together to form a single tenuous plasma.

Parker believed that solar corpuscular radiation and the extended solar corona must be the same. They both were, as he came to name it, the "solar wind." The auroras always were there, to a greater or lesser extent; the earth's magnetic field always was fluctuating somewhat; comet tails always were being blown very strongly away from the sun; and interplanetary space always was filled with the constantly expanding solar corona, moving outward from the sun.

An examination of the equations describing the dynamical behavior of the hot solar atmosphere in the presence of the powerful gravitational field of the sun showed that, with the extended high temperature deduced by Chapman, the corona is approximately static near the sun, but gradually expands with velocities that increase to 500 to 1,000 kilometers per second at large distances from the sun. The expansion reaches supersonic speeds at a distance of several solar radii and continues to accelerate for as far out as the temperature is maintained.

Parker realized that to develop the theory of the solar wind, even with fully supporting mathematical equations, and to have it accepted by the scientific community would be quite a task. In 1958, Parker wrote a paper titled "Dynamics of the Interplanetary Gas and Magnetic Fields." He reconciled Chapman's work on the expansion of the solar corona with Biermann's findings on solar corpuscular radiation. The paper contained equations developed by Parker showing supersonic velocities for the solar wind of several hundred kilometers per second. When the paper reached the *Astrophysical Journal*, however, it was rejected during the screening process, but without any indication of any scientific or mathematical error. It was a major set-back, but a colleague, Subrahmanyan Chandrasekhar, who was the editor of *Astrophysical Journal*, informed Parker that the referees of his paper were experts in the field, and they asserted that the outward acceleration of the corona to supersonic speeds was scientifically absurd, and in view of this expert opinion, it might be reasonable to withdraw the paper. Parker pointed out to Chandrasekhar that the referees had failed to find any error in the calculations and that he wished to go ahead with publication. Chandrasekhar believed he had given adequate warning, and since no mathematical error was evident, he accepted the paper.

With the publication of Parker's paper and its mathematical prediction of the solar wind, all that remained to be accomplished was an actual "sighting." Instruments designed by Soviet scientist K. I. Gringauz and carried aboard a Luna satellite were the first to detect a gas moving past the earth at some speed in excess of 60 kilometers per second—a supersonic velocity that confirmed Parker's prediction.

It would be several more years before the phenomenon of the solar wind was accepted as a fact by the scientific community. Subsequently, the actual velocity was determined by several U.S. satellites to vary from 300 to 1,000 kilometers per second.

Impact of Event

The discovery of the solar wind has added to the knowledge and understanding of the origin, evolution, and the continuing operation of the universe. Besides giving the correct explanations for the auroras, magnetic disturbances, and the behavior of comet tails, understanding the solar wind gives scientists a perspective on the activity of the solar system and adds to the knowledge of stars. Most other stars have their own stellar winds along the same general lines as the solar wind.

The traditional view of stars saw them as tranquil objects, shining away for billions of years and eventually going out. It has been learned that a star is very active, yet very mysterious. For example, the origin of the magnetic field inside the sun is not understood yet. Although it has been established that the luminosity of the sun varies by one part in six hundred, there is evidence from other sun-type stars that it could vary at times by one part in one hundred, in the space of a few years; that would be sufficient to cause substantial changes in the earth's climate. A decrease in luminosity of that magnitude would cause the polar ice caps to advance, thus producing a small ice age. In the absence of any other explanation, the substantial variations in climate recorded over the past thousand years suggest strongly that there are substantial variations in the luminosity of the sun.

There is no basis for thinking that a change of 1 percent would create the same conditions that caused any of the several major periods of glaciation dating as far back as 570 million years ago. Nevertheless, it easily could be equivalent to the Little Ice Age, which began in the thirteenth century and reached its maximum around the middle of the eighteenth century, at which point glaciers were more extensive on Earth than at any other time. The Little Ice Age affected global agricultural output, leading to hardship in China and in Europe. Killing frosts in the

North American Great Plains were commonplace each summer.

Even if the luminous intensity of the sun does vary, it is an occurrence that takes place only over a period of centuries, making it impossible to measure over any useful human period of time and difficult to predict and adjust. To overcome that difficulty, a group of Harvard University researchers is using the 152-centimeter telescope at Mount Wilson to conduct a ten-year study of about fifty sun-type stars. By being able to detect the warning signs of a major climate-altering change early enough, preparations could be made to accommodate a significant change in the earth's climate.

Understanding the solar wind shows scientists that the sun is losing mass at the rate of about 1,000,000 tons per second. That, however, is not a problem. Because of the immense size of the sun, the loss it has experienced has amounted to only one-ten-thousandth of its original mass.

Bibliography

Menzel, Donald H., and Jay M. Pasachoff. *Stars and Planets.* Boston: Houghton Mifflin Company, 1983. An excellent book for the novice astronomer/astrophysicist who wishes to become familiar with the night sky, the backdrop of comet shows. Provides the reader with understandable explanations of the "operation" of the sun and other stars.

Mitton, Simon, ed. *The Cambridge Encyclopaedia of Astronomy.* New York: Crown, 1977. The book carries the distinction of having an internationally eminent advisory board. They have succeeded in creating not only a reference work of the highest scientific standard and of lasting value but also one that is a challenge and a pleasure to read. A broadly based survey of the field of astronomy, with descriptive sections on planets, Earth's sun, other stars, and cosmology.

Muirden, James. *The Amateur Astronomer's Handbook.* 3d ed. New York: Harper & Row, 1987. Recognized as a standard work, this book has all the information necessary for establishing an amateur observatory to examine "the place of business" of the astrophysicist. Muirden explains the ways many observers have overcome the drawbacks of modest equipment by teaching themselves to excel in technique.

The Rand McNally New Concise Atlas of the Universe. New York: Rand McNally, 1989. Contains an atlas of Earth from space, an atlas of the Moon, an atlas of the solar system, and an atlas of the stars. Much of the material in this book has been made available by the U.S. Geological Survey and the National Aeronautics and Space Administration (NASA).

Zeilik, Michael. *Astronomy: The Evolving Universe.* 2d ed. New York: Harper & Row, 1979. Clear, simple writing is used. The evolution of the ideas about the universe—from superstition and myth to contemporary science—is traced. Zeilik introduces the idea of the scientific model, a simple concept that need not scare the nonscientist.

John M. Shaw

Cross-References

Hale Establishes Mount Wilson Observatory (1903), p. 194; Hartmann Discovers the First Evidence of Interstellar Matter (1904), p. 213; Russell Announces His Theory of Stellar Evolution (1913), p. 585; Lyot Builds the Coronagraph for Telescopically Observing the Sun's Outer Atmosphere (1930), p. 911; Chandrasekhar Calculates the Upper Limit of a White Dwarf Star's Mass (1931), p. 948.

THE UNITED STATES LAUNCHES
ITS FIRST ORBITING SATELLITE, EXPLORER 1

Category of event: Space and aviation
Time: January 31, 1958
Locale: Cape Canaveral, Florida

With the launch of Explorer 1, the United States entered the space age, bolstering the nation's pride in its technology and preparing for a manned spaceflight

Principal personages:

DWIGHT D. EISENHOWER (1890-1969), the thirty-fourth president of the United States, who cautiously committed the country to the development of a satellite program

WILLIAM H. PICKERING (1910-   ), a New Zealand-born rocket engineer and theorist, who directed the Jet Propulsion Laboratory's configuration of the Jupiter C rocket

HOMER J. STEWART (1915-   ), a Jet Propulsion Laboratory scientist who chaired the Department of Defense's Advisory Group of Special Capabilities, which selected the first satellite program

WERNHER VON BRAUN (1912-1977), a German-born rocket scientist, who developed the launch vehicle that placed Explorer 1 in orbit, and a guiding spirit for the United States' space program

JAMES A. VAN ALLEN (1914-   ), an astronomy and physics professor at the University of Iowa and a high-altitude researcher who designed Explorer 1 and the experiment that detected the radiation belt, now named after him

Summary of Event

According to a White House announcement in 1955, the United States government was sponsoring a program to place satellites in orbit for the advancement of science, but, in fact, President Dwight D. Eisenhower's reasons were far more complex: The United States' prestige as the world's technological vanguard, national defense, and international law were as important. The complex motivations sometimes hindered as much as helped the fledgling space program, so that by the time Explorer 1 circled the earth on January 31, 1958, the United States was already behind in the space race. The Soviet Union's Sputnik 1 had achieved orbit four months earlier. Nevertheless, Explorer 1 achieved its most important goals, and it produced a scientific surprise that proved to be fundamentally important to planning later manned spaceflights.

In *The Heavens and the Earth: A Political History of the Space Age* (1985), Walter A. McDougall argues that the first government support for a satellite program resulted from the nuclear arms race: Eisenhower wanted a spy satellite that could warn of a Soviet attempt to launch intercontinental ballistic missiles (ICBMs), then being developed by both the United States and the Soviet Union. Yet, there was a problem. If the military (which possessed the most advanced research facilities) pursued satellite testing, it was feared that the Soviets would accuse the United States of using space for aggression. They would try to make flyovers of their territory illegal in international law. Eisenhower insisted that, unlike national airspace, outer space should be free of restrictions.

An opportunity for peaceful use of spacecraft presented itself in the International Geophysical Year (IGY, July, 1957, through December, 1958), with an effort to encourage worldwide cooperation in science. In 1955, at the urging of the National Science Foundation, the United States government began plans to celebrate IGY by orbiting a satellite. Eisenhower's advisers were confident that no objections could be raised to the project, since it was ostensibly a purely civilian research effort. Once a satellite had been orbited, precedent would be set for unrestricted use of outer space. Meanwhile, the Soviet Union had begun a similar project.

The Department of Defense was placed in charge and established an advisory committee of nine members headed by Homer Stewart of the Jet Propulsion Laboratory (JPL) to select a vehicle and payload. There were three candidates: the Air Force's World Series satellite based on the Atlas ICBM; the Army and JPL's Explorer, which used a modified Redstone missile; and the Navy's Vanguard satellite and Viking booster. Even though the Army's proposal showed the clearest promise for an early launch date, the committee chose the Navy's Viking-Vanguard by a one-vote margin.

Vanguard was beset with problems from the outset. The Department of Defense allocated funding priority to warhead-carrying ICBMs, so the satellite project was chronically underfunded. As the Viking booster had to be redesigned after early testing failures, delay followed delay. Pressure mounted steadily for a successful launch, especially after the Soviets placed Sputnik 1 in orbit on October 4, 1957, followed by Sputnik 2 on November 3. The Navy team rushed to get Vanguard into space; the first attempt failed spectacularly. On December 6, 1957, it rose a few feet above its launchpad, then sank back to Earth in flames.

Although it had not received authorization, the Army satellite team had been working quietly on its rejected candidate, with Stewart's unofficial encouragement. Headed by Dr. Wernher von Braun, it assembled and tested a workable launch vehicle, the Jupiter C, and waited on the sidelines in case the Navy Vanguard project failed, as the first attempt did. When malfunctions delayed a second attempt to launch Vanguard on January 27, 1958, the secretary of defense, Neil H. McElroy, told the Army to try Explorer.

Four days later, at 10:38 P.M., the four-stage Jupiter C rocket successfully blasted off from Cape Canaveral, Florida. Reaching a speed of about 29,000 kilometers per hour, it lifted the 13.9-kilogram last stage and instrument payload into an elliptical orbit, with a high point of 2,554 kilometers and a low point of 352 kilometers. The news of success cheered the nation; Explorer not only had equaled the achievement of the Sputniks but also had reached a higher orbit.

The Jupiter C rocket was a direct descendant of the German V-2 rockets used to bombard England during World War II. Von Braun, who had designed the V-2, had come to the United States in hopes of using his skills to build spacecraft. He adapted and enlarged the V-2 design for that purpose, even though the Army had instructed him to work primarily on building weapon-delivering rockets. The first stage of the Jupiter C was von Braun's 21-meter-tall Redstone rocket fueled by liquid oxygen and hydrogen, which boosted to an altitude of 85 kilometers in 145 seconds. It then detached, and the remaining three stages, all clusters of solid-fuel rockets, coasted to an altitude of approximately 341 kilometers. One after another, von Braun's assistants rapidly ignited these stages by remote control until the final one accelerated to orbital velocity. The whole assembly was set spinning before takeoff to stabilize the rocket in flight. This multistaged design had been developed at JPL, under the direction of William H. Pickering.

James A. Van Allen designed and built the Explorer 1 payload at the University of Iowa. A tube 1.8 meters by 20.3 centimeters in length and 15.2 centimeters in diameter (including the final booster), the satellite contained instruments for measuring temperature and radiation levels in space and detecting the impacts of micrometeoroids, as well as two radios for transmitting the data back to Earth.

The Geiger counter aboard the Explorer led to the first major scientific discovery by a space probe. Van Allen had expected to encounter increased radiation above the earth's atmosphere, but the instrument became so saturated with high-level radiation that at first he thought it had malfunctioned. Later satellites recorded similar intensities; Van Allen eventually mapped the two toroidal zones of high radiation that gird the earth, now known as the Van Allen radiation belts.

Impact of Event

Explorer 1 boosted the United States' technological self-esteem, sagging after the Soviet Union achieved orbit first. Yet, its real importance lay in its contribution to the understanding of outer space and the establishment of the National Aeronautics and Space Administration (NASA).

The interservice rivalry among the Army, Navy, and Air Force for research money was as much responsible for delaying the nation's entry into the space age as the difficulties in developing the new technology. That fact was evident to the scientists at work in rocketry research and to the politicians who oversaw expenditures. It became abundantly clear to President Eisenhower and Senate Majority Leader Lyndon B. Johnson, who led the congressional initiatives for space exploration, that space research and development had to be removed from the control of the military. They thought that only an independent agency would assure efficient use of money, produce the safest vehicles, and allow the widest application of space technology through public access to the fruits of the research.

So, on October 1, 1958, NASA began operation, taking over many of the facilities and research staffs devoted to satellites by the armed services. If such an agency had not been created, and created quickly, the space program of the United States might well have stayed a poor stepchild of military ICBM programs and been drastically delayed in realizing manned spaceflights, deep-space exploration by scientific probes, and the many practical benefits to weather forecasting and communications made possible by satellites.

Van Allen's discovery of the radiation zones, which extend 48,000 to 64,000 kilometers from Earth, affected the design of manned space capsules, since the radiation could injure astronauts. NASA learned to calculate flight paths to avoid areas of intense radiation and to include shielding to protect humans and delicate instruments. The radiation belts also modified theories about the earth's magnetic fields and the nature of cosmic rays.

Furthermore, von Braun's Redstone rocket proved to be a reliable launch vehicle. The thorough testing conducted during the early Explorer launches, in part, qualified it as the booster for the United States' first manned spaceflight in 1961. To keep weight to a minimum, Van Allen also pioneered techniques to miniaturize instrumentation and telemetry components.

Perhaps the most revealing fact about the launch of Explorer 1 and the United States' entry into the space age was how readily the nation accepted the venture. Dissenters decried the vast amounts of money devoted to space as wasteful of tax dollars better spent on social programs, but they were relatively few. The majority of Americans either approved of or did not object to space exploration and the technocracy it entailed. Development of the frontier had always been part of the American mentality, and space became a new frontier.

Bibliography

Bilstein, Roger E. *Orders of Magnitude: A History of the NACA and NASA, 1915-1990.* NASA SP-4406. Washington, D.C.: Government Printing Office, 1989. This official history of NASA and its predecessor, the National Advisory Committee for Aeronautics, provides only basic information on Explorer 1. It summarizes the various political influences and research efforts that preceded the launch. It also presents a readable, if sometimes rosy, overview and contains many photographs.
Green, Constance M., and Milton Lomask. *Vanguard: A History.* NASA SP-4202. Washington, D.C.: Smithsonian Institution Press, 1971. This detailed history of the early satellite programs concentrates on Vanguard but also chronicles the achievements of its chief rival: the Explorer series. What emerges most clearly is the consternation of scientists involved in the project, who endured ridicule and pressure from the constant media scrutiny of their failures.
McDougall, Walter A. *The Heavens and the Earth: A Political History of the Space Age.* New York: Basic Books, 1985. McDougall's critical study of the military and political support for the United States' venture into space is the best available. The story of Eisenhower's goal in funding satellite research and the chagrin and confusion of the scientists involved is especially well told and thoroughly documented. McDougall also philosophizes provocatively on the dangers of aerospace

technocracy, a welcome change from the unanalytical enthusiasm of most histories of spaceflight.

Newell, Homer E. *Beyond the Atmosphere: Early Years of Space Science.* NASA SP-4211. Washington, D.C.: Government Printing Office, 1980. A NASA scientist and administrator, Newell gives an insider's account of the background of NASA's creation. The focus is therefore on organizational history; but along the way, the Explorer project receives attention as—along with Vanguard—one of the primary examples of why a unified, nonmilitary agency was needed to develop the nation's space program.

Porter, Richard W. *The Versatile Satellite.* New York: Oxford University Press, 1977. Porter summarizes the progress of satellite history trenchantly, but his book is particularly valuable to those new to space science for its lucid explanations of basic rocketry, the nature and value of the scientific discoveries that satellites have made possible, and their many practical uses. Contains a wealth of color and black-and-white photographs, illustrations, maps, graphs, and tables.

Sullivan, Walter. *Assault on the Unknown: The International Geophysical Year.* New York: McGraw-Hill, 1961. Chapters 5 and 6 give a well-written critical account of the satellite race and its place in the celebration of IGY. Written shortly after the events, the book reveals the temper of the time: optimism in the technological future. Sullivan also explains the nature of the radiation belt in detail and provides helpful illustrations.

Roger Smith

Cross-References

The First Rocket with More than One Stage Is Created (1949), p. 1342; Sputnik 1, the First Artificial Satellite, Is Launched (1957), p. 1545; Tiros 1 Becomes the First Experimental Weather Reconnaissance Satellite (1960), p. 1667; Echo, the First Passive Communications Satellite, Is Launched (1960), p. 1677; Telstar, the First Commercial Communications Satellite, Relays Live Transatlantic Television Pictures (1962), p. 1728; The First Permanently Manned Space Station Is Launched (1986), p. 2316.

A CORRODED MECHANISM IS RECOGNIZED AS
AN ANCIENT ASTRONOMICAL COMPUTER

Category of event: Archaeology
Time: 1959
Locale: Athens, Greece

The studies of de Solla Price on an ancient Greek mechanism showed that the technology of the ancient world was much more advanced than previously recognized

Principal personages:
DEREK DE SOLLA PRICE (1922-   ), an American historian of science specializing in the history of clocks and timekeeping mechanisms
SPYRIDON STAIS (1860-1931), a Greek historian and minister of education who initiated the excavation of the Antikythera shipwreck
JOANNES N. SVORONOS (1863-1922), a Greek historian who performed much of the initial description and interpretation of the Antikythera Mechanism
ALBERT REHM (1871-1949), a German classical scholar who deciphered some of the inscriptions on the Antikythera Mechanism

Summary of Event

In the early spring of 1900, a party of Greek sponge fishermen were returning home from their fishing grounds off North Africa when they were driven off course by storms and took refuge off the island of Antikythera, between the southern tip of mainland Greece and the island of Crete. After the storm abated, they decided to try diving for sponges in this unfamiliar site. At a depth of 42 meters, diver Elias Stadiatis found the remains of an ancient ship and returned to the surface with the arm of a bronze statue. After carefully noting the location of the site, the divers returned to their home port and spent the next six months deliberating on what to do about their find. They finally decided to report the find to the authorities and did so on November 6.

The Greek authorities acted quickly. The divers were hired to recover artifacts from the wreck, and a naval vessel was detailed to support the expedition. This was the first submarine archaeological investigation. Diving continued from late November, 1900, until September 30, 1901, without benefit of any underwater breathing apparatus. Divers could remain submerged for only a few minutes at a time, and because of the great water depth, could dive only twice a day. Free diving (without breathing devices) in such deep water is very dangerous; one diver died and two were permanently disabled during the operations.

The wreck yielded many amphorae (oil jars) and marble and bronze statues, which eventually allowed archaeologists to date the shipwreck at about 65 B.C. During the reassembly of the large bronze statues, small unidentified pieces of bronze were kept in a storage area until they could be fitted into place. On May 17, 1902, Spyridon Stais noted that one of the scraps bore an inscription. Further study by Joannes N. Svoronos revealed the imprint of gears in the corroded bronze. Additional scrutiny revealed portions of several rotating dials. The nature of the device was the subject of immediate controversy. Some researchers considered the device to be an astrolabe (an early navigation instrument). Others considered the gearing far too complex for such a device and argued that it was part of a water clock or planetarium of a sort described by ancient writers, but not previously known to have survived. A few scholars argued that the device was so complex it could not have been ancient, but must have been lost on the site of the shipwreck at a much later date.

Over the next half century, additional descriptions of the device, which came to be called the Antikythera Mechanism, were published by researchers like Ioannes Theophanidis and Albert Rehm. Although additional details of its construction were clarified, little new insight into its function resulted. In 1951, the device attracted the attention of Derek de Solla Price, a historian of science with an interest in timekeeping devices. He studied newly available photographs of the artifact and was able to examine the device in person in 1958. Based on analysis of the visible gears in the device and the inscriptions on it, he concluded that it was a computing device for calculating the positions of the Sun and Moon; the results were published in 1959.

Despite Price's studies, too little of the device was visible for a detailed reconstruction of its action. After two thousand years in sea water, the original bronze had altered to a mass of copper and tin compounds, and it was impossible to dismantle the object. In fact, the mechanism was in several pieces and some of it had crumbled away. Price considered X-raying the device, but initially no suitable facilities were available. In 1971, Price learned of an alternative technique, gamma-radiography, which used a small amount of radioactive material as a radiation source. With the cooperation of the Greek Atomic Energy Commission, gamma radiographs were made in 1971. Eventually X-ray photographs were made.

The radiographs revealed a total of twenty-two gears in four layers, which formed part of a compact apparatus originally measuring about 15 centimeters wide and 30 centimeters high. The gears had triangular teeth, easy to fabricate by hand with a file, but less efficient than modern gear design. The Antikythera Mechanism is the only complex mechanical device known to have survived from antiquity. Although the radiographs helped enormously in interpreting the device, they did not answer every question. None of the gears was complete enough or visible enough to allow an unambiguous count of their teeth. Because the gears are not perfectly circular and the teeth are not perfectly uniform in spacing, the tooth counts could be off by one or more teeth for some gears. A difference of one tooth (47 versus 48 or 127 versus 128 teeth) can be of considerable significance in interpreting the astronomical function of the clock. Fortunately, it is possible to rule out many alternative gear schemes because they conflict with the arrangement of other gears or dials on the device.

The Antikythera Mechanism was driven by a shaft that entered one side of the device. The shaft turned a toothed drum, or contrate gear, which in turn meshed with a large gear at right angles to the shaft. Five turns of the shaft resulted in one turn of the main drive gear, which represented a year. The other gears were used to display the positions of the Sun and Moon on dials. Letters on one of the dials appear to correspond to a list of heliacal risings and settings of major stars, a common timekeeping device in ancient calendars. Heliacal rising is the first appearance of a celestial body before sunrise; heliacal setting is the last appearance of an object after sunset.

The gear ratios in the device show that it was used to simulate several major solar and lunar cycles. The phases of the Moon fall on the same date after an interval of nineteen years. This cycle, the Metonic cycle, was known in antiquity. Nineteen years corresponds to 254 sidereal revolutions (revolutions of the Moon with respect to the stars), and the Antikythera Mechanism is geared to reflect these cycles. Because a whole number of years occur in the Metonic cycle, after each cycle the Earth, Sun, and Moon have the same positions relative to the stars. The Moon makes 235 revolutions with respect to the Sun (synodic revolutions) in a Metonic cycle. That is, there are 235 lunations, or intervals from new moon to new moon in a Metonic cycle. It is physically possible that other planetary motion gears could have fitted within the space available in the device, but no such gears survived.

The 235 revolutions are the most startling feature of the Antikythera Mechanism. It would be possible to produce this cycle with a separate gear, but there are no gears with the necessary number of teeth. The device actually produces the cycle by subtracting the 19 revolutions of one gear from the 235 revolutions of another. Such an arrangement, called a differential gear, was not suspected of being known in antiquity. The earliest differential gear known before Price's study dated from 1575, more than sixteen hundred years later than the Antikythera Mechanism.

Impact of Event

The study of the Antikythera Mechanism has shown that ancient technology was capable of much more sophistication than anyone had hitherto suspected. The Antikythera Mechanism was not an attempt to model the physical behavior of the heavens. Instead, it was a mechanized version of mathematical formulas used for predicting the cycles of the Sun and Moon. In modern terms, it was a mechanical calculator or analog computer. The exact purpose of the device is still unknown. It may have been used as a portable calculating device. Alternatively, it could have been part of a larger display in a temple or other public building, as other timekeeping devices of the period were. It was definitely not a navigation instrument for the ship, but an artwork like much of the rest of the cargo.

A device as complex as the Antikythera Mechanism cannot have been an isolated creation. It verified an extensive and elaborate gear-making tradition. The impression of the ancient world created by its most imposing artifacts (statues and buildings) is incomplete. The lack of perishable materials (paper, cloth, wood, and even most metal) creates an erroneous impression of a lack of advanced technology. To some extent, this lack is filled by ancient writers who have left descriptions of mechanical devices, yet even these descriptions are incomplete. Often they were written by members of the educated class, who may have been intrigued by the devices but lacked the technical expertise to describe them correctly. Even in the few cases of writings left by ancient technologists, the record is incomplete. For example, the Roman military engineer Vitruvius has left one of the best records of ancient technology, but it mostly concerns heavy military engineering. Someone like Vitruvius would be unlikely to have described the Antikythera Mechanism. The apparent lack of ancient advanced technology often has been attributed to slavery; as Price notes, the Antikythera Mechanism "gives the lie to an historical theory that has long been outworn and is now unworthy of serious consideration."

The Antikythera Mechanism and the rare devices related to it that have survived from later times help solve the mystery of one of the modern world's most fundamental devices. One of the salient features of Western European civilization is its emphasis on time and timekeeping. Mechanical clocks appeared abruptly in history, fully developed and highly sophisticated. Indeed, some of the most complex clocks in existence are among the earliest. If clocks are regarded solely as timekeeping devices, they appear to have come mysteriously from nowhere. Many early clocks, however, included astronomical displays, and these devices, as the Antikythera Mechanism shows, have a very ancient history. Thus, it appears that clocks, so influential in regulating the modern world, evolved out of astronomical mechanisms. Their development was stimulated more by a desire to model the movements of the heavens rather than simply to keep time.

Bibliography

De Camp, L. Sprague. *The Ancient Engineers.* Garden City, N.Y.: Doubleday, 1963. A comprehensive survey of technology from earliest times to the beginning of the Renaissance, written in nontechnical language. De Camp makes extensive use of the writings of ancient technologists and briefly describes the Antikythera Mechanism.

North, J. D. "The Astrolabe." *Scientific American* 230 (January, 1974): 96-106. A summary of one of the most beautifully crafted and deeply ingenious ancient scientific instruments. For a time, the Antikythera device was thought to be an ancient astrolabe.

Price, Derek de Solla. "An Ancient Greek Computer." *Scientific American* 200 (June 1959): 60-67. The result of Price's first detailed analysis of the Antikythera Mechanism. Although made without benefit of radiography, Price's study was confirmed largely by his later work. This article contains a number of diagrams showing the probable original design of the Antikythera device.

_____. *Gears from the Greeks: The Antikythera Mechanism, a Calendar Computer from c. 80 B.C.* New York: Science History Publications, 1975. A reprint of a lengthy journal article in which Price describes his findings. Includes many radiographs and diagrams of the gear arrangements as well as a thorough history of investigations into the Antikythera Mechanism. By far the most thorough account of the mechanism.

_____. "Piecing Together an Ancient Puzzle: The Tower of the Winds." *National Geographic* 131 (April, 1967): 586-596. A description of a building in Athens that once housed an elaborate public timekeeping display. Although the device in this building probably was not similar to the Antikythera Mechanism, the investigation nevertheless sheds light on the use of mechanical timekeeping devices in the ancient world.

Steven I. Dutch

Cross-References

Evans Discovers the Minoan Civilization on Crete (1900), p. 67; The French Expedition at Susa Discovers the Hammurabi Code (1902), p. 169; Libby Introduces the Carbon-14 Method of Dating Ancient Objects (1940's), p. 1160; Renfrew, Dixon, and Cann Reconstruct Ancient Near Eastern Trade Routes (1962), p. 1718.

HOPPER INVENTS THE COMPUTER LANGUAGE COBOL

Category of event: Applied science
Time: 1959
Locale: Washington, D.C.

Hopper helped develop COBOL, the first user-friendly computer programming language

> *Principal personages:*
> GRACE MURRAY HOPPER (1906-   ), a mathematician and recipient of more than thirty honorary doctorates for her work with computers
> HOWARD HATHAWAY AIKEN (1900-1973), a mathematician who conducted pioneering work with computers

Summary of Event

In 1959, Grace Murray Hopper had been involved with digital computers and computer languages almost as long as electronic digital computers had existed. Hopper, a mathematician, had been on the faculty at Vassar College when World War II began. She enlisted in the Navy and was assigned to the Bureau of Ordnance Computation Project to work with missile ballistics problems in 1943. In 1944, the Navy began using one of the first electronic computers, the Automatic Sequence Controlled Calculator (ASCC), designed by a team of IBM (International Business Machines Corporation) engineers headed by Howard Hathaway Aiken, to solve these problems.

IBM had given the completed machine, which was 15.5 meters long and 2.4 meters high, to Harvard University in 1944. The most advanced electronic calculating machine of its time, it performed approximately three mathematical operations per second, a speed that seemed very fast at the time. The ASCC became known as the Mark I and after the Mark I was pressed into service by the Navy, Hopper became the third person to work as its programmer.

Hopper's interest in computer programming continued after the war ended. The first electronic computer, the Mark I, had been built by IBM, but other business machine companies quickly began their own research and development programs. Instead of returning to her teaching career after the war, Hopper worked at Remington Rand and later Sperry Corporation. While she continued to serve as an officer in the Naval Reserve, she worked on software for the various successors to the Mark I, including UNIVAC, the first large-scale commercial computer. By the early 1950's, Hopper's work with programming languages had led to her development of FLOW-MATIC, the first English-language data processing compiler. Hopper's work on FLOW-MATIC paved the way for her later work with Common Business Oriented Language, or COBOL.

Until Hopper developed FLOW-MATIC, digital computer programming was all machine-specific and written in machine code. A program for one computer could not be used automatically for another. Every program was both machine-specific and problem-specific in that the programmer would be told what problem the machine was going to be asked to solve and then would write a complete new program for that specific problem in machine code. Machine code was based upon the programmer's knowing the physical characteristics of the computer as well as the requirements of the problem to be solved; that is, the programmer had to know what was happening within the machine as it worked through a series of calculations, which relays tripped when and in what order, as well as what mathematical operations were necessary for the problem to be solved. Programming was a highly specialized skill requiring a unique combination of linguistic, reasoning, engineering, and mathematical abilities that not even the mathematicians and electrical engineers who designed and built the early computers could be sure of possessing. Machine code is both complex and time-consuming to write, and while every computer still operates in response to the instructions or programming built into it, which is formatted in machine code, modern computers now can accept programs written in nonmachine code—that is, in various automatic programming languages. They are able to accept nonmachine code programs because specialized programs now exist to translate those programs into the appropriate machine code. These translating programs are known as compilers or assemblers, and FLOW-MATIC was the first natural language assembly program.

Hopper developed FLOW-MATIC after realizing that a need existed both to eliminate unnecessary steps in programming and to make computers more accessible to users. FLOW-MATIC was based, in part, on Hopper's recognition that certain elements, or commands, were common to many different programming applications. Rather than writing a lengthy series of instructions in machine code, for example, to instruct the computer to begin a series of operations, Hopper theorized that it would be possible to develop commands in an assembly language in such a way that a programmer could write one command, such as the word *add*, that would translate into a sequence of several commands in machine code. Hopper's successful development of a compiler to translate programming languages into machine code thus meant that programming became faster and easier. From assembly languages such as FLOW-MATIC, it was a logical progression to the development of high-level computer languages, such as Formula Translation or FORTRAN and COBOL.

High-level computer languages were developed to enable the programmer to write a personal program in a form close to English or standard mathematical notation, that is, in a form that the user was comfortable using. FORTRAN, a programming language developed primarily for use in science and engineering, is an example of a language that relies on mathematical notation and symbolism. Jean Sammet argues that FLOW-MATIC—one of the first intermediary languages between machine code and modern high-level languages—was particularly significant for two reasons: the use of understandable English words for the operations to be performed and the data on which they are to operate, and the realization that the data designs can and should be written completely independently of the procedures to be executed. Prior to the development of FLOW-MATIC, the programmer had to translate the operations and data into machine code; following FLOW-MATIC, the compiler performed those operations.

Between 1955 (when FLOW-MATIC was introduced) and 1959, a number of attempts at developing a specific business-oriented language were made. IBM and Remington Rand believed that the only way to market computers to the business community was through the development of a language that business people would be comfortable using. Remington Rand officials were committed especially to providing a language resembling English. The company position was that business people were not interested in writing symbolic formulas and would, in addition, prefer to write complex operations as a series of individual statements rather than nesting them. They also thought that any mathematical symbolism was unsuitable for a business data processing language. They argued that the average business person would prefer to enter programming commands not as (a × b), for example, but instead as MULTIPLY A BY B or A TIMES B. None of these attempts at developing a business-oriented language succeeded, however, and by 1959 Hopper and others in the U.S. Department of Defense had persuaded representatives of different companies of the need for cooperation.

On May 28 and 29, 1959, a conference sponsored by the Department of Defense was held at the Pentagon. Approximately forty representatives from government agencies, computer manufacturers, and other interested parties met to discuss the problem of establishing a common language for the adaptation of electronic computers for data processing. Three committees were created: the Short Range, Intermediate Range, and Long Range. The Short Range Committee adopted the ambitious goal of meeting its objective within three months. Members of the Short Range Committee consisted of representatives from six manufacturers and two government agencies. This committee represented the first attempt ever to have an intercompany committee specify a machine-independent language, and Sammet reported that many participants initially were not very optimistic about their chances of success.

Surprisingly, the committee succeeded, and the first distribution of COBOL was accomplished on December 17, 1959. Sammet reports that while there were numerous people involved with the development of COBOL, Hopper played an especially crucial role. Not only did Hopper find solutions for technical problems but also she succeeded in the task of selling the concept of a common language from an administrative and managerial point of view. Hopper recognized that while the companies involved in the commercial development of computers were in competition with one another, the use of a common, business-oriented language would contribute to the growth of the computer industry as a whole, as well as simplifying the training of computer programmers and operators. The form COBOL assumed as a language may have been the result of discussions within a committee, but its existence as a common language within the computer industry resulted from Hopper's salesmanship before the committee met.

Impact of Event

Common Business Oriented Language, or COBOL, was the first procedure-oriented natural language, machine-independent computer program developed for business data processing operations. Its development simplified the training required for computer users in business applications as well as demonstrating that computers could, indeed, be practical tools in government and industry as well as in science. Prior to the development of COBOL, electronic computers had been criticized as merely expensive oversized adding machines that were adequate for doing time-consuming mathematics but lacking the flexibility business people required.

In addition, the development of COBOL freed programmers not only from the need to know machine code but also from the need to be as cognizant of the physical characteristics of the machine as they must be of the characteristics of the problems they hope to solve. There is no longer a need to know what specific hardware instructions are required to activate the computational and logical processes or what registers are available. In short, programmers can write programs without knowing much about the specific physical characteristics of the machines on which the program is to be run. This means that, unlike the early programs of the 1940's and 1950's, programming languages can now be written that are both machine-independent and almost universally convertible from one computer to another.

Finally, because Hopper and the other committee members worked under the auspices of the Department of Defense, the software was not copyrighted, and COBOL became widely available to anyone who wanted to use it in a comparatively short period of time. It diffused rapidly within the industry and contributed to the widespread adaptation of computers for use in a countless number of settings.

Bibliography

Hodge, Marie. "An Admiral's Amazing Grace." *50 Plus* 26 (October, 1986): 16-17. Report on Hopper's retirement after serving forty-two years in the Navy.

Hopper, Grace M. "Admiral Hopper Talks to AAAS Staff." *Science* 223 (September 5, 1986): 1095-1096. Discusses the future of computers and the need to educate workers.

_____, et al. "What Lies Ahead." *Byte* 14 (January, 1989): 343-349. Brief reminiscences about early days of computers as well as speculations about future developments.

Keerjoda, Eileen. "The Grand Old Lady of Software." *Newsweek* 101 (May 9, 1983): 13-14. Brief biography of Hopper.

Sammet, Jean E. *Programming Languages: History and Fundamentals.* Englewood Cliffs, N.J.: Prentice-Hall, 1969. Thorough explanation of computer languages that not only explains how they work but also explicates the principles underlying them.

Sanderson, Peter C. *Computer Languages: A Practical Guide to the Chief Programming Languages.* London: Newnes-Butterworths, 1970. Explains FORTRAN, ALGOL 60, COBOL, and PL/I.

Shurkin, Joel. *Engines of the Mind: A History of the Computer.* New York: W. W. Norton, 1984. A general history of the computer focusing on priority disputes. Mentions Hopper only in passing, but is interesting in providing background on the early years in the industry.

Nancy Farm Mannikko

Cross-References

Eckert and Mauchly Develop the ENIAC (1943), p. 1213; The First Electronic Stored-Program Computer (BINAC) Is Completed (1949), p. 1347; UNIVAC I Becomes the First Commercial Electronic Computer and the First to Use Magnetic Tape (1951), p. 1396; Backus' IBM Team Develops the FORTRAN Computer Language (1954), p. 1475; Kemeny and Kurtz Develop the BASIC Computer Language (1964), p. 1772.

A RADIO ASTRONOMY TEAM SENDS AND RECEIVES RADAR SIGNALS TO AND FROM THE SUN

Category of event: Astronomy
Time: 1959
Locale: Stanford University, California

The radio astronomy team of Eshelman, Barthle, and Gallagher transmitted and detected the first radar wave reflections from the sun

Principal personages:
VON RUSSEL ESHELMAN (1924-   ), an American astrophysicist
ROBERT C. BARTHLE (1928-   ), an American astronomer
PAUL B. GALLAGHER (1926-   ), an American physicist

Summary of Event

As in military radar, radio astronomy encompasses "passive" and "active" branches. In the former, receive-only radio telescopes study radiation naturally emitted by celestial objects. In the latter, or radar case, radio or microwave signals are transmitted from Earth, and echoes are received after reflection and scattering from astronomical targets. Active radar astronomy has the advantage that signals can be chosen specifically to transmit through gas clouds and resolve spatial structures inaccessible to visual telescopy. Its chief limitation arises from significant losses caused by progressive geometrical spreading and attenuation with range.

Since the late 1930's, numerous radar investigations of meteors were conducted with what were essentially military systems. Nevertheless, only after World War II were the first deliberate efforts made to send and receive radar echoes specifically to and from other bodies in the solar system. As in military and air traffic control radar units, astronomical radars include a transmitter and antenna array to radiate short pulses of electromagnetic energy, a small fraction of which returns as echoes to the antenna following reflection from a solid body, or ionized gas cloud. The distance from array to reflector can be determined directly from one-half the measured elapsed travel time multiplied by the speed of light.

Assessment of total radar capability to detect a given distant target can be made via the radar equation. The radar equation is a simple measure of radar performance, defined in terms of transmitted power, signal-to-noise ratio, antenna gain, antenna area, target reflector cross section, and antenna-target distance. The signal-to-noise ratio for a given radar reflector depends on the specific array geometry used, transmitted peak power, and the receiver frequency bandwidth. Whereas the former two factors are more or less fixed by hardware, the last can be chosen to exclude ambient noise without rejecting echo energy. The target area of a reflector, measured in square meters, is its effective radar cross section, usually different from its simple geometric area. Because of its symmetrical shape, a true sphere, for example, exhibits the same radar cross section at all aspect angles, and in the so-called optical regime (where sphere radius is much larger than incident wavelength), the radar cross section is independent of wavelength. The simplest radar reflection to interpret is so-called specular (mirrorlike), or planar reflection, defined as reflection from a sufficiently smooth interface according to the Lord Rayleigh roughness criteria. Greater surface roughness causes some impinging power to be more randomly ("diffusely") scattered or lost in other than the straightline direction of propagation.

In 1945, the first radar echoes were detected from the Moon. F. J. Kerr, in England and Australia, published the first theoretical computations defining the kinds of radar power and antenna required for attempts to detect radar echoes from specific regions of the sun. As established by visual astronomy, the sun is divided into photosphere, chromosphere, and corona. The chromosphere is basically a thin, ionized gas layer overlying the photosphere. The corona is the outer part of the solar atmosphere, which can, at times of high solar activity, extend great distances outward from the sun.

Since its corona is very hot (10^6 Kelvins), it was necessary first to consider carefully the effects of refraction-bending, scattering, and collisional attenuation losses for proposed radar sounding signals. In addition to Kerr, Soviet experts, and later noted radio astronomer Robert N. Bracewell, theoretically examined, in 1955, the maximum expected penetration of radar waves, as a function of frequency and assumed raypath, into the ionized solar corona as limited by magnetic field and absorption. This is considerably more complex a computation than parameterizing the radar equation. A theoretical formula by Baumbach and Allen (1947) was used by Kerr and Bracewell to predict the varieties and properties of radar wave propagation paths through the magnetized ion clouds of the corona. An optimum frequency of a difference of 25 to 30 megacycles per second was determined. It was not until mid-1958, however, that sufficiently precise and powerful radar units became available, first at the Lincoln Laboratory of the Massachusetts Institute of Technology (MIT) and shortly thereafter at Stanford University. In early February, 1958, Robert Price and others at MIT made two attempted observations of reflected radar signals from Venus, which was expected to return an echo 5 million times weaker than that returned from the Moon. Although planetary echoes were made on this occasion, the returned echoes were too weak compared to ambient noise level to make detection clear and repeatable. In contrast to the near-exclusive focus of nascent radar astronomy on nearby planets, in early 1959, Von Russel Eshelman, Robert C. Barthle, and Paul B. Gallagher of Stanford University's Radio Physics Center made the first successful radar contact with the sun. The Stanford experiment was undertaken at a frequency of 25.6 megacycles per second. The radar system included 40 kilowatts transmitted by deploying a broadside array of four rhombic-shaped antenna elements covering more than 5.6 hectares of ground. The radar transmissions were pulsed alternatingly on and off at thirty-second intervals for fifteen minutes, slightly less than the theoretical round-trip travel time for radar signals between the earth and the sun. The received signal was amplified, filtered, frequency-modulated, and recorded on magnetic tape. The observed reflected radar echoes were much less in amplitude than the solar and cosmic background noise levels and required additional careful filtering and other data processing to ensure clear detection.

The taped records were converted from analog to digital form at the high sampling rate of 4,096 samples per second, and the absolute (positive) amplitude values of these sampled signals binned together and summed for periods of one second. This widely used bin-sum process is equivalent to one-second integration. The sums were then cross-correlated, a mathematical technique to measure similarity between two curves, with a unit square wave of one-minute period, in an attempt to bring out any specific periodicities at this frequency. If the received solar echoes were an ideal square wave of one-minute period, in the absence of noise, cross-correlation or similarity curves would be perfectly triangular in shape with symmetrical straight-line sides. Since the solar echoes received were not perfect square waves nor noise-free, but were noisy envelopes of many echo square waves arriving over a group of adjacent time delays, the triangular correlation curve appeared jagged and truncated. The amount of truncation served as a direct measure of the depth of penetration of radar signals into the solar corona, experimentally confirming that the corona was not a single or uniform specular reflector. The effect of solar and cosmic background noise on the triangular correlation curves was to generate further fluctuations from the ideal signal response. Only when the triangular curve sufficiently exceeded the magnitude of noise fluctuations could a radar echo signal be identified definitively as present.

To confirm further their data analysis for a definitive source of solar echoes (and not statistical artifacts), the Stanford team made two additional test records on numerically simulated test data. An initial tape encompassed only received radar band noise, while a second tape contained the same noise, plus a one-cycle-per-second square wave signal approximately one hundred times weaker than the noise. Processing both tapes as above, the triangular similarity curves were obtained. This permitted the experimenters to conclude safely that the signal-to-noise ratio of the received radar echoes from the sun was between a difference of 21 and 25 decibels, so that solar echo energy over the measurement period was a difference of 23 decibels less than the combined solar and cosmic ambient noise.

Although no direct measurement of the sun's radar cross section was made during the 1959 experiment, Barthle subsequently made an indirect cross section estimate in 1960. Using empirical relations for the cosmic radio noise background versus frequency at 26 megacycles per second, an approximate noise level of 3×10^{-19} watts per cycle per second was computed. The radar echo power received by the Stanford antenna was estimated to be 1.5×10^{-21} watts per cycle per second. Comparing correlated amplitude curves versus time, the Stanford results first indicated that radar energy was reflected apparently from a solar depth interval of between 1 and 3 solar radii.

Impact of Event

As a consequence of these results, regular radar studies of the sun were initiated by MIT's Lincoln Laboratories as well as other institutions. MIT employed a large cross-polarized array at El Campo, Texas, with the first extended observations in April, 1961, using a more powerful continuous-wave transmitter broadcasting at approximately 38.25 megacycles per second. Observations of solar radar returns were made as the sun passed across the antenna's beam area. The improved depth resolution of this array detailed further finer scale structure of the solar interior. Strong solar noise bursts have occasionally decreased radar echo reception when noise frequencies overlap with those of radar, so that additional cross-correlational and deconvolutional (inverse waveform) filtering techniques were necessary to ensure reliable echo waveform detection. Doppler spreading of typically 30 to 40 kilocycles per second indicates strong plasma waves. The Doppler shift is the amount of change in the measured frequency of a (radar) wave caused by the relative motion of reflector with respect to trasmitter. The data from MIT's tests provided direct estimates of the sun's radar diameter. It was first recognized here that the sun's apparent radar cross section fluctuates notably with time between 0.5 and 2 degrees angular width. Similar variations in depth of radar penetration were noted (between 1.1 and 1.5 solar radii). Overactive coronal regions, such as the characteristic long streamers, were shown to have typically high ion particle densities approximately ten times higher than those previously predicted by the theoretical models of Kerr and Bracewell.

As a result, other more comprehensive models for solar radar propagation were developed, incorporating phenomenological models for random scattering and random reflection, as well as refraction, which notably advanced the state-of-the-art in the theory of wave scattering as a whole. The success of the Stanford radar experiment gave renewed impetus to use of radar for planetary exploration. Following its conjunction in 1961, Price and Gordon H. Pettengill of MIT, and researchers at Jodrell Bank, RCA Laboratories, and the Soviet Union all obtained sufficiently strong radar echoes from Venus with reasonably good mutual agreement. In June, 1962, the Soviet Union reported radar detection of Mercury, with subsequent radar measurements of Mars and Jupiter reported in spring and fall, 1963. The mandatory minimization of all Earth-end radar system noise brought notable engineering improvements in quieting electronic receiver and antenna noise, as well as increasing sophistication in signal modulation and detection algorithms.

Bibliography

Eshelman, V. R., R. C. Barthle, and P. B. Gallagher. "Radar Echoes from the Sun." *Science* 131 (1960): 329-332. Gives a brief semitechnical description of the Stanford experiment setup and results.

Kerr, F. J. "On the Possibility of Obtaining Radar Echoes from the Sun and Planets." *Proceedings of the IRE (Institute of Radio Engineers) (UK)* 40 (1952): 660-662. This paper, together with Kerr's tutorial published a few months before the Stanford experiment, accurately estimates antenna and radiated power requirements for Earth-based detection of solar radar reflections.

NATO Advanced Study Institute on Solar System Radio Astronomy. *Solar System Radio Astronomy*. Edited by Jules Aarons. New York: Plenum Press, 1965. Shows the rapid development of radio telescopy and astronomical radar in the years immediately following the Stanford experiment.

Page, R. M. *The Origin of Radar*. New York: Greenwood Press, 1979. A most comprehensive and readable introduction to the development of basic radar concepts and instrumentation.

Proakis, John G., and Dimitris G. Manolakis. *Introduction to Digital Signal Processing*. New York: Macmillan, 1988. The best introduction to correlational, multiplexing, and other basic filtering techniques employed in radio astronomy.

Stix, Michael. *The Sun: An Introduction*. New York: Springer-Verlag, 1989. A more advanced undergraduate text, requiring a second-year physics and mathematics background. Repays careful study.

Wentzel, D. G. *The Restless Sun*. Washington, D.C.: Smithsonian Institution Press, 1989. Accurately presents an elementary-level account of key concepts and methods with numerous illustrations.

Gerardo G. Tango

Cross-References

Lyot Builds the Coronagraph for Telescopically Observing the Sun's Outer Atmosphere (1930), p. 911; Jansky's Experiments Lead to the Founding of Radio Astronomy (1930), p. 934; Reber Makes the First Radio Maps of the Universe (1942), p. 1193; Ryle's Radio Telescope Locates the First Known Radio Galaxy (1946), p. 1271; Franklin and Burke Discover Radio Emissions from Jupiter (1955), p. 1492; Ryle Constructs the First Radio Interferometer (1955), p. 1496; The Jodrell Bank Radio Telescope Is Completed (1957), p. 1539.

LEAKEY FINDS A
1.75-MILLION-YEAR-OLD FOSSIL HOMINID

Category of event: Anthropology
Time: July 17, 1959
Locale: Olduvai Gorge, northern Tanzania, East Africa

The Leakeys found the first fossil hominid, which lived 1.75 million years ago at Olduvai Gorge in Tanzania (formerly called Tanganyika) in East Africa

Principal personages:
> L. S. B. LEAKEY (1903-1972), a man of varied interests beyond archaeology, paleontology, and prehistory who advanced scientific understanding of human biological and cultural evolution as well as stimulated popular interest in the subjects
> MARY LEAKEY (1913-   ), a leading prehistorian of the twentieth century and a dedicated and hardworking archaeologist who became Leakey's second wife; she contributed much to the knowledge of African prehistory and to the success of their joint efforts

Summary of Event

Olduvai Gorge in northern Tanzania was discovered in 1911 when a German butterfly collector happened upon it. Within two years of its discovery, a German expedition recognized the gorge as a fossil hunter's paradise.

The gorge owes its origins to massive geological faulting approximately 100,000 years ago. As a result of the changing geology, the Great Rift Valley was formed, which stretches over 6,400 kilometers in East Africa, from Jordan in the north through Kenya and Tanzania to Mozambique in the south. A newly formed river resulted from the rains and rapidly cut through the previously laid down strata. The strata was formed from a series of Ngorongoro and Lemagrut volcanic eruptions, combined with lake and river deposits laid down millions of years ago. The gorge has four distinct layers, or beds, labeled Bed I (at the bottom of the gorge) through Bed IV (nearest the top). Bed I is the oldest and has been dated to be more than 2 million years old. While Olduvai is more than 40 kilometers in length and grows to a depth of approximately 92 meters, it is a small portion of the Great Rift system. The gorge passes through the surrounding Serengeti Plain, a semiarid grassland plateau, which possesses an environment similar to that of the past few million years, as documented by information within Olduvai's strata.

Louis Seymour Bazett Leakey, born to English missionary parents in Kenya and initiated into the Kikuyu tribe as a young boy, had varied interests but was ultimately trained as an anthropologist at the University of Cambridge. In 1931, he was accompanied on his first paleontological expedition to Olduvai by Hans Reck, a German geologist. Reck, who had worked at Olduvai prior to 1914, discouraged Leakey from his hope to find evidence of prehistoric human activity at the gorge; however, within the first day of their arrival, a hand ax was discovered. Leakey recorded the site of this discovery as FLK, an acronym for "Frida" Leakey, his first wife, and *korongo*, a Swahili word for "gully." Leakey recognized this site as an important one, although it was to become famous twenty-eight years later with the discovery by Mary Leakey, his second wife, of their first hominid fossil, *Zinjanthropus boisei*.

Mary Douglas Nicol was born in England in 1913. She was a sixth-generation descendant of John Frere, a late eighteenth century antiquarian who discovered stone tools in association with the remains of extinct animals. Mary Leakey was also educated in England as an archaeologist. When she met Leakey in 1933, she was becoming well known for her illustrations of lithic tools. Indeed, it was soon after they met that Leakey asked her to undertake the drawings for the first edition of his book, *Adam's Ancestors* (1934). They were married on Christmas Eve, 1936, in England, only days before their departure for Kenya.

From the late 1930's until the discovery of their first fossil hominid in 1959, the Leakeys focused worldwide attention on prehistorians and paleontologists in East Africa with their introduction of a stone-tool technology encountered at Olduvai and with the discovery of several extinct vertebrates, including a 25-million-year-old primate, a member of the genus *Proconsul*. The "Oldowan" tool tradition, named for Olduvai, was introduced by the Leakeys and was dated to the Lower Pleistocene epoch, which, at the time, was believed to have begun about a million years ago. In the early 1960's, the date for this tool tradition was revised based upon the potassium-argon radiometric-dating technique. Specifically, the technique was applied to the volcanic rocks recovered from Olduvai and prompted the age to be extended by approximately another million years. This new date was confirmed by dating methods developed later, including fission track and paleomagnetism.

On the morning of July 17, 1959, L. S. B. Leakey awoke with a headache and fever. He wrote in *National Geographic Magazine* (1960, p. 431) that "Mary was adamant" and said, " 'I am sorry, . . . but you just cannot go out this morning, even though you want to. You're not fit for it, and you'd only get worse. We cannot risk having to go back. . . .' " Little could anyone know that during that morning's search of Olduvai, Mary Leakey would discover the remains for which she and her husband had long been searching: the animal believed to have made the previously discovered Oldowan tools. She had happened upon the upper dentition and a few fragments of a never-before-documented fossil hominid. The fossil was found very near the bottom of the gorge eroding out of an embankment representing Bed I. During the next nineteen days, the Leakeys recovered more than four hundred pieces from an almost complete skull. Similar fossil hominids, presently classified as members of the genus *Australopithecus*, had been found previously in South Africa by Raymond Arthur Dart in 1924 and Robert Broom in 1936. Yet, firm dates could not be established for the South African finds; evidence of associated tool use was not as accurately documented as that encountered at Olduvai. The hominid discovered by the Leakeys is suggested to have lived approximately 1.75 million years ago. They recognized the remains as those of a young adult male based upon the degree of dental eruption and development and evidence of extreme robustness. Furthermore, the dental, facial, and cranial morphology of the Leakey discovery was distinct from the hominids previously known from South Africa. As a result, the Leakeys placed their hominid into a new taxon. Specifically, the Leakeys classified their discovery into a new genus *Zinjanthropus*, and species, *boisei*. *Zinj* is Arabic for East Africa, *anthropus* is Greek for mankind, and *boisei* is a latinization of Boise, the family name of Leakey's benefactor, Charles Boise. Because of the specimen's cranial robustness, massive molars, and "molarized" premolars, the fossil's popular name became "Nutcracker man."

Impact of Event

The discovery of *Zinjanthropus* affected human paleontology in many ways. The age of the first hominids was pushed back dramatically. Although Dart, Broom, and others had previously given the world cause to accept the notion proposed by Charles Darwin in *The Descent of Man and Selection in Relation to Sex* (1871) that Africa would prove to be the cradle of humankind, the various hominid fossils recovered from South Africa (for example, *Australopithecus africanus, Paranthropus robustus*, and others) did not lend themselves to accurate dating. The discovery of *Zinjanthropus boisei* and the Oldowan tools from the volcanic contexts of Olduvai Gorge, however, allowed accurate radiometric dates to be applied. Thus, the age of this early hominid found by the Leakeys pushed the age of the earliest hominids well beyond that which previously had been suggested.

Additionally, the discovery of *Zinjanthropus* created controversy among paleontologists because Leakey introduced a new genus. Simply, some believed another taxonomic name was not warranted. While controversy exists among paleontologists over the interpretation of the hominid fossil record, *Zinjanthropus, Australopithecus, Paranthropus*, and other generic names previously introduced have been placed into the single genus *Australopithecus*. Furthermore, many specimens previously seen as members of distinct genera are now interpreted to be members of different species. The consensus is that what was once called *Zinjanthropus boisei* should best be known as *Australopithecus boisei*. Also, this particular species is viewed as having been much more robust than its nearest taxonomic relatives, *Australopithecus robustus* and *Australopithecus africanus*. The latter species is the least robust of the three. Furthermore, since paleontologists define hominids as habitually bipedal higher primates that use tools (as evidenced by the location of the foramen magnum beneath the skull), with the discovery of tools in association with "Zinj," one could no longer doubt that members of the subfamily *Australopithecinae* deserved to be classified as hominids.

Perhaps the most important impact of the Leakey discovery was that of public support. While the Leakeys had become well known among their scientific peers in archaeology, prehistory, and paleontology, the public became familiar with their work because of their discovery of *Zinjanthropus*. Most notably, the discussion of this discovery, complete with color photographs and L. S. B. Leakey's personal account in the September, 1960, issue of *National Geographic Magazine*, played an important role in obtaining public support in the quest to document the human paleontological record. The support offered by the National Geographic Society of Washington led to more than double the amount of earth excavated the following season. The increase in the recognition and support of paleontology has had a dramatic impact on the scientific search for human fossil ancestors.

Bibliography

Johanson, Donald C., and Maitland A. Edey. *Lucy: The Beginnings of Humankind*. New York: Simon & Schuster, 1981. A book coauthored by another prominent figure in the field of paleoanthropology. This volume offers a popular account of other hominid discoveries from the Pleistocene of East Africa. It addresses the financial problems encountered in such research as well as various strong personalities and controversies that have influenced attempts to document the human fossil record.

Leakey, Louis S. B. *By the Evidence: Memoirs, 1932-1951*. New York: Harcourt Brace Jovanovich, 1974. This volume addresses the period following Leakey's research post at the University of Cambridge until 1952. His divorce from Frida, his first wife, his marriage to Mary in 1936, his work with the Kenyan Criminal Investigation Department during World War II, his and Mary's return to paleontology following the war, and Mary's discovery of Proconsul in 1948 are all discussed.

_____. "Finding the World's Earliest Man." *National Geographic* 118 (September, 1960): 420-435. A popular version of the original *Nature* article describing the site at Olduvai Gorge (FLK) and *Zinjanthropus boisei*. It was written for what became one of the Leakeys' strongest supporters, the National Geographic Society, and further enhanced public support of the Leakeys' search.

_____. "A New Fossil Skull from Olduvai." *Nature* 184 (August, 1959): 491-493. This is the publication that announced the discovery of the first hominid remains recovered by the Leakeys at Olduvai Gorge. The site, the circumstances, and the fossil are described. The remains are described as being those of a young male and placed into a new genus and species, *Zinjanthropus boisei*.

Leakey, Richard E., and Roger Lewin. *Origins*. New York: E. P. Dutton, 1977. Drawing, in part, upon the work of his parents, Richard Leakey also discusses his paleontological discoveries at Lake Turkana in northern Kenya. This popular volume suggests that there may have been three or more species of hominids existing as contemporaries in East Africa approximately 2 million years ago. Central to the text's theme is the question of why the lineage of *Homo* survived and the others did not.

Pfeiffer, John E. *The Emergence of Humankind*. 4th ed. New York: Harper & Row, 1985. Although not written in the style of most textbooks, this volume is used frequently as a textbook in introductory physical anthropology courses. It addresses the various lines of research often employed by paleoanthropologists in their attempt to learn about the hominid fossil record.

Turhon A. Murad

Cross-References

Boule Reconstructs the First Neanderthal Skeleton (1908), p. 428; Zdansky Discovers Peking Man (1923), p. 761; Dart Discovers the First Recognized Australopithecine Fossil (1924), p. 780; Weidenreich Reconstructs the Face of Peking Man (1937), p. 1096; Ardrey's *The Territorial Imperative* Argues That Humans Are Naturally Territorial (1966), p. 1808; Simons Identifies a 30-Million-Year-Old Primate Skull (1966), p. 1814; Anthropologists Discover "Lucy," an Early Hominid Skeleton (1974), p. 2037; Sibley and Ahlquist Discover a Close Human and Chimpanzee Genetic Relationship (1984), p. 2267; Hominid Fossils Are Gathered in the Same Place for Concentrated Study (1984), p. 2279; Scientists Date a *Homo sapiens* Fossil at Ninety-Two Thousand Years (1987), p. 2341.

THE ST. LAWRENCE SEAWAY IS OPENED

Category of event: Applied science
Time: June 26, 1959
Locale: United States-Canadian border on the St. Lawrence River

The St. Lawrence Seaway opened ocean traffic 3,777 kilometers into the heart of North America

Principal personages:

DOLLIER DE CASSON (?-1701), a Canadian soldier and pioneer who made the first attempt to improve the St. Lawrence River by digging a canal to bypass the Lachine Rapids

WILLIAM HAMILTON MERRITT (1793-1862), an American-born Canadian businessman who developed the idea of the Welland Ship Canal to bypass Niagara Falls to get from Lake Erie to Lake Ontario

LIONEL CHEVRIER (1903-), a member of the Canadian Parliament and Minister of Transport who became the first president of the St. Lawrence Seaway Authority

LEWIS GOULD CASTLE (1889-1960), a former banker who was chosen to be administrator of the St. Lawrence Seaway Development Authority

ROBERT SAUNDERS (1903-1955), a former mayor of Toronto who became chairman of the Ontario Hydro Electric-Power Commission

ROBERT MOSES (1888-1981), the chairman of the Power Authority of the State of New York, which controlled power development of the United States side of the St. Lawrence River

Summary of Event

The dedication of the St. Lawrence Seaway on June 26, 1959, by President Dwight D. Eisenhower of the United States and Queen Elizabeth II of England and Canada climaxed the greatest joint international project in history. Never before had two countries worked in conjunction to achieve such an economic goal. The St. Lawrence Seaway opened a water route 3,777 kilometers into the heart of North America. This waterway would serve the economic needs of both nations and open their inland ports to the world. The dedication was the culmination of five years of construction and more than two centuries of speculation. The history associated with the St. Lawrence Seaway is as complex as the construction itself. Natural and man-made barriers contributed to the delay. National and international problems threatened what was to become the greatest international friendship venture ever undertaken by two bordering nations.

The St. Lawrence River flows northeast to the Atlantic Ocean. The problem was 1,609 kilometers up the river from its mouth, at Montreal, Canada. From there, the water rises to a height of 75 meters above sea level at Lake Ontario, and eventually at the other end of the Great Lakes rises to a height of 183 meters above sea level. A water route was needed to bypass the 304-kilometer rapids and unnavigable sections so ocean vessels could get to the inland ports of the Great Lakes.

Jacques Cartier discovered the 161-kilometer-wide gulf on St. Lawrence's Day in 1535. He sailed up the river, which he named after St. Lawrence, looking for a northwest passage to China. Samuel de Champlain, known as the father of Canada, came many years later and served the people along the river.

Dollier de Casson, Superior of the Sulpecian seminary, looked out over the Lachine Rapids and dreamed of a plan that would bring missionaries, settlers, trappers, and traders up the rapids and into the lakes beyond. He planned to build a canal to bypass the rapids. Unfortunately, by his death in 1701, only an 1,829-meter dike had been excavated.

William Hamilton Merritt, a businessman in the Niagara Peninsula, was a forerunner in canal building. He proposed the Welland Canal to bypass the rapids and falls on the Niagara River. The 1.2-meter-deep, 171-kilometer canal would connect Lake Ontario with Lake Erie. This canal would have an ascent of 109 meters accomplished by forty wooden locks.

By the beginning of the nineteenth century, the St. Lawrence River had established itself as a freight route to the east. A variety of flat-bottomed river boats carried wheat, flour, lumber, and other goods between Montreal and Quebec.

The Lachine, Beauharnois, and Cornwall canals and a second Welland Canal were built by the mid-1800's. At that time, a 2.7-meter-deep channel existed from the Atlantic Ocean to Detroit, Michigan, and Windsor, Ontario.

Severe northern winters closed the canals for five months every year. Shippers wanted to maximize their seven-month season. By 1904, a 4.2-meter channel ran from Lake Erie to Montreal. Connecting channels were constructed between Lake Huron and Lake Erie and through the Canadian Sault Canal to connect all of the Great Lakes. It was now possible for larger ships with greater amounts of cargo to pass through the canals.

The earlier part of the twentieth century saw ships getting larger and carrying greater amounts of cargo over the world's oceans. It was now time for serious consideration of a joint project to develop a seaway from Montreal to Lake Ontario. World Wars I and II delayed discussion of the project, and the United States Congress failed to pass legislation pertaining to the seaway.

Canada took the initiative after World War II in both improving the seaway and developing hydroelectric power projects. At one point, it even considered doing both projects alone. Lionel Chevrier, Canadian Minister of Transport in 1947, took a leading role in developing plans for both projects, as well as negotiating with representatives of the United States to find out their interests toward the projects. The power project received first attention.

Ontario Hydro-Electric Power and the Power Authority of the State of New York agreed to develop power on the St. Lawrence in 1950. These agencies were headed by Robert Saunders and Robert Moses, respectively. A powerhouse 1,006 meters long was to be built jointly west of Cornwall. The river would be backed up 45 kilometers, creating a 161-square-kilometer lake. Many farms and small villages as well as factories, roads, and railroads tracks would be under water. More than six thousand people would have to be relocated.

Two dams were also in their plans. The first, at Long Sault, would be 762 meters long and would control the water flow to the great powerhouse. The second, at Iroquois, would be 747 meters long and control the outflow from Lake Ontario. The cost to the two power agencies would total $650 million. This was the first great step to the development of the seaway.

The problem of moving towns, bridges, people, industry, and traveling routes fell to the power agencies. Even the river would be diverted in places during construction. New towns sprang up. The integrity of the land was preserved as many of the old homes blended with the new ones. The great advantage, however, was that now the seaway could become a reality.

Canada took the initiative. It was determined to move ahead whether or not the United States chose to participate. Chevrier was named president of the St. Lawrence Seaway Authority.

President Harry S Truman wanted the United States to participate, but Congress failed for a fourth time to authorize American participation. Only after President Eisenhower was elected did the United States move forward on the project. He signed an executive order giving the Power Authority of the State of New York the authority to represent the United States in the power venture.

In 1954, Congress passed the Wiley-Dondero Bill, allowing the United States to participate in the St. Lawrence Seaway project. It was a great victory for both countries. Governor Thomas E. Dewey of New York, Premier Leslie M. Frost of Ontario, and Prime Minister Louis St. Laurent of Canada met on August 10, 1954, to break ground. Lewis Gould Castle was chosen administrator of the St. Lawrence Seaway Development Authority, the U.S. agency set up to do work on the American side of the river. Work began immediately. The first contracts were out by October; both countries wanted to get started before winter set in.

Six main structures were constructed for the generation of power: a powerhouse across the north channel of the St. Lawrence connecting the Canadian mainland and Barnhart Island, a powerhouse spilling dam across the south channel connecting the United States with Barnhart Island, a control dam at Iroquois to regulate the overflow of Lake Ontario, dikes as necessary to regulate the pool level at and above Barnhart Island, a canal closure structure in the Canadian dike next to the powerhouse to maintain a 4.2-meter depth for navigation during construction, and a controlled intake at the mouth of the Messena Canal. Seven locks were built between Montreal and Lake Ontario. Three were in the International Rapids section. Eight locks remained on the Welland Canal between Lakes Erie and Ontario.

Work went extremely slowly at first. Millions of tons of clay had to be moved. The largest earth-moving machines in the world were brought in to do the work. Potsdam sandstone, one of the hardest rocks in the world, had to be drilled and blasted. Once this rock was removed, it was used in retaining dikes along the channel. Another problem encountered was the severe weather. Temperatures reached 35 degrees below zero. Concrete would freeze before it was set, so preheated sand, gravel, and water were used in the concrete mixture. In 1957, flood waters from hurricane Audrey threatened work.

In less than five years, one of the greatest projects undertaken by two nations was complete. Locks up to 9 meters deep, almost 274 meters long, and 24 meters wide now could handle ocean vessels of 10,000 tons and lake transports up to 25,000 tons if their draft was not more than 7.8 meters. The original twenty-two small locks had been replaced by seven large ones, making the ascent from Montreal to Lake Ontario an even water stairway. The total cost was $450 million. The final cost of the power and navigation projects was more than $1.2 billion.

It took ten years to complete the Suez Canal, twenty-four years to construct the Panama Canal, and more than thirty years to build the first St. Lawrence Canal system. Each phase of construction on the seaway was completed on time or ahead of time. The joint effort by all authorities involved proved that private, state, national and provincial groups could work together with the cooperation of two nations.

Impact of Event

The completion of the St. Lawrence Seaway opened a water route that stretches 3,777 kilometers into North America. The largest ships in the world can carry cargoes into and out of North America by the cheapest method—water.

More than $1 billion was spent on developing the power and seaway projects. More than twenty-two thousand people were employed on the projects. Indirectly, tens of thousands more were touched: those who made the machines used on the projects and those who transported them to the work sites. In addition to salaries paid to workers, the areas surrounding the seaway reaped its benefits.

The State of New York and the Province of Ontario receive power from the power plants on the St. Lawrence River. The potential "white power" to the area is between 25 and 30 million horsepower produced by water on its way to the sea. Fifty-seven million tons of coal would be needed annually to produce the same horsepower.

The area that is reached by shipping corresponds closely to the size of Western Europe. The opening of the seaway included a sharp drop in shipping costs and a downward press on shipping rates. New business was created for Quebec ports on the river as well as for both countries on the Great Lakes.

Grains, raw materials, and automobiles are shipped to world ports through the seaway. Until the mid-twentieth century, the great iron and steel producers were located on the Great Lakes, and these products also went to foreign and domestic ports via the seaway. The deep waterway permitted the movement of bulk goods in far more economic quantities.

United States and Canadian ports developed the capabilities for handling ocean shipping. The United States had a concentration of heavy industry in the Great Lakes area. Now, 80 percent of the world's ships could reach their ports. Chicago, Detroit, and Duluth joined Toronto and Hamilton as world ports. Milwaukee undertook a $5 million harbor improvement. Toledo considered a $20 million terminal. Buffalo spent $6 million on port improvements. Overseas traffic passing through the Welland Canal increased tenfold between the years 1946 and 1959.

The major development of the St. Lawrence Seaway is that it shows the world that two independent countries can build and manage a joint project of major proportion and live in harmony with its existence. An artificial boundary separates both countries along the whole of the waterway, yet both countries reap benefits from it. Cooperation and consideration between countries are possible, and a common objective can be reached.

Bibliography

Chevrier, Lionel. *The St. Lawrence Seaway.* Toronto: Macmillan, 1959. Chevrier relates the obstacles and problems associated with the development of such a large international program. Conveys the history of the idea of a seaway for more than one hundred years and goes into detail about the behind-the-scenes drama to get the seaway construction underway. Illustrated. For a wide audience.

Hills, Theo L. *The St. Lawrence Seaway.* New York: Praeger, 1959. Hills, an associate professor of geography at McGill University in Montreal, writes an excellent book that is illustrated throughout. He discusses all aspects of the St. Lawrence Seaway, including history, negotiations, politics, construction, and economic advantages to all areas touched by the project. A large section covers power projects, and the final chapter discusses the future of the seaway, including lists of foreign and domestic ship traffic.

Judson, Clara Ingram. *St. Lawrence Seaway.* Chicago: Follett, 1959. This book is designed for the younger reader. It is heavily illustrated and covers all aspects of the history and development of the St. Lawrence Seaway. Judson puts the entire area in perspective by providing good descriptions of early development and improvement.

Mabee, Carleton. *The Seaway Story.* New York: Macmillan, 1961. Mabee writes from a personal interest point of view. He watched the seaway being built and relates the story of the politics involved by the United States and Canada during the project. He gives adequate space to problems associated with the seaway, both natural and man-made. Illustrated.

Payne, Robert. *The Canal Builders: The Story of Canal Builders Through the Ages.* New York: Macmillan, 1959. Discusses the great canals of the world through history. Pages 248 to 261 discuss the St. Lawrence Seaway. The history of the waterway from 1535 through its opening, along with the construction and international problems, are briefly but accurately covered. The young reader can compare the seaway project with other major canal projects from around the world. Illustrated.

Sussman, Jennifer. *The St. Lawrence Seaway: History and Analysis of a Joint Water*

Highway. Montreal, Quebec, Canada: C. D. Howe Research Institute, 1978. This publication, part of the Canada-U.S. Prospects Series, examines the Canada-United States relationship in the context of contemporary domestic and international development and provides an analysis of the relationship. Chapters deal with economic, financial, and industrial matters related to the seaway. Contains graphs and charts. Illustrated.

Willoughby, William R. *The St. Lawrence Waterway: A Study in Politics and Diplomacy.* Madison: University of Wisconsin Press, 1961. This scholarly work discusses all aspects of the waterway project. Willoughby provides a thorough history of the idea to open a seaway and then tackles the political and natural obstacles that prevented it from happening for many years. He concentrates on the objective of navigation and the plans and proposals for navigation. Illustrated with a bibliography.

Larry N. Sypolt

Cross-References

Construction Begins on the Panama Canal (1904), p. 249; The Completion of Boulder Dam Creates Lake Mead, the World's Largest Reservoir (1936), p. 1075; The Verrazano Bridge Opens (1964), p. 1782.

LUNA 2 BECOMES THE FIRST MAN-MADE OBJECT TO IMPACT ON THE MOON

Category of event: Space and aviation
Time: September 13, 1959
Locale: Baikonur (Tyuratam), Soviet Union, and the Moon

The Soviet space probe Luna 2 became the first man-made object to make contact with the surface of another celestial body

Principal personages:
SERGEI VERNOV (1910-1982), a Russian physicist and cosmic-ray researcher who supervised the cosmic-ray observations in early Soviet space probes
ALEKSANDR CHUDAKOV (1921-   ), a Russian physicist who participated in cosmic-ray studies in early Soviet space missions
SIR BERNARD LOVELL (1913-   ), a British radio astronomer, a founder and former director of Jodrell Bank radio observatory

Summary of Event

Less than two years separated the launching of the first artificial satellite and the first human contact with the Moon. The principal obstacle to be overcome in reaching the Moon, in comparison to reaching Earth orbit, was reaching Earth's escape velocity, 11 kilometers per second, as opposed to 8 kilometers per second required to send a satellite into orbit around the earth. The first attempt to reach the Moon by spacecraft came on October 11, 1958, when the United States launched Pioneer 1. Pioneer 1 did not quite achieve escape velocity; it fell about 350 meters per second short of the required 10,800 needed to escape and fell back to Earth after reaching a maximum altitude of 115,000 kilometers. Pioneer 1 had been equipped with a retrorocket to slow it so that it could be captured into a lunar orbit, and when it became clear that Pioneer 1 would not reach the Moon, attempts were made to fire the rocket to put the probe into an elongated orbit around the earth. These attempts failed, and the probe was destroyed on reentry into the earth's atmosphere. The next probe, Pioneer 2, reached an altitude of less than 2,000 kilometers. Pioneer 3, launched on December 6, 1958, also fell short of its goal, reaching a maximum altitude of 107,000 kilometers.

The Soviet Union inaugurated its lunar exploration program on January 2, 1959, with the launch of the Soviet probe Luna 1, also called Mechta (Russian for "dream"). The official name for the Soviet lunar spacecraft series is Luna (Russian for "moon"), but with the memory of the first Sputnik earth satellites still vivid, the American press nicknamed the Soviet probes "Lunik," a name still found in many histories. The word "Lunik" does not exist in Russian; in fact, early Russian scientific reports on Soviet lunar missions did not even refer to the probes by name. Instead, they were simply called by generic terms like Space Rocket 1.

Luna 1 carried instruments to measure cosmic rays, charged particles from the sun, interplanetary gases and magnetic fields, and meteor impacts. On January 3, at a distance of 113,000 kilometers, Luna 1 released a cloud of sodium vapor as part of an experiment to study the earth's magnetic field. The next day, Luna 1 passed about 5,000 kilometers from the Moon and became the first space probe to orbit the sun. The final weight of Luna 1 and its booster stage was 1,472 kilograms, with Luna 1 itself weighing 361 kilograms. The United States probe Pioneer 4 was launched two months later, on March 3. The goal of Pioneer 4 had been to pass close by the Moon and enter an orbit around the Moon, but the probe actually missed it by 60,000 kilometers and went on to orbit the sun.

Luna 2 was launched on September 12, 1959. It was similar in instrumentation and appearance to Luna 1, a sphere about 120 centimeters in diameter. After a flight of thirty-six hours, it impacted on the Moon at 90223 P.M. (Greenwich mean time), or 4:02:23 P.M. eastern standard time, on September 13, 1959. Impact occurred at about 3 kilometers per second, about a minute and a half later than scheduled. The point of impact was 435 kilometers north of the visible center of the Moon, near the craters Archimedes, Aristillus, and Autolycus.

Luna 2 was tracked by the British radio telescope at Jodrell Bank, under the direction of Sir Bernard Lovell. At the time of impact, the Moon was below the horizon for most of the United States, though it was later learned that one military tracking facility in the eastern United States also detected the last minutes of data transmission before impact. As was usual for that time, there had been no prior announcement of the launch, but a teletype message from Moscow arrived at Jodrell Bank less than an hour after launch with precise information on transmission frequencies and the position of the spacecraft. In his account of the history of Jodrell Bank, Lovell expressed a conviction that the information must have been prepared before launch specifically for that tracking facility, and sent once the launch had gone successfully.

The sudden cessation of signals from Luna 2 did not persuade all observers that the probe had hit the Moon. In the suspicious political climate of the time, some Americans suspected that the probe might have missed the Moon and that its transmitter might have failed or been turned off. A crucial set of Jodrell Bank observations provided unambiguous proof that Luna 2 had, in fact, impacted on the Moon. As the probe neared the Moon, it accelerated under the influence of the Moon's gravity. As its speed increased, the frequency of its transmissions decreased because of the Doppler effect. The observations matched exactly the expected acceleration because of the Moon's gravity and showed that there had been no attempt to change the spacecraft's course before impact.

Data transmitted by Luna 2 were analyzed by Sergei Vernov, Aleksandr Chudakov, and other Soviet scientists. These data showed that the Moon did not lack an appreciable magnetic field; nor were there any radiation belts around the Moon, as there were around the earth. Luna 2 also found unexpected differences in the earth's radiation belts (Van Allen belts) compared to the findings of Luna 1. Luna 1 had found that the earth's outer radiation belt was strongest about 27,000 kilometers from the earth. Luna 2 found that the outer belt was strongest 17,000 kilometers from Earth, and the peak radiation intensity was about five times stronger than measured by Luna 1. Both spacecraft traveled similar paths with respect to the earth's magnetic field, except that the path of Luna 2 took it through a more sunward part of the earth's magnetic field. Luna 2 scientists suspected that the earth's magnetic field was being distorted by the flow of charged atomic particles from the sun, a hypothesis that was confirmed by later investigations by other space probes.

The micrometeorite detectors of Luna 2 were modified from those on Luna 1. In the 1950's, scientists tended to overestimate the hazard from meteorites. The detectors on Luna 1 recorded micrometeorites in three ranges, with the coarsest detector set to register objects heavier than one-tenth of a microgram. Also, the spacecraft was designed to transmit data only after the detectors had accumulated a certain number of impacts. The detection threshold of Luna 1 was so high that no data were transmitted. Luna 2 was designed to register every impact, and its coarsest detection range was sensitive to particles only one-sixth as heavy as that of Luna 1. Luna 2 recorded two impacts in thirty hours of data transmission. The detection limits on Luna 3 were reduced by an additional one-half, so that the coarsest particle detector was sensitive to particles weighing less than one hundredth of a microgram, and Luna 3 recorded seven impacts in six and one-half hours. Some of the observed difference was caused by variations in meteorite abundance as the earth swept through streams of meteor debris, but the Luna data showed that the hazard from micrometeorites was extremely small.

Impact of Event

The effects of Luna 2 were more symbolic—political and emotional—than scientific. The symbolic importance of Luna 2 was the first human contact with another celestial body. The political and emotional impact was a product of the rivalry between the United States and the Soviet Union. The launch of Sputnik 1 in 1957 had been a profound shock to Americans. In the early years of space exploration, there was great anxiety in the United States over an apparent Soviet superiority in space technology. The Soviet Union achieved major space objectives and launched heavier spacecraft one to two years before the United States matched the same accomplishments. The ability to send a 390-kilogram probe to the Moon was a striking demonstration of Soviet space capability, and its dramatic effect was heightened by the timing of the launch shortly before a visit to the United States by Soviet Premier Nikita S. Khrushchev.

The complexion of the early space age was colored by military decisions made some years before the first satellites were launched. The fundamental decision was the way the United States and Soviet Union chose to deliver nuclear weapons, which at that time were extremely bulky. The United States, which had access to bases close to Soviet territory, chose to defer development of intercontinental ballistic missiles (ICBMs) and rely on manned bombers until the weight and size of nuclear weapons decreased. The Soviet Union, with no bases close to American territory, chose to develop ICBMs powerful enough to carry the heavy warheads then in use. As a result, when military missiles were applied to launching space probes, the Soviet Union had a significant advantage in launch capability. Early American space probes, in contrast, were launched by upgraded medium-range missiles, and were therefore small.

The scientific achievements of Luna 2 were modest and largely overshadowed by the dramatic Luna 3 mission only three weeks later, which transmitted the first photographs of the far side of the Moon. From a technological standpoint, the major achievement of Luna 2 was the development of the ability to aim and navigate spacecraft accurately enough to hit a moving celestial target. At that time, space technology was rudimentary by contemporary standards, as demonstrated by the failures of the early Pioneer probes, and hitting the Moon was a considerable achievement. Luna 2 confirmed that the Moon lacked a magnetic field and provided hints of the complexity of solar interactions with the earth's magnetic field. Finally, the use of Doppler-shifted radio transmissions pioneered by Jodrell Bank later became a powerful tool in spacecraft navigation and a means of determining accurately the masses of planets visited by spacecraft.

Bibliography

Braun, Wernher von, Frederick Ordway, and David Dooling. *Space Travel: A History*. Rev. ed. New York: Harper & Row, 1985. A comprehensive history of space exploration, with lengthy coverage of the early history of rocketry. The emphasis is on manned spaceflight, but there is a good summary of planetary missions.

Canby, Thomas Y. "Are the Soviets Ahead in Space?" *National Geographic* 170, (October, 1986): 420-459. A well-illustrated examination of the Soviet space program with numerous diagrams and photographs of Soviet launch vehicles and spacecraft.

Ley, Willy. *Rockets, Missiles, and Men in Space*. Rev. ed. New York: Viking Press, 1968. A history of the early years of space exploration by one of its key participants. Useful for its descriptions of the political impact of early space events.

Lovell, Sir Bernard. *The Story of Jodrell Bank*. London: Oxford University Press, 1968. A history of the great Jodrell Bank radio telescope, by its founder and first director. Its chapters on the early years of space probe tracking provide some of the best available historical insights into these events.

Oberg, James E. *Red Star in Orbit*. New York: Random House, 1981. A detailed account of Soviet space exploration that attempts to penetrate the secrecy that surrounded the Soviet space program. The primary emphasis is on manned space exploration.

Wukelic, George E., ed. *Handbook of Soviet Space-Science Research*. New York: Gordon & Breach, 1968. Although superseded by many references with regard to recent space developments, this book contains photographs, diagrams, and technical data on most early Soviet spacecraft.

Steven I. Dutch

Cross-References

The First Rocket with More than One Stage Is Created (1949), p. 1342; Sputnik 1, the First Artificial Satellite, Is Launched (1957), p. 1545; Luna 3 Provides the First Views of the Far Side of the Moon (1959), p. 1619; Venera 3 Is the First Spacecraft to Impact on Another Planet (1965), p. 1797; The Lunar Orbiter 1 Sends Back Photographs of the Moon's Surface (1966), p. 1825; Mariner 9 Is the First Known Spacecraft to Orbit Another Planet (1971), p. 1944; Mars 2 Is the First Spacecraft to Impact on Mars (1971), p. 1950; Soviet Venera Spacecraft Transmit the First Pictures from the Surface of Venus (1975), p. 2042; Viking Spacecraft Send Photographs to Earth from the Surface of Mars (1976), p. 2052.

LUNA 3 PROVIDES THE FIRST VIEWS OF
THE FAR SIDE OF THE MOON

Category of event: Space and aviation
Time: October, 1959
Locale: Earth-Moon system

In one of the earliest missions of the space age, the Soviet Union's Luna 3 photographed the hidden side of the Moon, revealing a surprising topography and impressing the world

Principal personages:

SERGEI P. KOROLEV (1907-1966), the Chief Designer of the Soviet Union's rockets and spacecraft, driving force behind many of the successes of the Soviet space program, whose lifelong dream was to explore space

NIKITA S. KHRUSHCHEV (1894-1971), the Premier of the Soviet Union from 1958 to 1964, First Secretary of the Communist Party from 1957 to 1964, who used the victories of the space program for political gain

Summary of Event

In the early days of space exploration, the successes of Soviet space missions were politically rewarding to Premier Nikita S. Khrushchev and personally and technically rewarding to Chief Designer Sergei P. Korolev. Korolev engineered many of these achievements, but did not receive wide acclaim, as Khrushchev (and his successors) kept Korolev's identity a secret until after his death in 1966. In the meantime, Khrushchev instructed Korolev to continue to produce spectacular missions, and the Chief Designer enthusiastically complied, as he was given the resources to accomplish exciting goals faster than he had ever imagined possible. After three Sputniks impressed the world with their successes in Earth orbit, the Soviets set their sights on the Moon.

Following three launch failures in 1958, Luna ("Moon") 1 became the first spacecraft to fly by the Moon, passing within 6,000 kilometers in January, 1959. That accomplishment followed four failed efforts by the United States to send spacecraft to Earth's celestial neighbor. After one more unsuccessful launch by the Soviet Union came the flight of Luna 2 in September. It succeeded in hitting the Moon, radioing data back to Earth throughout its flight. The Soviet Union's next mission, Luna 3, was the most ambitious yet.

It was only the second anniversary of the launch of the first artificial satellite, Sputnik 1, when Luna 3 lifted off shortly before 7:00 A.M. (Moscow time) on October 4, 1959. The Soviet Union named this spacecraft the Automatic Interplanetary Station, and its goal was to provide humankind's first views of the far side of the Moon.

The forces of nature have conspired to make the rate of the Moon's revolution around Earth the same as its rotation on its own axis. The result is that residents of Earth are privileged enough to see only one side of the Moon. (A slight wobbling of the Moon actually allows 59 percent of its surface to be seen from Earth.) The other side always points away, so it cannot be seen directly from Earth. The target of Luna 3 was this hidden side.

The spacecraft was cylindrical with hemispherical endcaps sporting a number of antennas. With a mass of 278.5 kilograms, its length was 1.32 meters and its diameter was 1.19 meters. This was the first of the Luna series to use solar cells (common on later spacecraft) to recharge batteries, rather than relying on batteries alone. The spacecraft spun for gyroscopic stability (the same phenomenon that stabilizes a spinning bullet or football) and to distribute the heat from the sun uniformly over the exterior. Fans circulated air inside to keep the electronics between 25 degrees Celsius and 30 degrees Celsius, despite the extreme temperatures in the vacuum outside.

During its trip through space, sensors designed to detect micrometeoroids and cosmic rays relayed their measurements to Earth. Ground controllers received the scientific data and monitored the health and trajectory of the spacecraft.

Luna 3 coasted from Earth toward the space above the Moon's south pole. The trajectory was selected so that as the spacecraft approached the Moon, gravity would bend its flight path to carry it over the south pole, behind the Moon, and then over the north pole to head back toward Earth.

At 5:16 P.M. on October 6, Luna 3 passed a little more than 6,000 kilometers from the Moon. As viewed from Earth, the Moon was less than five days old— merely a crescent. This resulted from the fact that the Moon was nearly between Earth and the sun. Therefore, the far side of the Moon was well illuminated and presented a bright disc for Luna 3's inquisitive eyes.

Upon command from Earth, the spacecraft fired its tiny gas jets to stop its rotation. A sun sensor on one end guided Luna 3 so that its other end, containing the camera and a moon sensor, pointed roughly toward the Moon. A cover that had protected the camera during the trip through space was removed, and the Moon sensor helped the jets adjust the spacecraft's orientation to center the Moon for the camera. It was 6:30 A.M. on October 7 when Luna 3 began taking pictures 65,200 kilometers from the Moon, which appeared about six times larger at that range than a full moon does when seen from Earth.

For forty minutes, the camera recorded its unique views on a special film resistant to the cosmic rays impinging on the spacecraft during its flight. A telephoto lens picked up details of the lunar surface, and another lens captured wide-angle shots to aid in making a map and locating the detailed features. By the time the last photograph had been taken, Luna 3 had receded to 68,000 kilometers from the Moon. The spacecraft started its spinning again.

Luna 3 was equipped with a complete developing facility. The film was automatically drawn through a processor to develop and dry it. The negatives were then wound into a canister for storage until the time to radio the views to Earth.

After the Moon's gravity distorted its original orbit, Luna 3 was left in a large orbit that stretched to 480,000 kilometers from Earth. It reached that distance on October 10 and began the eight-day flight to the low point of its orbit, where it would be 47,500 kilometers away.

During the fall back toward Earth, the pictures were scanned one-by-one with a narrow beam of light. The amount of light transmitted by each point on the negative revealed how dark or light that spot was. Luna 3 radioed to Earth the intensity of the light that shone through each part of the pictures, and eager scientists used that information to reconstruct the precious images. These fuzzy pictures revealed craters, mountains, dark areas, and bright areas and were the subject of much analysis long after the mission had concluded.

Forty percent of the side seen from Earth is covered by vast smooth regions known as maria. Early astronomers thought these dark expanses were seas, but they are now believed to be the remains of enormous lava flows. The greatest surprise waiting on the other side of the Moon was the paucity of these features. The spacecraft had imaged 70 percent of the far side, and less than 10 percent was covered by maria. Instead, the terrain was dominated by craters and mountains.

Some of the features located on the visible side near the Moon's limb were included in Luna 3's photography, allowing these areas to be viewed without the foreshortening distortion that occurs when they are seen nearly edge-on from Earth. In addition, because their locations already were known, their appearances on the photographs allowed scientists to establish the positions of new features on the far side with great reliability. They also aided in estimating the quality of the images and in testing the scientists' abilities to interpret the pictures.

Luna 3 continued looping around Earth even after its job was completed. In November, 1959, its radio transmissions ceased, and its orbit eventually took it back to Earth's atmosphere in April, 1960. No one took notice when it burned up; but by then, the secrets it had uncovered already were well-known to the world.

Impact of Event

Luna 3's views of the Moon were exciting to scientists and nonscientists alike. The startling asymmetry between the near and far sides of the Moon remains a significant scientific mystery and is still accepted as the most important discovery of Luna 3. No theory for why the two sides should be so different has gained wide acceptance, despite many attempted explanations. Even after spacecraft orbited the Moon, landed on it, and returned samples from its surface, the answer remains unknown.

The Soviet Union used the stunning results of Luna 3 to bolster its prestige in the world. Claiming the rights to name its discoveries, the Soviet Union gave many of the new features names of national importance, such as the Sea of Moscow, the Gulf of Cosmonauts, Tsiolkovsky Crater, and the Soviet Mountain Range. Khrushchev enjoyed the growing impression, at home and throughout the world, of the Soviet Union as a rapidly advancing socialist nation, with him as the efficient and progressive leader. Yuri A. Gagarin, who later became the first person in space and one of his country's most beloved heroes, has said that the pride and excitement elicited by these images provided the final inspiration for him to apply to the cosmonaut program. Many Soviet scientists, engineers, and officials predicted that, with the Soviet Union's clear lead in space, their spacecraft soon would visit other planets and conduct many other bold missions throughout the solar system and beyond. Some politicians in the United States claimed the pictures were counterfeits, but that did little to mitigate the admiration and envy of the Soviet Union's accomplishment.

The early triumphs of the Soviet Union in exploring the Moon stood in stark contrast to the efforts of its competitor. After twelve complete or partial failures, the first fully successful probe by the United States was Ranger 7 in July, 1964, and the first photographs the United States took of the hidden side were made in 1966 by Lunar Orbiter 1.

After Luna 3's spectacular success in 1959, there was no doubt that the Soviet Union held a substantial lead in lunar exploration. For reasons unknown in the West, however, Luna 4 was not launched until 1963, and Lunas 4 through 8 all failed. In a related program, Zond ("Probe") 3 did image the remaining unseen portion of the far side in July, 1965. Following the five disappointments in the Luna series, the Soviet Union took the lead again in the use of unmanned spacecraft to study the Moon with Luna 9 making the first soft landing in February, 1966, and Luna 10 being the first to enter orbit about the Moon in April, 1966. After American astronauts landed on the Moon in July and November of 1969, Luna 16 succeeded in retrieving 101 grams of lunar soil in September, 1970. Luna 17 delivered the first remote-controlled rover to the Moon two months later. That same year, a crater 360 kilometers in diameter—one of the largest on the far side of the Moon—was named Korolev, honoring the genius this man applied to Luna 3 and other missions into space.

Bibliography

Harvey, Brian. *Race into Space: The Soviet Space Programme.* Chichester, England: Ellis Horwood, 1988. A complete description of Soviet unmanned and manned missions, ground facilities, key technical contributors, and the historical and political context in which the events occurred. Careful readers will find many small technical errors, but the breadth of this text makes it a rich source for all audiences.

Johnson, Nicholas L. *Handbook of Soviet Lunar and Planetary Exploration.* San Diego: Univelt, 1979. This book provides a very readable, detailed description of the history of the Soviet efforts to explore the Moon and planets. Suitable for college-level readers, it includes many technical descriptions and drawings of the spacecraft and their systems. Includes many references and an extensive bibliography.

Kopal, Zdeněk. *Exploration of the Moon by Spacecraft.* Edinburgh: Oliver and Boyd, 1968. Written by an expert in lunar research, this 88-page book explains how the spacecraft worked and how their results contribute to an overall understanding of the lunar surface environment. Since it was written before the series of Apollo landings, the text necessarily relies on conclusions and speculations supported by the early unmanned probes.

Moore, Patrick. *The Moon*. New York: Rand McNally, 1981. This well-illustrated book has only brief descriptions of the missions to the Moon but extensive and clearly presented information on the structure, composition, and evolution of the Moon. Many photographs and maps are included, with descriptions of the prominent features and an index to aid in locating features by name.

Wilson, Andrew. *Solar System Log*. London: Jane's, 1987. With a description of every mission to the Moon, planets, and comets, this book should be enjoyed by general audiences. It provides the essential facts from each flight and allows the reader to understand any flight in the context of humankind's efforts to explore the solar system.

Marc D. Rayman

Cross-References

Luna 2 Becomes the First Man-Made Object to Impact on the Moon (1959), p. 1614; Gagarin Becomes the First Human to Orbit Earth (1961), p. 1693; The Soviet Luna 9 Makes the First Successful Lunar Soft Landing (1966), p. 1819; The Lunar Orbiter 1 Sends Back Photographs of the Moon's Surface (1966), p. 1825; The First Humans Land on the Moon (1969), p. 1907; Apollo 12 Retrieves Surveyor 3 Parts from the Lunar Surface (1969), p. 1913; Mariner 9 Is the First Known Spacecraft to Orbit Another Planet (1971), p. 1944.

ANTHROPOLOGISTS CLAIM THAT ECUADORIAN POTTERY SHOWS TRANSPACIFIC CONTACT IN 3000 B.C.

Category of event: Anthropology
Time: The early 1960's
Locale: Valdivia, Ecuador

Anthropologists asserted that design similarities between five-thousand-year-old pottery from Ecuador and pottery of the same age from Japan show pre-Columbian contact between Asia and South America

Principal personages:

BETTY J. MEGGERS (1921-   ), an American anthropologist, author, research associate, and expert in archaeology at the Smithsonian Institution

CLIFFORD EVANS (1920-1981), an anthropologist and curator of archaeology, later chairman of the anthropology division, at the Smithsonian Institution

EMILIO ESTRADA (1916-1961), a prominent Ecuadorian businessman, widely respected amateur archaeologist, and sportsman who was greatly interested in diffusion from Asia to Mesoamerica

Summary of Event

Anthropologists agree that humanity had its origins in the Old World and migrated to the New World comparatively recently. While there is disagreement over the earliest date for humankind in the Americas, there is consensus that North and South America were populated by about 10,000 B.C. These early inhabitants were of Asian origin and migrated to the New World across the Bering land bridge, a vast, subarctic plain connecting present-day Alaska and Siberia. The land bridge was exposed by a fall in ocean levels resulting from the Ice Age. After the close of the last Ice Age, the sea level rose, submerging the land bridge and arresting land contact between Asia and the Americas. Some anthropologists have argued, however, that sporadic contacts between the Old and New Worlds continued and that these contacts had decisive impacts on the development of culture in America.

The possibility of pre-Columbian transoceanic voyages, particularly voyages between Asia and South America, has been one of the most debated issues in anthropology. It is important because it plays a key role in the debate between diffusionists and those who favor independent invention.

Diffusionists believe that human beings are, by nature, very conservative and that as a result, new social practices and forms of society are rarely invented. Accordingly, civilizations that include agriculture, urban centers, monumental architecture, writing, and complicated social organization are so intricate, they could not have been discovered more than once or twice in human history. Instead, diffusionists theorize, such civilizations have spread around the world through contact between groups. In the late 1800's, Friedrich Ratzel and the members of the German *Kulturkreis* school attempted to trace the spread of complex civilizations around the world. In the 1920's, Grafton Elliot Smith, a prominent British anthropologist, suggested that all complex society had developed in Egypt and diffused from there.

In the early twentieth century, under the purview of Franz Boas, most American anthropologists came to reject diffusionism in favor of independent invention. Boas and his followers were disturbed by scientific problems with diffusionism, as well as its often racist and ethnocentric overtones. While they did not reject diffusionism altogether, they argued that humankind is equally inventive everywhere. Consequently, civilizations rise in many places as the result of broadly similar conditions of population and environment. Unless contact between cultures can be scientifically proven, they insisted that similarities between them must be assumed to be the result of convergent or parallel cultural development, or chance. By the mid-twentieth century, American anthropologists overwhelmingly favored independent invention over diffusion. A small but highly vocal group of scholars, however, continued to support the diffusionist position.

For both groups, the high civilizations of the Americas were important test cases. If all contact between Asia and the Americans ended with the disappearance of the Bering land bridge twelve thousand years ago, then complex civilizations such as the Olmec, the Maya, and the Inca, which appeared only within the past few thousand years, must have been invented independently. If, however, transoceanic contact between Asia and the Americas continued, then there remained the possibility that the development of complex civilization in America had been critically influenced by voyagers from Asia, thus supporting the diffusionist view.

Despite the strength of academic opinion against diffusion, public interest in it remained strong. Numerous popular authors wrote about the similarities between American societies and Old World civilizations. Explorers such as Thor Heyerdahl captured the imagination with dramatic demonstrations showing that transoceanic voyages were possible with simple technology. Unfortunately, archaeologists working on scientific projects failed to find data that could confirm contact between Old and New Worlds. Without such reliable, scientifically collected data, arguments for diffusion remained weak.

In 1956, Emilio Estrada, a well-respected Ecuadorian amateur archaeologist, discovered fragments of ancient pottery near Valdivia on the Ecuadorian coast. Estrada was a businessman with a particular interest in world trade. He was interested in the possibility of pre-Columbian transoceanic voyages and favored a diffusionist explanation of New World civilization. Estrada enlisted the help of Smithsonian anthropologists Betty J. Meggers and Clifford Evans. Excavations at the Valdivia site continued from 1957 to 1961. Meggers and Evans published the results of their study in 1965 as the first volume of the prestigious Smithsonian Contributions to Anthropology. Even though Estrada died suddenly in 1961, he was listed as a coauthor of the book in honor of his important contributions. In their book, Meggers and Evans claimed that, at Valdivia, they had discovered the oldest pottery in the New World, dating to about 3000 B.C. They believed their finds proved that pottery must have been introduced from Asia to the Americas at that date. They reasoned that if pottery had been independently invented in America, the oldest pottery found should be quite simple and newer forms increasingly complex. The Valdivia pottery did not fit this pattern. It was the oldest found, and yet it was very complex. Further, they showed that the Valdivia pottery bore an uncanny resemblance to Early and Middle Jomon pottery from Japan, dating from about the same time period.

It was established that members of the Jomon culture practiced deep-sea fishing. Meggers and Evans hypothesized that a group of Jomon fishermen had been blown off course and eventually landed in Ecuador. There they found people who were culturally quite similar to themselves but lacked pottery. The fishermen introduced the technology for making pottery at Valdivia and from there it spread throughout the Americas.

For diffusionists, the effect of Meggers, Evans, and Estrada's work was electrifying. Internationally respected archaeologists, working in a strictly controlled scientific project, appeared to find strong evidence for transpacific contact and diffusion of an important aspect of culture from Asia to America. James A. Ford, a prominent archaeologist and supporter of diffusionism, wrote that Meggers and Evans had clearly demonstrated that culture was diffused rather than reinvented and that "human culture is a single connected story." In 1966, Meggers and Evans received the Gold Medal of the International Congress of Americanists for outstanding Americanist studies and the Decoration of Merit from the government of Ecuador.

Other anthropologists were not as sanguine and pointed to serious defects in Meggers and Evans' argument for diffusion. Archaeologists showed that many of the dates and design examples that Meggers and Evans had taken for Jomon pottery were found on Honshu, rather than Kyushu, an island farther to the southwest, where the voyages to Ecuador were alleged to have originated. David Collier of Chicago's Field Museum of Natural History noted that sailors adrift from Japan were very unlikely to reach Ecuador and concluded that they would probably have ended their trip in Southern California or Mexico. Many argued that even if a boatload of fishermen had landed in Ecuador, it was unlikely that there would be specialists on board capable of making pottery. The most telling blow against the diffusionists, however, was the discovery of older and simpler pottery in Colombia and Ecuador. This pottery bears no resemblance to Japanese work. Because of these flaws, the work did little to convince those who were not already supporters of diffusionism.

Impact of Event

There are very few anthropologists who support the contention that Jomon fishermen were responsible for the introduction of Valdivia pottery. Even staunch defenders of diffusion admit that, in the light of discoveries of ancient pottery made since the time of the Valdivia finds, a Japanese origin for American pottery is extremely unlikely. The debate between diffusionists and those who support the independent invention of culture continues.

Diffusionists have amassed a bewildering range of evidence showing the similarities between artifacts from New World cultures and those from China, Malaysia, the Mediterranean, Africa, India, and Southeast Asia. They argue that many of these similarities seem so unlikely that contact and diffusion are the best explanation of their presence. The sheer number of similarities, they say, makes any other interpretation unlikely.

Those who favor independent invention insist that even a very large number of design similarities between Old and New World artifacts would not prove contact, since coincidence or parallel cultural development cannot be ruled out. Startling similarities are frequently found in societies so greatly separated in time and space that no contact between them is possible. Author Nigel Davies, for example, points out that very unusual stirrup-spout bottles made in Africa in the 1930's are virtually indistinguishable from bottles made on the north coast of Peru in about 800 B.C. There is almost no chance of diffusion across more than twenty-five centuries.

According to John H. Rowe, a steadfast critic of diffusionism, "Direct contact is proved archaeologically by the identification of sites of actual colonies or trading posts or by the repeated occurrence of trade objects from one area in archaeological association in another." The only known example of a pre-Columbian site connecting Old and New Worlds that meets Rowe's criteria is the Norse settlement in Newfoundland, Canada, dated around A.D. 1000. This settlement seems to have had very little lasting impact on indigenous American culture.

Other anthropologists have reviewed several types of evidence that might be used to prove pre-Columbian contacts and diffusion. These include overwhelming architectural and city plan similarities between urban areas, as well as similarities in the structure, but not the vocabulary, of Old and New World languages, domesticated plants, and even in intestinal parasites. None of these investigations, however, has provided well-accepted, compelling evidence for contact.

Throughout the twentieth century, diffusionists have been unable to provide data for their case that satisfy the demands of those who favor independent invention. Unless they are able to do so in the future, the idea that complex culture arises very rarely and has been spread by diffusion will remain only a thought-provoking possibility. While transoceanic voyages cannot be ruled out, the hypothesis that contact between Old and New Worlds had a substantial impact on New World cultures remains unsubstantiated.

Bibliography

Davies, Nigel. *Voyagers to the New World*. New York: William Morrow, 1979. A generally skeptical account of various theories of contact between the Old and New Worlds. Davies briefly discusses Meggers and Evans' claims about Valdivia pottery but dismisses them as highly unlikely. He is more impressed by theories of contact between ancient Polynesia and the Americas. Davies credits the common biological inheritance of all peoples for the striking similarities between New and

Old World cultures. This book is a good choice for the reader who wants a general introduction to the problems of transoceanic contact and diffusion.

Jett, Stephen C. "Pre-Columbian Transoceanic Contacts." In *Ancient Native Americans*, edited by Jesse D. Jennings. San Francisco: W. H. Freeman, 1978. A compendium of evidence for diffusion to the Americas from Asia, Europe, and Africa by an anthropologist who is a firm supporter. Jett offers a large array of evidence, almost all of it based on similarities in design. He presents a great number of theories with relatively little comment on their credibility. A useful source for those who would like to see an enormous collection of diffusionist data.

Meggers, Betty J., and Clifford Evans. "A Transpacific Contact in 3000 B.C." *Scientific American* 214 (January, 1966): 28-35. A summary of Meggers and Evans' theory of transpacific contact written for a general audience. Contains illustrations of Valdivia and Jomon pottery as well as a map showing the probable course of a voyage between Japan and Ecuador.

Meggers, Betty J., Clifford Evans, and Emilio Estrada. *Early Formative Period of Coastal Ecuador: The Valdivia and Machalilla Phases*. Washington, D.C.: Government Printing Office, 1965. As the first volume of a new series, this book set a high standard of quality for publication in archaeology. Copiously illustrated and containing much well-presented data, it was written for a professional audience. The book combines a well-accepted traditional archaeological report of the digs in Valdivia and the more controversial presentation of the authors' theories on the connection between Jomon, Japan, and Valdivia, Ecuador.

Phillips, Phillip. "The Role of Transpacific Contacts in the Development of New World Pre-Columbian Civilizations." In *Handbook of Middle American Indians*. Vol. 4, *Archaeological Frontiers and External Connections*, edited by Gordon F. Ekholm and Gordon R. Willey. Austin: University of Texas Press, 1966. Phillips presents the scholarly case against the significance of transpacific contacts in the rise of American civilization. He argues that though transoceanic contacts are conceivable, the important developments in the rise of New World civilization are better explained without them.

Rowe, John Howland. "Diffusionism and Archaeology." *American Antiquity* 31 (1966): 334-337. A brief, but blistering, attack on the diffusionist position. Rowe lists sixty characteristics common to two cultures he considers completely unrelated. Intended for a professional audience but easily accessible to the layperson.

Richard L. Warms

Cross-References

Boas Publishes *The Mind of Primitive Man* (1911), p. 481; Bingham Discovers an Inca City in the Peruvian Jungle (1911), p. 491; Boyd Defines Human Races by Blood Groups (1950), p. 1373; Renfrew, Dixon, and Cann Reconstruct Ancient Near Eastern Trade Routes (1962), p. 1718; Radar Observations Show That Mayan Agricultural Centers Are Surrounded by Canals (1980), p. 2145.

THE PLASTIC IUD IS INTRODUCED
FOR BIRTH CONTROL

Category of event: Medicine
Time: The early 1960's
Locale: United States

The use of intrauterine devices as a form of birth control was revolutionized when modern IUDs made from plastic were introduced in the United States

Principal personages:

JACK LIPPES (1924-), an associate professor of obstetrics and gynecology who designed one of the first forms of plastic IUDs

HOWARD TATUM (1915-), a physician and professor of gynecology and obstetrics who designed the first T-shaped IUD, which conformed to the shape of the uterus

JAIME A. ZIPPER, a professor of physiology and obstetrics and gynecology who studied the effects of various metals on living tissue, which resulted in the production of IUDs containing copper

Summary of Event

The intrauterine device (IUD) is a small loop, coil, or ring made of plastic, copper, or stainless steel that is inserted into the uterus by a physician. Although often thought of as a form of birth control first introduced in the 1900's, primitive forms of the IUD have been in existence for some time. For many centuries in the Middle East, camel drivers prevented camels from becoming pregnant by inserting pebbles into the uteri of female camels. Cleopatra reportedly experimented with various materials, such as hardened sea sponge, as forms of primitive IUDs. During the Middle Ages, uterine plugs made of tightly bound paper tied with string were used by Persian women. The problem with these early forms of IUDs was that they were often inserted into the female reproductive tract under unsanitary conditions which often led to infections. In the 1920's, physicians in Germany developed a metal ring which could be inserted into the human uterus, but because of many cases of inflammation and infection, this form of birth control was soon abandoned.

With advances in plastic technology during the 1940's, there was renewed interest in the IUD as a form of birth control in Israel, Japan, and the United States. IUDs could now be formed in a variety of shapes including coils, loops, spirals, and bows. A new form of IUD introduced in the United States at this time was the "Lippes loop," developed by Jack Lippes. The loop and its inserter were first marketed in 1964. This plastic loop could be straightened and fitted into a tube for insertion and then positioned in such a way that it would resume its original shape in the uterus. Two threads attached to the loop extended through the cervix into the upper part of the vagina to allow the woman to check the placement of the loop. If pregnancy was desired, the loop could be removed by a physician simply by pulling on these threads. Studies found that there was much less chance of expulsion of the Lippes loop and other plastic IUDs, which increased their contraceptive effectiveness. In addition, the chance of serious infection occurring with the use of these IUDs was reduced with the development of antibiotic drugs.

The exact way in which Lippes loop and other IUDs prevent pregnancy is not known, although several hypotheses have been suggested. An IUD does not kill sperm or block the entrance to the uterus. Instead, it either prevents fertilization of the egg or implantation of the embryo in the uterus. Experiments done with monkeys indicate that the presence of the IUD may cause minute vibrations of the oviduct, speeding passage of the egg to the uterus before the uterus is ready to receive it. As a result, pregnancy does not occur. Other studies suggest that irritation of the lining of the uterus caused by the presence of the IUD prevents the implantation of the blastocyst or causes an implanted blastocyst or embryo to be sloughed off as part of menses. It may be possible also that the IUD immobilizes sperm as they pass through the uterine cavity.

The type of IUD a doctor selects depends upon the condition of the uterus, problems with menstruation or infection, and whether the woman has been pregnant. The IUD is an excellent form of birth control for women who have had at least one child, are involved in a monogamous relationship, and who do not wish to be sterilized. IUDs are not appropriate for women under twenty-five years of age or for those who have not had children, since there is a higher rate of IUD expulsion in these women. Women with heavy menses or severe menstrual cramps are also not good candidates.

The insertion of the IUD is a rather simple procedure for the physician. The patient is usually asked to sign an informed consent indicating that she understands the nature and limitations of the IUD. After explaining the procedure to the patient and describing the IUD, the physician performs a pelvic exam to rule out the possibility of pregnancy or an active pelvic infection. The cervix (opening to the uterus) is washed with an antiseptic solution and a local anesthetic may be applied at this time. A sterile IUD is then straightened and fitted into a sterile tube and the tube containing the IUD is passed through the vagina and cervix into the uterus. When the IUD is gently pushed out of its inserter tube, it resumes its original shape as it presses against the lining of the uterus. A small portion of the tail (threads attached to the IUD) is allowed to extend through the cervical canal to allow the woman wearing the IUD to check its placement from time to time. Most physicians prefer to insert an IUD during the menstrual period. At this time, the cervix is somewhat dilated, making it easer to insert the tube containing the IUD. The flow of blood from the uterus washes away bacterial contaminants and reduces the possibility of infection following the initial introduction of the IUD into the body. Also, the physician can be reasonably sure that the patient is not pregnant.

As with any contraceptive device, the IUD has several limitations and disadvantages. Approximately 10 to 15 percent of women will have their IUDs removed because of bleeding, spotting, or pain. Bleeding is related to the size of the IUD in relation to the size of the uterus. A tight-fitting IUD pressing against the walls of the uterus will cause more bleeding than one that does not exert as much pressure. If the tip of an IUD presses against the cervical canal, bleeding will result; thus, it is very important that the IUD be seated in the uterus in such a way that it does not protrude into the cervix. Spotting during the time of ovulation as well as immediately before and after menses is quite common in women wearing IUDs. Intermittent spotting and cramps usually cease after three months of use. The uterus often reacts to the presence of the IUD with strong contractions that can displace the IUD downward and push it through the cervix. Even more problematic is the complete expulsion of the IUD from the uterus. If this occurs, it usually does so in conjunction with menses, especially in the early months of use. Most expulsions are accompanied by strong cramping, although some women experience expulsion with no symptoms. Since the consequence of an unnoticed expulsion is often an unwanted pregnancy, it is important that a woman wearing an IUD frequently check the placement of the threads attached to the IUD and also examine her sanitary napkin or tampon during menses for an expelled IUD. If the IUD is expelled, another IUD of a different size and/or shape may be inserted, usually with no further complications.

Although rare, perforations of the uterus by the IUD are also possible. In most cases, however, these perforations occur during the time of insertion. Since perforations are often asymptomatic at first, they are rarely diagnosed at an early time. The absence of IUD strings or the inability to withdraw the IUD if the strings are in place may indicate that the IUD has perforated the uterus. At this time, an X ray or ultrasound can be used to locate the IUD. If the IUD is embedded in the muscle of the uterus, it can be removed vaginally; if the IUD has entered the abdominal cavity, it can be removed by laparoscopy.

The most serious complication related to the use of the IUD is a higher chance of developing pelvic inflammatory disease (PID). Most hospitalizations and deaths resulting from the use of the IUD result directly from PID. Chances of developing this infection are greatest during the first four months following insertion. A mild infection can be corrected with medical attention without ever removing the IUD. If a more serious infection develops, it is recommended that the IUD be removed. Symptoms of PID include a vaginal discharge; abdominal, back, or leg pain; fever; chills; and bleeding after intercourse. Treatment of pelvic infections includes the use of antibiotics and bed rest. Once an infection has occurred, a woman should wait three months to one year before having another IUD inserted.

Although the effectiveness rate of the IUD is very high, some pregnancies do occur. Pregnancies have even occurred in women where the IUD is properly in place; however, the possibility of pregnancy increases when the IUD is partially or fully expelled or if it perforates the uterus. A high percentage of women who become pregnant while wearing an IUD undergo spontaneous abortions. If spontaneous abortions do not occur and the pregnancy continues, the IUD cannot be removed unless the tail is visible; any attempt to remove the IUD directly from the uterus usually results in a miscarriage. Some women go to full term with these pregnancies, and evaluations of the infants show no increase in complications as compared to the population at large.

The IUD is a highly effective form of birth control (98 percent effective) and is second only to oral contraceptives in preventing unwanted pregnancies. The IUD has many advantages in that its insertion requires only one procedure and it does not interfere with the spontaneity of intercourse. The IUD provides long-term protection against pregnancy and does not have undesirable systemic effects. The IUD does not alter the hormone levels in the body. When a woman wearing an IUD wishes to become pregnant, the device can be removed by a physician. The cost of the IUD is much lower than any other form of birth control when used over a long period of time.

Impact of Event

The Lippes loop was the most widely used form of inert IUD during the 1960's and 1970's and was the standard against which other IUDs were usually compared. (Inert IUDs do not contain medication.) Many of the other inert plastic IUDs manufactured during the 1960's and 1970's were removed from the market because they did not prove to be superior to the Lippes loop, which had a high success rate in preventing pregnancy in 94 percent of the women who wore it.

In 1982, the National Survey of Family Growth indicated that 2.2 million women in the United States were using IUDs. Further advances in the field included an IUD developed by Jaime A. Zipper, professor of physiology, obstetrics, and gynecology at the University of Santiago in Chile, and Howard Tatum, professor of gynecology and obstetrics of the Emory University School of Medicine in Atlanta, Georgia. Studies by Zipper indicate that iron, zinc, and copper are toxic to the enzymes in the cells of the uterine lining that are necessary for the proper implantation of the embryo; copper also prevents fertilization of the egg. Zipper and Tatum added copper wire to the stem of a T-shaped IUD, which had been developed by Tatum. It resulted in a significant improvement in the contraceptive effect of the IUD. This new IUD was placed on the market by G. D. Searle and Co. in 1973. In the mid-1970's, the Alza Corporation manufactured Progestasert, an IUD that included a hormonal delivery system built into the device.

Despite these tremendous advances in the development of the IUD, a number of events occurred during the 1970's and early 1980's that resulted in a decreased number of women using the IUD as a form of birth control. One of the earlier forms of plastic IUDs known as the Dalcon shield (introduced in 1969) was reported to be associated with serious infections in women who became pregnant while wearing it. The infections began with flulike symptoms followed by septicemia; fifteen deaths resulted from these infections. In the months that followed, an increasing number of reports of infections related to the use of the IUD as well as papers citing complications, difficult removals, and perforations of the uterus caused by the IUD were published. These reports received widespread media attention, and soon all IUDs became tainted by the reputation of one faulty product. A large number of lawsuits by plaintiffs claiming that they had not been warned of potential serious pelvic infections eventually resulted in the withdrawal of most IUDs from the market. The Lippes loop was discontinued in September, 1985, by Ortho Pharmaceutical because of lack of use and increased litigation costs.

The history of the IUD came full circle in the late 1980's when public opinion of the IUD became more positive. In the late 1980's and early 1990's, four IUDs were marketed in the United States. They included a revised version of the original Lippes loop, which is nonmedicated and may remain in place indefinitely; the Cu-7, which is shaped like the number seven with pure copper wire wound around its base; the TCu 200, which is an older form of the copper IUDs but preferential to the Cu-7; and Progestasert, which is similar in structure to the TCu 200 except that instead of the copper wire it contains a special plastic that releases a tiny amount of progesterone onto the lining of the uterus over a period of a year. The Progestasert must be renewed each year. These IUDs are considered safe and effective forms of birth control by the World Health Organization, the Food and Drug Administration, and the United States Agency for International Development. When patients are properly selected and counseled and when IUDs are properly inserted and used, they remain one of the most effective forms of birth control on the market.

Bibliography

Corson, Stephen, Richard Derman, and Louise Tyrer. *Fertility Control*. Boston: Little, Brown, 1984. The editors have synthesized the works of many contributing authors in this reference book designed for students, resident physicians, and clinicians. Topics such as history of birth control, various forms of contraception, and ethical issues of birth control are discussed in a clear, concise manner. Illustrated, with an extensive list of references.

Duffy, Benedict, Jr., and M. Jean Wallace. *Biological and Medical Aspects of Contraception*. Notre Dame, Ind.: University of Notre Dame Press, 1969. Duffy and Wallace deal with contraception as a scientific problem that faces humans worldwide. Information on the biology of reproduction and the medical aspects of contraception is provided, with emphasis on the importance of education in dealing with fertility regulation on a global basis. Includes illustrations and glossary.

Hafez, E. S. E., ed. "Clinical Aspects of Inert and Medicated Intrauterine Devices." In *Human Reproduction: Conception and Contraception*. 2d ed. Hagerstown, Md.: Harper & Row, 1980. This chapter provides a detailed clinical discussion of all aspects of the IUD, including descriptions of various types of IUDs and their selection, insertion, advantages, disadvantages, and pregnancy in women wearing the IUD. Contains illustrations, tables, graphs, and an extensive list of references.

Hardin, Garrett. *Birth Control*. New York: Pegasus, 1970. Hardin presents a detailed explanation of the various forms of birth control, including the effectiveness, safety, advantages, and disadvantages of each type. As a biologist, Hardin presents a straightforward explanation of the anatomy and physiology of the reproductive system and the functioning of birth control methods as well as the moral and psychological issues concerned with birth control. This book is well written and includes illustrations and suggested readings.

Hatcher, Robert, and Gary K. Stewart. *Contraceptive Technology 1982-1983.* 11th rev. ed. New York: Irvington, 1982. This textbook provides family planning information as to the safety and effectiveness of various forms of contraception. In addition, this textbook is revised each year and provides up-to-date information on such topics as infertility, pregnancy, sexually transmitted diseases, and family health. Excellent reference. Includes illustrations, diagrams, reference tables, and bibliography.

Lieberman, E. James, and Ellen Peck. *Sex and Birth Control.* New York: Thomas Y. Crowell, 1973. Lieberman and Peck use this book as a vehicle for communication to young people about sex and contraception. They present facts and ideas in a clear, understandable manner and often incorporate real-life situations and quotes from teenagers expressing concerns about birth control. Enjoyable reading. Includes illustrations and bibliography.

Debra Zehner

Cross-References

Ivanov Develops Artificial Insemination (1901), p. 113; Ehrlich Introduces Salvarsan as a Cure for Syphilis (1910), p. 476; Papanicolaou Develops the Pap Test for Diagnosing Uterine Cancer (1928), p. 864; Birth Control Pills Are Tested in Puerto Rico (1956), p. 1512; Brown Gives Birth to the First "Test-Tube" Baby (1978), p. 2099; Baulieu Develops RU-486, a Pill That Induces Abortion (1982), p. 2185.

SPERRY DISCOVERS THAT EACH SIDE OF THE BRAIN CAN FUNCTION INDEPENDENTLY

Category of event: Biology
Time: The early 1960's
Locale: California Institute of Technology, Pasadena, California

By analyzing the behavior of split-brain patients, Sperry and his colleagues showed that the human brain is actually composed of two brains that may function separately, challenging the idea of a single consciousness

Principal personages:

ROGER W. SPERRY (1913-), a neurophysiologist who was awarded the 1981 Nobel Prize in Physiology or Medicine for his work on split-brain patients

MICHAEL S. GAZZANIGA (1939-), a graduate student of Sperry who was responsible for the psychological testing of split-brain patients

RONALD MYERS (1929-), a student of Sperry who carried out initial split-brain research on animals

JOSEPH BOGEN (1926-), a neurosurgical resident at White Memorial Hospital who performed human split-brain surgery

PHILLIP VOGEL (1906-), the chief of neurosurgery at White Memorial Hospital, who was in charge of split-brain surgery on humans

DOREEN KIMURA, a psychologist who showed the right brain's superiority in identifying musical melodies

JERRE LEVY (1938-), a student of Sperry who studied right-brain function

Summary of Event

The bilateral nature of the human organism means that many parts of the body come in two identical mirror images. These paired organs, such as the lungs, kidneys, and eyes, generally perform identical functions. It was long assumed that the two halves of the brain likewise have a single function. It therefore came as quite a surprise to scientists to discover not only that the two halves of the brain perform different activities but also that, in certain cases, each half can function independently.

This discovery was made in the 1960's in the laboratory of Roger W. Sperry, a neurophysiologist who had trained with the developmental biologist, Paul Weiss. Sperry was already well known for having shown that growing nerve fibers are guided to make predetermined connections. In the early 1950's, he began to research the function of the corpus callosum. This narrow bundle of some 200 million neurons connects the two halves of the brain. With his graduate student, Ronald Myers at the University of Chicago, Sperry cut a small piece of brain tissue from an animal, as well as other brain tissue connecting the two hemispheres. With a patch over the right eye, visual information stimulating the left eye would be able to enter only the left hemisphere of the brain. Myers then taught these animals a simple task.

When a cat was taught to solve a problem with its left eye, the information was stored in the left hemisphere. When the left eye was then covered, the cat, looking through its right eye, was unable to perform the same task. The information obviously could not pass to the right hemisphere when the corpus callosum was cut. The right hemisphere could, however, learn the task itself. It was possible, in fact, to teach each hemisphere of the cat to solve a single problem using two different methods. It was as if the cat had two separate brains in its skull, each of which could function independently when separated from the other.

Over the next several years, Myers and Sperry also showed that the brains of monkeys and chimpanzees are made up of two hemispheres that can be made to work independently. Yet, there was reason to doubt that these findings would be relevant to human brains. The corpus callosum had already been cut in a number of humans in a medical study by the neurosurgeons W. P. van Wagenen and Andrew Akelaitis in the 1940's. The surgery was performed as a last resort to control incapacitating epilepsy. The doctors reasoned that if the connection between the two hemispheres were severed, an epileptic seizure occurring in one half of the brain would leave at least half of the brain unaffected. Not only did the surgery prove effective in limiting the spread of epileptic seizures but also, for reasons still unknown, it actually decreased the frequency of such seizures. Fortunately for the patients, there were no obvious deficits in personality, intelligence, or mental functioning, suggesting to scientists that the corpus callosum has no important function in humans.

Sperry decided to conduct more careful studies of such split-brain patients. The surgery was performed by Phillip Vogel and Joseph Bogen at the White Memorial Hospital in California. Their first patient was known by the initials W. J., a forty-eight-year-old war veteran who had developed serious seizures. As expected, the surgery significantly improved his condition and did not seem to change his behavior in any obvious way.

More careful behavioral studies were begun by Michael S. Gazzaniga, a graduate student, in Sperry's laboratory, which was now relocated to the California Institute of Technology. The experimental procedure was simple: The subject was asked to keep his eyes focused on a point directly in front of him. A picture of some everyday object was then flashed for a fraction of a second to one side of this point, and the subject was asked to report what he saw. Visual information that enters the brain from the left visual field goes to the right hemisphere, while information from the right visual field is projected to the left hemisphere. A normal person would report having seen an object whichever field it was in. This was not the case for W. J. He accurately reported seeing an object in the right half of his visual field (perceived by the left hemisphere). When a picture was flashed to his left visual field (perceived by the right hemisphere), he denied having seen anything. The right hemisphere was not blind; it simply could not speak. When W. J. was asked to give a manual response by pointing to an object he had seen, he indicated that his right hemisphere could, in fact, perceive the object.

Sperry and Gazzaniga thus solved the problem of the elusive function of the corpus callosum. When a normal person saw an object in the left visual field, the right hemisphere, which obtained the information, sends it via the corpus callosum to the left hemisphere, which then can verbalize a response about what the individual saw. The corpus callosum thus allows communication between the two hemispheres.

Although the right hemisphere was initially considered inferior because it lacked the verbal ability of the left hemisphere, subsequent research showed that the right hemisphere can understand the vocabulary of a ten-year-old. Although unable to direct the mouth to speak, the right hemisphere could direct the left hand to move plastic letters so as to spell out the answers to certain questions.

As in the animal studies, each half of the human brain could learn new information, respond to questions, and store memories on its own, acting as if unaware of the second half of the brain. The left half of the brain was clearly superior in language skills and speech. It needed to be determined if the right half had other skills. Gazzaniga tested split-brain patients in another test, where they were required to arrange a set of blocks to match a design in a picture. The left hand (guided by the right half of the brain) was superior on this task. The scientists concluded that the right hemisphere is important for spatial skills.

The split-brain patient proved a valuable subject for allowing scientists to study where certain activities are localized in the human brain. The finding that the human brain is actually able to function as two separate brains in these patients raised the question as to the possible lateralization of functions in the normal intact brain. Jerre Levy, another student of Sperry, showed that the right hemisphere seems to be superior on spatial tasks in intact people as well. Particularly convincing is the work of Doreen Kimura, who developed tests to study information processing in normal individuals. She showed that the left hemisphere is better at interpreting verbal information, while the right hemisphere is better at identifying melodies. In other work, she showed that speech is processed differently in male and female brains.

While hemispheric specialization has become an accepted concept, the type of specialization is understood differently by different scientists. Some describe the left hemisphere as perceiving symbolic information, while the right hemisphere perceives nonsymbolic information. Others refer to the left hemisphere as dealing with verbal, logical, and mathematical skills, while the right hemisphere deals with spatial tasks, such as reading maps or remembering faces. Other scientists think of the left hemisphere as seeing things in a sequential, logical manner, while the right hemisphere sees things in a more holistic way.

Impact of Event

The idea of some dichotomy in the human mind has existed for centuries. Whether called active-passive, scientific-humanistic, or yin-yang, the human brain seems to appreciate the concept of a dual mind. The research on brain lateralization provided a biological explanation that could support such a duality: The two hemispheres could be thought of as two ends of a continuum. Books and articles began to appear in the popular press in the 1970's and 1980's, exhorting their readers to perform exercises to activate the right hemisphere and free the creative impulses supposedly hidden there. Claims were made that these exercises would make one more imaginative, creative, or a better artist or writer. There is not, in fact, any evidence to show that creativity is linked to one hemisphere. Even if it were, however, it is not clear that exercise will make it more efficient.

The acceptance of the idea of hemispheric specialization did have some positive effects in the general population, as people gained a better understanding of nonverbal forms of intelligence. While most intelligence tests measure what are considered left-brain activities, increasing emphasis is being given to measurements and appreciation of other types of intelligence that may be localized to the right brain. Educational practices also were affected by knowledge of the different functions of the brain hemispheres. The idea of nonverbal instruction was appreciated by many teachers, from sports to languages. These subjects, it was argued, could be learned more quickly by forcing the right hemisphere to learn by nonverbal imitation, rather than giving verbal instructions to the left hemisphere. While the scientific validity for this concept is uncertain, this attitude does seem to lead to a well-rounded education that will benefit many.

Sperry's studies also had some impact on the understanding of certain disorders. Dyslexia, for example, is a disorder of children who have difficulty learning to read. These children tend to show less than the usual right-hemisphere specialization for spatial relations. Although the data are not unequivocal, the idea that reading disorders are biologically based and not the result of children's misbehavior has led to more flexibility in dealing with these disorders.

The split-brain research raises certain philosophical considerations: Is the split brain also a split mind? Are there two separate consciousnesses in a single individual? Sperry argues that in a normal individual, the corpus callosum maintains an integrated sense of awareness. It is only after the split-brain surgery that two separate consciousnesses emerge. Bogen believes that there is a duality of consciousness in all normal minds, but it is made more apparent by split-brain surgery.

Gazzaniga and his student Joseph LeDoux have developed the concept of the "sociology of the mind," by which the mind is made of several parts—a verbal self, an emotional self, and a motor-action self—and these parts each have separate locations in the brain.

Julian Jaynes has looked at the religious implications of the split-brain research. He hypothesized that the right hemisphere produces ideas that are heard by the left hemisphere as "voices." He suggests that the prophets and seers of the distant past were responding with their left hemispheres to the voices in the right, which they interpreted as the voice of God speaking to them. Today, he suggests, people are culturally prejudiced to ignore these voices.

Controversy about the meaning of the split-brain research continues long after its original report in the 1960's. For stimulating this controversy, Sperry was awarded the Nobel Prize in Physiology or Medicine in 1981.

Bibliography

Baskin, Yvonne. "Emergence: Roger Sperry." In *The Omni Interviews*, edited by Pamela Weintraub. New York: Ticknor & Fields, 1984. In an interview with *Omni* magazine, Sperry describes his philosophy of consciousness as an emergent entity that is greater than the simple sum of awarenesses shown by the separate left and right hemispheres.

Gazzaniga, Michael S. *The Bisected Brain*. New York: Appleton-Century-Crofts, 1970. A useful description of the work conducted by Sperry from his early days in Sperry's laboratory to the beginning of his independent research program. Contains figures and references.

_____. *The Social Brain: Discovering the Networks of the Mind*. New York: Basic Books, 1985. An engaging account of split-brain research, written for general audiences by one of the leaders in the field. Offers personal insights into early work in Sperry's laboratory. Elaborates Gazzaniga's theory of brain modularity. His speculations about the implications for anthropology, religion, and social processes are thought-provoking, but highly speculative.

Segalowitz, Sid J. *Two Sides of the Brain: Brain Lateralization Explored*. Englewood Cliffs, N.J.: Prentice-Hall, 1983. The best general introduction to the field in a concise, easy-to-read volume. Although written for those with no background, the breadth of coverage and references to more technical papers make this useful also for more advanced readers. Contains balanced analyses of the opposing viewpoints of the principal investigators in the field. Includes discussion of differences in brain lateralization between individuals, between men and women, and between monolingual and bilingual people.

Sperry, Roger. "Some Effects of Disconnecting the Cerebral Hemispheres." *Science* 217 (1982): 1223-1226. Lecture delivered by Sperry in 1981, when he received the Nobel Prize. Unlike most of his writing, this is accessible to the layperson. Summarizes his split-brain work and his thoughts about its ramifications. References.

Judith R. Gibber

Cross-References

Pavlov Develops the Concept of Reinforcement (1902), p. 163; Berger Develops the Electroencephalogram (EEG) (1929), p. 890; Moniz Develops Prefrontal Lobotomy (1935), p. 1060; Cerletti and Bini Develop Electroconvulsive Therapy for Treating Schizophrenia (1937), p. 1086; Aserinsky Discovers Rapid Eye Movement (REM) in Sleep and Dreams (1952), p. 1424; Hounsfield Introduces a CAT Scanner That Can See Clearly into the Body (1972), p. 1961.

THE MÖSSBAUER EFFECT IS USED IN THE DETECTION OF GRAVITATIONAL REDSHIFTING

Category of event: Physics
Time: 1960
Locale: Harvard University, Cambridge, Massachusetts

The Pound-Rebka experiment made use of the Mössbauer effect to confirm the gravitational redshift that had been predicted by Einstein's theory of general relativity

Principal personages:

ALBERT EINSTEIN (1879-1955), a German physicist who was best known for his theories of special and general relativity

WALTER SYDNEY ADAMS (1876-1956), an American astronomer who conducted gravitational redshift studies of the white dwarf, Sirius B

RUDOLF LUDWIG MÖSSBAUER (1929-   ), a German physicist who discovered the effect which is named for him and for which he was awarded the 1961 Nobel Prize in Physics

ROBERT VIVIAN POUND (1919-   ), an American physicist

GLEN A. REBKA, a physicist who collaborated with Pound in conducting a gravitational redshift experiment

JESSE LEONARD GREENSTEIN (1909-   ), an American astronomer who conducted studies that confirmed gravitational redshifting in white dwarf stars

SIR ISAAC NEWTON (1642-1727), an English scientist-philosopher who developed the law of gravitation, laws of motion, and other pioneering concepts in the physical sciences and mathematics

Summary of Event

In 1916, Albert Einstein published the theory of general relativity. This revolutionary proposal was, in fact, an extended or generalized version of the theory of special relativity that was presented in 1905. The essential difference between the two is that the theory of special relativity involves high velocity, uniform motion, and flat space-time; the theory of general relativity permits curved space-time and accelerated motion. The theory of general relativity was Einstein's theory of gravity. Unlike Sir Isaac Newton's concept of gravity—a force acting over a distance—it was Einstein's contention that gravity is a consequence of the shape of space-time. Space-time, by Einstein's definition, consists of three spatial dimensions and time as the fourth dimension.

In 1665, Newton had worked out the universal law of gravitation. This law and Newton's laws of motion were extremely successful in predicting the motion of both falling bodies and orbiting bodies. One of the most spectacular successes of Newton's laws occurred in 1846 with the discovery of the planet Neptune. The planet had been discovered within one degree of its predicted position. At about the same time, a detailed study was initiated on the orbit of the planet Mercury. Although Newton's laws predicted that the orbit of Mercury would rotate very slowly around the sun, there was a 43 arc second per century advance that was not accounted for by theory. Some in the scientific community began to question the validity of Newton's laws. Others speculated on the possible existence of a planet inside the orbit of Mercury, while still others proposed that the sun is not symmetric about its core. When the curved space-time of the theory of general relativity was applied to the problem of Mercury's orbit, observations and calculations agreed.

To explain Einstein's concept of gravity, one might imagine a sheet stretched out and held tightly by each of its four corners. A ball placed in the center of the sheet would cause a slight depression. The more massive the ball, the greater the depression. Another ball being rolled near this depression would naturally follow the curve or shape of this depression. It was Einstein's contention that the sun warps the space-time around it, and Mercury follows this curvature in space-time. Other confirmations of the theory of general relativity were to follow in the years after its introduction. In 1919, Arthur Stanley Eddington led an expedition to an island off the coast of Africa to photograph a total eclipse of the sun. The photographs revealed an apparent shift in the background field of stars that matched the prediction of the theory of general relativity. Einstein had explained that light from stars would bend in the curvature of space-time caused by the sun; Eddington's work had proven this theory to be correct.

The theory of general relativity also predicted a phenomenon known as gravitational redshifting, or the Einstein shift. According to theory, as light escapes from the surface of a star, it loses some of its energy. This would cause the lengthening of the light waves. Since the longest visible light waves are red, lengthened waves would appear redder, hence the term "redshift."

The detection of gravitational redshifting in a star is extremely difficult. First, the motion through space and the rotation of the star itself would cause a red or Doppler shift far greater than that caused by gravitation. Second, convection currents operating on stellar surfaces would cause Doppler shifts ranging from blue to red. In spite of these difficulties, in 1925, the American astronomer Walter Sydney Adams studied the spectrum of the white dwarf companion of the star Sirius in search of evidence for gravitational redshifting. It was reasoned that since white dwarfs have gravitational fields thousands of times more intense than ordinary stars, gravitational redshifting might be observed more readily. Adams made observations that indicated the existence of gravitational redshifting, but this was not confirmed until the 1977 study by Jesse Leonard Greenstein and others. In this study, the spectra of more than twelve white dwarf stars were made with the Mount Palomar telescope. Analysis of these spectra proved the existence of gravitational redshifting.

All the tests conducted of the theory of general relativity were astronomical in nature. In 1960, an experiment was designed to test the validity of the theory in the laboratory. This test would make use of the Mössbauer effect.

To explain the gravitational redshift, suppose that a photon of light is fired upward from a source to a certain height where it impacts against a target. This collision would produce a positron and an electron by the process of pair production. The positron and electron would each fall back to the surface of the earth where, after the kinetic energy gained by the acceleration of gravity is extracted, they recombine into a photon identical to the original one. This sounds like a perpetual motion machine and the process, as stated, would indeed violate the law of conservation of energy. In reality, the photon climbing out of the earth's gravitational field would lose energy or become redshifted. The amount of energy lost would be exactly equal to the amount of energy gained by the electron-positron pair as they fell in the gravitational field.

In 1958, the German physicist Rudolf Ludwig Mössbauer discovered a method whereby atomic nuclei could be used as extremely sensitive clocks. Since atoms emit light at specific wavelengths and frequencies, they may be considered as being a type of clock. It is known that when a radioactive isotope of some element emits a gamma ray, it can absorb another gamma ray of exactly the same energy. This fact alone, however, does not allow the redshift to be measured. Thermal energy within a sample of any element will cause the nuclei of the atoms to oscillate. This motion will cause a Doppler shift in gamma-ray frequencies. When a nucleus gives off or receives a gamma ray, there is a slight recoil motion. This motion also causes a Doppler shift. It was Mössbauer's discovery that if the nuclei in question were embedded in the correct type of crystal, then the forces exerted by the surrounding atoms would reduce the thermal oscillations and virtually eliminate the recoil during emission and absorption of gamma rays. The gravitational redshift experiment was only one of many applications of this discovery, for which Mössbauer was awarded the 1961 Nobel Prize in Physics.

The Pound-Rebka experiment of 1960 was the first accurate measurement of the gravitational redshift to be performed under laboratory conditions. The experiment was performed in the Jefferson Physical Laboratory at Harvard University in Cambridge, Massachusetts. Gamma rays, which were emitted from a radioactive source located in the basement, traveled upward through holes drilled in the various floors to an absorber located in the penthouse. For the total distance of 22.5 meters, the calculated redshift was approximately two parts in a thousand trillion. If there was redshifting of the gamma rays from the emitter, these rays would not be absorbed by the absorbing crystal. It was found that gamma rays emitted at the bottom underwent a gravitational redshifting and were rarely absorbed at the penthouse level. The emitter was placed on a hydraulic lift that could be raised or lowered. By moving the emitter upward at a small velocity, a Doppler shift was set up that compensated for the gravitational redshift and allowed absorption.

About half of the total number of measurements were made, with the emitter located at the top of the tower and the absorber at the bottom. This reversal in location of the absorber and emitter allowed the blueshift to be measured. Again, when the platform was raised, a compensating redshift canceled out the amount of blueshift and made absorption possible. The results of the 1960 Pound-Rebka experiment agreed with the prediction of the theory of general relativity with an error of about 10 percent. An improved version of the experiment was completed in 1965 by Pound and an associate. The results of this experiment reduced the error to 1 percent.

Impact of Event

Prior to the 1960 experiment of Robert Vivian Pound and Glen A. Rebka, the gravitational redshifting predictions made by the theory of general relativity had not been verified under laboratory conditions. The problem with measuring the redshift was the infinitely small increments of time that had to be measured. With the discovery of the Mössbauer effect in 1958, the measurement of a gravitational redshift became possible. The precise frequencies of gamma rays emitted by radioactive nuclei such as cobalt or iron were within the range necessary to conduct an experiment. Mössbauer's discovery that thermal oscillations of nuclei and recoil from emission and absorption of gamma rays can be controlled significantly made it possible to detect the slightest amount of red- and blueshifting. Although the amount of redshift measured by Pound and Rebka was very small, it had significant implications. Not only did this experiment confirm the gravitational redshift predictions of the theory of general relativity but it also confirmed Einstein's contention that there is no such thing as a universal time.

Anything that oscillates or emits light on a periodic basis may be thought of as a clock. Examples of this might be a pendulum, an ordinary wristwatch operating on a mainspring, a quartz-controlled watch, or atoms that give off light or other forms of radiation. When atoms give off light, they do so with a definite wavelength and a definite frequency. By measuring this frequency, an accurate measurement of time can be made. Pound and Rebka found that radiation from atoms is redshifted as it travels upward against gravity. When any form of electromagnetic radiation is redshifted, its wavelengths become longer and its frequency becomes lower. In other words, Pound and Rebka had found that gravity causes the flow of time to slow. Thus, the concept of a universal time was shown to be invalid.

In his theory of special relativity, Einstein showed that time is relative to an inertial observer. Time differences between observers become apparent if there is a difference in motion between the observers. The time difference would no longer exist if both frames of reference were at rest relative to each other. In the theory of general relativity, Einstein had predicted that there would be a time difference for observers at rest if one were positioned "higher" than the other.

The data gathered by Pound and Rebka in their 1960 experiment verified the gravitational redshift predictions of the theory of general relativity with great accuracy. The prediction that the frequency of radiation traveling upward against gravitation is shifted toward the red end of the spectrum and radiation falling in a gravitational field is shifted toward the blue end of the spectrum was confirmed with an error of about 10 percent. The results of these experiments have influenced the acceptance of the theory of general relativity in the scientific community today.

Bibliography

Asimov, Isaac. *The History of Physics*. New York: Walker, 1984. This volume is a well-written history of physics from the ancient Greeks to modern developments in particle physics. It is intended for the layperson.

Calder, Nigel. *Einstein's Universe*. New York: Viking Press, 1979. This volume concerns both the theories of special and general relativity. Although somewhat detailed, the reader should have an understanding of basic physics and astronomy and perhaps some background in relativity theory.

French, A. P., ed. *Einstein: A Centenary Volume*. Cambridge, Mass.: Harvard University Press, 1979. This volume consists of a series of short articles by various authors on the life of Einstein and his contributions to science. The articles that pertain to the development of the theories of special and general relativity and quantum mechanics are quite technical.

Gardner, Martin. *The Relativity Explosion*. New York: Random House, 1976. An excellent volume for the layperson. Both theories of special and general relativity are explained as well as an introduction to such topics as quasars, pulsars, and black holes.

Kaufmann, William J. *The Cosmic Frontiers of General Relativity*. Boston: Little, Brown, 1977. This volume covers the theory of general relativity and its applications to such topics as stellar evolution, white dwarfs, pulsars, neutron stars, and the various types of black holes. Suitable for the informed reader.

Krane, Kenneth. *Modern Physics*. New York: John Wiley & Sons, 1983. A highly technical treatment of selected topics in physics such as the theories of special and general relativity, quantum mechanics, and nuclear physics. The volume was intended as a textbook for an advanced undergraduate course in modern physics.

Will, Clifford M. *Was Einstein Right?* New York: Basic Books, 1986. A volume covering the theory of general relativity and the evidence for the theory. Such topics as curved space-time, gravitational redshifting, gravity waves, and the frontiers of experimental relativity are discussed. Suitable for the informed reader.

David W. Maguire

Cross-References

Russell Announces His Theory of Stellar Evolution (1913), p. 585; Einstein Completes His Theory of General Relativity (1915), p. 625; Schwarzschild Develops a Solution to the Equations of General Relativity (1916), p. 630; Einstein's Theory of Gravitation Is Confirmed over Newton's Theory (1919), p. 684; Oppenheimer Calculates the Nature of Black Holes (1939), p. 1150; Wheeler Names the Phenomenon "Black Holes" (1968), p. 1881.

SCIENTISTS DEVELOP A TECHNIQUE TO DATE ANCIENT OBSIDIAN

Category of event: Archaeology
Time: 1960
Locale: Washington, D.C.

Geologists and archaeologists originated a technique to determine directly the date of manufacture of some stone artifacts

Principal personages:
IRVING FRIEDMAN (1920-   ), an American geologist who was the primary developer of obsidian hydration dating
ROBERT L. SMITH (1920-   ), an American geologist who collaborated with Friedman on obsidian hydration dating
CLIFFORD EVANS (1920-1981), an American archaeologist with the Smithsonian Institution who provided archaeological obsidian samples to Friedman and Smith and assessed the technique archaeologically
BETTY J. MEGGERS (1921-   ), an American archaeologist with the Smithsonian Institution who collaborated with Evans
DONOVAN L. CLARK (1919-   ), an American geologist who studied obsidian hydration dating

Summary of Event

From the beginnings of archaeology, archaeologists have struggled to date the objects that they unearth. This has not been easy, since some artifacts—particularly stone tools—have been made for hundreds of thousands or even millions of years and can bear considerable similarity to one another. Early archaeologists thought they had solved the problem when they reasoned that earlier tools would be simpler than later tools; to their minds, sophistication was a simple index of recency. Unfortunately, this notion was wrong. In North America, for example, one of the earliest stone spear point types also is one of the most technologically sophisticated and most aesthetically pleasing.

For decades, archaeologists were left with little choice but to date their sites by one of two methods: stratigraphy (based on the layering of earlier levels below later ones) and seriation (the placing of artifact forms in sequences where each form is only slightly different from its predecessor). Each of these methods, however, had significant drawbacks, and the dating of sites and artifacts remained contentious.

The development of radiocarbon dating at the midpoint of the twentieth century solved many archaeologists' problems and allowed them to begin turning more of their attention to some of the vexing issues of human behavior in the ancient past. Yet, there remained one difficulty. Radiocarbon dating is an isotopic method that relies on material that once was alive; it calculates how long since the death of the animal or plant from which the material came. Many archaeological sites contain only artifacts that cannot be dated by this technique. Even in the cases where charcoal or other radiocarbon-datable materials are present, it is not always clear that the charcoal is from the same date as the tools. Ground movement with frost, burrowing by rodents or even insects, and a host of other mechanisms can place a chunk of organic material next to an archaeological tool, though the two may come from eras millennia apart.

In the late 1950's, Irving Friedman and Robert L. Smith, geologists working with the U.S. Geological Survey, decided to solve the archaeologists' problem and to base their technique on obsidian.

Obsidian is a naturally occurring volcanic glass, usually black, but sometimes gray or even greenish. Obsidian occurs around the world, and wherever it has been available, people have used it to make flaked stone tools. Its earliest use probably was about one million years ago, since it has been found in Acheulean hand axes from the Kariandusi site in Kenya, where it dates to 900,000 B.C.; yet, it still is used occasionally by Australian aborigines.

Friedman and Smith based their technique on the recognition that the surfaces of obsidian were chemically distinct from the interior portions of a piece. Specifically, the outer surfaces were "hydrated"—they had molecules of water between the silica molecules that composed the obsidian. The hydrated rind, only a few microns thick and invisible to the naked eye, was denser than the interior surfaces and was visible under magnification by virtue of its higher refractive index and tiny cracks that developed at the line of contact between the hydrated and unhydrated portions. This was known from previous studies, but their prior work showed that the changes in the outer rind took place after its volcanic formation. Friedman and Smith also demonstrated that the changes were the result of a more or less straightforward diffusion process, where the water molecules mechanically seeped into the obsidian. Since diffusion is a well-known process that follows predictable and quantifiable rules, it seemed likely that the hydration process would take place at a more or less consistent rate, making obsidian hydration a good basis for a dating technique.

Primarily through the assistance of Betty J. Meggers and Clifford Evans, archaeologists at the Smithsonian Institution, Friedman and Smith obtained hundreds of archaeological specimens of obsidian that came from sites and levels that had already been dated by the radiocarbon dating technique. They reasoned that the hydration rind began forming the moment a tool was made by the removal of flakes. Assuming the radiocarbon dates to be accurate (as most were), they reasoned that the thickness of this rind would be greater for the older tools. Further, they reasoned that they could derive an equation to calculate the age of a specimen on the basis of the thickness of its hydration layer.

To test this hypothesis, Friedman and Smith cut thin sections of obsidian from each of the hundreds of tools provided by the archaeologists. Each of these was examined under a microscope, where the thickness of the rind was measured. On the basis of their results, they decided that their hypothesis was fundamentally correct:

Obsidian hydration layers become thicker with time at a regular rate and can be used for dating. A problem, however, became evident. Since diffusion processes proceed faster at higher temperatures, a tool from the tropics would appear falsely older than a tool of the same age from the Arctic. Friedman and Smith established several hydration rates to use in the calculation of dates on specimens from regions of different climates. Subsequent researchers have found it necessary to calculate local hydration rates for relatively small areas.

A further complication was noted by Friedman and Smith, though it was left for others to recognize its full significance: Obsidians of different chemical compositions have somewhat different hydration rates, even if held under identical temperatures. In 1961, Donovan L. Clark, then a graduate student working on his doctoral dissertation, recognized that relatively subtle chemical differences in obsidian could result in significantly different hydration rates. This meant that a few hydration rates for different temperatures no longer would suffice; each locality of obsidian potentially has a different composition from all others, so each type of obsidian needs its own family of hydration rates, one for each temperature. This made the situation much more complicated; therefore, for the next three decades, archaeologists calculated hydration rates for scores of different obsidian sources. Friedman advocated developing a general equation that would take composition of the obsidian into account in the calculation of a date, but no one has yet figured out how to do so.

A final difficulty with obsidian hydration is a mathematical one. The calculation of a hydration rate is a statistical process in which one attempts to summarize a series of findings with a single equation or curve. Unfortunately, the real world is an untidy and unpredictable place, and a series of tiny errors and chance variations make the data from which the curve or equation is constructed considerably less regular than one might wish. As a result, more than one equation can summarize the data; and, while most versions of the equation will give similar results, the results can be quite different for specific cases. Various researchers champion different forms of the equation.

Impact of Event

Obsidian hydration dating has failed to have the major impact on a variety of fields that radiocarbon dating has produced. The lingering technical problems noted make the application of obsidian hydration dating to a new area and new obsidian types a time-consuming task, since a considerable investment in time must be made to calculate the applicable hydration rates. Consequently, the use of obsidian hydration dating tends to be spotty, with intensive use in such areas as California, Mexico, and Japan.

Where it has been used, however, it has presented archaeologists with several important benefits. First, it is the only major dating technique available widely to archaeologists that permits the dating of the tool itself. Dates obtained by other methods always are subject to the criticism that the material that actually is dated may not truly be contemporary with the artifacts or other materials for which the date is desired. Second, the technique is inexpensive. Archaeological excavations operate under the same fiscal restraints as almost all other scientific research, and a technique that allows the researcher to stretch his or her budget a bit further is very welcome. For the cost of one radiocarbon date, an archaeologist can have about fifteen obsidian hydration dates. Since any single date (obtained by any technique) can be in error, a sizable array of dates is desirable, and this technique can provide them affordably. Further, the equipment necessary for the procedure is moderately simple, and the archaeologists often are able to save money by doing the obsidian hydration dating themselves, a luxury not afforded by radiocarbon dating and its complex apparatus.

While the impact of obsidian hydration has been strongest in archaeology, it has seen applications elsewhere. Geologists have used it to date obsidian flows and domes, which in turn have been used to date other geological events. There are limits, however, to the use of obsidian hydration dating in geology. Hydration rinds that exceed a certain thickness tend to chip off, making a specimen appear younger than it really is. The practical limit of the technique appears to be around one million years, a limit that encompasses nearly all of the archaeological record but only the most recent portion of the geological record.

Finally, art historians have used the technique to test the age of disputed artworks of obsidian, particularly prehistoric Mexican and Central American sculptures. Usually a thin wedge can be cut from the base of a piece without disfiguring it.

When Friedman and Smith introduced obsidian hydration dating, their article was paired with an archaeological assessment of the technique by Meggers and Evans. The archaeologists concluded that the technique had considerable promise if the problems surrounding the calculation of the hydration rate (or rates) could be solved. After years of attempts, the problems foreseen by Meggers and Evans have been only partly solved, and new ones unanticipated by them have also developed. Still, obsidian hydration dating has yielded thousands of accurate, low-cost dates to archaeology.

Bibliography

Ericson, Jonathan E. "Egalitarian Exchange Systems in California." In *Exchange Systems in Prehistory*, edited by Timothy K. Earle and Jonathan E. Ericson. New York: Academic Press, 1977. A good example of how obsidian hydration can be used in concert with other archaeological techniques to help reconstruct past behavior from archaeological remains. The author is a major proponent of obsidian hydration dating in archaeology.

Evans, Clifford, and Betty Meggers. "A New Dating Method Using Obsidian: Part II, An Archaeological Evaluation of the Method." *American Antiquity* 25 (April, 1960): 523-537. The companion article to the original treatment by Friedman and Smith, this article presents the first archaeological application and assesses the value of the technique. Many of the difficulties noted subsequently have been overcome. Examples used are from Latin America.

Friedman, Irving, and Robert L. Smith. "A New Dating Method Using Obsidian: Part I, The Development of the Technique." *American Antiquity* 25 (April, 1960): 476-522. This is the original article in which the technique of obsidian hydration dating was presented. While subsequent research has pointed out some areas of complication, the article remains substantially current.

Friedman, Irving, and Fred W. Tremblour. "Obsidian: The Dating Stone." *American Scientist* 66 (January/February, 1978): 44-51. While there are no summaries of obsidian hydration dating written for the layperson, this is the closest approximation. It is a highly readable, brief, nonjargonistic treatment that summarizes the technique, its assumptions, and some of its successes. Photographs illustrate obsidian artifacts and their obsidian hydration rinds, and charts graphically depict the hydration rates and results of analysis.

Michels, Joseph W., and Ignatius S. T. Tsong. "Obsidian Hydration Dating: A Coming of Age." In *Advances in Archaeological Methods and Theory.* Vol. 3, edited by Michael B. Schiffer. New York: Academic Press, 1980. An excellent summary of obsidian hydration dating, its history, its problems, and its future. The author presents a balanced discussion of relevant controversies and differing viewpoints. Technical.

Tite, M. S. *Methods of Physical Examination in Archaeology.* New York: Seminar Press, 1972. A basic handbook of scientific analytic methods in archaeology. The book is densely written and difficult, but it is a classic in its field. One portion of a chapter is devoted to obsidian hydration dating, but other dating techniques also are discussed.

Russell J. Barber

Cross-References

Elster and Geitel Demonstrate Radioactivity in Rocks, Springs, and Air (1901), p. 93; Boltwood Uses Radioactivity to Obtain the Age of Rocks (1905), p. 285; Libby Introduces the Carbon-14 Method of Dating Ancient Objects (1940's), p. 1160; Anthropologists Claim That Ecuadorian Pottery Shows Transpacific Contact in 3000 B.C. (1960's), p. 1624.

HESS CONCLUDES THE DEBATE ON
CONTINENTAL DRIFT

Category of event: Earth science
Time: 1960-1962
Locale: Princeton, New Jersey

Hess's seafloor spreading mechanism for the continental displacement theory rein-terpreted geologic paradigms and had the same impact that Darwin's evolution the-ory had on biology

> *Principal personages:*
> ALFRED LOTHAR WEGENER (1880-1930), a German scientist-explorer who proposed the first coherent theory of continental displacement in 1915
> H. H. HESS (1906-1969), an American geologist who revolutionized the earth sciences with his conclusion that seafloor spreading was the mechanism for a continental displacement theory
> ROBERT S. DIETZ (1914-   ), an American geologist who independently arrived at the seafloor spreading hypothesis and published it before Hess

Summary of Event

Princeton University professor H. H. Hess is noted for his scientific contributions to the field of geology, specifically his ground-breaking *History of the Ocean Basins* (1962), in which he proposed seafloor spreading as the long-sought-after mechanism for Alfred Lothar Wegener's continental drift theory. The elements of seafloor spreading, the rifting of the Pangaea continent into several continental-size plates, and lateral displacement of those plates to their present latitudes remain the dominant paradigm in the earth sciences, collectively known as plate tectonics. Yet, the idea of drifting continents was not original with Hess. The hostility the geologic community demonstrated toward the idea inhibited Hess initially from publishing his theory.

Wegener's 1915 theory of drifting continents lay dormant after his death in 1930. Several problems kept it from universal acceptance. First, the jigsaw puzzle fit was not exact. It did not account very well for Central America, and Ireland and New-foundland did not correlate geologically. Second, Sir Harold Jeffreys (1891-1977), leading geophysicist of the time, presented evidence in the 1923-1924 meeting of the British Association for the Advancement of Science that Wegener's forces were too small by three orders of magnitude to drive the drift mechanism. Other geophysicists questioned Wegener's objectivity and accused him of generalizing on generaliza-tions. A third problem was the repeated failure of Wegener's own test to prove his hypothesis. The timing of radio signals across the Atlantic in 1922, 1927, 1936, 1938, and 1948 did not reveal a widening of the Atlantic through progressively longer time intervals. Finally, in the eyes of the geologic community, Wegener was not a geologist but an outsider attempting to restructure their science.

Wegener's supporters tried to mollify his enthusiasm for the scientific community's acceptance of his theory. Harvard University geologist Reginald A. Daly (1871-1957), an ardent believer in continental drift, wrote in his 1926 book, *Our Mobile Earth*: "So obvious are his logical inconsequences and his failure properly to weigh ascertained facts that there is danger of a too speedy rejection of the main idea involved." Geologist Alexander L. du Toit of South Africa's Johannesburg University and S. Warren Carey of the University of Tasmania, Hobart, defended Wegener's theory in their 1937 publications, and it rallied again in England with the 1944 publication of Arthur Holmes's (1890-1965) textbook *Principles of Physical Geology*.

For the most part, resistance to Wegener's theory continued. World War II delayed research into the question, and from the 1930's to the mid-1950's, continental drift remained a paradigm held with great passion by a minority of geologists but deficient of evidence according to the majority. Bailey Willis, of Stanford University, criticized it in his 1944 article, "Continental Drift, Ein Märchen (a Fairy Tale)," published in the *American Journal of Science*. Even as supporting evidence was accumulating in the mid-1950's, *Crust of the Earth*, a 1955 landmark publication of the Geological Society of America, ignored continental drift, although it mentions both Wegener and du Toit in unrelated discussions. As late as 1966, University of Hamburg physicist Pascual Jordan described the theory as the geophysicists' "favorite fairy tale."

Postwar advances in technology, methodology, and the new science of paleomagnetism lent support to Wegener's theory. Paleomagnetism enabled scientists for the first time to reconstruct, from igneous rocks, a fossil imprint of the earth's earlier magnetic fields. Geologic research in these new areas continued to focus on data gathering, but now particularly in the oceans where the U.S. Navy had directed its interest to the ocean floor. Other seagoing nations also initiated active research programs that culminated in the International Geophysical Year (IGY, July, 1957, to December, 1958), the first multinational research effort. The result of this effort was that in almost every area of geologic research, scientists found the earth and particularly the ocean very different from what they had imagined originally. One of the most curious features was the Mid-Atlantic Ridge. Understanding it led to an understanding of plate tectonics.

Matthew F. Maury (1822-1891), director of the U.S. Navy's Department of Charts and Instruments, first recognized the Mid-Atlantic Ridge in 1850 while collecting bathemetric measurements aboard the USS *Dolphin*. Maury named it the "Dolphin Rise" and published a map of it in his *The Physical Geography of the Sea* (1855). Data from HMS *Challenger* expedition (1872 to 1876) supplemented Maury's map, but the details of the Mid-Atlantic Ridge remained vague until the German meteor expedition of 1925 to 1927 led by Nobel laureate Fritz Haber. The expedition collected much oceanographic data and utilized an echo sounder to map the ocean floor. In 1933, German oceanographers Theodor Stocks and Georg Wust produced the first detailed map of the ridge noting a valley that seemed to be bisecting it. Later, in 1935, geophysicist Nicholas H. Heck found a strong correlation between earthquakes and the Mid-Atlantic Ridge.

Interrupted by World War II, oceanic exploration resumed in the late 1940's as a predominantly American venture. These studies produced a host of seemingly divergent data. In 1950, Maurice Ewing (1906-1974) of the Lamont-Geological Observatory established that no continental crust exists beneath the ocean basins. In 1952, Roger Revelle, director of Scripts Institute of Oceanography at La Jolla, California, and his student Arthur E. Maxwell determined the rate of heat flow from the earth's interior in the Pacific Ocean. They found it was similar to continental heat flow rates that E. C. Bullard of the University of Cambridge first described in 1935, except over the oceanic ridge, where the rate was substantially higher. The idea of a structurally active ridge received further support in 1954 when Jean P. Rothé, director of the International Bureau of Seismology in Strasbourg, mapped a continuous belt of earthquake epicenters from Iceland through the mid-Atlantic around South Africa, through the Indian Ocean, and on to the African Rifts and the Red Sea. In 1956, Maurice Ewing and Bruce C. Heezen continued the German technique of echo soundings at Lamont-Geological Observatory and found that the Mid-Atlantic Ridge was more than 64,000 kilometers long and, more important, that it had a rift (tensional) valley along the entire crest. In 1961, Ewing and Mark Landisman discovered that this ridge system extends throughout all the world's oceans, is seismically and volcanically active, continues to exhibit a tensional valley, and is mostly devoid of sediment cover.

Ivan Tolstoy and Ewing first characterized the geologically important question of sediment cover in 1949, describing a main ridge of thin sediment and flanks of thick sediment. The age of the sediments increased from the ridge toward the continents, the oldest being only Cretaceous in age (65 million years). In 1959, Victor Vacquier discovered that enormously long faults crossed the oceans' floor in many places. The faults have offsets of hundreds of kilometers but do not extend into the continents.

Central to the interpretation of this ocean mountain range were the early 1950's paleomagnetic researches of Patrick M. S. Blackett and his student, Keith Runcorn, at the University of Manchester. Their studies of fossil magnetism suggested that in the geologic past, the inclination, declination, and even the polarity of the earth's magnetic field had been very different from current orientations. The seemingly chaotic data formed a consistent pattern only upon assuming that the continents had moved relative to the magnetic poles and to one another. Magnetic studies of the seafloor by oceanographers R. G. Mason, A. D. Raff, and Vacquier revealed a symmetrical, zebralike pattern about the midoceanic ridge in 1957.

By the end of the 1950's, it was clear that existing geologic theories clearly had failed to predict or explain these seemingly unrelated phenomena; the new data required a new paradigm. In 1960, Hess circulated among his colleagues his theory of seafloor spreading to illuminate the working of Wegener's continental displacement hypothesis.

Impact of Event

The period between 1960 and 1965 was one of great uncertainty and multiple directions for geologists. In 1960, Hess synthesized the oceanic data of the 1950's into a bold new theory. Hess's paradigm was so novel and radical that he did not attempt to publish it in the usual professional journals, but included it in a 1960 report to the Office of Naval Research. Hess also widely circulated reprints among his colleagues.

In his 1960 report, Hess proposed that the midoceanic ridges were the loci of upwelling mantle convection cells that progressively moved the seafloor laterally and eventually under the continents. (Nearly thirty years earlier, in 1931, Arthur Holmes, of the University of Edinburgh, proposed that convection currents may exist in the mantle.) This driving mechanism brought together the divergent data of post-World War II research into one coherent theory. This creation of new seafloor from the upwelling of the mantle explained the high heat flow above the midoceanic ridge, the tensional rift-valley in the middle of the ridge, the correlation of the ridge with earthquake epicenters, the transform faults associated with the ocean floor, the continuation of the ridge throughout the oceans, the absence of continental-type rocks in the oceans, the thin sediment in the middle of the ridge and its thickening toward the edges, the symmetrical paleomagnetic zebra patterns, and the energy of the convection currents that was sufficient to drive the continents.

Robert S. Dietz, working for the Navy Electronic Laboratory in San Diego, published virtually identical ideas and coined the phrase "seafloor spreading" in a 1961 article "Continent and Ocean Basin Evolution by Spreading of the Sea Floor," published in *Nature*. Hess's reluctance to publish in mainstream scientific journals muddles the question of intellectual priority. He had scheduled his theory for publication in a multivolume set *The Sea, Ideas and Observations*, but delays kept it from the presses until 1963. Meanwhile, Hess was aware of Dietz's 1961 article, and in November, 1962, he published his ideas through a more expedient route, a collection of essays dedicated to his former teacher, *Petrologic Studies: A Volume in Honor of A. F. Buddington*. Dietz acknowledged Hess's priority of the mobile seafloor theory, and Hess credited Dietz for coining the term "seafloor spreading."

With the theory of seafloor spreading fully illuminated by both Hess and Dietz, the geologic community began reevaluating data and redesigning field studies to test it. One of the first tests occurred in 1963, following a prediction by Drummond H. Mathews and his student Frederick J. Vine at the University of Cambridge. They hypothesized that the magnetic pattern of polar reversals should be symmetrical along the axis of the oceanic ridge and correlate with its morphology. Their hypothesis proved correct and initiated a revolution in the earth sciences. In 1966, in recognition of his scientific breakthrough, Hess received the Geological Society of America's Penrose Medal, the geologist's equivalent of the Nobel Prize. By 1967, seafloor spreading was the dominant paradigm, and virtually all earth science specialists began to reinterpret their data in the light of the new paradigm.

Bibliography

Engel, A. E. J., H. L. James, and B. F. Leonard, eds. *Petrologic Studies: A Volume in Honor of A. F. Buddington*. New York: Geological Society of America, 1962. This is the primary source for Hess's theory based on his earlier Report to the Office of Naval Research, *Evolution of Ocean Basins*, Contract No. 1858(10), NR 081-067. This may be appropriate for the more advanced reader.

James, H. L. "Harry Hammond Hess." *National Academy of Sciences Biographical Memoirs* 43 (1973): 108-128. This biographical sketch yields insight into Hess, the man, and the full scope of his career and scientific work. For a wide audience.

Le Grand, Homer E. *Drifting Continents and Shifting Theories*. New York: Cambridge University Press, 1988. A very comprehensive work illustrating how science works in periods of revolution. Although written for an advanced audience, there is much here for the reader at any level. Comprehensive bibliography.

Scientific American. *Continents Adrift*. San Francisco: W. H. Freeman, 1973. This is an excellent collection of landmark papers (1952 to 1970) from the geologic revolution. Designed for the general reader, with typically excellent illustrations and photographs.

Sullivan, Walter. *Continents in Motion: The New Earth Debate*. New York: McGraw-Hill, 1974. This book has something for the reader at any level of geologic sophistication. Extremely readable and well written, with comprehensible drawings and photographs. Develops like a detective story rather than a textbook.

Young, Patrick. *Drifting Continents, Shifting Seas*. New York: Impact Books, 1976. This is an introductory book to the story of plate tectonics. The emphasis is on the people and chronological development. Very readable and well illustrated.

Richard C. Jones
Anthony N. Stranges

Cross-References

Wegener Proposes the Theory of Continental Drift (1912), p. 522; Langevin Develops Active Sonar for Submarine Detection and Fathometry (1915), p. 620; The German *Meteor* Expedition Discovers the Midatlantic Ridge (1925), p. 805; Heezen and Ewing Discover the Midoceanic Ridge (1956), p. 1508; The *Glomar Challenger* Obtains Thousands of Ocean Floor Samples (1968), p. 1876.

A VACCINE IS DEVELOPED FOR GERMAN MEASLES

Category of event: Medicine
Time: 1960-1969
Locale: Bethesda, Maryland; West Point, Pennsylvania

Parkman, Meyer, and Hilleman discovered that it was possible to attenuate the rubella virus and use it as an effective vaccine to prevent German measles

Principal personages:
  PAUL D. PARKMAN (1932-   ), an American physician who developed
    and tested a rubella vaccine with Meyer
  HARRY M. MEYER, JR. (1928-   ), an American physician who developed and tested a rubella vaccine with Parkman
  MAURICE R. HILLEMAN (1919-   ), an American physician who developed and tested a number of rubella vaccines

Summary of Event

Rubella, also known as German measles, lasts less than two weeks in children. They suffer from swollen glands, a low fever, and a transient three-day rash. In pregnant women, however, the virus that causes German measles can infect the developing fetus, especially during the first three months of the pregnancy; it can cause serious developmental defects. Approximately 15 to 20 percent of pregnant women that acquire German measles during the first three months of gestation give birth to infants that have one or more of the following problems: heart defects (50 percent), deafness (50 percent), eye defects and blindness (40 percent), mental retardation (40 percent), blood defects such as anemia and bleeding (30 percent), bone lesions, enlarged liver, enlarged spleen, and hand abnormalities. About 10 percent of babies born with congenital rubella die, while severe infections of the fetus result in spontaneous abortion.

The most severe defects occur when the infection occurs during the first two months of pregnancy. Studies show that 50 percent of pregnant women infected during the first month give birth to defective babies, but only about 10 percent of the babies had defects when the mothers were infected during the third month. Less than 5 percent of pregnant women infected in the fourth month of gestation have defective babies. Infections after the fourth month cause less serious and cryptic defects in the fetus.

The reported incidence of German measles in the United States during the early 1960's usually ranged between forty thousand and forty-five thousand cases per year. In the spring of 1964, an especially severe epidemic of rubella occurred that resulted in approximately seven thousand fetal deaths and twenty thousand babies with congenital defects. It is estimated that twenty-five hundred babies died. Serum from the babies with congenital defects contained antibodies against the rubella virus and many had viruses in their throat secretions, urine, cerebrospinal fluid, and most tissues. The rubella virus interferes with the development of many organs and continues to cause damage to many infants after they are born. Nearly 10 percent of the infants with congenital rubella still shed viruses ten to thirteen months after their birth. About 35 percent of these babies have extremely low platelet counts that result in spontaneous bleeding. Low numbers of red blood cells, inflammation of the liver, and bone disease afflict many of the bleeding babies, who often die in the first year after birth. The rubella virus has been shown to inhibit the division of human embryonic cells in cell cultures and cause chromosome breaks. This may explain why infants with congenital rubella generally have organs that are reduced in size.

Congenital rubella represented an important public health problem before the development of vaccines because affected newborns shed the virus for up to a year after their birth. This exposed pregnant women and personnel at doctors' offices to the virus. Newborns with congenital rubella also were a problem in hospitals because secreted viruses would infect other newborns in pediatric wards. The development of a safe vaccine was an important first step in reducing the incidence of congenital rubella.

A 1962 paper by Paul D. Parkman describes how his research group isolated, propagated, and characterized the agent responsible for German measles. His associates collected throat washings from hospitalized patients who had signs and symptoms of German measles. Also collected from all patients were blood samples. The throat washings were mixed with African green monkey kidney cells, and the cells were then grown in culture. The agent collected from the patients produced no visible changes in the cells; however, the agent's presence was detected by adding the echo virus. If the rubella virus was infecting the monkey cells, the cells would be resistant to the echo virus, but if they were not infected, the cells would lyse.

Parkman's group found that sixteen (80 percent) of twenty throat washings from patients diagnosed with rubella interfered with echo virus lysis of the cells. Fourteen (67 percent) of twenty-one patients with probable rubella had viruses in their throat washings. Only one (4 percent) of the twenty-five patients diagnosed with scarlet fever and four (30 percent) of thirteen patients with atypical skin rashes were found to have rubella virus in their throat washings. These data suggested that a common virus was found in the throat washings of persons with German measles.

It was found that patients with German measles all developed antibodies against the rubella viruses. The concentration of antibodies was shown to increase eight- to sixteen-fold in the two-week period following the rubella rash. The antibodies were specific, having no inhibitory effect on a number of other viral types. In addition, the cultured rubella virus was not neutralized by antisera against other viruses.

With the development of immunological methods for identifying the rubella virus, Parkman's research group showed that the virus reproduces in the throat for about two weeks before symptoms appear. Viruses are found in the blood as much as a week before the rash. The two-week incubation period is followed by swelling of the lymph nodes behind the head and ears. A few days later, the rash develops as well as antibodies against the virus. Over the next two weeks, the viral infection diminishes but viruses can still be isolated from the throat in many cases. The shedding of viruses for as much as a week before symptoms appear, as well as after symptoms disappear, makes this disease difficult to control by isolating patients.

Parkman, Harry M. Meyer, Jr., and their associates found that some viral strains changed as they were transferred repeatedly to fresh monkey cells. One virus, transferred seventy times, became very aggressive toward rabbit kidney cells, lysing them after a week's growth. Viruses from the first cell cultures did not lyse the rabbit cells. Also, it was found that the viruses from the later monkey cell cultures induced much higher levels of interferon than low-passage viruses (viruses transferred only a few times).

An important consideration in developing an attenuated vaccine was to find a virus that would not be shed. This would prevent vaccinated children from infecting pregnant women. An attenuated virus might still be dangerous to a fetus. Monkeys were used to determine whether high-passage viral strains (those transferred seventy or more times) were sufficiently attenuated, induced antibodies, or were shed. Parkman and his associates found that low-passage viral strains produced clinical signs of rubella in monkeys as well as neutralizing antibodies. In addition, these viruses were shed from the throat and rectum and transmitted to other monkeys. Viruses were found in the blood also. In contrast, high-passage viral strains were not shed from the throat or rectum and were not transferred to other monkeys. Also, these viruses were not found in the blood. Nevertheless, the high-passage viral strains induced neutralizing antibodies. Experiments using monkeys were fine, but it was not known if the virus would have the same characteristics in humans.

Meyer, Parkman, and Theodore C. Panos experimented with forty-two children, thirty-four who were inoculated with the high-passage rubella virus and eight who were not exposed and served as controls. None of the forty-two children involved developed swollen lymph nodes, a fever, or a rash. Past experiments with unmodified rubella viruses had always led to swollen lymph nodes, a fever, and a rash. In each of the thirty-four inoculated children, neutralizing antibodies developed by the thirtieth day after inoculation. None of the blood samples taken from the inoculated children contained detectable viruses. Viruses were detected in throat samples from twenty-three (68 percent) of the thirty-four inoculated children between days seven and twenty-four. Nevertheless, these viruses did not infect the uninoculated control children, because none of these children developed neutralizing antibodies against the rubella virus and none had viruses reproducing in their throat. A natural infection by rubella virus among a group of eleven children contrasted with the infection by the attenuated virus. Nine of the children developed a rash, three children had viruses in their blood, and all eleven children shed viruses in their throats. Measurements showed that one hundred times more virulent viruses were shed than attenuated viruses.

By 1968, four different research groups had developed rubella vaccines with attenuated viruses. Parkman and Meyer had obtained theirs in monkey cells, another doctor grew his virus in rabbit cells, Stanley A. Plotkin obtained his virus in diploid human cells, while Maurice R. Hilleman had attenuated his virus in duck cells. The danger of preparing vaccines in mammalian (monkey, rabbit, human) cells was that they often harbored a variety of viruses or proviruses that might infect humans and cause cancer. To avoid this possibility, Hilleman grew attenuated viruses in duck cells. The cells were from birds that developed spontaneous tumors very infrequently.

A comparison of Hilleman's vaccine with that developed by Parkman and Meyer showed that a number of Hilleman's viral strains were effective and not passed on to contacts. Vaccination of 265 rubella-susceptible children with the Parkman-Meyer virus grown in duck cells resulted in 256 (97 percent) of the children developing antibodies. None of the children, however, had clinical signs of rubella. In addition, none of the 262 siblings or 34 parents who functioned as controls developed antibodies, indicating that the secreted viruses produced no apparent infections in contacts.

Hilleman and his associates tested the Parkman-Meyer virus on susceptible women of childbearing age. In this group, the attenuated viruses were more virulent than in the children tested. Thirty-five women were inoculated with rubella vaccine. Unlike the results obtained with children, the symptoms of mild clinical rubella developed in twenty women (fifteen showed no signs or symptoms). Fifteen suffered with pain in their joints (arthritis), eight developed a rash, six felt poorly, five had swollen nodes, and three had no appetite. Thirty-four (97 percent) of the thirty-five women developed antibodies against the rubella virus. These results indicated that the Parkman-Meyer vaccine was more virulent for adults than for children.

Impact of Event

In 1969, a number of vaccines were licensed for general use. The Parkman-Meyer attenuated virus was grown in dog kidney cells by Parkman and Meyer but in duck embryo cells by Hilleman. These vaccines were designated DK-12 and DE-5, respectively. Another viral vaccine produced using rabbit kidney cells became known as RK, or the Cendehill strain. The Plotkin vaccine made from viruses grown in human diploid cells was designated as RA 27/3. From 1970 to 1975, more than 55 million children and women of childbearing age in the United States were vaccinated. The vaccination program had a dramatic effect on the epidemiology of German measles. The most obvious effect was that the incidence of German measles in the United States dropped from forty thousand to about twelve thousand cases. Before the vaccine, epidemics of German measles occurred every six to nine years. The vaccine prevented the severe epidemics expected in the 1970's and 1980's. Nevertheless, there was a slight increase in the incidence of rubella from 1975 to 1977. From 1977 through 1989, the incidence of German measles decreased from about sixteen thousand to less than four hundred cases per year. In 1990, the incidence of German measles increased 2.5 times to more than one thousand cases. This increase may have reflected the fact that more and more children were not being vaccinated in the 1980's before they entered school. Many states still do not have mandatory vaccination for rubella. Most of the children acquiring rubella come from economically disadvantaged homes, where the parents do not have the money for vaccinations and do not understand the public health importance of vaccination.

The safety of vaccines developed by each of the groups is being studied. The DK-12 vaccine developed by Parkman and Meyer was associated with many more cases of pain in the joints, arthritis, and nerve damage than other vaccines. Also, the DK-12 vaccine produced more severe symptoms. Therefore, it was removed from distribution in the early 1970's. The other vaccines appeared to be equally effective and safe.

A number of studies have indicated that immunized children are not contagious. No examples of vaccinated children transmitting the attenuated virus to their susceptible mothers or other contacts have been documented. Thus, vaccination of young children is an effective measure for blocking wild-type infections that are frequently transmitted from young children to their pregnant mothers.

Data on fifty-six susceptible women who were inadvertently vaccinated shortly before or after conception suggest that there is a small risk of fetal infection by the attenuated viruses. Twenty-three (41 percent) of these women gave birth to normal babies with no evidence of rubella viruses. Twenty-eight (50 percent) had abortions because of the fear of giving birth to defective children. There was no information on the state of the aborted fetuses. Apparently, they were normal. Yet, the gestational tissues of five women (9 percent) contained viruses. Whether this would have led to some cases of congenital rubella is not known. These limited data indicated that the incidence of congenital rubella, when pregnant women are vaccinated within the first three months of their pregnancy, would be less than 2 percent.

A study of vaccinated children indicates that the antibodies against the rubella virus persist for as long as seven years. Reinfection of these children with wild-type rubella virus protects most of them from developing any signs or symptoms of German measles. No viruses are found in their blood. This suggests that pregnant women, previously vaccinated, have little chance of being reinfected by a wild-type virus. Even if they should be infected, the virus would not be able to migrate through the blood to the fetus.

Since the mid-1970's, use of the rubella vaccine has prevented the birth of more than five thousand children per year with congenital rubella. At least two epidemics in the 1970's and 1980's were avoided, saving an additional thirty thousand to forty thousand children from congenital rubella. It is estimated that an equal number of abortions because of rubella infections during pregnancy have been avoided.

Bibliography

Cooper, Louis Z. "German Measles." *Scientific American* 215 (July, 1966): 30-37. This paper explains how German measles was defined as a separate and distinct disease in the 1800's and how in the 1940's congenital rubella in newborns was associated with German measles in pregnant women. Most of the paper is concerned with the symptoms of congenital rubella. Drawings illustrating the defects that may occur in the heart and eye are very informative. Photographs of cultured cells infected by rubella viruses demonstrate the cytopathic effects of the attenuated virus obtained by Parkman and Meyer.

Hilleman, Maurice R., Eugene Buynak, Robert E. Weibel, and Joseph Stokes. "Live, Attenuated Rubella-Virus Vaccine." *The New England Journal of Medicine* 279 (August 8, 1968): 300-302. This paper considers four rubella vaccines that had been developed by 1968 and compares the Parkman and Meyer strain with a viral strain developed by Hilleman at the Merck Institute for Therapeutic Research at West Point, Pennsylvania. This paper clearly illustrates the concern scientists had that their vaccines might not be safe and the number of clinical trials performed before any vaccine could be licensed.

Krugman, Saul, and Samuel L. Katz. "Rubella Immunization: A Five-Year Progress Report." *The New England Journal of Medicine* 290 (July 13, 1974): 1375-1376. This short paper reported on the effectiveness and safety of the rubella vaccines licensed in 1969. One vaccine, which was developed by Parkman and Meyer in dog kidney cells (DK-12), was recalled because of the high incidence of joint pains, arthritis, and neurological problems associated with it.

Meyer, Harry M., Paul D. Parkman, and Theodore C. Panos. "Attenuated Rubella Virus, II. Production of an Experimental Live-Virus Vaccine and Clinical Trial." *The New England Journal of Medicine* 275 (September 15, 1966): 575-580. This paper describes the clinical results obtained with the Parkman and Meyer vaccine. It was found that the vaccine was safe in children. None of the children developed a rash or enlarged lymph nodes. Viruses could not be isolated from any blood samples. Nevertheless, a number of children shed the virus in their throats. This article is worthwhile reading because it shows how scientists go about testing a new vaccine and what results concern them.

Parkman, P. D., E. L. Buescher, and M. S. Artenstein. "Recovery of Rubella Virus from Army Recruits." *Proceedings of the Society for Experimental Biology and Medicine* 111 (1962): 225-230. This paper describes how Parkman and his research group at the Walter Reed Army Institute of Research in Washington, D.C., characterized the agent responsible for German measles and demonstrated that it was a virus. Also noteworthy was the discovery that the virus could be identified by antibodies developed in rabbits against a strain of the rubella virus grown and maintained in African green monkey cells.

Parkman, Paul D., Harry M. Meyer, Ruth L. Kirschstein, and Hope E. Hopps. "Attenuated Rubella Virus. I. Development and Laboratory Characterization." *The New England Journal of Medicine* 275 (September 15, 1966): 569-574. This paper describes how Parkman and Meyer attenuated a rubella virus and discovered that it might be a good candidate for making a safe vaccine. The paper shows precisely how a group of scientists obtained an attenuated virus and how they tested it to determine whether it had the characteristics they thought were important in a rubella vaccine.

Weibel, Robert E., Joseph Stokes, Eugene B. Buynak, and Maurice R. Hilleman. "Rubella Vaccination in Adult Females." *The New England Journal of Medicine* 280 (March 27, 1969): 682-685. This paper illustrates how an attenuated rubella virus may produce more severe infections in one group of humans than another. The Parkman and Meyer viral strain grown in duck cells by Hilleman produced no signs and symptoms in hundreds of children tested but produced signs and symptoms of German measles in 57 percent of the women of childbearing age.

Jaime S. Colome

Cross-References

Rous Discovers That Some Cancers Are Caused by Viruses (1910), p. 459; Calmette and Guérin Develop the Tuberculosis Vaccine BCG (1921), p. 705; Zinsser Develops an Immunization Against Typhus (1930), p. 921; Theiler Introduces a Vaccine Against Yellow Fever (1937), p. 1091; Salk Develops a Polio Vaccine (1952), p. 1444; Sabin Develops an Oral Polio Vaccine (1957), p. 1522; A Genetically Engineered Vaccine for Hepatitis B Is Approved for Use (1986), p. 2326.

ORÓ DETECTS THE FORMATION OF ADENINE FROM CYANIDE SOLUTION

Category of event: Biology
Time: Spring, 1960
Locale: Houston, Texas

Oró was the first scientist to focus on the synthesis of biological molecules from hydrogen cyanide, which now occupies a key role in models for the origin of life

Principal personages:
   JUAN ORÓ (1923-   ), a Spanish-American chemist whose career has centered on pathways to organic molecules on the primitive earth and in comets
   AUBREY PIERCE KIMBALL (1926-   ), a biochemist who helped identify the products obtained from the cyanide reaction
   LESLIE ELEAZER ORGEL (1927-   ), an English-American chemist whose contributions to the study of life's origins began with the mechanism of adenine synthesis
   JAMES PETER FERRIS (1932-   ), an organic chemist who has conducted extensive research on the synthesis of biological molecules from hydrogen cyanide

Summary of Event

The question of life's origin has engaged the minds of intellectuals since ancient times, but during the twentieth century this subject has moved from the philosopher's court to the scientist's laboratory. A major figure in this transformation was the Soviet biochemist Aleksandr Ivanovich Oparin, who articulated the paradigm that has guided research in this field: The origin of life can be viewed as a gradual, cumulative process marked by successive stages of increasing complexity. Just as molecular biology has revealed different levels of organization in biochemical systems, the study of primordial life could be approached in a modular fashion, beginning with the synthesis of organic molecules from the primitive atmosphere.

When Juan Oró enrolled in graduate school at the Baylor College of Medicine in 1952, few scientists had a serious interest in the question of how life began. Experiments in several laboratories in the United States and Germany had shown that carbon dioxide could be converted to formaldehyde and other simple products, but no complex molecules had been synthesized. In 1953, however, a second-year graduate student named Stanley Miller at the University of Chicago published a report of amino acids (the constituents of proteins) formed by the action of simulated lightning in a model atmosphere containing methane, ammonia, hydrogen, and water. The use of methane as a carbon source marked a departure from earlier practice, but this mixture had been suggested by Harold C. Urey as representative of the primordial atmosphere. Although scientists now believe that the Miller-Urey experiment overestimated the amounts of methane and ammonia on primitive earth, the dramatic synthesis of amino acids stimulated many researchers to enter the field of prebiotic chemistry.

Oró had decided to focus on the origins of life even before Miller published his seminal communication. He had graduated from the University of Barcelona with a degree in chemistry. On his way to Houston, Texas, to attend Baylor University, he stopped in New York to meet a fellow Spaniard named Severo Ochoa. At the age of forty-six, Ochoa was a well-known biochemist who would later win the 1959 Nobel Prize in Physiology or Medicine for his research on the artificial synthesis of polynucleotides. Ochoa encouraged Oró to pursue his goal of developing prebiotic pathways to sugars and related molecules. Oró obtained a position as chemistry instructor at the University of Houston in 1956. His doctoral research on formate metabolism in animals had given him valuable experience in laboratory techniques for biochemical analysis, which were also essential for the research he planned in prebiotic chemistry. Indeed, his early work focused on improvements in these analytical methods. After some initial experiments on the synthesis of amino acids from formaldehyde, Oró turned his attention to cyanide.

Miller had shown that hydrogen cyanide (HCN) was an important intermediate in the synthesis of amino acids during the electric discharge reaction. Other investigators such as Philip Abelson, the director of the geophysical laboratory at the Carnegie Institution, had repeated the Miller-Urey experiment using a variety of gas mixtures and confirmed the formation of HCN, leading Abelson and others to conclude that this molecule was probably an important constituent of the primordial atmosphere. While these reactions yielded glycine and other amino acids, they also produced a brown tar that had not been characterized. During a conference in 1959, Abelson and Oró speculated on the origin of this solid residue, which they viewed as extended chains, or "polymers," of HCN molecules. Oró therefore decided to shift his research to the products that might be formed from cyanide.

Hydrogen cyanide is well known for its acute toxicity, but Oró fortunately had acquired experience while in Spain working with this dangerous substance. During his first studies at Houston, he bubbled HCN into a solution of ammonia to give ammonium cyanide, which then reacted with itself to give more complex molecules. The reaction itself was accompanied by a series of visible changes: from colorless to yellow, then orange, and finally to red, as a dark precipitate began to form. This "alchemist's brew," as Oró called it, was heated overnight at just below its boiling point, after which the liquid was analyzed for biological molecules.

The detection technique employed in these studies was paper chromatography, where a tiny drop of an unknown mixture is separated on a long sheet of porous paper that is dipped into a suitable liquid, which carries some components a greater distance than others. When Oró first analyzed the liquid from the cyanide reaction, he found significant amounts of amino acids, along with a very faint trace of adenine, one of the essential bases in deoxyribonucleic acid (DNA) and ribonucleic acid (RNA). He subsequently treated the solution with acid and concentrated the product for further characterization: Paper chromatography (using several different solvents and a variety of visualization techniques) provided much stronger evidence for the presence of adenine. Oró demonstrated that the chemical and physical properties of an authentic sample of adenine were the same as those of the isolated product, thus confirming its identification. This discovery marked the first synthesis of adenine under presumed prebiotic conditions. Oró published his results in the June, 1960, issue of *Biochemical and Biophysical Research Communications.*

Further characterization of the products formed from ammonium cyanide was carried out by Oró and his graduate student, Aubrey Pierce Kimball. In addition to adenine, they found two imidazole derivatives, one of which was proposed as a precursor to adenine. Oró and Kimball regarded the formation of imidazoles as significant, because such compounds play a catalytic role in biochemistry and because the modern biosynthesis of adenine proceeds through similar molecular species. They also confirmed the formation of amino acids, including glycine, alanine, and aspartic acid, from the heating of ammonium cyanide solutions. The production of adenine and amino acids from a mixture of ammonia and HCN was also verified by a British group under the direction of Roy Markham at the University of Cambridge.

For Oró, the cyanide studies marked the beginning of a long career devoted to understanding the origins of life. A major focus of his subsequent research has been the related molecule—cyanamide—which can be formed from ammonium cyanide by the action of ultraviolet light. Oró and his coworkers have utilized cyanamide in the synthesis of oligonucleotides, oligopeptides, and lipids (the building blocks of nucleic acids, proteins, and membranes, respectively). He also served on National Aeronautics and Space Administration (NASA) teams for the analysis of lunar rocks from the Apollo missions and for the interpretation of data from the Martian Viking probes. His contributions have thus extended from the development of prebiotic pathways to the search for life in the universe.

Impact of Event

The formation of adenine from a solution of ammonium cyanide marked an important advance in prebiotic chemistry both because of the simplicity of the starting materials and because the reaction yielded amino acids. Since proteins and nucleic acids are essential for modern life, the detection of constituents from both classes of molecules served to heighten interest in cyanide chemistry. Nevertheless, Oró had employed hot temperatures (near boiling) and high concentrations, conditions that many scientists regarded as too restrictive. Leslie Eleazer Orgel at the Salk Institute in California pointed out that even the most optimistic estimate of the cyanide content of the primordial ocean would be well below that used to prepare adenine. A further limitation of Oró's pathway was that it relied on formamidine (an adduct of HCN and ammonia), which is formed only at high concentrations and is highly unstable in water.

Together with research associates James Peter Ferris and Robert Sanchez, Orgel set out to develop a more general route to adenine starting from HCN. They found that the polymerization of cyanide does indeed occur under more dilute conditions, although a lower limit is eventually reached. In a thorough mechanistic study, they showed that the HCN tetramer (diaminomaleonitrile) is a more likely precursor than the HCN trimer (aminomalononitrile) proposed by Oró. Orgel and Ferris demonstrated that the tetramer can be converted by the action of ultraviolet light into an imidazole derivative that ultimately yields adenine upon further reaction with HCN. Orgel also suggested a clever process by which high concentrations of cyanide could be achieved on primitive earth: The freezing of ponds or lakes could remove much of the water, creating a potent HCN solution in the remaining liquid. The Salk group thus improved on Oró's discovery by demonstrating the synthesis of adenine and its precursors under more natural conditions.

Since 1967, Ferris has led his own research effort devoted to the synthesis of biological molecules from HCN. In his laboratory at Rensselaer Polytechnic Institute in upstate New York, many biochemicals have been detected after the initial products of HCN polymerization are heated in an alkaline solution. The Rensselaer scientists also isolated a diverse array of other molecules that are either components of modern proteins and nucleic acids or are precursors to the constituents of these biopolymers. For example, they found a substance known as orotic acid, which they irradiated with ultraviolet light to form uracil, a major constituent of RNA.

Additional studies of HCN chemistry have been carried out by several other scientists, including Alan Schwartz at the University of Nijmegen in The Netherlands. He and his assistant, Andries Voet, isolated an HCN pentamer that serves as a precursor to adenine. They also demonstrated that uracil can be formed under conditions that do not require ultraviolet light. The conclusion that can be drawn from these diverse investigations is that HCN can provide a rich source of biological molecules and therefore probably played a significant role in the synthesis of the molecular precursors of early life. The detection of HCN and related compounds in comets and in interstellar space has reinforced the primordial importance of cyanide chemistry. Oró's pioneering synthesis of adenine from ammonium cyanide thus opened new pathways in the elucidation of the origins of life.

Bibliography

Day, William. *Genesis on Planet Earth: The Search for Life's Beginning*. 2d ed. New Haven, Conn.: Yale University Press, 1984. A well-written, nontechnical account of research on the origins of life, with many references to Oró. Includes an extensive list of primary sources.

Ferris, James P., and David A. Usher. "Origins of Life." In *Biochemistry*, edited by Geoffrey Zubay. 2d ed. New York: Macmillan, 1988. A brief summary written by two knowledgeable participants; the level of discussion requires a background in college chemistry.

Oparin, A. I. *The Origin of Life*. Translated by Sergius Morgulis. New York: Macmillan, 1938. First published in Russian in 1936, this translation provided many English readers with their first view of Oparin's model. The opening chapters provide a succinct history of ideas on the origin of life.

Orgel, L. E. *The Origins of Life: Molecules and Natural Selection*. New York: John Wiley & Sons, 1973. Although somewhat dated, this book offers an introduction and selected bibliography for the advanced high school student or general reader.

Oró, J. "Prebiological Chemistry and the Origin of Life: A Personal Account." In *Reflections on Biochemistry*, edited by A. Kornberg, B. L. Horecker, and L. Cornudella. New York: Pergamon Press, 1976. An autobiographical essay with emphasis on Oró's scientific work.

Raymo, Chet. *Biography of a Planet: Geology, Astronomy, and the Evolution of Life on Earth*. Englewood Cliffs, N.J.: Prentice-Hall, 1984. A highly illustrated survey, ranging from the origin of the solar system to early human evolution, with a brief discussion of prebiotic synthesis. Appropriate for high school students.

William J. Hagan, Jr.

Cross-References

Hopkins Discovers Tryptophan, an Essential Amino Acid (1900), p. 46; Lemaître Proposes the Big Bang Theory (1927), p. 825; Gamow and Associates Develop the Big Bang Theory (1948), p. 1309; Ochoa Creates Synthetic RNA (1950's), p. 1363; Lippmann Discovers Acetyl Coenzyme A (1951), p. 1390; Watson and Crick Develop the Double-Helix Model for DNA (1951), p. 1406; Miller Reports the Synthesis of Amino Acids (1953), p. 1465; Calvin Wins the Nobel Prize for His Work on Photosynthesis (1961), p. 1703; Deep-Sea Hydrothermal Vents and New Life-Forms Are Discovered (1977), p. 2058; Cech Demonstrates That RNA Can Act as an Enzyme (1982), p. 2190.

TIROS 1 BECOMES THE FIRST EXPERIMENTAL WEATHER RECONNAISSANCE SATELLITE

Categories of event: Earth science and space and aviation
Time: April 1, 1960-June 14, 1960
Locale: United States

The Tiros series of cloud-cover meteorological satellites pioneered reconnaissance of large-scale weather systems and led to vast improvements in weather forecasting capabilities

Principal personage:
> HARRY WEXLER, director of National Weather Bureau meteorological research at the time of Tiros 1 operations

Summary of Event

The first experimental weather satellite, Tiros 1, was launched from Cape Canaveral on April 1, 1960, by a Thor-Able launch vehicle. Tiros 1 was inserted into an elliptical orbit ranging from 696 to 749 kilometers. This orbit was inclined 49.3 degrees to the equator; thus Tiros flew over a large portion of Earth's inhabited land masses. As a result, Tiros covered the area from Montreal, Canada, to Santa Cruz, Argentina, in the Western Hemisphere. Tiros completed an orbit every ninety-nine minutes and, when launched, was expected to survive at least three months in space, returning thousands of images of large-scale weather systems.

Tiros 1 was built in the shape of an 18-sided drum, 48.25 centimeters high and 106.7 centimeters in diameter. It weighed a mere 123 kilograms. The polygonal drum shape maximized available surface area on the spin-stabilized satellite for solar cells to gather solar radiation and generate electricity. A total of 9,260 solar cells covered the top and sides of Tiros 1. These charged a nickel-cadmium battery pack to which all electrical systems were connected. Images taken by Tiros optical systems were transmitted to ground stations by a pair of 2-watt FM transmitters operating at 235 megacycles.

Tiros 1 was equipped with a pair of vidicon scanner television cameras, one equipped with a wide-angle lens and the other with a narrow-angle lens. Both cameras created pictures with five hundred lines per frame at a shutter speed of 1.5 milliseconds. Each television camera's imaging data were stored on their own magnetic tape storage unit for downloading when Tiros 1 was in contact with a ground station. A total of thirty-two images could be stored on each tape unit during a single orbit. The wide-angle lens provided a low-resolution view of a coverage area of 2,048 square kilometers. The narrow-angle lens had a resolution of half a kilometer, but covered only 205 square kilometers.

The imaging system operated in two different modes. When Tiros was in contact with a ground station, the television cameras could bypass the tape-recording system and transmit data directly to Earth. When out of range of a ground receiving station, the television cameras recorded images on magnetic tape every thirty seconds until a maximum of thirty-two pictures were stored. Once back over a ground station, data would be downlinked. It required less than eight minutes to play back completely thirty-two recorded images. Typically, a pass within range of a ground station would last twelve minutes; thus live images were possible after downloading those images recorded when out of radio contact.

Tiros transmitted its data to ground stations, which displayed the data on televison displays. Photographs of these displays were then made for permanent records. Tiros weather data were sent to the Naval Photographic Interpretation Center for detailed meteorological analysis. Next, the photographs were passed along to the National Weather Bureau for further study. Tiros was controlled principally from two ground stations, one operated by the Army Signal Corps located at Fort Monmouth, New Jersey, and one operated by Lockheed Missile and Space Division located at Kaena Point, Hawaii. In addition to these primary ground stations for satellite data retrieval and control, backup ground stations at Cape Canaveral and in Princeton, New Jersey, were available for data acquisition only. An onboard electronic timing system could be set five hours in advance of execution by ground control commands from either Fort Monmouth or Kaena Point. Then the electronic timing mechanism would trigger selectively the camera shutters for proper exposures to image selected weather systems and record electronically the image on magnetic tape.

Tiros caused some controversy because it was able to image large areas of the communist world: the Soviet Union, Cuba, and Mongolia. The weather satellite's imaging system was not particularly useful as a spy satellite. The highest resolution available on Tiros photographs was only 0.3 kilometer; thus only large-scale surface features were visible in the images. Nevertheless, the National Aeronautics and Space Administration (NASA) skirted adverse international reactions by carefully scrutinizing Tiros images for evidence of sensitive surface features before releasing them publicly.

Tiros could image weather systems only for certain periods of each orbit. The satellite was constructed so that its receiving antenna was on the top surface and the two television cameras and four transmitting antennas were mounted on the satellite's bottom surface. Tiros was spin-stabilized, rotating twelve times per minute about its symmetry axis, which was aligned in inertial space rather than simply pointing down to the earth. As a result, Tiros was able to image weather only on the daylight side of an orbit, when the satellite's bottom faced toward Earth. The combination of Tiros orbital mechanics and Earth's rotation permitted the satellite to provide intermittent coverage of the area between north and south 50 degrees latitude.

Tiros 1 was not in orbit very long before it made significant and startling discoveries. This satellite was the first to document that large storms have vortex patterns, unmistakable pinwheel swirl patterns. Within its lifetime, Tiros photographed more than forty northern mid-latitude storm systems, and each one had a vortex at its center. These storms were in various stages of development and were between 800 and 1,600 kilometers in diameter. The storm vortex in most of these was located inside a 560-kilometer-diameter circle around the center of the storm's low-pressure zone. Nevertheless, Tiros images did not reveal at what stage in a storm's development the vortex pattern formed. This was typical of Tiros data. The satellite was truly an experiment and, like most initial experiments, various new phenomena were uncovered but not fully understood. Tiros data showed clearly that weather systems could be investigated from orbit and future weather satellites could be outfitted with sensors that would lead to better understanding of meteorology on a global scale.

Tiros 1 did suffer from a few difficulties during its lifetime on orbit. Low contrast in the television imaging system often made it difficult to distinguish between cloud and snow cover. Following the twenty-second orbit only, the satellite's high-resolution television camera was no longer capable of recording images on magnetic tape for later playback. Tiros responded to Earth's magnetic field in a way that tended to move it away from an advantageous Earth observation attitude. Experience with Tiros 1 led to improvements on later Tiros and other weather satellites.

After completing 1,302 orbits, the operational lifetime of Tiros 1 concluded. Between launch and June 14, 1960, fourteen thousand useful photographs had been collected by the experimental weather satellite, proving the utility of an orbital imaging platform for the collection of meteorological data. Tiros 1 data provided information about large-scale meteorological structures not known previously to exist. The success of Tiros 1 justified the existence of the Tiros program and ultimately led to nine other Tiros satellites and the modern weather satellites available for weather monitoring and forecasting.

Impact of Event

The space age has spawned numerous important benefits to daily life and accelerated the evolution of several existing technologies. Three decades after Sputnik 1, many of these space-derived technologies are taken for granted: high-speed global communication, vast memory computer systems, and worldwide weather forecasting, for example. Prior to Tiros 1, weather monitoring was done with networks of ground-based instrumentation centers, airborne balloons, and instrumented aircraft. Brief high-altitude rocket flights provided limited coverage of cloud systems from above. Tiros 1 was the first step in the development of a permanent monitoring of weather systems. The resulting savings in both property damage and loss of human life from hurricanes alone that has resulted from early detection and accurate tracking of such storms by weather platforms in space has paid for the development and operational costs of all weather satellites from Tiros to the present many times over.

The first suggestion of using a space-based platform for weather observation appears to have been included in a 1951 Rand Corporation report to the United States Air Force written by Stanley M. Greenfield and William W. Kellogg. In 1954, Harry Wexler, of the National Weather Bureau, proposed providing such a space-based platform with television cameras, infrared sensors, and radar. Serious work on a weather satellite began in 1957, when researchers at the Air Force Geophysics Research Directorate outlined a design for the infrared sensors that would be used ultimately on Tiros 1. The remainder of Tiros systems were defined the following year by the Advanced Research Projects Agency. Shortly thereafter, Tiros project authority was transferred to the newly formed civilian NASA space program. NASA awarded the contract to build Tiros 1 to the RCA Astro-Electronics Division.

Tiros was designed purely as an experimental project, not as an operational weather satellite. The Weather Bureau, indeed, was divided on the usefulness of such a satellite for meteorological studies. Those who were in favor of Tiros were surprised at how powerful a tool a weather satellite could be, and those who were dubious prior to Tiros 1 were convinced that weather satellites were indispensable to the future of meteorological research. Wexler said that he found the quality of Tiros television images to be an unexpected, pleasant surprise. Tiros had exceeded his best hopes. He and other meteorologists were totally surprised at some of the data returned by Tiros 1.

As a result of the Tiros 1 experiment, meteorologists were not ready to discard ground-based and airborne weather systems in favor of orbital platforms. Such systems could not provide data about pressure, humidity, and temperature, for example. Because of Tiros 1, meteorologists clearly viewed weather satellites as a necessary supplement to ground-based and airborne systems for large-scale monitoring of weather systems and storms. Satellites could provide more reliable expansive coverage at a far lower cost than a large contingent of aircraft. Tiros 1 was followed by nine other similar spacecraft and paved the way for modern operational weather satellite systems.

Bibliography

Alexander, George. "Tiros 1 Shows Large Storms Have Vortex." *Aviation Week and Space Technology* 74 (February 6, 1961): 74-75. Scientific discussion of early results from Tiros 1. Revelation of structure inside large cyclonic storms.

Bilstein, Roger E. *Orders of Magnitude: A History of the NACA and NASA, 1915-1990.* NASA SP-4406. Washington, D.C.: Government Printing Office, 1989. For the general reader. Describes numerous experimental satellite programs, such as Tiros, in addition to manned spaceflight activities of NASA. Places unmanned probes, such as Tiros, in the overall setting of space achievement and improvement of life on Earth.

Bird, John. *The Upper Atmosphere: Threshold of Space.* NASA SP-105. Washington, D.C.: Government Printing Office, 1988. Thorough explanation of atmospheric structure and phenomena. Describes for the layperson what current satellite technology can reveal about atmospheric conditions, weather, pollution, and the like. Contains many diagrams and photographs.

Clark, Evert. "Tiros Exceeds Weather Bureau Hopes." *Aviation Week and Space Technology* 72 (May 2, 1960): 30. Provides initial evaluation of preliminary Tiros 1 data. Quotes from project scientists express their optimism for future weather system understanding and prediction.

Cortright, Edgar M. *Space Exploration—Why and How.* NASA EP-25. Washington, D.C.: Government Printing Office, 1965. General description of weather, communications, and interplanetary spacecraft. Provides several early Tiros weather photographs.

Kolcum, Edward H. "Gamble on Tiros Satellites Is Paying Off." *Aviation Week and Space Technology* 75 (October 2, 1961): 70-74. Tiros was an evolving series of weather satellites. Eighteen months after the first Tiros launch, this article describes how much the Tiros program changed the nature of weather forecasting.

Lewis, Craig. "NASA Tiros 1 Demonstrates Potential Satellite Reconnaissance Utility." *Aviation Week and Space Technology* 72 (April 11, 1960): 28-30. Describes launch and early work of the Tiros satellite. Speculates on the prospects for operational weather reconnaissance from space. Photograph of launch and several early Tiros weather images.

"Tiros Defines Weather Systems, Land Areas." *Aviation Week and Space Technology* 72 (April 18, 1960): 34. Brief article provides a number of Tiros 1 images of large-scale atmospheric systems.

"Tiros 1 Will Scan Cloud Cover, Earth Temperature." *Aviation Week and Space Technology* 72 (March 14, 1960): 26-28. Describes Tiros spacecraft systems and mission profile. Explains how Tiros data was collected and transmitted to Earth for analysis.

David G. Fisher

Cross-References

Bjerknes Publishes the First Weather Forecast Using Computational Hydrodynamics (1897), p. 21; Fabry Quantifies Ozone in the Upper Atmosphere (1913), p. 579; Manabe and Wetherald Warn of the Greenhouse Effect and Global Warming (1967), p. 1840.

THE FIRST LASER IS DEVELOPED
IN THE UNITED STATES

Categories of event: Applied science and physics
Time: July, 1960
Locale: Hughes Research Laboratories, Southern California

Maiman succeeded in putting into operation the theoretical principles of the laser

Principal personages:
CHARLES HARD TOWNES (1915-   ), an American physicist who was a cowinner of the 1964 Nobel Prize in Physics
ARTHUR L. SCHAWLOW (1921-   ), an American physicist who, together with Townes, formulated the basic principles of the laser
THEODORE HAROLD MAIMAN (1927-   ), an American physicist who designed apparatus that put into operation the principles formulated by Schawlow and Townes

Summary of Event

Lasers were once called optical masers. MASER is an acronym, standing for Microwave Amplification by the Stimulated Emission of Radiation; LASER is an acronym for Light Amplification by the Stimulated Emission of Radiation. Both masers and lasers operate on the same principle to provide a beam of electromagnetic radiation that is monochromatic (consisting of a single wavelength), highly directional, and coherent (the waves' crests and troughs aligned).

A laser beam, launched from Earth, produced a spot a few kilometers wide on the Moon, nearly 400,000 kilometers away. Ordinary light would have spread so much as to have produced a "spot" several times wider than the Moon. Also, laser light can be concentrated to a spot yielding an enormous intensity of energy, more than that at the surface of the Sun, an impossibility with ordinary light.

In order to appreciate the difference between laser light and ordinary light, one must examine how light of any kind is produced. In a light source, such as a fluorescent lamp, the atoms of gas the lamp contains must be excited to a state of higher energy than their normal, or ground, state. This is accomplished by flipping a switch, which sends a current of electricity through the lamp; the current jolts the atoms into the higher-energy state. This excited state is unstable, however, and the atoms will spontaneously return to their ground state by ridding themselves, in the form of light, of the excess energy they had acquired. The atoms return to the ground state "individualistically," the light emitted by one atom unrelated to the light emitted by any other. The light emitted by a lamp full of atoms, therefore, is disorganized, emitted in all directions and randomly in time. This type of light, common to all ordinary sources, from fluorescent lamps to the sun, is ordinary, incoherent light.

Laser light is different. The excited atoms in a laser do not emit their excess energy as individualists, but in a collective manner. The atoms remain in the excited state until there are a great many excited atoms. Then, they are stimulated to emit, not independently, but in an organized fashion, with all their light waves traveling in the same direction, crests and troughs perfectly aligned. This type of light is called coherent.

The concept of coherence did not arise in connection with lasers nor did stimulated emission, a subject studied by Albert Einstein in 1917. Maser and laser physicists introduced the idea of collecting a great many excited atoms, then stimulating them so as to amplify their radiation. Lasers could have been developed well before 1960, since optical spectroscopy was an established field a century ago. The laser's precursor, the maser, however, could not have been produced before World War II, when microwave research began. Despite optical spectroscopy's seniority, the maser preceded the laser because amplification was associated with electrical circuits, of which microwave devices had been components since the war. Thus, the laser's tardy appearance can be attributed to conceptual, rather than technical, obstacles.

The idea of stimulating an assemblage of excited atoms to emit their excitation energy in masers was introduced independently in the Soviet Union by Nikolay Gennadiyevich Basov and Aleksandr Mikhailovich Prokhorov, and in the United States by Charles Hard Townes and his students at Columbia University and by Joseph Weber at the University of Maryland. The first masers were followed by speculation about how to extend the amplification principles to light. In 1958, Townes, together with Arthur L. Schawlow, explored the requirements in a theoretical paper. They stated that, in principle, a laser could be constructed; they went on to describe its features. It would employ a technique called optical pumping to excite the atoms. (Optical pumping had been developed by Alfred Kastler several years earlier to study the excited states of atoms; he won the 1966 Nobel Prize in Physics for his efforts.) Schawlow and Townes added, however, that it would be difficult to make a laser in practice, because the energy required for optical pumping was greater than could be obtained from lamps then available. Nevertheless, Theodore Harold Maiman, at the Hughes Research Laboratories, designed apparatus to provide more energy than had been thought possible. In 1960, he constructed the first laser in the United States.

The material of which the laser is made is of prime importance; it must be one in which the atoms' excited state lasts long enough for many excited atoms to accumulate. The next phases of laser action—stimulation and amplification—are engineering problems: how to construct the laser from the selected material.

It is a property of stimulated emission that stimulated light waves will be aligned exactly, crest to crest, trough to trough, and with respect to direction, with the radiation that does the stimulating. From the assemblage of excited atoms, one atom returns to its ground state, emitting light. That light hits one of the other excited atoms and stimulates it to fall to *its* ground state and emit light; stimulating and stimulated light are exactly in step. The light from these two atoms hits other excited atoms, stimulates them to emit in step, and the light from these stimulates still more atoms, until that first atom that returned to its ground state has produced a cascade.

If, while the light from the first atom is being amplified in this coherent fashion, another atom falls and emits in a different direction, its light will be amplified also, but will have a disturbing effect because of its lack of coherence with the light initiated by the first atom. The disturbing light must be eliminated. Engineering comes into play at this point. Maiman's laser, a single crystal of synthetic pink ruby, was machined to form a cylindrical rod about 4 centimeters long and 0.5 centimeter across. The ends, polished flat and made parallel to within about a millionth of a centimeter, were coated with silver to make them mirrors.

If the first atom emitted light in a direction parallel to the length of the cylinder, all the light stimulated by that initial light would travel along the length of the cylinder. At the end of the cylinder, the mirror there would reflect the light back along the length to stimulate more light in the same direction. All the light would hit the mirror at the other end, be reflected back, stimulate more light, all in the same direction and, thus, steadily build up an increasing intensity of light.

If the disturbing atom emits light in a direction other than parallel to the length of the cylinder, either immediately or after a few reflections at the mirrors, the disturbing light would exit through the curved nonreflecting walls of the cylinder. The result is that no light, except that traveling along the length of the cylinder, builds up in intensity (is amplified). If the mirror at one end of the cylinder is constructed to let through a fraction of the light, the beam will emerge straight ahead with almost no spread.

To produce the initial excitation, which Schawlow and Townes believed could not be achieved with lamps available at that time, Maiman used a lamp similar to those used by photographers, which emitted an enormous burst of ordinary light in a fraction of a second. His lamp, helical in shape, was wrapped around his ruby rod, so that as much of the exciting light as possible would reach the rod. The lamp was connected to a large bank of condensers carrying a tremendous electrical charge, which produced sufficient energy to excite the atoms of the ruby to lase.

In the Soviet Union, F. A. Butayeva and V. A. Fabrikant amplified light in 1957, using mercury; however, their work was not published for two years and was published in a memorial volume (not a scientific journal) to a scientist little known outside his country. The work of the Soviet scientists, therefore, received virtually no attention in the Western world. Yet, the 1964 Nobel Prize in Physics, recognizing those who had formulated the fundamental principles, was awarded to Basov, Prokhorov, and Townes.

Impact of Event

When the laser was introduced, it broke all records for immediacy of impact. In the eighteen months following Maiman's announcement that he had succeeded in producing a working laser, about four hundred companies and several government agencies embarked on similar work involving lasers. Activity centered on searching for new materials from which to construct lasers—solid, liquid, and gaseous—and on improving existing lasers. New materials were superior to the ruby because they did not require as much energy for excitation; others provided light of a different color from the characteristic red of the ruby. Substitutes were found for the metal end mirrors, which burned up after a few bursts of laser light. Effort was devoted also to exploring applications of lasers; much of the effort was directed toward the use of lasers in communications. Because of the extremely high frequency of visible light, a single laser beam had more information-carrying capacity than all the radio, television, and other communications channels in existence. At the same time, there was equal activity in publicizing the near-miraculous potentialities of the device, in applications covering the spectrum from death rays to sight-saving operations. A popular film in the James Bond series, *Goldfinger* (1964), had the hero under threat of being sliced in half by a laser beam—an impossibility at the time the film was made because of the low power output of the early lasers.

In the first decade after Maiman's laser, there was some disappointment. Lasers were used with much success in some areas of medicine, such as repairing detached retinas, and in scientific applications, particularly in connection with standards— the speed of light had been measured with great accuracy, as was the distance to the moon—but communications proved an area difficult for the laser to conquer. The difficulty was that light, including laser light, is scattered by clouds and fog. By 1990, however, partly because of advances in other fields, essentially all of the laser's promise had been fulfilled, including the death ray and James Bond's slicer. The new field of fiber optics had produced light pipes, which solved communications problems; in medicine, laser surgery took off from the modest welding of detached retinas. As other fields arose and progressed, the laser found its place in technologies not envisioned at the time of the first laser; for example, lasers are found in computer printers, in compact disc players, and even in former president Ronald Reagan's controversial "Star Wars" program.

Bibliography

Bertolotti, M. *Masers and Lasers: An Historical Approach*. Bristol, England: Adam Hilger, 1983. Gives a detailed discussion on the development of the laser and maser. Also discusses work being conducted at the same time in the Soviet Union. Written for those with a background in physics.

Hecht, Jeff, and Dick Teresi. *Laser: Supertool of the Eighties*. New York: Ticknor & Fields, 1982. Includes a discussion of the use of lasers in medicine, publishing, the arts, communications, energy production, and warfare. Contains a section on the history of the laser. For a wide audience.

Lasers and Light: Readings from Scientific American. Introductions by Arthur L. Schawlow. San Francisco: W. H. Freeman, 1969. This is a fine compendium of articles, written by distinguished scientists, on subjects that provide a background for understanding lasers or that elaborate on topics, such as optical pumping. The first section, "Light," contains an article on how light interacts with matter, another on how light is analyzed. There is a section on the chemical and biological effects of light, an article on the maser, and an article on fiber optics. Two sections are devoted to lasers. The collection in its entirety makes an interesting, entertaining, informative package for those with an interest in lasers.

Schawlow, Arthur L. "Advances in Optical Masers." In *Lasers and Light: Readings from Scientific American*. San Francisco: W. H. Freeman, 1969, and in *Scientific American* (July, 1963). This article relates, as its title states, the advances made in the approximately two years following the construction of the first laser.

_____. "Optical Masers." In *Lasers and Light: Readings from Scientific American*. San Francisco: W. H. Freeman, 1969, and in *Scientific American* (June, 1961). This early article written for the general public by the coinventor of the laser is perhaps the best on this level. It is well written, nicely illustrated, and the explanations are clear and understandable.

Grace Marmor Spruch

Cross-References

Gabor Develops the Basic Concept of Holography (1947), p. 1288; Lasers Are Used in Eye Surgery for the First Time (1962), p. 1714; Optical Pulses Shorter than One-Trillionth of a Second Are Produced (1974), p. 2020; Tunable, Continuous Wave Visible Lasers Are Developed (1974), p. 2025; The First Commercial Test of Fiber Optic Telecommunications Is Conducted (1977), p. 2078; Compact Disc Players Are Introduced (1982), p. 2200; Optical Disks for the Storage of Computer Data Are Introduced (1984), p. 2262.

ECHO, THE FIRST PASSIVE COMMUNICATIONS SATELLITE, IS LAUNCHED

Category of event: Space and aviation
Time: August 12, 1960
Locale: Cape Canaveral, Florida

The world's first passive communications satellite was launched, paving the way for the many communications satellites that now circle the globe

Principal personages:
> WILLIAM J. O'SULLIVAN, JR., an aeronautical engineer at the National Advisory Committee for Aeronautics
> JOHN R. PIERCE (1910-?), a researcher at Bell Telephone Laboratories

Summary of Event

On August 12, 1960, the Echo I passive communications satellite was launched from Cape Canaveral (later Cape Kennedy), Florida, atop a Delta Thor launch vehicle. Then United States president Dwight D. Eisenhower spoke via a prerecorded message, which was conveyed from the National Aeronautics and Space Administration (NASA) communications facility at Goldstone, California, to Holmdel, New Jersey. The first-ever two-way message was sent the next day, August 13, between Richardson, Texas, and Cedar Rapids, Iowa. The world's first reported picture transmission took place on August 19, this time originating at Cedar Rapids, Iowa, and received in Richardson, Texas. With these amazing technological advances, Echo I opened a new era of world communications.

The Echo program developed initially from a project on air density run by the National Advisory Committee on Aeronautics (NACA, later to become NASA), in response to the International Geophysical Year (IGY). (The IGY was an international program to increase knowledge about the earth and its environment.) William J. O'Sullivan, Jr., of the NACA Langley Research Facility, had studied prospective projects designed to measure the air density of the atmosphere and proposed a large, inflatable balloon to detect the aerodynamic drag. Although two launches with an Echo-type balloon were attempted, launch-vehicle failures plagued the efforts. In further study, O'Sullivan decided that radio beacons, attached to the balloon, would allow tracking during a greater period of each orbit. A reflector of some type, bouncing signals back to the transmitter, could increase the tracking to an almost continual basis, he concluded. After that, it followed simply that the balloon could bounce back communications signals, and the concept of Echo I was born. Two new requirements became necessary: The balloon had to be increased in size and made more reflective.

John R. Pierce, of Bell Telephone Laboratories, had considered the concept of a passive communications satellite since 1955. (A passive satellite is one that simply bounces signals back to Earth. An active communications satellite receives and transmits.) As early as April, 1958, a small, 3.66-meter inflatable sphere was deployed, launched by a Nike-Cajun launch vehicle. Balloon satellites were launched twice more in 1958, one in May, still only 4.1 kilograms, but reaching a height of 80 kilometers. The second, on October 22, was called Explorer 6 (not related to the later Explorer program). It was only 3.66 meters in diameter and did not achieve the correct orbit.

By 1959, Bell Telephone Laboratories and NACA scientists were working jointly on the Echo project. NACA scientists at Langley worked on three developmental projects for the Echo: a sufficiently reflective material, a mode of inflating the balloon, and a delivery cannister. E. I. du Pont supplied the material, an aluminized Mylar film 0.5 millimeter in thickness. The G. T. Schjeldahl Company fitted together the 82 gores of material to form the globe, which was 30.48 meters in diameter. The sublimating medium (a medium that goes from solid to gas without going through a liquid phase) was chosen: benzoic acid. The cannister was made of metal, impregnated with plastic. This spherical container was constructed by Kaiser-Fleetwing.

A 0.76-meter balloon was launched aboard a Vanguard launch vehicle, but the Vanguard failed. Between April and September, 1959, Langley personnel constructed a 30.48-meter inflatable sphere, destined for another deployment. Project Shotput, lofted by a Sergeant-Delta launch vehicle on October 28, flew to 400 kilometers before the sphere ruptured. The second Project Shotput was launched on January 16, 1960, with the same launch vehicle, and again achieved 400 kilometers in height before the cannister ruptured. A bit more than a month later, on February 27, a third Shotput flight resulted in a radio transmission originating in Holmdel, New Jersey, and sent to Round Hill, Massachusetts. Once again the sphere ruptured. On April 1, 1960, the by now uniform-sized sphere (30.48 meters) was successfully launched and inflated at 380 kilometers in altitude. Launch vehicle malfunction, this time by a Thor-Delta, caused the failure of the Echo A 10 on May 13, destroying the spacecraft upon reentry when the attitude control jets on the second stage failed. Finally, on August 12, Echo I was launched and fully deployed. The metal cannister was injected into orbit after deployment of the balloon, as planned. For four and a half months, the satellite was utilized for experimentation by the Jet Propulsion Laboratories (JPL) in California and Bell Telephone Laboratories. Despite damage from micrometeoroid particles (minute particles in space), the Echo I was still useful for communications experiments, including PAGEOS I, which garnered geodetic information such as mapping data. The programmed cost for the entire Echo I project was $21,998,000. Echo I reentered the earth's atmosphere on May 24, 1968.

Echo I was a balloon of 30.5 meters in diameter, constructed of bright silver aluminum-covered Mylar polyester film and weighing 76 kilograms. It was folded into the gray, magnesium cannister, which measured 0.67 meter in diameter and weighed almost 11 kilograms. Residual air, benzoic acid, and anthraquinone were used to inflate the giant sphere. The extremely bright surface of the balloon reflected 98 percent of the signals transmitted at 20,000 megacycles. Two radio beacons, each weighing 312 grams, were each powered by five nickel-cadmium batteries, in turn powered by seventy solar cells per beacon. These radio beacons were used for survey and tracking purposes. The two beacons were attached to 25-centimeter disks that were mounted on opposite sides of the balloon. A small whip antenna was provided for each beacon.

The Delta launch vehicle carried three stages, with a gross liftoff weight of approximately 50,817 kilograms. The entire vehicle stood 28 meters tall, and had a diameter of almost 2.5 meters. The solid fuel first-stage Thor booster was modified for the Echo project and delivered 333,708 newtons of thrust. Liquid propellant powered the second-stage rocket engine, with 1,685 newtons of thrust. Powered by the AJ 10 142 engine, this stage was 0.8 meter in diameter. The radio command guidance and the flight controller were contained within the second stage. The third stage, which injected the cannister into orbit, was an Altair solid fuel rocket power plant. Injection was achieved with 674 newtons of thrust during forty seconds of firing. The cannister separated with spring action, freeing the sphere, which was then inflated.

Two more Echo I satellites were launched during 1962. Echo (Big Shot 1) was launched on January 15, and Echo (Big Shot 2) on July 18. Plans for further Echo-type satellites were dropped as active communications satellite technology was developed.

Impact of Event

Probably the most immediate impact of the Echo I program was the visual proof of the utilization of space for peaceful purposes. Echo I could be seen from Earth and proved to be an impetus to the exploration of space, exciting the interest of the world and the pride of the American public.

The success of Echo I gave birth to six different types of communications satellites between 1962 and 1963. American Telephone and Telegraph developed the low-altitude, random-orbit Telstar. Hughes Aircraft put a high-altitude, stable-orbiting Syncom into the skies. Project Relay was an active repeating satellite, built by Radio Corporation of America. The NASA Rebound program was based on the Echo satellite itself but was soon abandoned for more advanced technology. Project Advent, a Department of Defense program, utilized an active repeater, developed by Bendix. A sixth, vastly different defense program conceived of placing a mass of small copper wires into an equatorial orbit, forming a belt.

President Eisenhower foresaw a need for legislation concerning the ownership and operation of space communications satellites. At the end of his term of office, he set early guidelines for this new age of space, just prior to the inauguration of incoming president John F. Kennedy. The ownership of devices designed by a private company, under contract to government entities such as NASA, came under scrutiny. President Kennedy advanced what amounted to the first space legislation on February 7, 1962, when he made a proposal to Congress that would establish free enterprise in space. The proposal would permit private companies to own and operate satellites and ground stations. A private corporation would be set up by the government, with both private-sector and corporate ownership. A long legislative battle ensued, with communications companies lobbying strongly for their interests and with many legislators concerned about an uncontrollable monopoly.

Space exploration received a hefty boost, because a large launch vehicle, necessary to put larger, heavier satellites into orbit, became a higher priority. The end result was the development of heavy launch vehicles such as the Saturn, which put astronauts on the Moon.

Probably the most long-lasting result of Echo I was the increased cooperation and communication among nations. Exchanges in culture via television broadcasts, language modification, and licensing agreements to handle the increased demand on the frequencies used in space communications systems (between 1,000 and 20,000 megacycles) are three examples of the aftereffects of Echo. These effects helped spur cooperative space efforts such as the Apollo-Soyuz joint American-Soviet mission. Senator Warren Magnuson from Washington stated in 1961: "The communications satellite, in my opinion, can be the most valuable instrument of good will and understanding in the history of the world."

Bibliography

Caprara, Giovanni. *The Complete Encyclopedia of Space Probes and Satellites*. New York: Crown, 1986. A beautifully illustrated, oversized book. Chapters are arranged by type of satellite. A pleasure to use.

Cox, Donald W. *The Space Race: From Sputnik to Apollo . . . and Beyond!* Philadelphia: Chilton Co., 1962. A political history of the major space events and of their impact on the international scene. Technical details are at a minimum. College-level reading.

Ezell, Linda Newman. *NASA Historical Data Book*. Vol. 2, *Programs and Projects, 1958-1968*. NASA SP-4012. Washington, D.C.: Government Printing Office, 1988. A comprehensive study of all the NASA programs during a critical decade in space development.

Ley, Willy. *Rockets, Missiles, and Space Travel*. Rev. ed. New York: Viking, 1958. Written by one of the most prolific writers on space and space travel. Gives a layperson's view of the development of rocketry and satellites as well as understandable explanations of satellite orbitry.

Rosenthal, Alfred. *Satellite Handbook*. Greenbelt, Md.: NASA/Goddard Space Flight Center, 1981. A complete listing of NASA space missions between 1958 and 1980. Gives launch vehicle and spacecraft description, project objectives, spacecraft payload, test results, and major participants.

Ellen F. Mitchum

Cross-References

Sputnik 1, the First Artificial Satellite, Is Launched (1957), p. 1545; The United

States Launches Its First Orbiting Satellite, Explorer 1 (1958), p. 1583; Tiros 1 Becomes the First Experimental Weather Reconnaissance Satellite (1960), p. 1667; Telstar, the First Commercial Communications Satellite, Relays Live Transatlantic Television Pictures (1962), p. 1728; The First Tracking and Data-Relay Satellite System Opens a New Era in Space Communications (1983), p. 2245.

HORSFALL ANNOUNCES THAT CANCER RESULTS FROM ALTERATIONS IN THE DNA OF CELLS

Category of event: Medicine
Time: 1961
Locale: Sloan-Kettering Institute for Cancer Research, New York

Horsfall's discovery that all cancer is attributable to alterations in the nucleic acids of cells provided a unifying concept regarding the genesis of cancer

Principal personages:

FRANK L. HORSFALL, JR. (1906-1971), a brilliant clinician, virologist, and president and director of the Sloan-Kettering Institute for Cancer Research

MACLYN MCCARTY (1911-   ), a research scientist at Rockefeller University and Horsfall's colleague, who discovered that genes are composed of DNA

Summary of Event

The history of a search for the genesis of cancer, according to Frank Horsfall, began with the first demonstration that factors such as X rays, certain organic chemicals, or viruses could induce the disease. While these findings were reported in the early 1900's, in relation to a more contemporary concept of cancer, the search began much later. In 1944, researchers Avery MacLeod and Maclyn McCarty announced that deoxyribonucleic acid (DNA) induced transformation of pneumococcal (bacteria) types, thus providing the first decisive evidence that nucleic acids possess biological activity. This discovery initiated a revolution in the biological sciences and eventually led to the demonstration that nucleic acids provide the chemical counterparts of the gene of heredity. Broad acceptance of the central and controlling role of nucleic acids, however, had occurred in the late 1950's, only a few years before Horsfall's discovery.

The demonstration of the chemical nature of the transforming principle not only initiated studies on the nature and functions of nucleic acids but also provided the first example of a guided and directed mutation with precisely predictable features. The "heritance" (permanent and irreversible change) of an acquired character was no longer a controversial and unsubstantiated theory. It was found, for example, that bacterial cells produced a new type of capsular polysaccharide when new genes were introduced in the form of nucleic acids derived from different bacterial cells. The new characteristic so acquired continued to appear in their daughter cells; thus, the change was enduring and inherited. Also, bacterial cells transformed in type by such nucleic acids became capable of producing the same nucleic acid, which could in turn transform other bacterial cells in an identical manner. Both the new character and its new genetic basis were handed down from one cell to another in enduring continuity.

Besides marking the beginning of a new era in biological thought, the implications of this new concept soon became apparent to physical scientists. Consequently, the fields of nucleic acid chemistry, genetics, virology, and immunology were being largely rewritten. The gap between the smallest unit accessible to biologists—a virus particle—and the largest unit available to biochemists—a protein or nucleic acid macromolecule—had been bridged. While the absolute distance was not great, it took much time to span. In relation to the natural history of humans, Horsfall believed that the implications of this new knowledge had as great a potential for a fuller understanding of the genesis of malignant tumors, behavioral disorders, and degenerative processes as it did for metabolic aberrations, endocrine dysfunctions, and infectious processes.

Historically, knowledge of cause has been the most important factor in the development of specific treatment and effective prevention. In Horsfall's time, the remarkable advances in the control of various infectious diseases would have been impossible without a knowledge of the causes of these diseases. He believed that one of the most pressing questions in cancer research was discovering the necessary and sufficient causes of the disease.

During the period of his discovery, research studies on the causes of cancer consisted of the following: Radiant energy at certain wavelengths and in certain quantities, as in X rays and ultraviolet light; organic chemical compounds of special types, such as some of those present in coal tar; and a large number of animal viruses of numerous species. Despite the multiplicity of factors that were known to be capable of inducing cancerous changes in cells, Horsfall believed it probable that the necessary and sufficient alterations in the cell itself were similar, if not identical, in every case. Significant to the development of this general concept was the discovery that the inducing factor has relevance to cancerous changes in cells only at their inception. Once the properties that characterize cancer cells appeared, the cells were observed to produce more cells with similar properties during growth and division, as is the case with various bacterial strains such as pneumococci, lysogenic bacteria, or toxigenic diphtheria bacilli. Horsfall observed that this process could continue indefinitely under laboratory conditions. In cell cultures, the cancerous alteration, once it first appeared, continued to characterize the cell's offspring in the absence of the inducing factor that initiated the change. Thus, Horsfall realized that the new characteristics of the cell were enduring and transmissible in biological continuity; it seemed likely to him that they resulted from changes produced in the genetic machinery (DNA) of the cell.

Because the new characteristics could be made to appear through the influence of environmental factors, he believed that these characteristics were acquired; because the new characteristics were transmissible in series in the absence of the initiating factor, he believed that they were heritable. Thus, Horsfall assumed that cancer represented one more example of acquired characters at the level of the individual cell;

the only significant way in which it differed from the bacterial examples cited was that cancer involved the cells of animals, including humans. In this unifying concept of the genesis of cancer, Horsfall observed that virus-induced cancers do not differ in any recognizable feature from those of similar type occurring in humans. Like human cancers, virus-induced cancers grow in an uncontrolled manner, produce metastases (transformations), and eventually lead to the death of the host.

When normal cells are converted to cancer cells by viruses, new properties appear that are expressed commonly as alterations in cell form, in growth rate, in metabolism, and in chromosome pattern or number. The cancerous change in cells has the hallmarks of a change in genetic make-up—that is, in gene complement—and so were considered to have formal correspondence to a mutation. Permanent hereditary changes (mutations) induced by viruses were well known in bacteria and in certain flowering plants. That such changes could also be produced in animal cells seemed probable to Horsfall, from his work with cancer-inducing viruses.

Horsfall observed that cancer could be induced both in animals and humans by radiant energy at certain wavelengths and intensities. Such radiant energy markedly increased the frequency and occurrence of a number of mutations and was known to produce permanent and transmissible alterations in the genetic apparatus. The effects of X rays on chromosomes and even on the fine structure of nucleic acids was only beginning to be understood. Similarly, several organic chemical compounds of special character were found to be mutagenic and induce cancers in animals or humans. As with the alterations produced by X rays or viruses, the new characters acquired by cells exposed sufficiently to such compounds persisted and were discovered to be transmitted from cell to cell in continuing series. Thus, in all the examples cited, the evidence indicated that the effects of the various cancer-inducing factors were similar and attributable to alterations produced in the nucleic acids (DNA) that control the genetic machinery.

Impact of Event

The revolution in biology implied much for the understanding of the genesis of cancer (oncogenesis). With Horsfall's announcement, an accumulation of seemingly unrelated details began to come together in a meaningful way and eventually rested upon a framework of principles that was solidly based. Horsfall's belief that cancers in general could represent the heritance of acquired characters at the cellular level provided a concept that embraced all the types of cancer cells that had been previously studied. His work ultimately provided a basis for research on the necessary and sufficient causes of malignant growth.

Horsfall's discovery that nucleic acids possess biological activity, that they orient and direct genetic properties, has raised the possibility that they represent the chemical counterparts of biological genes. Also, his detailed investigation of viruses has been of major importance to advancement of knowledge in this field and has served to unify the physical and the biological sciences. The new concepts that have developed in molecular biology have had a great impact on the tactics and strategy of cancer research. The discovery that a molecule can reproduce itself in a biological environment, that it carries in its chemical structure vast amounts of coded information, and by virtue of chemical necessity, controls the synthesis of its complementary partner with such precision that mistake, or mutation, occurs less than one in a million replications was not only impressive but also far-reaching.

During his lifetime, Horsfall predicted what the future impact of his discoveries might be. On the basis of his knowledge of the chemical counterpart of genes, he believed that the fine structure of the nucleic acids of cancer cells would not be found to be identical with that of normal cells. To explain such a continuing genetic alteration, there seemed to be only two acceptable hypotheses: It may be attributable either to a mutation, a copying mistake in nucleic acid replication, or to the introduction of new genetic material, as from a virus, into the hereditary apparatus of the cell.

In the years since Horsfall's predictions, great strides have been made in discovering the link between chromosomal abnormality and cancer. The nucleic acids of cancer cells were found to be different from cancer cells. Regarding his two hypotheses, however, rather than being an either-or question, researchers have learned that some cancers are caused by mutations and the introduction of new genetic material. Four categories of cancers have been found to arise, for example, from chromosomal abnormalities: first, cancers arising from the inherent instability of the genetic material and the unavoidable exposure to a certain low level of mutagens in the environment (these cancers can never be eradicated); second, tumors that result from mutagenic exposure in excess of the baseline level (the person's constitutional capacity to handle mutagens may be sufficient to deal with the background load but is unable to cope with the additional requirements); third, cancers that result from a relative genetic insufficiency to tolerate carcinogen exposure (the constitutional ability to respond is below normal capacity); finally, those cancers in which the environmental influence seem to be insignificant.

Bibliography

Comings, David E. "A General Theory of Carcinogenesis." *Proceedings of the National Academy of Sciences* 70 (1973): 3324-3328. While there are many theories about what causes cancer, Comings attempts to unify all the current concepts about the biology of cancer and cell transformation into a general hypothesis, which may have some relevance to mechanisms of carcinogenesis. Although somewhat technical, this article is useful in providing a general overview of some of the strides made in a unified theory of carcinogenesis since Horsfall.

Hirst, George K. "Frank Lappin Horsfall, Jr." In *Biographical Memoirs of the National Academy of Sciences* 50 (1979): 233-267. This useful article provides the most complete biographical data available on Horsfall's life; although it does not describe the scientist's research in any depth, it does offer the reader a glimpse into the major discoveries. Also includes a complete bibliography of Horsfall's publications.

Horsfall, Frank. "Current Concepts of Cancer." *Canadian Medical Association Journal* 89 (1963): 1224-1229. Horsfall describes his work on the genetic transfer of information in cancer cells in the context of contemporary theories of the origin of cancer. Accessible to the layperson, the article provides an interesting picture of how Horsfall's discovery was built upon the relationship of DNA to cancer.

_____. "Heritance of Acquired Characters." *Science* 136 (1962): 472-476. Horsfall puts forth his unifying concept on the genesis of cancer. He gives a historical introduction to the theory and discusses several possible applications of this theory to research on cancer-inducing viruses.

_____. "On the Unity of the Sciences." *Science* 133 (1961): 1059-1060. While Horsfall does not mention his own work specifically, he discusses the interactions among the physical and biological sciences and shows their unification as a progressive process. Interesting and informative article.

Genevieve Slomski

Cross-References

Rous Discovers That Some Cancers Are Caused by Viruses (1910), p. 459; Papanicolaou Develops the Pap Test for Diagnosing Uterine Cancer (1928), p. 864; Avery, MacLeod, and McCarty Determine That DNA Carries Hereditary Information (1943), p. 1203; Watson and Crick Develop the Double-Helix Model for DNA (1951), p. 1406; A Gene That Can Suppress the Cancer Retinoblastoma Is Discovered (1986), p. 2331.

NIRENBERG INVENTS AN EXPERIMENTAL TECHNIQUE THAT CRACKS THE GENETIC CODE

Category of event: Biology
Time: 1961
Locale: National Institutes of Health, Bethesda, Maryland

Nirenberg unraveled the genetic coding problem, developing a breakthrough experimental method

Principal personages:

MARSHALL W. NIRENBERG (1927-   ), the American biochemist who developed the experimental technique that elucidated the genetic code and cowinner of the 1968 Nobel Prize in Physiology or Medicine

J. H. MATTHAEI, a postdoctoral fellow from Germany who collaborated in the code-cracking research

FRANCIS CRICK (1916-   ), the British biologist who, together with James D. Watson, discovered the structure of DNA; cowinner of the 1962 Nobel Prize in Physiology or Medicine

GEORGE GAMOW (1904-1968), the Russian theoretical physicist and cosmologist who defined the nature of the coding problem and proposed some early (incorrect) solutions

MARIANNE GRUNBERG-MANAGO, a French biochemist who discovered an enzyme that could be used to produce synthetic RNA with known base sequences

RICHARD E. MARSHALL, an American biochemist who helped establish the theory that the genetic code is essentially the same in all living species

Summary of Event

Nucleic acids somehow carry the blueprint for the building of proteins; this had been confirmed by 1944 and accepted conclusively by 1952. Nevertheless, it took James D. Watson and Francis Crick's discovery of the molecular structure of deoxyribonucleic acid (DNA), in 1953, to suggest how the necessary processes of information storage, replication, and transmission might occur. Their model served to fix the course of subsequent research that would eventually lead to a deciphering of the genetic code and an understanding of the relation between protein and the genetic material.

Proteins make up most cellular structures and also serve as catalysts for almost all chemical reactions in living organisms. Proteins are polymers (molecular chains composed of similar chemical units) that are made of amino acids, of which there are twenty main types. The linear sequence of amino acids is the primary structure of the protein, and their order causes the molecule to fold into a three-dimensional form. The final shape of the molecule is the most important factor in determining its function; therefore, proteins are direct products of the primary sequence of amino acids. DNA is also a polymer, but it is composed of four different types of links, called nucleotides, or bases, which are attached to a backbone of alternating phosphate and sugar groups. Two chains usually intertwine together in the characteristic double-helical form so that the bases pair up in a regular fashion. There are four major types of bases, called adenine (A), guanine (G), thymine (T), and cytosine (C); they join by hydrogen bonds so that A's always pair with T's, and G's always pair with C's. Ribonucleic acid (RNA) has a similar structure, but uracil (U) replaces thymine.

In 1953, George Gamow, a theoretical physicist who had been inspired by the Watson-Crick DNA model, came up with an idea that would define the discussion of the coding problem. Noting the four-base linear structure of DNA and the linear primary structure of proteins, he theorized that the order of the former completely determined the latter, rather like a template, and so reasoned that the problem was to figure out how the four-letter "alphabet" of nucleic acid bases could be formed into "words" that would translate into the twenty-letter alphabet of amino acids. If the words were one letter long, then four nucleotides could obviously code only for four amino acids. Two-letter sequences could combine to get only sixteen. A three-letter sequence, which could allow sixty-four combinations, called "codons," was therefore the minimum needed to get the magic twenty amino acids. Together with his statement of the problem, published in *Nature* in 1954, Gamow proposed an ingenious three-letter solution, the "diamond" code, based upon what he took to be twenty types of diamond-shaped pockets (into which he thought the amino acids could fit) formed by the bases in the double-helix. This proposal spurred interest in the coding problem, and a flurry of theoretical work followed.

Gamow's diamond code, however, ran into immediate difficulties. There were mechanical and chemical problems; for example, the model required that protein production take place in the cell nucleus, whereas evidence suggested that this occurred in the cytoplasm, perhaps mediated in some way by RNA (as was later shown to be). Also, in order to fit the spacing of the diamonds to typical amino-acid spacing, the code had to be fully overlapping; that is, each code letter in a chain would be used in three codons in a row. This overlapping structure, however, ruled out certain sequences that were known to exist. A variety of other overlapping codes were suggested, but it was eventually shown to be impossible for a fully overlapping structure to work. If the code was nonoverlapping and was to be read as a series of triplets, then the problem of punctuation arose. Unless there was something that functioned like commas, there was no way for the cell to know where a triplet began. To avoid this problem, creative attempts were made to devise codes that included "nonsense" triplets (that is, ones that did not correspond to any amino acid), and there was some excitement when mathematical permutations of this approach were discovered that produced codes with exactly the magic number of twenty "sense" combinations. This approach, however, implied that DNA molecules in all species should have more or less the same composition; but as the data on this increased, it was seen that the ratio of A-T pairs and G-C pairs could vary tremendously. Another approach assumed that the combination of bases in a triplet and not their order was important, but mechanisms that might accomplish this seemed physically implausible. The theorists might have continued in this fashion, but numerological speculation was cut off abruptly when the key to the code was provided by an experimentalist.

In the summer of 1961, the Fifth International Congress of Biochemistry was held in Moscow. Crick was among the some six thousand participants as was Marshall W. Nirenberg, a young unknown researcher from the National Institutes of Health in Bethesda, Maryland. Nirenberg was slated to give a ten-minute talk, and the pre-printed abstract gave no hint of the discovery (which he had made after submitting the abstract) he would report. Crick, however, was alerted to the content of the paper and was so impressed that he invited Nirenberg to read it again at a much larger session over which he was to preside. Crick recalls that the audience was "startled" and "electrified" by the report; Nirenberg had shown experimentally that the triplet UUU was a codon for the amino acid phenylalanine; the first word of the genetic code had been translated.

Nirenberg and his associate J. H. Matthaei had discovered how to add an RNA message to a test-tube system that synthesized proteins and how to find out what amino acid was synthesized by it. The technique involved extracting the protein synthesis machinery (ribosomes, messenger RNA, and enzymes) from *Escherichia coli*, the bacillus that inhabits the human gut. Such extracts, when given an energy source such as adenosine triphosphate (ATP), are called "cell-free systems" and are able to incorporate amino acids into protein. Cell-free systems had been developed by other researchers several years earlier but were unreliable because of rapid disintegration of the enzymes and messenger RNA. Nirenberg and Matthaei were able to increase stability by adding a chemical that allowed them to freeze the system for storage without loss of activity. The twenty amino acids, radioactively labeled with carbon 14, were added to the system. When these ingredients were mixed, only a very little incorporation of amino acid into protein occurred, as revealed by measurements of radioactivity. Next, the artificial RNA message was added, a sequence consisting entirely of uracil bases. (The process of getting a synthetic RNA of known base sequence had been developed by Marianne Grunberg-Manago. In 1955, Severo Ochoa, following Grunberg-Manago's discovery, developed the enzyme, polynucleotide phosphorylase, which catalyzes such synthesis.) This produced an eight-hundred-fold increase in the radioactivity level; amino acid had been incorporated into protein. Subsequent tests with different mixtures containing only one radioactive amino acid at a time revealed that it was phenylalanine.

Impact of Event

After Nirenberg's discovery in 1961, work proceeded rapidly. By the following year, Crick's laboratory had confirmed by genetic studies that the code was indeed a triplet code. Nirenberg, Ochoa, Grunberg-Manago, and other researchers had correctly decoded thirty-five of the triplets by 1963. A refined trinucleotide binding test developed in Nirenberg's laboratory increased the number to fifty, and by 1966 all but three of the sixty-four possible triplets had been assigned to their corresponding amino acid; most had been reconfirmed in different laboratories by more than one experimental method. The final three triplets, UAA, UAG, and UGA, were revealed to be chain terminators—punctuation that specified the end of an amino acid "sentence"—and this brought the coding problem, as it was originally conceived, to a final solution.

Answers, however, always generate more questions. It had been shown in 1944 by Oswald Avery and his colleagues that DNA was the genetic material among almost all species of organisms, but it was not known if the genetic code was universal. Some of the theoretical arguments that had been made before Nirenberg's breakthrough had relied upon the assumption of universality, based upon the idea that physical and chemical properties of the twenty amino acids would constrain possible codon assignments. After it was learned that "suppressor" mutations can change a codon reading, universality could no longer be taken for granted. Experimental work on the question, however, has for the most part confirmed the code's universality. Richard E. Marshall, C. Thomas Caskey, and Nirenberg performed the most extensive research, and their results were published in 1967 in *Science*. Making use of the trinucleotide-binding technique, they showed that cell-free preparations from a bacterium (*E. coli*), a mammal (guinea pig), and an amphibian (toad) gave almost identical results for most of the fifty different RNA codons tested. Confirming evidence was quickly obtained in studies using various techniques and a wide variety of organisms and cell types, for example, tobacco mosaic virus, plant coat proteins, rat liver, and human hemoglobins. A very few exceptions have been found, particularly in mitochondria, but these are best regarded as evolutionary deviations from a single standard code.

From a theoretical standpoint, the near universality of the code supports the hypothesis that all forms of life on Earth are related to one another by common evolution; at some point very early in the evolution of life, a single chemistry emerged as adaptively successful and all subsequent variation has built upon that structure. From the standpoint of applied science, the universality of the code simplifies the technology of bioengineering, since it allows bits of DNA from one organism to be spliced into that of another organism. The impact of this technology, which was made possible by building upon the sorts of techniques developed to elucidate the code and its related chemical mechanisms, is only beginning to be felt, and it has given rise to new legal and ethical problems that have yet to be resolved.

Bibliography

Crick, Francis. *What Mad Pursuit: A Personal View of Scientific Discovery.* New York: Basic Books, 1988. Crick's intellectual autobiography is a highly readable history of the key events in the investigation of the structure of DNA and the genetic code. Chapters 8 through 12 describe, from Crick's point of view, the nature of the coding problem and the research conducted on the problem. An appendix gives a clear introduction to the basic molecular mechanisms needed for an understanding of genetics, and a second appendix gives the complete code.

Haseltine, William A. "The Genetic Code." In *The Microverse*, edited by Byron Preiss and William R. Alschuler. New York: Bantam Books, 1989. Written as an approachable introduction for the layperson, this is a good first source for an overview of the current state of the art in molecular genetics. Of particular interest is the description of advances in understanding of genetic mechanisms that have occurred since the breaking of the code, especially the relevance of genetics to cancer and AIDS research.

Lappé, Marc. *Broken Code: The Exploitation of DNA*. San Francisco: Sierra Club Books, 1984. Outlines advances following the breaking of the code that resulted in recombinant DNA (rDNA) technology, but the focus of the book is on the ethical ramifications of genetic engineering as they have been debated in the public and political arenas. The book contains an index, glossary of terms, bibliographical references following each chapter, and useful appendices.

Lewin, Benjamin. *Genes III*. 3d ed. New York: John Wiley & Sons, 1987. A popular introductory college-level textbook on the molecular biological basis of genetics. Clear explanations are given of the current view on key genetic concepts and biomolecular mechanisms. A complete glossary defines all technical terminology, and there is an exhaustive index.

Nirenberg, Marshall W. "The Genetic Code: II." *Scientific American*, March, 1963, 80-94. Describes the technique Nirenberg used to match nucleotide triplets to the amino acid they code for. Some material has been superseded. Interesting to compare this article with the ones by Francis Crick that appeared in *Scientific American* in October, 1962 ("The Genetic Code") and October, 1966 ("The Genetic Code: III") to get a sense of how quickly the field developed.

Ycas, M. *The Biological Code*. Amsterdam: North-Holland, 1969. Although somewhat technical in orientation this book should nevertheless be accessible to a dedicated reader; however, because so much has been learned since it was published, it should not be consulted for timely material. Useful for its explanations of important experimental work and its extensive bibliography. Contains name and subject indexes.

Robert T. Pennock

Cross-References

Hopkins Discovers Tryptophan, an Essential Amino Acid (1900), p. 46; Avery, MacLeod, and McCarty Determine That DNA Carries Hereditary Information (1943), p. 1203; Ochoa Creates Synthetic RNA (1950's), p. 1363; Watson and Crick Develop the Double-Helix Model for DNA (1951), p. 1406; Cohen and Boyer Develop Recombinant DNA Technology (1973), p. 1987; Berg, Gilbert, and Sanger Develop

Techniques for Genetic Engineering (1980), p. 2115; Murray and Szostak Create the First Artificial Chromosome (1983), p. 2251; A Genetically Engineered Vaccine for Hepatitis B Is Approved for Use (1986); p. 2326; A Gene That Can Suppress the Cancer Retinoblastoma Is Discovered (1986), p. 2331; The Search Continues for the Gene That Begins Male Development (1987), p. 2346.

GAGARIN BECOMES THE FIRST HUMAN
TO ORBIT EARTH

Category of event: Space and aviation
Time: April 12, 1961
Locale: Baikonur Cosmodrome at Leninsk, Soviet Union

Gagarin became the first human to orbit Earth, furthering the efforts of space exploration by the Soviet Union

Principal personage:
> YURI A. GAGARIN (1934-1968), a Soviet cosmonaut who became the first man in space

Summary of Event

Yuri A. Gagarin, born in Gzhatsk in the Smolensk Region of the Soviet Union, studied at the Saratov flight school, and eventually joined the Soviet Air Force in 1956. In 1959, Gagarin volunteered to be a cosmonaut, before a call was made for Air Force test pilots between the ages of twenty-five and thirty-five to volunteer. The initial screening for cosmonauts was made in October of 1959. Gagarin was chosen as one of the first twenty cosmonaut candidates on his twenty-sixth birthday. Not even his wife Valentina was allowed to know of the highly secretive project.

On March 14, 1960, the cosmonauts went into training. They were, at first, housed in a building at Khodynskoye Field at the Frunze Central Airfield. Lectures began with aviation medicine, but the twenty cosmonauts soon began to lose interest, and discussions were added on spacecraft design and orbital theory. Only six of the candidates were chosen for physical training, because of the limited training space and equipment. These men underwent survival training, jet flight piloting, parachuting, centrifuge and isolation chamber training, physical fitness exercises, and education in spacecraft design and function.

On April 3, 1959, official approval was given for a manned launch. Two men had been selected from the six who trained: Gherman Titov and Gagarin. A week later, on April 10, the two men were informed that Gagarin was to be the first man in space. Titov underwent all of the procedures leading up to the actual launch, however, in case Gagarin should be unable to fly.

Approval for flight leading to manned space travel was made as early as November, 1958. Design of Vostok 1 began in 1959. The design and manufacture of Vostok was done in a parallel manner. Thus it was that while the prototype was complete in March, 1959, the advanced design model was accomplished in May of 1960. The first landing test was performed during the early part of 1960. The design team was headed by Sergei Korolev, with Alexei Ivanov, Yevgeni Alexandrov, and Noraiv Sisakazan. When complete, the craft would contain 15,000 meters of electrical wiring, 240 valves, and 6,000 transistors.

The spacecraft, Vostok 1, was constructed in two parts: The upper part was a 2.5-meter sphere, weighted on one end with heat shielding. This added weight automatically tilted the sphere with the heavy end down, in preparation for the heat of reentry. The cosmonaut lay on the couch in this upper part, surrounded by three small windows, television cameras, film cameras, a two-way radio system, control panels, life-support systems, and food and water dispensers. Food and water were provided for ten days, as insurance against retrorocket failure. (The low orbit would naturally decay in ten days if the retrorockets did not take the spacecraft out of orbit.) Two antennas sat atop the capsule.

The lower portion of the spacecraft was the TDU-1 (Braking Engine Installation) retrorocket system. It had a forty-five-second ignition time and carried about 275 kilograms of fuel. Amine/nitrous oxide self-igniting propellant was used to produce 1,615 kilograms of thrust. Small round tanks of compressed air were attached to the area between the two parts of the spacecraft. The entire capsule, with cosmonaut payload, weighed 4,725 kilograms.

Unlike the American spacecraft, which are mounted vertically onto the launch pad, the Vostok 1 was mounted horizontally and raised, intact, to the vertical. The "A" rocket booster, with strap-on A-1 boosters, put the capsule into an orbital apogee of 327 kilometers and a perigee of 181 kilometers. The strap-on tanks fell away 119 seconds after launch. After 156 seconds, a protective shroud around the capsule was jettisoned. The booster core burned out after 300 seconds, and orbital insertion occurred at 676 seconds following launch.

The Vostok launch system differed greatly from the early American system. The cosmonaut was ejected with his seat from the capsule at 7,000 meters; he separated from the seat at 4,000 meters. Both the cosmonaut and the capsule descended by parachute. The capsule had a landing velocity of 10 meters per second, producing a possible 100 gravities of deceleration. The cosmonaut sustained half of the velocity, 5 meters per second. This ejection system was necessary because the descending combined weight would have required a huge parachute and probably another set of retrorockets to assist in a soft landing. The added weight of this equipment would have prevented the launch.

During 1960 and 1961, a series of Korabl-Sputnik (Spaceship Satellite) test launches were made. Sputnik 1 was the world's first artificial satellite. Sputnik 2 carried the world's first live space traveler, a dog named Laika. Unfortunately, the spacecraft could not be recovered, and Laika died by injection after seven days of travel. The third craft, Sputnik 3, launched on May 15, 1960, was an electrical analog, carrying heavy instrumentation. It carried no heat shield and was reported to have been a planned nonrecovery. Sputnik 4, launched on July 23, reportedly carried no biological experiments. It did not reach orbit, and the spacecraft was not recovered. In fact, when the retrorockets were fired for reentry, the capsule was facing away from Earth, and the spacecraft went into a higher orbit, where it stayed for four years. Later research indicates that a dummy astronaut was possibly the payload.

On August 19, Strelka and Belka, the world's first recovered cosmonaut dogs, were launched aboard Sputnik 5, along with rats, white mice, flies, plant seeds, fungi, chlorella algae, and a spiderwort plant. Counterparts of each experiment were maintained on Earth to compare for possible damage from space travel. These biological experiments underwent a one-day orbit, after which the animals were ejected to land safely within 10 kilometers of their land target. Toward the end of 1960, on December 1, Sputnik 6 was launched. Pchelka and Mushka were the two dogs on this disastrous flight. A lower orbit was used, similar to that projected for manned flight. A new solar orientation system was used, instead of the infrared attitude control used previously. Unfortunately, the capsule did not reenter at the proper angle, and the spacecraft was burned. Sputniks 7 and 8 were satellite probes sent to Venus. Venera 1 did not perform as planned, and was reported to be a one-day orbiting Sputnik 7. Venera 2 (Sputnik 8) succeeded in its interception of Venus.

Beginning in 1961, three man-rated spacecraft were delivered to the launch site. The first two launches were made with dogs. Sputnik 9 was launched on March 9 with the dog Chernushka and other specimens. After a complete orbit, the craft and specimens were recovered. Another dog, named Zvezdochka, was launched on March 25 aboard Sputnik 10, and was again successfully recovered after one orbit. These two flights, called Vostok A and B, were preparatory to Vostok 1, the launch of the first human into space.

Gagarin was awakened almost four hours prior to his 9:07 A.M. launch. Only one hitch marred the launch; it was corrected by opening the hatch and resealing it. Gagarin was literally only a passenger in the spacecraft. The controls were locked, and he would control the craft only in case of an emergency. An envelope containing the combination to the locked controls was in the craft for that purpose. Gagarin sent greetings to the nations of the world as he orbited past and kept the ground control apprised of his physical condition. He tried to eat paste-type space food from squeeze tubes and to drink water, as an experiment. Vostok's flight objective was to check the mechanics and the effects of space travel on humans. It was enough that Gagarin was in the spacecraft. Gagarin landed at 11:05 A.M., 26 kilometers southwest of Engels in the Saratov Region of the Soviet Union.

Impact of Event

Gagarin proved that humans could be launched into space, orbit the earth, and be safely recovered. It was a colossal feat, and a necessity before the course of space exploration could be set by any nation. The courage and determination displayed by this act impressed the entire world, especially when his gentle personality and lack of ego was noted. His attitude set a new standard, which astronauts and cosmonauts alike have maintained during the years of spaceflight.

Gagarin's flight spurred both the United States and the Soviet Union to pursue aggressively more ambitious projects. The American space program had lagged under the administration of President Dwight D. Eisenhower, who was not convinced that humans belonged in space. Gagarin's flight made the American public and the Congress take a hard look at the world and at the leadership position of the United

States. The next president, John F. Kennedy, announced the goal of landing on the Moon not long after the promptings of the Vostok 1 flight. In fact, the reason given by staff members recommending the lunar program was to increase the prestige of the United States. Suddenly, funding was available, and the National Aeronautics and Space Administration (NASA), with its strong skills in organization and administration, was allowed to forge ahead with plans to put a human on the Moon. The American public aligned firmly behind the grand vision of President Kennedy, and the huge amounts of funding remained in place for technological developments.

The Soviet Union had experienced an extraordinary tragedy attempting to launch a satellite under pressure from government entities at the same time the Vostok flights were being readied. Several men died, including an outstanding scientist. The project directors refused ever again to allow political pressures to force a disregard for safety precautions during launch. This, however, did not stop the progress of the Soviet space program but taught the Soviets that caution was needed in the years ahead. The Soviets responded to the unofficial American challenge, and the space race was on. When the large launch vehicles planned for use in launching a lunar mission kept failing, the program was abandoned in favor of space station development.

The world's first transnational telecast, featuring interviews with Gagarin, was watched avidly by peoples of all nations. Gagarin became a world celebrity overnight and had difficulty finding privacy anywhere. Soviet Premier Nikita S. Khrushchev used the amazing flight to try to sway the world toward his ideology and to show the United States that Soviet technology was superior. What he accomplished was the unification of the American people behind the president and behind the American space program. This gave a tremendous boost to American technological developments and opened up the field of space to the world. The entire world suddenly acquired a real hero in Gagarin, and they responded accordingly. Gagarin's feat of courage appealed universally to the best of humankind and has reserved him a place in history among all nations.

Bibliography

Clark, Phillip. *The Soviet Manned Space Program: An Illustrated History of the Men, the Missions, and the Spacecraft*. New York: Orion Books, 1988. A large-format, color-illustrated book, with more detailed information concerning the history and development of the various Soviet space programs. It also gives brief biographies of the cosmonauts and of their missions.

Dzyubenko, Galina, comp. *The Man from a Legend: A Collection of Essays*. Translated by Sharon McKee. Moscow: Progress Publishers, 1988. An unusual collection of views on the lives of well-known Soviet leaders. Gagarin is the first to be described. The personal side of Gagarin is noted, along with the progress of the Vostok program. His love of country, his family, and his common roots are discussed. A fascinating portrayal of Gagarin.

Hart, Douglas. *The Encyclopedia of Soviet Spacecraft*. New York: Bison, 1987. This coffee table book, with spacecraft listed alphabetically, is accompanied by beautiful, large color photographs and diagrams. Basic flight information is given on each mission, with a paragraph concerning the flight objectives.

Harvey, Brian. *Race into Space: The Soviet Space Programme.* Chichester, England: Ellis Horwood, 1988. The subheadings in this book make research a pleasure. The information is very up-to-date and interesting to read. A chronology of major events and a record of Soviet space missions are included in the appendix.

Johnson, Nicholas L. *Handbook of Soviet Manned Space Flight.* San Diego: Univelt, 1980. An excellent resource for more detailed research on the spacecraft design, variations between missions, and the launch vehicles used. It covers Vostok through Soyuz, including the Salyut space station and the Progress cargo ship.

Ellen F. Mitchum

Cross-References

The First Rocket with More than One Stage Is Created (1949), p. 1342; Sputnik 1, the First Artificial Satellite, Is Launched (1957), p. 1545; The United States Launches Its First Orbiting Satellite, Explorer 1 (1958), p. 1583; Shepard Is the First United States Astronaut in Space (1961), p. 1698; Glenn Is the First American to Orbit Earth (1962), p. 1723.

SHEPARD IS THE FIRST
UNITED STATES ASTRONAUT IN SPACE

Category of event: Space and aviation
Time: May 5, 1961
Locale: Cape Canaveral (now Cape Kennedy), Florida

Shepard was the first American launched into space, proving that manned space-flight was feasible

Principal personages:
    ROBERT R. GILRUTH (1913-   ), the head of the Space Task Group and the manager of the Mercury Program
    WERNHER VON BRAUN (1912-1977), a pioneer in rocketry who developed the Redstone launch vehicle
    ALAN B. SHEPARD (1923-   ), the astronaut who was the pilot of the Mercury *Freedom 7* flight

Summary of Event

In the late 1950's and early 1960's, space had become a tool of the Cold War and a source of malcontent to the American public. The Soviets had repeatedly captured the record for "firsts" in space, including the first human in space, the first space walk, and the first woman in space. The Soviet flight of Yuri A. Gagarin, the first human in space, made Alan B. Shepard's flight, only weeks later, a trifle anticlimactic. The United States government's policy of freely disseminated information on the space program, however, provided the world with film footage of the event and made Shepard's flight seem more real than the Soviet flight. Shepard's flight also evoked intense pride in the American public and helped ensure the future funding of the American manned space program.

Shepard was educated at the U.S. Naval Academy, and took flight training at Corpus Christi, Texas, and Pensacola, Florida, receiving his wings in 1947. He was chosen with the first draft of astronauts, the original seven, on April 9, 1959. At 9:34 A.M. on May 5, 1961, the Mercury-Redstone 3 lifted off from Cape Canaveral (now Cape Kennedy), Florida. Forty-five million people, glued to their television sets, heard him transmit, "Yes, Sir, reading you loud and clear. This is *Freedom 7.* The fuel is Go . . . 1.2 G . . . cabin at 14 psi . . . oxygen is Go. *Freedom 7* is still Go!" Shepard had been enclosed in the capsule since 5:20 that morning, awaiting his historic, precedent-setting flight into history. The flight lasted only about fifteen minutes, and Shepard experienced weightlessness for approximately five minutes. He traveled 495.3 kilometers from the launch site and attained 191 kilometers in altitude, pulling 6 gravitational loads upon launch and 11 gravitational loads upon reentry.

Plans for a manned satellite program were approved on October 7, 1958, by National Aeronautics and Space Administration (NASA) Administrator T. Keith Glennan. Bids were requested on both launch vehicle and spacecraft, and the Space Task Group was organized at Langley Research Center in Virginia, headed by Robert R. Gilruth. The development of Project Mercury set important precedents. First of all, the technology available at the time would be used as much as possible, cutting down on research. Second, failure of any system would be covered by a back-up system. In other words, there were two of each critical system. In the case of guidance, however, pilot ability was utilized should there be a failure. Third, the system of testing made it possible to use the same basic design, adding new devices to succeeding test flights. This caused rapid improvements and advancements in the systems. (The Soviets used a different system, in which they varied new systems constantly, thereby unable to correct problems systematically.)

Several major developmental projects were identified: testing of a modified Redstone launch vehicle; development and testing of an escape system; capsule environment; heat shield and heat ablation (device whereby the burning off of material dissipates reentry friction heat); and development of the capsule's retrorockets, which were needed to angle the spacecraft into the proper reentry angle. The launch vehicles were supplied by military services, the Atlas from the Air Force, and the Redstone from the Army. The Atlas was used for a variety of testing purposes. The Jupiter-C modification of the Redstone was further modified to ensure safety measures were added. For example, alcohol was used as a fuel because of lower toxicity, while the structural changes included the permanent mounting of the lower two stages and the addition of the capsule adaption segment atop the launch vehicle.

North American Aviation designed and constructed the airframe for Little Joe I for the escape system test series. Little Joe I, with a boilerplate (prototype) spacecraft atop, was used to test the escape system, which comprised a tower assembly, powered by solid-fuel rockets. When fired by any one of various sensors or by the astronaut, the entire tower, atop the capsule, would be shot away from the launch vehicle, pulling the astronaut away from a possible launch vehicle failure.

Many of the biologic requirements of the Mercury astronaut were established by an early balloon ascension program called "Operation Manhigh." In this program, a series of experimental pilots were lifted to the very edge of space in a gondola. Earlier experiments using mice and other small animals helped establish the amount of life-support needed for a human in Manhigh. The 100 percent oxygen, a "scrubber" to rid the air of carbon dioxide, cooling and heating, and waste collection were only a few of the prime considerations. The original seven astronauts banded together on certain vital issues. One of them was the inclusion of a large window, to ease claustrophobic feeling and to be able to catch a unique view of the world. The spacecraft itself was small; the diameter of the cone at the widest point was 2.1 meters, and the length was 3.4 meters between the nose and the retrorockets. The unique Mercury spacecraft shape, rather like a bell with a domed bottom, was designed to withstand the intense heat of reentry. Since drag created by the friction of reentry was used to slow the capsule, the larger surface of the bottom of the bell was the hottest surface. It was covered with the ablative material to protect the craft from combustion. The rest of the capsule was tiled with beryllium.

During the two years of equipment, launch vehicle, and spacecraft testing, Shepard was going through the most thorough testing procedures ever created for astronauts. After selection from the records of an initial 508 test pilots, 32 volunteers were sent to the Lovelace Medical Clinic in Albuquerque, New Mexico, where they underwent endurance capability and psychological evaluations. All but one were deemed in top condition and were then sent to Wright-Patterson Air Force Base in Ohio. From the top eighteen candidates, seven were chosen who seemed to relate well to one another. Each of the seven Mercury astronauts undertook the mastering of one aspect of the launch. Virgil I. (Gus) Grissom worked on the capsule, and John H. Glenn, Jr., worked on the instrument panel layout. M. Scott Carpenter became expert on communications, and Walter M. (Wally) Schirra on the pressure suit. Both L. Gordon Cooper and Donald K. (Deke) Slayton worked closely with the builders of the booster. Shepard undertook probably the most complex subject: the complicated tracking systems.

Shepard, and each of the Mercury space travelers, named his own craft. "Freedom" is self-explanatory; however, the "7" started out because his launch vehicle was the seventh produced, the spacecraft was also number seven. Also, the "7" came to stand for the spirit and incredible courage of the original seven astronauts, and each, in turn, named his craft with a "7" following the chosen name. Shepard's remarkable attitude and raw courage set the standards for American astronauts and lives on today.

Impact of Event

Following the launch of the first world coverage communications satellite, President Dwight D. Eisenhower expressed two major concerns in relation to the future of space. He was worried that there would be problems regarding who controlled worldwide communications, and he believed that only unmanned spaceflight should be explored. In fact, there was considerable debate about the direction of the space program. One faction wished to continue development of space via satellites and defense weaponry and the other wished to launch humans into space. It was against a backdrop of great controversy, and under a new presidency (with John F. Kennedy) that Project Mercury began. It was not until October of 1958 that NASA gave its consent to the project, in spite of the fact that Wernher von Braun had made recommendations years before and had projected a possible launch date of April, 1959. The interagency jealousies of the time prevented the launch that could have put the first human in space before the Soviets could develop the necessary technology.

It was of prime importance that Project Mercury succeed, therefore, to illustrate the feasibility of humans in space. Once Shepard returned to a hero's welcome and presidential honor, Senator Hubert H. Humphrey quickly proposed on May 6, 1961, an International Space Year to foster international space cooperation and to secure peace in space. In the proposition, he suggested that the United Nations charter be extended outward into space. Humphrey hoped for world cooperation in weather prediction, even weather control, in addition to global communications.

Project Mercury had already done much to dampen military interservice jealousies, as facilities were used as needed, not taking into account whether the Air Force, Navy, or Army ran the facility. The astronauts themselves did much to unite the country and to place the space program in the foremost of the American scene. They placed little importance on which branch of the military they represented, emphasizing only their nationality. They worked extremely well together, in spite of the fact that they were all very aggressive, success-oriented people. Their spirit, enthusiasm, and teamwork gave NASA the clean, positive image that pulled together the governmental factions, allowing space research and development to progress during the following years.

Probably the most far-reaching impact of Shepard's flight is the change in viewpoint from around the world. Once the public saw Earth from space, realization began to set in that all nations should pull together. Somehow, disputes among nations seemed petty when thinking of other worlds. Although the Soviet-American race into space continued for a number of years, consideration of joint projects began to surface. Now, commercial launch vehicles of various nations offer launching of spacecraft to many nations. The future of space travel may well involve joint planetary expeditions, utilizing the specialities of various nations. The flight of *Freedom 7* led the way into a new generation of exploration whose end is not yet in sight.

Bibliography

Cipriano, Anthony J. *America's Journeys into Space: The Astronauts of the United States.* New York: Wanderer Books, 1979. Beautifully illustrated biographical data book with approximately two pages devoted to each astronaut. Missions are described briefly, making a very readable, informative book. Basic biographical details are in chart form, and spaceflight details are in narrative form. Astronaut portraits were drawn by William Joffe Numeroff.

Cox, Donald W. *The Space Race: From Sputnik to Apollo, and Beyond.* Philadelphia: Chilton Books, 1962. A detailed history of the space program, its development, and its ramifications. It deals with behind-the-scenes political, economic, and historical causes and consequences, making for fascinating reading. It also traces the "space race" between the Soviet Union and the United States, and attempts to lay a rationale for the future of space, as seen from the early 1960's.

Engle, Eloise, and Arnold S. Lott. *Man in Flight: Biomedical Achievements in Aerospace.* Annapolis, Md.: Leeward, 1979. The book was written in celebration of the fiftieth anniversary of the Aerospace Medical Association. It gives an excellent history of the interaction of various biomedical organizations and the story of the oftentimes unseen medical personnel who helped make spaceflight possible.

Ezell, Linda Neuman. *NASA Historical Data Book.* Vol. 2, *Programs and Projects 1958-1968.* NASA SP-4012. Washington, D.C.: Government Printing Office, 1988. An invaluable source of raw data on the space program. Charts give chronological history, launch vehicle and spacecraft data, and compact, informative narrative. A little difficult to follow unless the reader has some background in technical terms.

Needell, Allan A. *The First Twenty-five Years in Space.* Washington, D.C.: Smithsonian Institution Press, 1983. The Smithsonian Institution's National Air and Space Museum, in cooperation with the National Academy of Sciences, compiled this book, based on the symposium held on October 14, 1982. These readings on the first twenty-five years of space deal with the rationale behind the entry of the United States into space exploration, the events, and its meaning.

Roland, Alex. *A Spacefaring People: Perspectives on Early Spaceflight.* NASA SP-4405. Washington, D.C.: Government Printing Office, 1985. Essays on early spaceflight, dealing with such topics as domestic and international consequences of spaceflight and the reasons for spaceflight, including the history behind the early spaceflight programs. It also includes the management developmental history of early space programs.

Time-Life Books Editors. *Life in Space.* Alexandria, Va.: Time-Life Books, 1983. This large size coffee-table book contains beautiful photography. The chapters deal with each American space program, beginning with Mercury and ending with the sixth flight of the Space Shuttle, including a chapter on unmanned deep space exploration. Narrative was written by consultants from the Smithsonian Institution's National Air and Space Museum.

Ellen F. Mitchum

Cross-References

The United States Launches Its First Orbiting Satellite, Explorer 1 (1958), p. 1583; Gagarin Becomes the First Human to Orbit Earth (1961), p. 1693; Glenn Is the First American to Orbit Earth (1962), p. 1723; The First Space Walk Is Conducted from Voskhod 2 (1965), p. 1787.

CALVIN WINS THE NOBEL PRIZE FOR HIS WORK ON PHOTOSYNTHESIS

Category of event: Chemistry
Time: December, 1961
Locale: University of California, Berkeley

The 1961 Nobel Prize was awarded to Calvin for his studies of photosynthesis, which forms the basis for nutrition of all living things

Principal personages:
> MELVIN CALVIN (1911-   ), an American chemist and biochemist who was the winner of the 1961 Nobel Prize in Chemistry for his work on photosynthesis
> MICHAEL POLANYI (1891-1976), an English professor of chemistry at the University of Manchester and a Fellow of the Royal Society with whom Calvin studied from 1935 to 1937

Summary of Event

Unraveling the mystery of how green plants transform energy from the sun and carbon dioxide into sugars and oxygen has been a subject of interest and speculation for a long time. It was not until Melvin Calvin published *The Path of Carbon in Photosynthesis* (1957) that the process was well understood. Calvin won the Nobel Prize in Chemistry in 1961 for his work.

Calvin's interest in the fate of carbon in photosynthesis, a fundamental biochemical reaction, began while studying in England as a postdoctoral fellow with Michael Polanyi at the University of Manchester from 1935 to 1937. During these years, Calvin's work involved coordinated metal compounds, molecules that have organic components attached to metals. There are many coordinated metal compounds that are significant biologically, such as heme found in red blood cells and chlorophyll found in green plants. In 1937, Calvin left England and returned to the United States to teach at the University of California at Berkeley. From 1941 to 1945, Calvin's work was directed at the war effort; this included two years on the Manhattan Project.

In 1946, Calvin was appointed director of the bioorganic division of the Lawrence Radiation Laboratory at Berkeley. His work centered on photosynthesis, the process that used light energy, water, and carbon dioxide to produce oxygen and carbohydrates (sugars). Despite the pivotal role that photosynthesis plays in life, the process was not well understood, and the exact nature of the molecules involved in this series of reactions was unknown. Calvin approached the problem on two fronts: determining how light energy is utilized and how complex sugars and other molecules are formed. There had been speculation, even before 1940, that the conversion of carbon dioxide to carbohydrate might be a dark reaction, separate from the conversion of water to oxygen. In 1937, Robert Hill had proven that oxygen could be produced from illuminated plant material when carbon dioxide was replaced. The reaction that occurs in the light, in addition to producing oxygen, formed high-energy reducing agents. These reducing agents, then, could convert carbon dioxide to sugar with no additional light. Calvin confirmed this observation by depriving plants of carbon dioxide while illuminating them so that they had the opportunity to store the high-energy reducing agents. When placed in a darkened environment, the plants were able to take up large amounts of carbon dioxide. Thus, incorporation of carbon dioxide depended on the reducing agents produced by light energy, rather than the light itself.

Calvin reasoned that if all chemicals involved in photosynthesis were identified, the sequence of reactions could be understood. Practical difficulties in such an undertaking were immense. Since all plant life is based on carbon, he needed to determine how carbon derived from carbon dioxide could be distinguished from carbon from other sources. Calvin postulated that if the carbon of carbon dioxide could somehow be "tagged," the carbon might be followed in its path to carbohydrates or traced. The discovery of the long-lived radioactive isotope of carbon, carbon 14, by Samuel Ruben and Martin Kamen provided such a tool. In 1945, an inexpensive and plentiful supply of carbon 14 was available with the construction of nuclear reactors. Carbon dioxide could be produced in which the carbon was radioactively tagged. Even when this carbon dioxide was transformed by the plant into other molecules, the source of the carbon would be announced to the researchers by its radioactivity. Naturally occurring carbon would not be detected in this way, so it could be ignored. Carbon dioxide entering plants appears eventually in all plant materials. In his Nobel address, Calvin described his strategy to investigate the chemicals that the carbon passes through by shortening "time of travel." If the reactions that transform the carbon into various chemicals could be stopped before the carbon had progressed into too many intermediates, the identity of the molecules between carbon dioxide and sugars could be determined.

Many of the techniques that ultimately unlocked the secrets of the dark reactions of photosynthesis were developed as part of the war effort: radio isotopes, ion exchange, and paper chromatography. The apparatus used for Calvin's studies was nicknamed the lollipop because of its shape. The alga *chlorella* was placed in the thin disklike apparatus and exposed to light and carbon dioxide. The tracer experiment was performed by substituting radioactive carbon dioxide in the stream. All chemical reactions were stopped by dropping the algae suspension into alcohol. This step also dissolved the organic molecules, separating them from the solid plant material, which could be analyzed for radioactivity. Traditional methods to purify such compounds were laborious and did not provide sufficient amounts of the materials to be analyzed. Calvin turned to ion exchange resins. When experimental mixtures were passed through columns of various resins and washed through with liquid, different compounds would pass out of the column at different speeds and thus could be separated.

It became obvious to Calvin that after only a few seconds the radioactive carbon had passed into a range of different compounds. The development of paper chromatography provided the means to separate the radioactive components of the photosynthetic process without knowing their identity. When different chemicals are placed on a porous sheet of paper and liquid is allowed to move up the paper, different molecules will move up the paper at varying speeds and are separated. If the paper is turned and liquid is allowed to move up at 90 degrees to its original direction, then the different compounds will be spread over the surface of the sheet. The location of molecules with radioactive carbon could be marked by allowing the paper to come into contact with photographic film. The areas of the film in contact with radioactive material would be exposed, creating dark patches. Some information to the identity of the molecules represented by dark patches was provided by subjecting the paper to analysis. More commonly, the separated materials were removed from the paper and subjected to chemical tests. The sequence of reactions suggested by these results proved to be complex. By charting the amount of a particular molecule as it appeared and disappeared, Calvin could place that substance in a sequence. The photosynthetic reactions form a cycle, albeit not a logical one, at first glance. Three molecules of carbon dioxide combine with three molecules of ribulose biphosphate (RuBP, a five-carbon molecule). The result of the enzyme catalyzed reaction is three molecules of a six-carbon molecule, which is bound to the enzyme. The molecules are cleaved into six three-carbon molecules, which have a phosphate group added to them by a highly energetic molecule adenosine triphosphate (ATP), produced in the light reaction. These products react with a reducing molecule from the light reactions of photosynthesis to produce six three-carbon molecules. One of these molecules is combined with an identical molecule from a second turn of the cycle. The remaining five molecules are transformed by a series of reactions to three molecules of RuBP, which can feed back into the cycle. At the time of the Nobel award, Calvin attributed the idea for the convoluted pathway to a trip he took with his wife. Inspiration came to him as he sat waiting in his car.

Impact of Event

The insight into the photosynthetic processes provided by Calvin and coworkers at Berkeley present a complex cyclic series of chemical reactions. This progression of reactions is referred to as the reductive pentose phosphate, or Calvin cycle. Calvin was able to demonstrate the generality of the process he described as it occurred in a range of organisms from bacteria to higher plants. The light-dependent conversion of light energy to chemical energy as ATP and reduced nicotinamide adenine dinucleotide phosphate (NADP) serves to transform reductively carbon dioxide to more complex organic molecules. The molecules that result from photosynthesis—often referred to as photosynthates—form the basis for nutrition of all living things. Furthermore, they are the precursors to oil, fuel, petrochemicals, and all other materials derived from them, such as pharmaceuticals, plastics, feedstocks, and dyes. It is difficult to imagine a world without the products of photosynthesis, either directly or indirectly, since they touch almost every aspect of human life. Coupled with the knowledge Calvin provided into the molecular results of photosynthesis, an understanding of the energy utilization, or quantum conversion steps, has been strengthened. Calvin demonstrated that the structures involved with photosynthesis can be isolated and, moreover, the carbon dioxide reducing enzymes could be washed off, leaving only the equipment used for quantum conversion. Structural studies provided additional information about the chemical biodynamics of the photosynthetic transformation.

The work honored by the Nobel committee was characterized by its ambitious nature, coupled with enormous attention to detail. Efraim Racker of the Public Health Research Institute of New York, an expert in photosynthesis also, said that "there was a lot of confusion in the field before Calvin. But he came up with the concept of the major cycle whereby carbon becomes sugar." Noting there were many contributors in the field, Racker said, "Others helped, but Calvin instituted a broad attack on it. It was his imagination and brilliant conception that did it." In addition to the enormous contributions to the biochemical field, Calvin creatively applied a wide range of analytical techniques to the project. Many of the techniques that proved pivotal to the work came out of the war effort.

Calvin proved to be a popular Nobel laureate. *Time* magazine referred to him as the "jolly biochemist" who had long been known as "Mr. Photosynthesis." Calvin's communication skills allowed his work to be widely understood and accepted.

Bibliography

Bassham, J. A., and M. Calvin. *The Path of Carbon in Photosynthesis.* Englewood Cliffs, N.J.: Prentice-Hall, 1957. A more technical discussion of the work, less accessible to the nonscientist than the Nobel lecture (cited below). Includes detailed descriptions of the experiments performed and the rationale for the work. Contains a historical perspective of the photosynthesis problem. Bibliography.

Calvin, Melvin. "The Long Journey." In *Science and Scientist*, edited by M. Kageyama, K. Nakamura, T. Oshima, and T. Uchida. Tokyo: Japan Scientific Societies Press, 1981. Calvin discusses, for the nonscientist, the generation of fuels and related materials by biological means. Calvin's concern is to replenish the dwindling reserves of the products of "ancient photosynthesis." The article describes the chemical history of fuel stocks and informs the reader of research being done at Berkeley in Calvin's laboratory on fuel-producing organisms.

_____. "The Path of Carbon in Photosynthesis." *Science* 135 (March 16, 1962): 879-889. The article is the lecture that Calvin delivered on receiving his Nobel Prize. Although this is a technical discussion, Calvin's delivery is such that the nonscientist should follow it easily. Includes personal insights and cites major influences. Contains pictures of the lollipop apparatus used, the photographic film showing the blackened areas, detailed graphs illustrating some of the experiment, and diagrams indicating the cycle of reaction in detail.

Farber, Eduard. "Melvin Calvin." In *Nobel Prize Winners in Chemistry, 1901-1961.*

Rev. ed. New York: Abelard-Schuman, 1963. This article provides biographical information on Calvin. Quotes freely from the Nobel lecture but allows the non-scientist to follow the sequence of events more easily.

Foyer, Christine H. *Photosynthesis*. New York: Wiley-Interscience, 1984. A textbook on photosynthesis with a broad base. The general concepts chapter will provide the nonscientist with a good overview of the topic. Includes a clear, concise diagram to illustrate the text and many examples of experimental data. A technical bibliography is provided at the end of each chapter.

Susan J. Mole

Cross-References

The First Synthetic Vat Dye, Indanthrene Blue, Is Synthesized (1901), p. 98; Hopkins Suggests That Food Contains Vitamins Essential to Life (1906), p. 330; Wilstätter Discovers the Composition of Chlorophyll (1906), p. 345; Krebs Describes the Citric Acid Cycle (1937), p. 1107; Lippmann Discovers Acetyl Coenzyme A (1951), p. 1390; Miller Reports the Synthesis of Amino Acids (1953), p. 1465; Kornberg and Coworkers Synthesize Biologically Active DNA (1967), p. 1857; Cech Demonstrates That RNA Can Act as an Enzyme (1982) p. 2190.

GIACCONI AND ASSOCIATES DISCOVER THE FIRST KNOWN X-RAY SOURCE OUTSIDE THE SOLAR SYSTEM

Category of event: Astronomy
Time: 1962
Locale: American Science and Engineering, Inc., Cambridge, Massachusetts

Giacconi and his colleagues launched a rocket-borne X-ray telescope that detected X rays from the constellation Scorpius

Principal personages:

RICCARDO GIACCONI (1931-   ), an Italian-American physicist who studied cosmic radiation and X-ray astronomy

HERBERT FRIEDMAN (1916-   ), an American cosmic-ray physicist who first detected X rays from the sun using X-ray detectors launched aboard captured German V-2 rockets

HERBERT BRIDGE (1919-   ), an American physicist at the Massachusetts Institute of Technology who studied cosmic rays and other high-energy particles

MARTIN ANNIS (1922-   ), an American cosmic-ray physicist

BRUNO ROSSI (1905-   ), an Italian-American physicist at the Massachusetts Institute of Technology

JOHN LINDSAY (1916-1965), an American X-ray astronomer at the NASA Goddard Space Flight Center

HERBERT GURSKY (1930-   ), an American physicist at Princeton University, American Science and Engineering, Inc., and the Harvard/Smithsonian Center for Astrophysics

NORMAN HARMON (1928-   ), an American cosmic-ray physicist and senior scientist at American Science and Engineering, Inc.

FRANK BETHUNE MCDONALD (1925-   ), an American astrophysicist at the NASA Goddard Space Flight Center

Summary of Event

All stars in the universe emit electromagnetic radiation as a result of the enormous thermonuclear reactions and complex chemical reactions of which they are composed. Electromagnetic radiation comes in many forms having particular frequencies and wavelengths. All electromagnetic radiation travels at the speed of light (300 million meters per second). The electromagnetic spectrum ranges from low-frequency, long-wavelength radiations such as radio, television, microwaves, and visible light to higher-frequency, shorter-wavelength radiations such as ultraviolet, X rays, gamma rays, and cosmic rays.

High-frequency ionizing radiation (ultraviolet, X rays, gamma rays, cosmic rays)

are mostly blocked by Earth's atmosphere. The thin ozone layer in the upper stratosphere acts as a chemical shield that reacts with these radiations as they bombard the
earth's atmosphere. Consequently, physicists and astronomers who wish to study
extraterrestrial high-energy (high-frequency) radiations must place measuring instruments into orbit above the earth's atmosphere.

With the explosion of astronomical research in the early twentieth century and the
harnessing of atomic energy during World War II, scientists gained considerable understanding of electromagnetism and stellar astrophysics. Scientists who had worked
on weapons, materials research, radar, and the atomic bomb during the war refocused their efforts toward the peaceful applications of science. These efforts included the field of high-energy physics.

Riccardo Giacconi received a doctorate in physics from Milano University in 1954.
In 1956, he moved to the United States, where he served on the physics faculty at
Indiana University (1956-1958) and Princeton University (1958-1959).

During the late 1950's, a group of physicists at the Massachusetts Institute of
Technology (MIT) in Cambridge, Massachusetts, established a company whose pri-
mary focus was high-energy physics and space research. The company, American
Science and Engineering, Inc., was headed by an American cosmic-ray physicist,
Martin Annis, and an Italian-American physicist, Bruno Rossi (chairman of the board
of trustees). In 1959, with the Cold War space race accelerating between the United
States and the Soviet Union, Annis and MIT physicist Herbert Bridge encouraged
Giacconi to join their company to establish a space science research division.

Giacconi joined the company, and he and his colleagues focused their research on
extraterrestrial radiation sources such as the Van Allen radiation belts surrounding
the earth-moon system. In collaboration with the National Aeronautics and Space
Administration (NASA), American Science and Engineering decided to test the emission of X rays from stars. This work had been started in the late 1940's by the
American physicist Herbert Friedman of the Naval Research Observatory. Friedman
launched X-ray detectors above the earth's atmosphere aboard captured German V-2
rockets and demonstrated that the sun emits X rays.

During 1960 and 1961, Giacconi, Frank Paolini, and Norman Harmon devised a
small, highly sensitive X-ray telescope that could detect faint X-ray emissions from
specific regions in space and that could fly aboard conventional Aerobee rockets
capable of achieving an altitude of about 160 kilometers. They attempted several
launches of X-ray telescopes from White Sands Missile Range in New Mexico beginning in the fall of 1961. Several of these early launches failed because of rocket
or equipment malfunctions, but they finally succeeded at midnight on June 18-19,
1962, with a six-minute suborbital flight. The X-ray telescope, a Geiger-counter-like
device, received and recorded stellar X-ray emissions on film.

Careful analysis of the X-ray film showed a higher emission of X rays emanating
from the southern constellation Scorpius. They named this X-ray source Scorpius
X-1, the first extrasolar X-ray source. Friedman's research group quickly confirmed
Giacconi's discovery. Other high-energy astrophysicists entered the field and dis-

covered additional X-ray sources, including Cygnus X-1 and the Crab nebula in Taurus.

Following the discovery of Scorpius X-1, Giacconi and his colleagues proceeded to develop more ambitious projects for stellar X-ray detection. These experiments involved the development of more sensitive rocket-borne X-ray telescopes, the mapping of more stellar X-ray sources across the sky, and the mapping of X-ray emissions from the sun's surface. Their ultimate goal was to place a series of orbiting X-ray telescopes around Earth for precise measurements of hundreds of stellar X-ray sources. They planned the development of these satellites in coordination with astronomers John Lindsay and Frank Bethune McDonald of the NASA Goddard Space Flight Center in Greenbelt, Maryland.

During the late 1960's, Giacconi and his colleagues continued their work on a proposed orbiting X-ray telescope. Friedman's group at the Naval Research Laboratory in Washington, D.C., and McDonald's group at the Goddard Space Flight Center independently were approaching the same goal. Funding for this project was limited, as NASA's budget was devoted to the Apollo manned lunar landing program, but the X-ray satellite project was completely funded by 1970. On December 12, 1970, the Cosmic X-Ray Explorer satellite was launched from an oil rig located off the coast of Kenya. Kenya was chosen because from there the satellite could easily enter an equatorial orbit, an orbit that would carry the satellite around the earth's equator, enabling the X-ray telescope to detect X-ray sources from practically every direction around Earth. X-ray data were relayed to a ground-based control station. The X-Ray Explorer, termed Small Astronomy Satellite I (SAS-1), was nicknamed Uhuru, the Kenyan word for freedom, because it was launched on Kenya's Independence Day.

Uhuru identified and mapped X-ray sources from deep space for prolonged periods of time. The immense data accumulated from the mission not only helped astrophysicists to locate cosmic X-ray sources but also enabled scientists to study periodic changes in each X-ray source over time, giving researchers clues as to the physical nature of these X-ray sources and the stellar chemical processes that stimulate X-ray emission. Many X-ray sources were identified as sunlike stars and galactic nuclei. Still other sources were determined to be superdense collapsed stars called neutron stars. Other scientists speculate that some X-ray sources (Cygnus X-1) may be black holes, gravitational singularities that are collapsed stars so dense that matter and light cannot escape.

Additional Small Astronomy Observatory Satellites were launched during the early 1970's, each satellite carrying a variety of high-energy detection equipment designed by Giacconi, Friedman, McDonald, and other physicists. Giacconi, McDonald, and Herbert Gursky of the Harvard/Smithsonian Astrophysical Observatory pushed successfully for the funding and development of a more advanced high-energy detection satellite series. The High Energy Astronomy Observatory (HEAO) program consisted of three satellites (HEAO-1, HEAO-2, HEAO-3) containing instrument packages for detecting high-energy radiation from space.

HEAO-2, also called the Einstein X-Ray Observatory in honor of the centenary of the great physicist's birth, was launched in 1978 and was operational through 1981. It contained a powerful X-ray telescope that detected X-ray emissions from quasars (quasi-stellar radio sources), the most distant and oldest objects yet discovered in the universe. The Einstein X-Ray Observatory also was useful for mapping the locations of these quasars and other cosmic X-ray sources. The Einstein X-Ray Observatory was a major culmination of Giacconi's career that was intricately dependent upon his 1962 discovery of Scorpius X-1, an X-ray emitting variable blue star twice the size of Earth's sun.

Impact of Event

Giacconi's discovery of the first extrasolar X-ray source was a tremendous astronomical achievement that changed scientists' view of the universe and led to a greater understanding of stellar astrophysics. The knowledge that many objects, including stars, planets, galaxies, and quasars, emit X rays has enabled scientists to comprehend the nature of these objects and the processes that occur within them. Giacconi's discovery launched the field of X-ray astronomy, an explosive branch of astronomy that continually yields new information about the universe.

The first X-ray telescopes, launched aboard sounding rockets by Giacconi and Friedman, pioneered later missions (Uhuru, Einstein X-Ray Observatory) that revealed many cosmic X-ray emitters. With succeeding X-ray telescope missions, X-ray sources were discovered in every section of the universe, enabling a comprehensive map of stellar X-ray emission to be generated.

X rays usually are produced by two specific processes, high-temperature plasmas, and molecular collisions and interactions. Within stars, temperatures exceed 1 million Kelvins. At such extreme temperatures, matter exists in a vaporized ionized state called plasma. The collision of plasma ions generates X rays. Stars, such as the sun, emit X rays in all directions (isotropically) similar to light emission. At the same time, high-energy particles are ejected from stars, a phenomenon known as solar wind. When these particles strike molecules such as the Moon's surface or the thick atmosphere of Jupiter, X rays are produced. Intense magnetic fields, such as those found around the gas giants (Jupiter, Neptune), can generate X rays.

The X-ray telescopes designed by Giacconi and his associates were very sensitive receivers whose collecting areas ranged from 1 square centimeter to 150 square centimeters. The greater sensitivity of succeeding X-ray telescopes enabled astronomers to detect very distant galaxies and quasars and helped astrophysicists to analyze exotic stars such as neutron stars and black holes.

Neutron stars were first hypothesized by the Indian astrophysicist Subrahmanyan Chandrasekhar and the Bulgarian-American astrophysicist Fritz Zwicky in the 1930's. Black holes, whose existence has not yet been verified, have been advocated for several decades by a host of prominent astrophysicists, including the German physicist Karl Schwarzschild, the American physicists John A. Wheeler and Kip S. Thorne, the Soviet physicists Yakov Borisovich Zel'dovich and Igor Novikov, and the English physicists Stephen W. Hawking and Roger Penrose. Both types of stars are superdense supernova remnants whose gravity can bend light.

The X-ray data gleaned from Giacconi and Friedman's experiments identified pulsars (Crab nebula) and potential black holes (Cygnus X-1), providing experimental support for theoretical astrophysics. Further X-ray studies have indicated the presence of black holes in galactic nuclei (including the centers of our Milky Way galaxy and the neighboring Andromeda galaxy) and enabled scientists to understand better quasars, the oldest, most distant objects yet discovered in Earth's universe.

Bibliography

Bartusiak, Marcia. *Thursday's Universe.* New York: Times Books, 1986. This excellent book is a history of the major astronomical achievements of the twentieth century. It is very enjoyable reading for a general audience. Chapter 2, "A Twilight's Last Gleaming," describes the discovery of Scorpius X-1 by Giacconi, Gursky, and their colleagues.

Grindlay, Jonathan E. "X Ray Astronomy." In *Encyclopedia of Astronomy and Astrophysics*, edited by Robert A. Meyers. San Diego: Academic Press, 1989. This survey article is a thorough discussion of X-ray astronomy. It provides detailed information and outstanding computer-generated images of X-ray sources obtained from Uhuru and the Einstein X-Ray Observatory.

Israel, Werner. "Dark Stars: The Evolution of an Idea." In *Three Hundred Years of Gravitation*, edited by Stephen W. Hawking and Werner Israel. Cambridge, England: Cambridge University Press, 1987. This extensive article is a history of the scientists who conceptualized the superdense neutron stars and black holes. The article discusses complex topics in simple terms and provides a lengthy reference list. The discovery of X-ray sources is discussed briefly.

Novikov, Igor. *Black Holes and the Universe.* Translated by Vitaly Kisin. Cambridge, England: Cambridge University Press, 1990. This outstanding little book is a clear presentation of black holes and their properties. Written by a leading Soviet theoretical physicist and a pioneer in black hole research, the book is both comprehensive and entertaining.

Rolfs, Claus E., and William S. Rodney. *Cauldrons in the Cosmos: Nuclear Astrophysics.* Chicago: University of Chicago Press, 1988. This textbook for advanced astronomy and physics students is a summary of current knowledge about stars and stellar processes. The chemistry and mathematics are very sophisticated. Chapter 1, "Astronomy—Observing the Universe," discusses quasars, radio stars, and results from the Einstein X-Ray Observatory.

Serway, Raymond A., and Jerry S. Faughn. *College Physics.* 2d ed. Philadelphia: Saunders College Publishing, 1989. This algebra-based textbook is an excellent introduction to physics for undergraduate science majors. It is clearly written, contains numerous sample problems, and provides superb illustrations and examples. Chapter 23, "Electromagnetic Waves," discusses the various types of electromagnetic radiation in detail, including high-energy X rays and cosmic rays.

Tucker, Wallace, and Karen Tucker. *The Cosmic Inquirers: Modern Telescopes and Their Makers.* Cambridge, Mass.: Harvard University Press, 1986. This book is a history of radio, X-ray, and gamma-ray astronomy. It provides the reader with a unique glimpse into the lives of several major American astronomers. Part 2, "A High-Energy Astrophysicist and the Einstein X-Ray Observatory," is an in-depth summary of Giacconi's life and scientific career.

Zeilek, Michael, and Elske V. P. Smith. *Introductory Astronomy and Astrophysics.* 2d ed. Philadelphia: Saunders College Publishing, 1987. This excellent introductory astronomy textbook for undergraduate science majors is a well written, extensively detailed survey of astronomy. The mathematics and physics are primarily algebra-based. Numerous photographs, illustrations, and references serve to illustrate key concepts. Chapter 18, "Variable and Violent Stars," discusses X-ray emitting stars and their nature.

David Wason Hollar, Jr.

Cross-References

Reber Builds the First Intentional Radio Telescope (1937), p. 1113; Reber Makes the First Radio Maps of the Universe (1942), p. 1193; Ryle's Radio Telescope Locates the First Known Radio Galaxy (1946), p. 1271; Ryle Constructs the First Radio Interferometer (1955), p. 1496; Parker Predicts the Existence of the Solar Wind (1958), p. 1577; Schmidt Makes What Constitutes the First Recognition of a Quasar (1963), p. 1757; Penzias and Wilson Discover Cosmic Microwave Background Radiation (1963), p. 1762; Bell Discovers Pulsars, the Key to Neutron Stars (1967), p. 1862.

LASERS ARE USED IN EYE SURGERY
FOR THE FIRST TIME

Category of event: Medicine
Time: 1962
Locale: New York University; Stanford University

The first significant clinical ophthalmic application of any laser system was the treatment of retinal tears with a pulsed ruby laser

Principal personages:
> CHARLES J. CAMPBELL (1926-   ), an ophthalmologist who began experimenting with ruby laser photocoagulation of the retina in animals in the early 1960's
> H. CHRISTIAN ZWENG (1925-   ), an ophthalmologist who treated human patients shortly after the invention of the ruby laser
> MILTON M. ZARET (1927-   ), an ophthalmologist who began using ruby laser photocoagulation of the retina in animal experiments in the 1960's
> THEODORE HAROLD MAIMAN (1927-   ), the physicist responsible for the development of the first laser

Summary of Event

The term "laser" is an acronym for *l*ight *a*mplification by the *s*timulated *e*mission of *r*adiation. Substances have the property to "lase," that is, to absorb energy in one form (either thermal, mechanical, electrical or light—all ophthalmic lasers use light as the stimulating source) and to emit a new form of light energy that is more useful. The utility of laser light is caused by a number of its unique properties; particularly useful is the concentration or brightness of the light. In fact, a laser produces the brightest light source known to humans. The development of the laser for ophthalmic use arose from the initial concentration of conventional light by magnifying lenses.

A substance that has the ability to lase possesses the unique property of transferring electrons from one orbital to a second orbital of higher energy. The theory of Niels Bohr states that each orbital is spaced by a precise energy interval. When most electrons have been energized sufficiently by the stimulating source so that they are in an orbital of higher energy, they may jump suddenly at the same time to their original orbital of lower energy. This sudden jump to a lower-energy level causes the emission of a new form of light energy (laser light), which has a single wavelength corresponding to the exact energy difference between the second orbital and the original orbital. It is coherent because all electrons jump at the same time and thus form a light wave that begins at the same time and is therefore in the same phase. The light then oscillates back and forth within the laser cavity (usually a tube with a mirror at each end, one mirror being highly reflective and the other mirror allowing some laser light to pass through for use in the eye). The laser light that passes through the partially reflective mirror may be altered in several ways to make it more effective for ophthalmic use, one of which is to concentrate further the laser light into a small interval of higher intensity.

Theodore Harold Maiman, formerly a research scientist at Hughes Aircraft Research Laboratories, was one of the few scientists interested in the use of solid materials—namely, ruby crystals—as a laser material. On July 7, 1960, Maiman made public his discovery of the first laser—a ruby laser. Shortly thereafter, ophthalmologists began using ruby lasers for medical purposes.

The first significant medical (ophthalmic) uses of the ruby laser occurred in 1961, with experiments on animals conducted by Charles J. Campbell, H. Christian Zweng, and Milton M. Zaret. Zaret and his colleagues produced photocoagulation of the eyes of rabbits by flashes from a ruby laser. Sufficient energy was delivered to cause instantaneous thermal injury to the retina and iris of the pigmented rabbit. The beam also was directed to the interior of the rabbit eye, resulting in retinal coagulations. He examined the retinal lesions and pointed out both the possible advantages of laser as a tool for therapeutic photocoagulation and the potential applications in medical research.

In 1962, Zweng, along with several of his associates, began experimenting with laser photocoagulation on the eyes of monkeys and rabbits to establish parameters for the use of lasers on the human eye. In their experiments with humans, all patients were treated with the experimental laser photocoagulator without anesthesia. Although usually no attempt was made to seal holes or tears, the diseased portions of the retina were walled off satisfactorily so that no detachments occurred. When attempts to obliterate microaneurysms were unsuccessful, the researchers postulated that the color of the ruby pulse so resembled the red of blood that the light was reflected rather than absorbed. They believed that another lasing material emitting light in another part of the spectrum might have performed more successfully.

Campbell and his colleagues also began experimenting on human subjects (in addition to animals) in 1962. Their clinical trials on adult pigmented rabbits, using both the laser and the xenon arc photocoagulator, indicated that, qualitatively, the lesions produced by these two instruments appeared to be similar, but the laser coagulations were located at a relatively more external level of the retina. Microscopic sections confirmed that the laser, with proper power controls, produced not destructive pathologic changes but therapeutic coagulations. They also produced therapeutic retinal burns in a series of human subjects and successfully treated retinal tears. In their research, they found that coagulations formed by the laser were smaller than those produced by the xenon arc and concluded that the laser was a desirable and feasible way of producing coagulations of the human retina.

Previously, xenon-arc lamp photocoagulators had been used to treat retinal tears, but the long exposure time of these systems (250-1,000 milliseconds, as opposed to the ruby laser's 0.2-1.0 milliseconds), combined with their broad spectral range emission (versus the single wavelength output of a laser), made the retinal spot on which the xenon arc could be focused too large for many applications. Focused laser spots on the retina could be as small as 50 microns.

The vitreous body, which usually fills the vitreous cavity of the eyes of younger individuals, commonly shrinks with age, with myopia, or certain pathologic conditions, causing it to separate from the adjacent retina. In some patients, the separating vitreous produces a traction (pulling) on an area of vitreo-retinal adhesion, causing a retinal tear to form. Through this opening in the retina, liquefied vitreous can pass to a site underneath the retina, producing retinal detachment and visual loss. The purpose of photocoagulation of a retinal tear is to cause an adhesive scar to form between the retina surrounding the tear and the underlying layers so that, despite traction, the retina does not detach. If more than a small area of retina has detached, the laser often is ineffective and major retinal detachment surgery must be performed. Thus, in the experiments of Campbell and Zweng, the ruby laser was used to prevent, rather than treat, retinal detachment.

Impact of Event

The first laser in ophthalmic use by Campbell, Zweng, and Zaret, among others, was a solid laser—Maiman's ruby laser. While the results they achieved with this laser were more impressive than with the previously used xenon arc, in the decades following these experiments, argon gas replaced ruby as the most frequently used lasing material in treating retinal tears.

Argon laser energy is delivered to the area around the retinal tear through a slit lamp or by using an intraocular probe introduced directly into the eye. The argon wavelength is transmitted through the clear structures of the eye, such as the cornea, lens, and vitreous. This beam is composed of blue/green light and is highly absorbed by the retinal pigmentation's hemoglobin and melanin and is absorbed only minimally by the normal ocular media, allowing the selective placement of argon laser energy at the desired level within the eye. Nevertheless, it can be absorbed by cataracts and by vitreous or retinal blood, decreasing its effectiveness.

While the ruby laser was found to be highly effective in producing an adhesive scar, it was not useful in the treatment of vascular diseases of the eye. A series of laser sources, each with different characteristics, have been considered, investigated, and used clinically for various durations during the period that followed Campbell and Zweng's experiments.

Subsequently developed lasers in the solid state include the YAG, a laser made of a synthetic crystal originally developed as a gemstone, Yttrium Aluminum Garnet— abbreviated YAG. Other laser types that are being adapted for use in ophthalmology are: CO_2 lasers for scleral (the tough, white, fibrous membrane covering the entire eyeball except the area covered by the cornea) surgery, eye wall resection, dye lasers for photodynamic inactivation of tumors, eximer lasers for their ability to break down corneal tissue through a photochemical nonthermal process that dissolves organic molecular bonds without tissue heating, and pulsed erbium lasers used to cut intraocular membranes.

Bibliography

Apfelberg, David B., ed. *Evaluation and Installation of Surgical Laser Systems.* New York: Springer-Verlag, 1987. This excellent work is intended to be a complete information source both for those relatively unfamiliar with the laser as well as for the experienced laser user. All details of laser biophysics, safety, and specialty uses are explained. In addition, the administrative, organizational, financial, and legal implications are outlined. Includes 103 illustrations and 33 appendices, as well as a glossary of terms.

Ball, Kay. *Lasers: The Perioperative Challenge.* St. Louis: C. V. Mosby, 1990. This well-written book provides an extensive overview of past and present advances in laser technology and use. It can be used as a fundamental reference tool for general knowledge as well as specialized knowledge in the field. Contains color plates, a glossary of terms, and suggested readings at the end of each chapter.

Goldman, Leon, and R. James Rockwell. *Lasers in Medicine.* New York: Gordon & Breach, 1971. This thorough and very informative work reviews the extensive and detailed work of a group of investigators who have been responsible for much of the developmental research in laser medicine and biology. The authors provide a general overview of the history and physics of laser emission, characteristics and measurement of laser radiation, laser biology, safety, as well as applications in ophthalmology, dermatology, and cancer research. Includes many graphs, charts, and illustrations.

McGuff, Paul E. *Surgical Applications of Laser.* Springfield, Ill.: Charles C Thomas, 1966. The general scope of this brief and somewhat dated work is laser surgery, with special reference to the application of laser in the treatment of malignancy and, specifically, malignant tumors. The effects of laser energy on human malignant tumors are studied, and concepts and hypotheses derived from experimental studies are formulated. Also included is a chapter on the present status of laser applications in biology, medicine, dentistry, and surgery. Contains appendices, a glossary of laser terms, and a bibliography.

Wolbarsht, M. L., ed. *Laser Applications in Medicine and Biology.* Vol. 2. New York: Plenum Press, 1974. This lengthy and detailed investigation of the rapid advances in laser technology gives an insightful view into the use of lasers in areas such as ophthalmology, holography, surgery, and dentistry. The work also discusses the issue of protective standards for the patient and the operator. Contains numerous graphs, charts, and illustrations.

Genevieve Slomski

Cross-References

The First Laser Is Developed in the United States (1960), p. 1672; Optical Pulses Shorter than One-Trillionth of a Second Are Produced (1974), p. 2020; Tunable, Continuous Wave Visible Lasers Are Developed (1974), p. 2025.

RENFREW, DIXON, AND CANN RECONSTRUCT ANCIENT NEAR EASTERN TRADE ROUTES

Categories of event: Archaeology and earth science
Time: 1962-1967
Locale: Cambridge Mineralogy and Petrology Department, England

Renfrew, Dixon, and Cann devised a method for tracing ten-thousand-year-old Near Eastern trade routes by means of trace-element analysis of obsidian

Principal personages:
> COLIN RENFREW (1937-   ), a British archaeologist from the Department of Ancient History, University of Sheffield, England
> J. E. DIXON, a British geologist in the Department of Mineralogy and Petrology, University of Cambridge, England
> J. R. CANN, a British geologist in the Department of Mineralogy and Petrology, University of Cambridge, England

Summary of Event

Scholars have long been intrigued by the rapid spread of Neolithic farming throughout southwestern Asia and the Mediterranean. The fact that isolated, widely scattered small villages made the transition from hunting and gathering to farming almost simultaneously suggested that these early communities had somehow been in contact. The problem, however, was to devise a way to trace the trade network and thereby confirm the existence of communication between the ten-thousand-year-old settlements.

In the early 1960's, Colin Renfrew and his colleagues, J. R. Cann and J. E. Dixon, realized that a comparative study of artifacts from the centers of early agricultural development might hold the clue needed to reconstruct prehistoric trade networks. Previous comparative studies had attempted mostly to analyze techniques of manufacture or stylistic similarities: If two cultures used pottery decorated in identical ways, it suggested the two had been in contact. This type of interpretation was limited, however, for the two societies might have devised the same techniques independently. Renfrew, Dixon, and Cann suggested that the raw materials from which tools were manufactured might hold more promise as a diagnostic of contact. If the materials recovered from the archaeological deposit do not occur naturally in the region, they must have been obtained in trade from another population.

The first problem faced by the researchers was to choose what material to study. They decided on obsidian, the easily chipped volcanic glass used by early tool makers throughout the world. Obsidian artifacts are found all over the Mediterranean basin and southwest Asia, but obsidian source areas occur only in regions that have seen recent volcanic activity: Italy, the Aegean, Turkey, and Iran. The next question was how to trace the obsidian to its source area. Obsidian tools often appear in archaeological deposits hundreds of kilometers from the nearest source. Tracing the tools to particular source areas was difficult, for obsidians from a single volcanic deposit may differ greatly, while those from different deposits might seem outwardly quite similar. Microscopic examination revealed little because early tool makers had always favored obsidian of uniform structure, free of the inclusions that sometimes distinguish one source from another. Nor did chemical analysis offer much information, for obsidians are all essentially identical in gross chemical makeup.

In 1962, the researchers turned to the relatively new field of trace-element analysis. The theory behind trace-element analysis is that each rock or mineral source has a trace-element pattern distinct from any other—a sort of chemical fingerprint made up of elements that are present in minute amounts. No matter how many flows might be represented in a single source site—and regardless of their outward appearance—all would display essentially the same trace-element pattern because they all derived from the same volcanic source.

Renfrew, Dixon, and Cann decided to use a method known as optical spectrography, an analytic tool already proven useful in archaeological studies of metal artifacts. Optical spectrography involves heating a powdered sample of material to incandescence. The light that results from this heating process is passed through a prism that spreads out the wavelengths of the light spectrum and makes it possible to measure them. The types and relative amounts of the trace elements present then can be determined because each element emits a characteristic wavelength (or color) of light at a level of intensity proportionate to the amount of the element in the sample. An advantage of the method is that it accurately measures the trace element makeup of very small samples.

Beginning with samples of well-known obsidian sources in the Mediterranean basin, the researchers set out to determine if the sources could be distinguished by their trace element makeup. They found that the elements barium and zirconium showed the most noticeable concentration differences in the samples, and often the relative proportions of those two elements alone were sufficient to distinguish one obsidian source area from another. The team then decided to test their thesis with a study of the ancient obsidians from the island of Malta, south of Sicily. Earlier archaeologists speculated that the obsidian on Malta was shipped by Minoan traders from Mílos, an island 966 kilometers away. Trace-element analysis suggested, instead, that the Neolithic people on Malta had sailed to the small island of Pantelleria, 240 kilometers north, for their obsidian. Further tests revealed that the obsidians found by Sir Arthur John Evans during his excavations on Crete in the early 1900's came from the Aegean islands of Giali (north of Rhodes) and Mílos. Therefore, by the early Neolithic, the Minoans were accomplished sailors and merchants already, plying their trade throughout the islands of the Aegean and the settlements of mainland Greece and Turkey. Renfrew and his colleagues were able to distinguish six sources for obsidian in the Mediterranean during Neolithic times: Sardinia, west of Italy; Palmarola, Pantelleria, and Lipari in the central Mediterranean; and the islands of Giali and Mílos, in the Aegean. They concluded also that there were two distinct trade regions: the central Mediterranean and the Aegean. Within each region, obsidian was often shipped long distances from its origin point, and a single site might yield samples of obsidian from two or more source areas. There seemed, however, to be no trade between the two regions.

Dixon, Cann, and Renfrew next applied their method to a study of obsidians from the earliest settled communities in the "fertile crescent" of Egypt, Palestine, Anatolia, and Mesopotamia. There they found abundant obsidian materials in early Neolithic village sites, but few obsidian source areas. Their studies of the obsidian revealed eight different types, some of which could not be matched to the known source areas in ancient Armenia (eastern Anatolia), Cappadocia (central Anatolia), or Ethiopia. Careful detective work, based on a comparison of the composition of the samples in various regions, led to the discovery of some of the missing source areas and a clearer picture of the patterns of trade in operation at the beginning of the Agricultural Revolution.

The Near Eastern research showed that the entire region of the Fertile Crescent (including the island of Cyprus) was supplied with obsidian from two major source areas: the Armenian and the Cappadocian. Renfrew found that obsidian distribution was surprisingly regular—within 240 to 320 kilometers of a source area, 80 percent of the chipped stone tools found at early Neolithic village sites were made of obsidian. Outside that radius, the amount of obsidian present at a particular site depended on its distance from the "supply zone." The drop-off of obsidian in this "contact zone" was a nearly perfect exponential function of distance: The farther from the supply zone, the fewer obsidian tools. Several sites in Palestine yielded obsidian artifacts from both source areas, a fact that the researchers suggest might have resulted from trade with two different groups: the nomads of the semiarid zone and the coastal farmers.

Renfrew, Dixon, and Cann concluded from their research that the regularity of obsidian distribution patterns in the early Neolithic settlements of the Mediterranean and Near East was the result of continuous, regular trade from as early as 8000 B.C. With trade came the cultural contact so important in the spread of ideas throughout the area.

Impact of Event

Questions about the origins of agriculture have fascinated scholars for decades, for the transition from hunting and gathering to food production was a monumental change in humankind's cultural adaptations. For the first time in 2 million years of prehistory, people were no longer forced to pursue wild food resources in endless, seasonal cycles of nomadic movement. They now controlled the animals and plants they needed for food. Food production was also the modification that made possible the later development of civilization, for the Neolithic farmer provided the economic base necessary to support the specializations and specialists of the Bronze Age world.

Trade was probably not an innovation of the Neolithic. There is ample evidence of trade in obsidian, flint, amber, and other raw materials from upper Paleolithic times, and the Neolithic obsidian trade would have been a logical outgrowth of these early contacts. One must be careful, as Renfrew and his colleagues point out, not to read too much complexity into this early exchange or overestimate the amount of actual face-to-face contact that resulted from it. Nevertheless, where there was exchange of materials there might have been the potential for exchanging ideas as well, and therein lies the real importance of establishing the existence of trade routes in antiquity.

At the time Renfrew and his colleagues developed their method of obsidian tracing in the mid-1960's, a major issue facing scholars doing Neolithic studies was the question of origins. Evidence of early farming had been uncovered in at least three centers within the greater Fertile Crescent area: Palestine, southern Anatolia, and the Zagros range of Mesopotamia. Much effort had been spent to determine which of these areas was the first farming community or if each had independently invented the process. Radiocarbon dating, unfortunately, was inexact enough to fuel a controversy, and scholars become involved in a rather heated argument of the issue.

The Renfrew, Dixon, and Cann research did not provide a definitive answer to the question of origins, but it did provide a mechanism to help trace the channels of communication in place at the time. As they pointed out, the Neolithic Revolution was not as abrupt a change as its name implied, but rather a gradual process that probably took several centuries or longer to mature fully. Given the existence of widespread trade (and therefore communication) among the cultures in the area, it would be difficult to conceive of such a series of changes taking place without some knowledge of those changes (if not the domesticates themselves) making their way to others in the trade network.

Renfrew, Dixon, and Cann's successful reconstruction of the Mediterranean obsidian trade gave rise to dozens of similar investigations in Europe, North America, Mexico, New Zealand, and Africa—virtually everywhere ancient peoples used obsidian for their tools. The increased knowledge of trade patterns resulting from this research has greatly enhanced an understanding of the development of prehistoric culture and the process of cultural change throughout the ancient world.

Bibliography

Cann, J. R., J. E. Dixon, and Colin Renfrew. "Obsidian Analysis and the Obsidian Trade." In *Science in Archaeology*, edited by Don Brothwell and Eric Higgs. Rev. ed. New York: Praeger, 1970. An article that deals specifically with the application of optical spectrography, the trace element method used in the obsidian studies carried out by Renfrew and his colleagues. A somewhat technical but interesting discussion of how characterization studies can be used in the field of archaeological analysis. Includes graphs and illustrations.

Cann, J. R., and Colin Renfrew. "The Characterization of Obsidian and Its Application to the Mediterranean Region." *Proceedings of the Prehistoric Society* 30 (1964): 111-133. The landmark article that launched the researchers' obsidian characterization and trade studies. Outlines the method of trace-element analysis and the technique of optical spectrography using test materials from the west Mediterranean. A classic study that showed the great potential of such studies to an understanding of cultural process.

Dixon, J. E., J. R. Cann, and Colin Renfrew. "Obsidian and the Origins of Trade." *Scientific American* 218 (March, 1968): 38-46. A general article that discusses obsidian characterization studies and the origins of trade in both the Mediterranean and the Near Eastern areas. A good summary article covering the first five years of their research. Written for an audience with less scientific background. Good pictures and illustrations.

Renfrew, Colin. "Trade as Action at a Distance: Questions of Integration and Communication." In *Ancient Civilization and Trade*, edited by Jeremy A. Sabloff and C. C. Lamberg-Karlovsky. Albuquerque: University of New Mexico Press, 1975. A theoretical study of the obsidian trade that applies system theory and locational analysis in the reconstruction of the formation of civilization. Useful for those interested in the application of model building in archaeological analysis. Good bibliography.

Renfrew, Colin, J. E. Dixon, and J. R. Cann. "Further Analysis of Near Eastern Obsidians." *Proceedings of the Prehistoric Society* 34 (1968): 319-331. A follow-up on the original study of Near Eastern obsidians. This article gives new information about the Anatolian sources and some revised results for the early Neolithic obsidian trade pattern. Useful illustrations and charts.

_____. "Obsidian and Early Cultural Contact in the Near East." *Proceedings of the Prehistoric Society* 32 (1966): 30-72. An extensive article on the obsidian trade in the Near East. Uses the same characterization methods as the original west Mediterranean study with similar, impressive results. Contains several charts and graphs. Excellent maps and bibliography.

Suzanne Knudson Engler

Cross-References

Evans Discovers the Minoan Civilization on Crete (1900), p. 67; Libby Introduces the Carbon-14 Method of Dating Ancient Objects (1940's), p. 1160; Scientists Develop a Technique to Date Ancient Obsidian (1960), p. 1645.

GLENN IS THE FIRST AMERICAN TO ORBIT EARTH

Category of event: Space and aviation
Time: February 20, 1962
Locale: 261 kilometers above Earth

By becoming the first American to orbit Earth, Glenn provided further impetus for the United States space program

Principal personages:

JOHN H. GLENN, JR. (1921-   ), a lieutenant colonel in the U.S. Marine Corps and pilot of the *Friendship 7* spacecraft who later became a senator from Ohio

M. SCOTT CARPENTER (1925-   ), a U.S. Navy lieutenant commander, backup pilot for the mission, and pilot of the subsequent Mercury-Atlas 7 flight

ALAN B. SHEPARD (1923-   ), a U.S. Navy lieutenant commander who was the first American in space

VIRGIL I. ("GUS") GRISSOM (1926-1967), a U.S. Air Force captain, capsule communicator at the Bermuda tracking station

L. GORDON COOPER (1927-   ), an Air Force major, capsule communicator at the Muchea, Australia tracking station

WALTER M. SCHIRRA (1923-   ), a U.S. Navy lieutenant commander, capsule communicator at the Point Arguello, California, tracking station

DONALD K. ("DEKE") SLAYTON (1924-   ), a U.S. Air Force major, blockhouse capsule communicator at Cape Canaveral

Summary of Event

Stunned by the Soviet accomplishment of 1961 and able to place a manned spacecraft only into suborbital flight, the National Aeronautics and Space Administration (NASA) was anxious to get John H. Glenn, Jr., into orbit. It had been only four years since the United States placed its first, tiny spacecraft into low Earth orbit, but president John F. Kennedy had set a goal for sending astronauts to the Moon within eight years, and NASA could not get Glenn off the ground.

The program to send Americans into space was originally called the Manned Satellite Project. Its objectives were "to achieve at the earliest practicable date orbital flight and successful recovery of a manned satellite, and to investigate the capabilities of man in this environment." These goals would be accomplished using the most reliable, available boost system. The spacecraft would be placed in an orbit high enough to permit a twenty-four-hour satellite lifetime. A retropropulsion system would be used to bring the craft out of orbit, and parachutes would lower it back to Earth. The spacecraft would be large enough to accommodate a single passenger but small enough to be carried on the nose of its booster. It would have high aerodynamic drag to slow it during reentry and would be capable of withstanding all the environmental changes placed upon it during flight.

In order to guarantee general use by contractors, the press, and the public, a short name was chosen for the project early in the fall of 1958. After rejecting names that might overemphasize the personality of the astronaut in the project or any military connotation, NASA officials formally announced that the manned satellite program would be called Project Mercury. The Olympian messenger Mercury already was a familiar name to most Americans by virtue of the chemical element and automobile bearing his name.

On May 5, 1961, slightly more than three weeks after Soviet cosmonaut Yuri Gagarin became the first human to fly in space, Alan B. Shepard was launched by a modified Redstone missile on a ballistic trajectory that took him and the *Freedom 7* spacecraft 188 kilometers high and 486 kilometers downrange. The feat was duplicated by Virgil I. ("Gus") Grissom two months later in *Liberty Bell 7*. Less than two weeks later, the Soviets again upstaged the United States by orbiting Gherman Titov for nearly a day.

NASA's first opportunity to launch Glenn came on January 27, 1962. Excessive cloud cover forced the Mercury-Atlas 6 mission to be canceled less than thirty minutes before lift-off. Weather and a slight problem with an insulation-retaining bulkhead in the Atlas booster delayed the mission six more times. At 11:30 P.M. on Monday, February 19, the second half of the final countdown began.

Glenn was awakened at 2:20 A.M. on February 20. He showered, got dressed, and ate breakfast. He was given a physical examination, had biomedical sensors placed on his body, and put on his silver-colored pressure suit. At 5:05 A.M., two hours before the scheduled launch, Glenn entered the transfer van to take him to Launch Pad 14. After the two-minute ride, he rode an elevator to the "white room" enclosing the tiny *Friendship 7* spacecraft.

In the military tradition, Glenn had been given the privilege of naming his craft. He elected to hold a family competition, and the name was chosen because friendship was what he wanted to spread as he circled Earth. The number 7 was a carryover from Shepard's capsule, *Freedom 7*. Shepard's capsule was production number 7, his booster was Redstone number 7, and his was to be the first of seven manned Redstone suborbital flights. It was only coincidental that there were seven Mercury astronauts, but the group thought that it would be appropriate to continue the 7 designation for all of their craft.

Glenn climbed into his spacecraft, and, after a brief delay caused by a broken microphone bracket in his helmet, the hatch was sealed. One of the hatch's bolts was found to be broken and had to be replaced. The countdown was stopped for the repairs. The hatch was reinstalled and the countdown resumed at 8:05 A.M. Several brief holds delayed the flight, but at 9:47:35 A.M., Atlas 109 lifted off into the blue Florida sky four seconds later. "Roger. The clock is operating. We're underway," radioed Glenn in a brisk, businesslike manner. He watched Earth fall away in his rear-view mirror, as the vibrations started to build. "Little bumpy along about here." The Atlas strained to overcome the bonds of gravity. As the air thinned, the ride began to smooth. At two minutes, twelve seconds into the flight, the two outboard booster engines on the Atlas shut down and were jettisoned. Also jettisoned was the now-unneeded launch escape tower. Three minutes later, the sustainer engine ran out of fuel and *Friendship 7* separated from the Atlas. John Glenn was in orbit.

The planned three-orbit mission went well. Glenn changed the spacecraft's attitude by moving a hand controller, which operated small hydrogen peroxide jets around the perimeter of the capsule. He made visual observations and took photographs; he checked the status of his craft and ate some food out of toothpaste tubes; he watched the sun set and then rise again forty minutes later. Looking out his window, he noticed luminous particles which he described as "fireflies" and which seemed to follow him. The particles are believed to be snowflakes from water vapor released by the capsule's cooling system, as well as paint and other material from the capsule.

Glenn had some problems with his autopilot and one of his thrusters, but he was able to complete most of his tasks. The ground tracking stations had received a signal indicating that the heat shield at the blunt base of the capsule might have come loose. If it were to separate from the craft during reentry, *Friendship 7* and its passenger would disintegrate in the intense heat. Ground controllers decided to leave the retropack attached during reentry in the hope that it would keep the shield in place until atmospheric pressure had built up sufficiently to retain it.

Friendship 7's three retrorockets ignited in sequence. The spacecraft slowed sufficiently to be captured by Earth's gravity and began its fiery plunge back down. Through his window, Glenn saw chunks of the retropack burn off and fly past him. He described the reentry as a "real fireball," though no one heard his radio transmission. He was in an ionization field created by the interaction of his capsule with the air molecules. Several minutes later, Glenn reestablished radio contact and reported that his stabilizing drogue parachute and his main parachute had deployed on time. After four hours, fifty-five minutes, twenty-three seconds in flight, *Friendship 7* was bobbing in the Atlantic Ocean. Several minutes later, Glenn, still strapped into his contour seat, was plucked from the water and placed on board the U.S. Navy destroyer *Noa*.

Impact of Event

Friendship 7 provided the U.S. space program with a needed impetus. Overshadowed by Soviet accomplishments in space and plagued by setbacks, NASA was being pressured by the press and by Congress to realize the manned moon landing goal.

Three months after Glenn's flight, M. Scott Carpenter verified that the United States could orbit a manned spacecraft and that Glenn's journey was not a fluke. In October, 1962, Walter M. Schirra flew a six-orbit mission, leading to the final Mercury mission in May, 1963. L. Gordon Cooper's flight met the goal of placing a manned spacecraft into orbit for twenty-four hours. Six of the Mercury astronauts flew during the program. Donald K. (Deke) Slayton, scheduled to pilot the Mercury-Atlas 7 mission, was grounded from flight because of an idiopathic atrial fibrillation (occasional irregularity of a muscle at the top of the heart), caused by unknown factors. In March, 1972, he was returned to flight status following a comprehensive review of his medical status. He flew as docking module pilot on the joint Soviet/American Apollo-Soyuz mission in 1975.

John Glenn became the most celebrated national hero since Charles Lindbergh and was approached by President Kennedy to run as a Democrat for a Senate seat from Ohio. Glenn had planned to stay with NASA to be part of the Apollo program, but he retired on January 16, 1964, to campaign for the Senate. Unfortunately, on February 26, 1964, he suffered a head injury from a fall, which forced him to postpone his senatorial quest. He worked as an executive in the private sector until his election to the U.S. Senate in 1974.

The Mercury Project teams shifted to the Gemini Program in early 1964 with great ease. The Gemini spacecraft was an enlarged, two-man version of the Mercury capsule. It offered many improvements, including a modular design for replacement of equipment. Gemini developed the techniques of orbital rendezvous and docking, as well as extravehicular activity (space walking), necessary to accomplish the goals of Apollo.

The Mercury spacecraft was a marvel of compactness. There were no integrated circuits or miniaturized components. The geniuses behind the program developed the technological roots for every subsequent American manned space flight and quite a few unmanned ones. In little more than three years, NASA went from placing small satellites in space to launching manned spacecraft. It had taken humans more than fifty years to get from the Wright Brothers to Sputnik.

Bibliography

Boynton, John H., ed. *First United States Manned Three-Pass Orbital Mission (Mercury-Atlas 6, Spacecraft 13): Part I—Description and Performance Analysis*. Washington, D.C.: Government Printing Office, 1964. This is part of the official NASA report on the Mercury-Atlas 6 flight. A description of the space vehicle and launch vehicle is presented, detailing each of the major systems as configured for the mission. The sequence of events is enumerated along with trajectory data. Black-and-white photographs, line drawings, and a brief reference list are included.
Carpenter, M. Scott, et al. *We Seven, by the Astronauts Themselves*. New York: Simon & Schuster, 1962. The seven *Mercury* astronauts describe the man-in-space program. The main focus is on Glenn's flight. The stories are personal narratives of many aspects of the project, including the spacecraft and the flights that preceded Glenn's. There are many black-and-white photographs and an index.
Chapman, John L. *Atlas: The Story of a Missile*. New York: Harper & Brothers, 1960. This is the "biography" of America's premier intercontinental ballistic missile, which would soon be used to put an astronaut into orbit. Although the infor-

mation in this work is very dated and limited, it provides an insight into the creation of a missile.

Grimwood, James M. *Project Mercury: A Chronology.* NASA SP-4001. Washington, D.C.: Government Printing Office, 1963. This is NASA's official record of Project Mercury, covering events on a day-to-day basis. Included in the coverage are the development of the spacecraft and launch vehicles, astronaut training, and mission results. Contains many black-and-white photographs and line drawings of components. Appendices provide a summary of the Mercury flights: mission objectives, orbital activities, and experiments.

McKann, Robert E., ed. *First United States Manned Three-Pass Orbital Mission (Mercury-Atlas 6, Spacecraft 13): Part II—Flight Data.* Washington, D.C.: Government Printing Office, 1964. This is part of the official NASA report on the Mercury-Atlas 6 flight. In this volume, actual flight data are presented. Contains a complete presentation of the data record. Includes charts, tables, and line drawings. A reference list is provided.

NASA Manned Spacecraft Center. *Results of the First United States Manned Orbital Space Flight, February 20, 1962.* Washington, D.C.: Government Printing Office, 1962. Describes the spacecraft and launch vehicle. Details each of the major systems as configured for the mission. Includes black-and-white photographs, line drawings, and a brief reference list.

Swenson, Loyd S., Jr., James M. Grimwood, and Charles C. Alexander. *This New Ocean: A History of Project Mercury.* NASA SP-4201. Washington, D.C.: Government Printing Office, 1966. One title in *The NASA History Series*, this book chronicles Project Mercury, from its conception to the flight of Gordon Cooper in Mercury-Atlas 9. Contains many black-and-white photographs. Line drawings show the inner workings of much of the equipment related to the missions. An impressive appendix lists source notes and bibliographic references.

Wolfe, Tom. *The Right Stuff.* New York: Farrar, Straus & Giroux, 1979. Interesting book about the team who flew in Project Mercury and about Chuck Yeager, the "loner" of X-1 fame. For a wide audience.

Russell R. Tobias

Cross-References

The Wright Brothers Launch the First Successful Airplane (1903), p. 203; Sputnik 1, the First Artificial Satellite, Is Launched (1957), p. 1545; The United States Launches Its First Orbiting Satellite, Explorer 1 (1958), p. 1583; Luna 2 Becomes the First Man-Made Object to Impact on the Moon (1959), p. 1614; Gagarin Becomes the First Human to Orbit Earth (1961), p. 1693; Shepard Is the First United States Astronaut in Space (1961), p. 1698; The Orbital Rendezvous of Gemini 6 and 7 Succeeds (1965), p. 1803; The First Humans Land on the Moon (1969), p. 1907.

TELSTAR, THE FIRST
COMMERCIAL COMMUNICATIONS SATELLITE,
RELAYS LIVE TRANSATLANTIC TELEVISION PICTURES

Category of event: Space and aviation
Time: July 10, 1962
Locale: Andover, Maine; Pleumeur-Bodou, France

Telstar I, the world's first commercial communications satellite, opened the age of live, worldwide television with the first transmission between the United States and Europe

Principal personages:
ARTHUR C. CLARKE (1917-   ), a British science fiction writer who first proposed the use of artificial Earth satellites as communications relays in 1945
JOHN R. PIERCE (1910-   ), an American engineer who worked on the Echo and Telstar satellite communications projects

Summary of Event

In 1945, Arthur C. Clarke proposed that a satellite orbiting high above the earth could serve as a communications relay station, overcoming the line of sight limitation on television transmission. Writing in the February, 1945, issue of *Wireless World*, Clarke said artificial satellites "could give television and microwave coverage to the entire planet." The first practical demonstration of the satellite relay principle came on December 18, 1958, when the United States Air Force launched the Project Score satellite. A 68-kilogram radio relay on Score accepted and retransmitted signals, including President Dwight D. Eisenhower's Christmas message to the world, between ground stations in Texas, Arizona, and Georgia.

In 1956, even before the launching of the first satellite, John R. Pierce at the Bell Telephone Laboratories of the American Telephone and Telegraph Company (AT&T) urged development of commercial orbital radio relays. He saw communications satellites as a replacement for the ocean bottom cables then being used to carry transatlantic telephone calls. In 1950, a total of 1.5 million transatlantic calls were made, but this was expected to grow to 3 million calls by 1960, straining the capacity of the existing cables; 21 million calls were made by 1970.

Communications satellites offered a viable alternative to building more transatlantic telephone cables. Economic calculations indicated that a satellite system, capable of handling one thousand calls simultaneously, and the ground stations could be built for about $100 million and maintained for $20 million per year. The potential revenue from such a system was estimated to be about $100 million per year. A satellite could also relay television, which could not be done by the transatlantic cable.

On January 19, 1961, the Federal Communications Commission (FCC) authorized AT&T to establish, at its own expense, an experimental satellite communications link across the Atlantic Ocean. The Bell Telephone Laboratories initiated Project Telstar, the first commercial communications satellite, in an agreement with the National Aeronautics and Space Administration (NASA) in July, 1961, under which AT&T was to develop and construct the Telstar satellite and ground communications stations. AT&T would pay NASA $3 million for each Telstar launch. The Telstar project involved about four hundred scientists, engineers, and technicians at the Bell Telephone Laboratories, twenty more technical personnel at AT&T headquarters, and the efforts of more than eight hundred other companies that furnished equipment or services. By July, 1962, AT&T had invested more than $50 million in research, development, and construction of the satellite and support facilities.

Telstar I was shaped like a faceted sphere, 88 centimeters in diameter and weighing 80 kilograms. Most of its exterior surface, sixty of the seventy-four facets, was covered by thirty-six hundred solar cells to convert sunlight into 15 watts of electricity to power the satellite. Each solar cell was covered with man-made sapphire to reduce the damage caused by the high-energy particles in the Van Allen radiation belt. As an experimental satellite, Telstar I carried a variety of instruments to evaluate its performance and monitor the effects of radiation on its electronics. The main instrument was a communications transponder, a radio receiver operating at 6,390 megahertz, and a transmitter operating at 4,170 megahertz, capable of relaying six hundred simultaneous telephone calls or one television channel. The transmitter output was only 2.25 watts, less than one-thirtieth that of a household light bulb.

Large ground antennas were required to receive Telstar's faint signal. The principal ground station was constructed by AT&T on a hilltop, informally called Space Hill, in Andover, Maine. A horn-shaped antenna, weighing 380 tons, with a length of 54 meters and an open end with an area of 1,097 square meters was mounted so that it could rotate to track Telstar across the sky. To minimize the stresses from wind and weather, the antenna was built inside an inflated dome, 64 meters in diameter and 49 meters tall. It was, at the time, the largest inflatable structure ever built. A second, smaller horn antenna in Holmdel, New Jersey, built by Bell Telephone Laboratories for experiments with the Echo I balloon satellite, was modified to receive signals from Telstar.

In February, 1961, the governments of the United States and England agreed to a collaboration between the British Post Office and NASA for testing experimental communications satellites. The British Post Office constructed a 26-meter-diameter steerable dish antenna of their own design at Goonhilly Downs, near Cornwall, England. Under a similar agreement, the French National Center for Telecommunications Studies constructed a ground station, almost identical to the Andover station, at Pleumeur-Bodou, Brittany, France.

The Telstar satellite was assembled and vibration tested at AT&T's Hillside, New Jersey, laboratory and then moved to Murray Hill, New Jersey, for transmission checks. The satellite was then placed in a thermal-vacuum chamber, where it was cooled to 149 degrees Celsius, heated by arc lamps mimicking the sun, and exposed to a vacuum simulating the space environment.

Following testing, Telstar I was moved to Cape Canaveral, Florida. and attached to the Thor-Delta launch vehicle built by the Douglas Aircraft Company. The Thor-Delta was launched at 3:35 A.M. eastern standard time (EST) on July 10, 1962, carrying Telstar I into an elliptical orbit with a low point of 953 kilometers and a high point of 5,655 kilometers. Telstar I took 157.8 minutes to circle the globe. The satellite was within range of the Andover antenna from 60 to 260 minutes a day. Telstar came within range of the Andover station on its sixth orbit, and a television test pattern was transmitted to the satellite at 6:26 P.M. EST. At 6:30 P.M. EST, a tape recorded black-and-white image of the American flag with the Andover station in the background, transmitted from Andover to Holmdel, opened the first television show ever broadcast by satellite. Live pictures of Vice President Lyndon B. Johnson and other officials gathered at Carnegie Institution in Washington, D.C., followed on the AT&T program carried live on all three American networks.

Up to the moment of launch, it was uncertain if the French station would be completed in time to participate in the initial tests. At 6:47 P.M. EST, however, Telstar's signal was acquired by the station in Pleumeur-Bodou, and Johnson's image became the first transatlantic television transmission. Pictures received at the French station were reported to be so clear that they looked like they were sent from only 40 kilometers away. Technical difficulties prevented reception of a clear signal at the English station.

American television viewers saw their first satellite transmissions from Europe on the night of July 11, 1962. At 6:35 P.M. EST, the French station broadcast a seven-minute taped program which included Yves Montand singing "La Chansonette." The English complained that this broadcast violated an agreement that the first Europe-to-America transmission would be a program produced by Eurovision, scheduled for the following week. The French replied that their transmission was only a "test." The English, who had corrected the difficulties at their station, transmitted the first live television between Europe and the United States on the next orbit. At 9:21 P.M. EST, American viewers saw an English test pattern.

The first formal exchange of programming between the United States and Europe occurred on July 23, 1962. This special eighteen-minute program produced by the European Broadcasting Union included Austria, Belgium, Denmark, Finland, France, West Germany, Ireland, Italy, Luxembourg, Monaco, The Netherlands, Norway, Portugal, Spain, Sweden, Switzerland, England, and Yugoslavia. It consisted of live scenes from major cities throughout Europe and was transmitted from Goonhilly Downs to Andover via Telstar. The European program, broadcast live on network television in the United States, depicted the heritage of Europe.

On the previous orbit, a program entitled "America, July 23, 1962," showing scenes from fifty television cameras around the United States, was beamed from Andover to Pleumeur-Bodou and seen by an estimated 100 million viewers throughout Europe. Telstar I functioned until February 21, 1963, except for an interruption from November 23, 1962, to January 4, 1963.

Impact of Event

Telstar I was the first space project originated and paid for by private enterprise. Telstar's launching marked the entry of private enterprise into space, and communications satellites quickly became the first viable space business venture. On the first day of trading after Telstar's launching, AT&T stock rose from 109.875 to 113.25 on the New York Stock Exchange.

The day after the launch of Telstar I, President Kennedy initiated a study of the new opportunities and problems arising from satellite communications technology. This study resulted in passage of the Communications Satellite Act on August 27, 1962. The act established the Communications Satellite Corporation (COMSAT) as the only United States entity permitted to enter into international communications agreements. This law effectively prohibited AT&T from operating its own commercial international telecommunications system. AT&T continued with the development of a second experimental satellite, Telstar II, but the Andover station was eventually sold to COMSAT.

COMSAT became the manager of the space segment of the International Telecommunications Satellite Consortium (INTELSAT), with an initial membership of eleven nations. By 1970, seventy-four nations, representing more than 96 percent of the world's telecommunications traffic, had joined INTELSAT. Within a decade, a single INTELSAT IV communications satellite demonstrated a transmission capacity of six thousand two-way telephone calls, exceeding the capability of all the world's international underwater telephone cables, or twelve simultaneous color television programs.

The significance of global satellite communications, however, went far beyond the world of private enterprise. In signing the COMSAT legislation, President Kennedy forecast: "The ultimate result will be to encourage and facilitate world trade, education, entertainment, and many kinds of professional, political and personal discourses which are essential to healthy human relationships and international understanding."

Telstar I and its successors revolutionized the television news and sports industries. Prior to the communications satellite, television networks had to rely on shipping film across the oceans, meaning delays of hours or days between the time an event occurred and the broadcast of pictures of that event on television on another continent. Now, news events of major significance, as well as sporting events, can be viewed live around the world. The impact on international relations also was significant, with world opinion becoming able to influence the actions of governments and individuals, since those actions could be seen around the world as the events were still in progress.

More powerful launch vehicles allowed new satellites to be placed in geosynchronous orbits, circling the earth at a speed the same as the earth's rotation rate so, when viewed from the ground, these satellites appeared to remain stationary in the sky. This allowed continuous communications and greatly simplified the ground antenna system. By the late 1970's, private individuals were able to build small antennas in their backyards to receive television signals directly from the satellites.

Bibliography

Clarke, Arthur C. *Voices from the Sky: Previews of the Coming Space Age.* New York: Harper & Row, 1965. This collection includes essays that explore the social consequences and impact on international relations of the instant, worldwide communications made available with satellites and describe Clarke's early role in suggesting such satellites. It includes a reprint of one of Clarke's 1945 *Wireless World* articles describing communications satellites.

Cook, Rick, and Frank Vaughn. *All About Home Satellite Television.* Blue Ridge Summit, Pa.: TAB Books, 1983. This well-illustrated volume describes the history of satellite television, explains the various types of satellites, and discusses the evolution of communications satellites from the earliest efforts to the modern, high-power satellites that can be received by individuals with personal antennas.

Edelson, Burton I. "Global Satellite Communications." *Scientific American* 236 (February, 1977): 58-68. This well-illustrated article traces the growth of the communications satellite industry, with particular emphasis on the economics of operation and the INTELSAT series of communications satellites.

Gatland, K. W., ed. *Telecommunication Satellites.* Englewood Cliffs, N.J.: Prentice-Hall, 1964. A detailed history of the first five years of communication by satellite. Chapter 3 focuses on Project Telstar, describing the satellite and its instrumentation, its orbit, and the reason for its eventual radiation-induced failure. Chapter 7 discusses the prospects for Europe, including descriptions of the European ground stations, a chronology of the first two weeks of transatlantic communications via Telstar I, and photographs of the first black-and-white and color television signals transmitted across the Atlantic to the English station at Goonhilly Downs.

Jaffe, Leonard. *Communications in Space.* New York: Holt, Rinehart and Winston, 1966. This well-illustrated monograph, written by the official who directed NASA's communications satellite effort from 1959 to 1963, describes the history of communications satellites and the expected societal impact of worldwide satellite communications. Includes an extensive reference list, and is intended for general audiences.

Ordway, Frederick I., III, Carsbie C. Adams, and Mitchell R. Sharpe. *Dividends from Space.* New York: Thomas Y. Crowell, 1971. Chapter 8 traces the history of communications satellites, the formation of the COMSAT and the INTELSAT, and the economic development of the communications satellite industry. Intended for general audiences, this book emphasizes the economic and public benefits of satellite communications.

Pierce, J. R. *The Beginnings of Satellite Communications.* San Francisco: San Francisco Press, 1968. This insider's account, written by the director of communications for the Bell Telephone Laboratories, describes the motivation for commercial communications satellites and traces their early history, with particular emphasis on the Telstar project.

George J. Flynn

Cross-References

Elster and Geitel Devise the First Practical Photoelectric Cell (1904), p. 208; Einstein Develops His Theory of the Photoelectric Effect (1905), p. 260; Bell Telephone Scientists Develop the Photovoltaic Cell (1954), p. 1487; The First Transatlantic Telephone Cable Is Put Into Operation (1956), p. 1502; Van Allen Discovers the Earth's Radiation Belts (1958), p. 1572; Echo, the First Passive Communications Satellite, Is Launched (1960), p. 1677.

MARINER 2 BECOMES THE FIRST
SPACECRAFT TO STUDY VENUS

Category of event: Space and aviation
Time: August, 1962-January, 1963
Locale: Cape Canaveral, Florida

In December of 1962, Mariner 2 became the first spacecraft to visit another planet and return useful data to Earth

Principal personages:
>JAMES RAYMON DEMPSEY (1921-   ), the president of Convair Astro-
>nautics
>JACK N. JAMES, the project manager of the Mariner program
>MARSHALL S. JOHNSON, the director of Mariner spaceflight operations
>ROBERT J. PARKS (1922-   ), the planetary program director of Jet Pro-
>pulsion Laboratory
>WILLIAM H. PICKERING (1910-   ), the director of Jet Propulsion Lab-
>oratory
>NICHOLAS A. RENZETTI, the director of the Deep Space Instrumentation
>Facility
>DAN SCHNEIDERMAN, the Mariner spacecraft systems manager

Summary of Event

In 1960, the National Aeronautics and Space Administration (NASA) formulated a plan that called for the launching of a spacecraft to the vicinity of the planet Venus. The launch window was to be a fifty-six-day period extending from July to September, 1962. Originally, the plan called for the building and launching of two spacecraft in this new Mariner series. The first craft, Mariner A, would be launched toward Venus. The second craft, Mariner B, would be sent to Mars.

The launch vehicle was to be the Atlas-Centaur two-stage rocket. The first stage, the Atlas, was the Air Force's Intercontinental Ballistic Missile. This particular variation, the Atlas-D, produced some 360,000 pounds of thrust at launch and had a range of about 10,000 kilometers. The vehicle was capable of accelerating a payload to more than 25,000 kilometers per hour.

The Atlas-D was made up of two main sections, a body and a booster-engine section. The booster section consisted of two 154,000-pound-thrust engines, which were jettisoned after they burned out. Two small vernier engines were installed on opposite sides of the rocket to help provide stability. The Atlas was finless and used a gimbal system of swiveling the engine thrust chambers for control. The vehicle was approximately 30 meters long, with a diameter of about 3 meters at its base.

The Centaur second stage, which was then under development by NASA's Lewis Research Center, was to develop some 30,000 pounds of thrust from two main engines. This powerful combination of the Atlas and the Centaur would make it possible for the Mariner spacecraft to be in the 450 to 560 kilogram class.

By the summer of 1961, it became apparent that the Centaur upper stage would not be available because of developmental problems. The replacement would be the reliable, but much less powerful, Agena-B. The Agena-B, as used in the Mariner program, weighed 765 kilograms and developed 16,000 pounds of thrust. The vehicle was 7.5 meters in length, with a diameter of 1.5 meters. It had the ability to be restarted in space. This feature enabled the spacecraft's orbital attitude to be changed. The restarting ability also allowed larger payloads to be carried into space.

Because the thrust output of the Agena-B was considerably less than that of the proposed Centaur, the weight of the Mariner spacecraft had to be reduced to about 200 kilograms. A spacecraft incorporating features of both the original Mariner A and the Ranger 3 unmanned lunar landing vehicle was proposed by scientists at the Jet Propulsion Laboratory (JPL). As a result of this recommendation, NASA decided to build two of the smaller Mariner spacecraft and launch both vehicles to the vicinity of Venus in 1962. Key personnel involved in the Mariner project included Jack N. James, Dan Schneiderman, James Raymon Dempsey, Marshall S. Johnson, Nicholas A. Renzetti, and Robert J. Parks and William H. Pickering of JPL.

By the time it was decided to use the smaller spacecraft, NASA had eleven months only until the launch date. Because there was no time for a completely new design, components that had been used in earlier space missions were redesigned quickly for use in the Mariner.

The basic structure of the spacecraft was a hexagonal frame made of magnesium and aluminum. A tubular aluminum superstructure, sun sensors, a transmitting antenna, gas jets (which enabled the attitude of the spacecraft to be controlled), and a small rocket engine for in-flight course corrections were attached. The rocket motor, which was located in the center of the hexagonal base, developed about 50 pounds of thrust. Six rectangular cases were attached to the frame of the spacecraft. These structures housed the circuitry for the scientific experiments and for communications and control. Other cases held a computer, the data encoder, and a silver-zinc storage battery. The battery was charged by some ten thousand solar cells, which were located on the Mariner's solar panels. Because of the battery and the mechanism for recharging, the Mariner spacecraft was self-sufficient in power.

The instruments that would conduct experiments in space were attached, as well as a nondirectional antenna. The instruments consisted of a magnetometer, Geiger-Müller tubes, an ion chamber, a cosmic dust collector, and both microwave and infrared radiometers.

When assembled and ready for launch, the spacecraft measured 1.5 meters in diameter and about 3 meters in height. With the solar panels and the directional antenna deployed, as they would be during the major portion of the flight, the Mariner spacecraft was 4.95 meters wide and about 3.6 meters high. The total weight of the spacecraft was 201.2 kilograms.

There were six major groups of experiments carried on the Mariner spacecraft:

the microwave radiometer, infrared radiometer, magnetometer, cosmic dust detectors, charged particle detectors, and the solar plasma spectrometer. In the radiometer experiment, both microwaves and infrared wavelengths were to be gathered simultaneously by the two radiometers as they scanned the planetary surface. The microwaves were to be collected by a small parabolic receiving antenna and focused into a receiving horn. The infrared radiation was passed through a series of filters to separate two distinct wavelength regions. The encoded data were then to be returned to Earth. One of the purposes of this experiment was to observe limb brightening and darkening of Venus during the encounter in an attempt to determine the source of the high surface temperatures that were detected from Earth.

A sensitive fluxgate magnetometer was carried aboard Mariner 2 so that it could detect magnetic fields both in the vicinity of Venus and during the flight to Venus. Measurements of the local magnetic field were to be taken every twenty seconds during the flight.

Several instruments on the Mariner spacecraft were used to detect charged particles. The ionization chamber used in this experiment consisted of a volleyball-sized sphere that contained a pressurized inert gas and a central electrode. The spacecraft power supply would charge the ionization chamber during the experiment, and, as high-energy particles were encountered, the chamber would discharge slowly. This information, along with particle count data taken by three Geiger-Müller tubes, would allow the determination of individual particle energy and types of particles encountered.

The cosmic dust experiment consisted of a piezoelectric crystal composed of lead zirconate attached to a magnesium sounding plate. Any impact on the sounding plate would send out tiny shock waves. The piezoelectric crystal would be compressed slightly as the waves passed through it, and a voltage, which would depend on the momentum of the impacting meteoroid, then would be emitted by the crystal.

The solar plasma spectrometer would detect and study the stream of charged particles, or solar wind, from the sun. The device consisted of a pair of curved, gold-plated, magnesium plates. An electrical voltage was applied across the plates, which would cause positively charged particles, such as protons and alpha particles, to travel a curved path and impact against a collector. The voltage was adjusted so that only particles of known energy could pass between the plates and be received by the collector.

Early in June of 1962, two Mariner spacecraft and two Atlas-Agena rockets arrived at Cape Canaveral. The intent of NASA was to launch both of these vehicles toward Venus during July and August. Mariner 1 was launched at 4:21 A.M. on July 22. Because of an error in the computer software, the Atlas-Agena went out of control and had to be destroyed by the range safety officer. Mariner 1 landed in the Atlantic Ocean about 4.5 minutes after its launch.

After the failure of Mariner 1, Mariner 2 was moved to the launch pad with a scheduled launch date of August 24. Several technical difficulties postponed the launch until 2:53 A.M. on August 27. The Atlas carried the spacecraft to an altitude of about 160 kilometers and an attitude roughly parallel to Earth's surface. At this point, the Agena second stage ignited, sending the spacecraft into orbit around Earth. When the spacecraft had coasted into the correct position for departure toward Venus, the Agena was restarted. The ninety-five-second burn provided the velocity necessary to escape the earth's gravitational field and begin an interplanetary voyage.

At a distance of approximately 2.4 million kilometers from Earth, a midcourse correction was made. It was concluded that the course Mariner 2 was on would carry it too far from Venus. The small rocket motor attached to the Mariner was fired for twenty-nine seconds to act as a brake and allow a closer encounter with Venus. Early in the morning of December 14, 109 days into the flight, Mariner 2 arrived in the vicinity of Venus, and its instruments began to scan the surface of the planet. Data were received from the spacecraft until January 2, 1963, when Mariner 2 was 86.8 million kilometers away from Earth. At that time, radio contact with Mariner 2 was lost.

Impact of Event

The flight of Mariner 2 to Venus represented the first time that instruments had been sent to another planet and data had been returned successfully to Earth. This historic mission enabled scientists to revise many long-held views about interplanetary space and Venus.

It was found during the flight that the space between Venus and Earth contained a cosmic dust density about ten thousand times lower than the near-Earth region. The detector plate was positioned approximately perpendicular to the plane of the ecliptic during the experiment and was facing in the direction in which the spacecraft was flying. It was noted that Mariner survived two fairly major impacts on the way to Venus. Near Venus, there was no evidence of a concentration of particles similar to that which surrounds Earth. In fact, the number of particles detected near Venus was not significantly greater than the number recorded during the flight.

The spacecraft's magnetometer detected slight magnetic fields in interplanetary space, which confirmed a number of widely accepted beliefs. As Mariner 2 passed by Venus, there was no evidence of a magnetic field along the spacecraft's trajectory or any regions of trapped charged particles as there are near Earth. Since Mariner's closest approach was 35,000 kilometers, these data did not prove that Venus has no magnetic field at all. A weak field would be compressed to an area close to the planet's surface by the solar wind and thus remain undetected by the spacecraft's magnetometer.

During the flight, there was always a detectable, although widely fluctuating, stream of solar plasma. The velocities of the charged particles ranged from 320 to 770 kilometers per second. It was concluded by scientists that astronauts traveling in this region of space could not be harmed by this intensity of radiation.

Radiometer data revealed that the cloud-top temperature readings are about -35 degrees Celsius at the center of the planet and down to about -50 degrees Celsius at the limbs. This data indicated that there was an apparent limb-darkening effect and that the planet has a surface temperature of approximately 400 degrees Celsius on both its light and dark sides.

The flight of Mariner 2 allowed for a more accurate calculation of the mass of Venus. When first launched, the shape of its path through space was dominated by Earth. Later in the flight, the sun became the dominant factor, and then finally, Venus. Through careful measurements, it was found that the path of Mariner 2 was deflected some 40 degrees by the gravity of the planet. When a body of known mass and velocity is deflected by a second gravitational body, application of the laws of Sir Isaac Newton and Johannes Kepler allow the calculation of the mass of the second body. It was found that the mass of Venus, in relation to Earth, is 0.81485, with an error probability of 0.015 percent.

Bibliography

California Institute of Technology, Pasadena. Jet Propulsion Laboratory. *Mariner-Venus 1962: Final Project Report*. NASA SP-59. Washington, D.C.: Government Printing Office, 1965. Prepared as a project report on the Mariner 2 spacecraft. Begins with background material on the formation of the program and the pre-Mariner concepts on the nature of Venus and continues into a technical description of the spacecraft and the launch vehicle. Discusses in detail the scientific experiments on board the spacecraft and the data received from the flyby. The reader should have a scientific background.

Corliss, William R. *Space Probes and Planetary Exploration*. Princeton, N.J.: D. Van Nostrand, 1965. Begins with a general history of rocketry from the ancient Chinese to Mariner 4, then progresses into a fairly technical treatment of such topics as interplanetary transportation, space mechanics, and spacecraft design. Concludes with a highly technical description of the scientific apparatus flown on Mariner and Pioneer spacecraft. The reader should have an engineering or technical background.

Glasstone, Samuel. *Sourcebook on the Space Sciences*. Princeton, N.J.: D. Van Nostrand, 1965. Covers a wide range of topics, from historical background of space exploration, orbits, trajectories, and propulsion units to a general description of the sun, the planets, and the universe. The technical level varies with the subject area covered, but for the most part, the reader should have an elementary knowledge of physics, chemistry, and mathematics.

Sobel, Lester A., ed. *Space: From Sputnik to Gemini*. New York: Facts on File, 1965. A nontechnical volume. Provides a history of the space age from the launching of the Soviet satellite Sputnik 1 in 1957 to the Gemini missions and lunar probes of 1965. A chapter is devoted to each year from 1957 through 1965, in which the significant events in the space race between the United States and the Soviet Union are covered.

Wheelock, Harold J., comp. *Mariner Mission to Venus*. New York: McGraw-Hill, 1963. Covers the Mariner 2 spacecraft from the planning stages to its launch and flight to Venus. Describes in detail the spacecraft, the launch vehicle, the tracking network, the flight, the scientific experiments, and the data returned. Well illustrated; suitable for general readers.

David W. Maguire

Cross-References

Venera 3 Is the First Spacecraft to Impact on Another Planet (1965), p. 1797; Soviet Venera Spacecraft Transmits the First Pictures from the Surface of Venus (1975), p. 2042.

CARSON PUBLISHES *SILENT SPRING*

Categories of event: Earth science and biology
Time: September 27, 1962
Locale: Silver Spring, Maryland

Carson evoked public debate on the hazards of chemical pesticides, triggering a wave of protest that marked the genesis of the modern environmental movement

Principal personages:

RACHEL CARSON (1907-1964), a biologist and author of *Silent Spring* (1962) and three books on marine life

CLARENCE COTTAM (1899-1974), a biologist and assistant director of the United States Fish and Wildlife Service

ABRAHAM A. RIBICOFF (1910-   ), a U.S. senator from Connecticut who initiated congressional hearings on environmental pollution and the pesticide problem

Summary of Event

The publication of *Silent Spring* in 1962 is often cited as the landmark event that triggered the modern environmental movement. The book is the result of a rare combination of scientific training, dedicated research, and literary skill. Through her subject—contamination of the earth from unabated proliferation of chemical pesticides—Rachel Carson captured international attention as she turned a debate previously restricted to scientific circles into a public political issue, profoundly influencing the broader shaping of the environmental policy of the United States.

Carson's decision to write the book came after receiving a letter from her friend, Olga Huckins of Duxbury, Massachusetts. In the summer of 1957, a state-hired airplane had crisscrossed Huckins' two-acre wooded lot, making several aerial treatments of dichloro-diphenyl-trichloroethane (DDT) for mosquito control. The following day Huckins found seven dead songbirds in her yard. Faced with another scheduled round of spraying the next summer, Huckins wrote to Carson, asking whether she knew of anyone in Washington who could help. In the course of making inquiries for her friend, Carson became alarmed at how serious the pesticide problem had become. She resolved to alert the public through a book.

This was not the first time, however, that Carson had thought of writing about DDT. She had become interested in the insecticide in the mid-1940's while working for the U.S. Fish and Wildlife Service. Two of her associates there, Clarence Cottam and Elmer Higgins, had warned the public—in scientific papers—of the potential for DDT to harm wildlife.

Classified as a chlorinated hydrocarbon, DDT is a synthetic organic insecticide, characterized by high toxicity to a wide variety of insects and by its persistence (it does not degrade quickly in the environment). Although it was first synthesized in 1874, DDT was not found to be an effective insecticide until 1939, in time to be used during World War II to dust the clothing of soldiers for protection against typhus (spread by lice) and malaria (spread by mosquitoes).

In December, 1944, entomologists warned that DDT might kill many beneficial insects and upset nature's economy. This concern also was the message of articles by scientists published in *Harper's* and *The Atlantic Monthly* in 1945. Carson was aware of these reports and she, too, became concerned that DDT could upset the balance of nature. Anxious to supplement her income through free-lance writing, she queried the editors of *Reader's Digest* to see if they would be interested in an article on the new insecticide. Unfortunately, the magazine declined her offer, and for Carson the idea lay dormant until the arrival of Olga Huckins' worrisome letter, thirteen years later.

By the 1950's, royalties from her books had permitted Carson to resign from the Fish and Wildlife Service to write on a full-time basis. She spent most of the period from 1958 to 1962 reviewing scientific literature and writing *Silent Spring*. A condensed version, about one-third of the text, was published in *The New Yorker* as a three-part weekly series, the first of which appeared on June 16, 1962; publication of the book followed on September 27.

Carson began her book with a fable, a description of a pleasant rural town suddenly stricken by a mysterious blight that had caused massive sickness and death among the town's people and animals. The residents, it turned out, had brought this "silent spring" upon themselves, a result of their liberal use of chemical pesticides. The problems of the fictitious town, Carson explained, were representative of tragedies that had actually occurred in separate American communities. The remainder of her book was methodically ordered, like a legal brief, presenting scientific evidence to expose the threat posed by persistent pesticides. She described how laboratories had created hundreds of synthetic chemicals to kill pests and how the "fittest" insects had built up tolerances to these chemicals, forcing the development of increasingly lethal compounds to kill the super races that had survived and reproduced. Carson argued that chemical pesticides often caused severe consequences for wildlife and also produced long-term effects on human health.

One example made famous by Carson's book was her account of the contamination of Clear Lake, California, a popular fishing spot located about 145 kilometers north of San Francisco. To eradicate a small gnat that had become a nuisance both to tourists and residents, local officials there treated the lake in 1949 with DDD (dichloro-diphenyl-dichloroethane), an insecticide closely related to DDT. The chemical worked well, it seemed, killing most of the gnat larvae in the bottom sediments and providing effective gnat control for years. Then, in 1954, another treatment became necessary. The first sign of trouble came the following winter when more than one hundred of the lake's western grebes were found dead. More grebes died after a third application of the insecticide in 1957. Although the treatment had been highly diluted, the strongest dose was only one part insecticide to 50 million parts of water. An analysis of the fatty tissues of the grebes indicated a DDD concentration of sixteen hundred parts per million. According to Carson, the chemical had been absorbed by plankton, which were then eaten by fish. Western grebes preyed upon the fish. Scientists had found an increase in the concentration of DDD with each step up the food chain. The substance did not break down and disappear in the environment as presupposed. Rather, it persisted and became more concentrated in the fat of animals as it moved up the food chain. The experience at Clear Lake, Carson suggested, made the use of chemicals (even in low concentrations) a serious risk to top predators, including humans.

Carson called attention to examples of reckless use of insecticides in large-scale programs by the United States Department of Agriculture (USDA) to eradicate pest insects such as the gypsy moth and the fire ant. The gypsy moth had plagued New England states with occasional serious infestations for nearly a century. In 1956, the USDA initiated a program to eradicate the pest by spraying nearly one million acres with DDT. Damage from this spraying provoked citizens on Long Island to halt through litigation a second treatment scheduled for 1957. Nevertheless, a court injunction to stop the spraying was denied. After the treatment, fish, songbirds, and beneficial insects, such as bees were found dead; leaf crops were badly damaged; vegetables were coated with spray residues; and milk was contaminated by pesticide residues on the grasses consumed by dairy cattle.

Carson described a similar experience with the fire ant, an insect that had come into the United States from South America after World War I. At worst, the fire ant had become a minor nuisance in southern states, occasionally stinging people and building large mounds that sometimes hindered farm machinery. In 1957, however, through an outpouring of press releases, newspaper stories, and films, the USDA suddenly began to portray the fire ant as a major pest, dangerous to livestock, wildlife, and people. Ignoring the protests of state conservation agencies, the USDA launched a spraying program that treated one million acres in 1958 with heptachlor and dieldrin, two of the most toxic chlorinated hydrocarbon insecticides. Through her correspondence with Cottam, who was surveying the damage, Carson learned of the consequences of the massive spraying campaign. The effects were beginning to sound familiar: Songbirds, game birds, pets, poultry, cows and other livestock and wildlife were killed; and milk was contaminated. After the spraying stopped, officials in Louisiana and Florida reported greater infestations of fire ants than when the eradication program had begun. Carson's central argument was that the idea of eradication—the complete extermination of pest insects—was imprudent. Humans, she contended, must relinquish the notion of conquering nature. The aim, instead, should be to reduce pest damage through the safest and most practical means. She did not advocate complete abandonment of chemicals, rather an integrated approach to pest management, minimizing chemical applications and employing biological and cultural controls whenever possible.

Impact of Event

Silent Spring was embroiled in controversy even before it was published. One Chicago-based chemical company tried to prevent its publication by threatening a lawsuit over alleged inaccuracies. Carson's publisher, however, verified the facts in question and proceeded with publication. The company did not pursue litigation. Later, the same company was found responsible for discharging waste products into the lower Mississippi River containing residues of the pesticide endrin—a substance Rachel Carson had described as "the most toxic of all the chlorinated hydrocarbons." Investigators from the U.S. Public Health Service found that the chemical had caused massive fish deaths during the early 1960's. When the investigation was made public in 1964, it reinforced Carson's message on the environmental hazards of chemical pesticides.

In the wake of the controversy over *Silent Spring*, President John F. Kennedy requested a study of the pesticide issue. A panel was formed from the President's Science Advisory Committee; in 1963, the committee released its findings in a report entitled *Use of Pesticides*. The report credited Carson with having alerted the public to the problem and recommended that the government warn people of the hazards as well as the benefits of pesticides. The report supported Carson's argument that the safety of pesticides should be determined before they were allowed to be used. The report also criticized government insect eradication programs.

Carson's warning about the impact of human activity on the environment became the central theme of the new environmental movement. After reading Carson's book, Senator Abraham A. Ribicoff initiated Senate committee hearings to review all federal programs related to environmental pollution, including air and water pollution, as well as contamination from radiation, and pesticides. After fifteen months of hearings, Ribicoff noted that pesticide regulation was based on the notion that control chemicals remained at the treatment site, while scientific evidence demonstrated otherwise. Pesticide residues often were highly mobile. When Carson testified before the Ribicoff Committee, she explained how chemicals from aerial spraying could attach to particles of dust and drift for long distances. DDT residues were found even in Antarctica, where the substance had never been used. The committee's 1964 report, *Pesticides and Public Policy*, did not recommend abandonment of persistent pesticides but urged substantive federal support for research on the environmental and human health effects of pesticides.

In assessing the safety of pesticides, Carson had tried to enlarge the focus of concern about direct acute poisoning to include attention to the potential for long-term health effects, such as the risk of cancer. She succeeded in creating the conditions that would permit more research in this area. In 1969, the National Cancer Institute released a study showing that chronic exposure to low levels of DDT could produce cancer in laboratory animals. This study later motivated officials to regard DDT as "potentially" carcinogenic to humans, an important consideration in the decision to ban the substance. Other studies showed that DDT induced reproductive failure in peregrine falcons and eagles.

By 1969, states began to take individual action against DDT. Arizona passed a one-year ban on DDT and DDD. Michigan became the first state to pass a permanent ban on DDT after the USDA had seized 22,000 pounds of Lake Michigan salmon contaminated by high levels of the insecticide. Following six months of hearings initiated by the Environmental Defense Fund, Wisconsin also passed a law banning DDT, effective in March, 1970. Finally, in 1972, after seven months of hearings, William Ruckelshaus, administrator of the new U.S. Environmental Protection Agency, placed a federal ban on DDT.

Carson's book had prompted calls for a complete overhaul of the nation's environmental policies. In 1969, Congress officially recognized the importance of environmental quality when it passed the National Environmental Policy Act, a sign that renovation was under way.

Bibliography

Brooks, Paul. *The House of Life: Rachel Carson at Work*. 2d ed. Boston: Houghton Mifflin, 1989. A personal account of the life and work of Rachel Carson by her editor. Brooks includes excerpts from Carson's early works as well as from *Silent Spring*. Drawing upon their personal association, Brooks provides a popular biographical treatment of Carson. Illustrated, with an index.

Carson, Rachel. *Silent Spring*. Boston: Houghton Mifflin, 1962. A landmark in environmental history, *Silent Spring* warns of the menace of DDT and other pesticides to the health of all living creatures and urges people to change their view of nature as something to be conquered to a view that recognizes mutual dependencies within the web of life. In her graceful prose, Carson provides numerous examples of the toxic effects of pesticides and encourages people to demand alternatives to chemicals. Carson's training as a biologist enabled her to interpret existing scientific literature and present it clearly for a broad public readership. Index.

Dunlap, Thomas R. *DDT: Scientists, Citizens, and Public Policy*. Princeton, N.J.: Princeton University Press, 1981. A good comprehensive source for the DDT story and economic entomology, including the prelude to and aftermath of *Silent Spring*. Dunlap places the use of DDT and other insecticides in historical context and devotes a chapter specifically to the public policy controversy created by Carson. The book provides an account of the Wisconsin DDT hearing and the Environmental Protection Agency DDT hearing. Includes bibliography and index.

Graham, Frank, Jr. *Since "Silent Spring."* Boston: Houghton Mifflin, 1970. A journalist's account of the controversy surrounding *Silent Spring*, and developments of the pesticide debate in the years immediately following the publication of Carson's book (prior to the 1972 banning of DDT). Graham offers a useful description of the continuing pesticide problem during the 1960's.

Strong, Douglas H. "Rachel Carson." In *Dreamers and Defenders: American Conservationists*. Lincoln: University of Nebraska Press, 1988. An abbreviated account of Rachel Carson and the significance of *Silent Spring* is encapsulated in one short chapter of this book. Although not intended to be comprehensive, the major issues are presented in historical context. Illustrated.

Robert Lovely

Cross-References

Steinmetz Warns of Pollution in *The Future of Electricity* (1908), p. 401; Insecticide Use Intensifies When Arsenic Proves Effective Against the Boll Weevil (1917), p. 640; Müller Discovers That DDT Is a Potent Insecticide (1939), p. 1146; Manabe and Wetherwald Warn of the Greenhouse Effect and Global Warming (1967),p. 1840; The United States Government Bans DDT Use to Protect the Environment (1972), p. 1982; Rowland and Molina Theorize That Ozone Depletion Is Caused by Freon (1973), p. 2009; The British Antarctic Survey Confirms the First Known Hole in the Ozone Layer (1985), p. 2285.

THE CASSETTE FOR RECORDING AND PLAYING BACK SOUND IS INTRODUCED

Category of event: Applied science
Time: 1963
Locale: The Netherlands

The first self-contained audio cassette made it possible to record and repeatedly play back sound without threading tape, a major breakthrough destined to make audiotape competitive with long-play disc recordings in the music recording industry

Principal personage:
> FRITZ PFLEUMER, a German engineer whose work on audiotapes paved the way for audio cassette production

Summary of Event

The introduction of magnetic audio recording tape in 1929 was met with great enthusiasm, particularly in the entertainment industry, and specifically among radio broadcasters. Although somewhat practical methods for recording and storing sound for later playback had been around for some time, audiotape was much easier to use, store, and edit, and much less expensive to produce. It was Fritz Pfleumer, a German engineer, who in 1929 filed the first audiotape patent. His detailed specifications indicated that tape could be made by bonding a thin coating of oxide to strips of either paper or film. Pfleumer also suggested that audiotape could be stripped to films to provide higher-quality sound than was available with the film sound technologies in use at that time. In 1935, the German electronics firm AEG produced a reliable prototype of a record/playback machine based on Pfleumer's idea. By 1947, the American company 3M had refined the concept to the point where it was able to produce a high-quality tape using a plastic-based backing and red oxide. The tape recorded and reproduced sound with a high degree of clarity and dynamic range. It would soon become the standard in the industry.

Still, the tape was sold and used in a somewhat inconvenient open reel format. The user had to thread it through a machine and onto a take-up reel. This process made using audio recording machinery somewhat cumbersome and complicated for the layperson. Sound recording technology remained primarily a professional and industrial tool for many years.

In 1963, the first audio cassette was introduced by the Netherlands-based Philips company. This device actually embodied several innovations, each of which contributed to its immediate acceptance and extraordinary popularity from the beginning. First, the cassette could be inserted into a machine without threading. This was a convenience that reduced the amount of time and effort required to mount, search, and rewind a tape. Since there was no threading required, a tape could be inserted into a machine and played immediately. Rewind and fast-forward were faster, and it made no difference where the tape was stopped prior to ejection of the cassette. On the other hand, open reel audiotape required that the tape be wound fully onto one or the other of the two reels to which it was attached during recording or playback before it could be taken off the machine.

Second, because refinements in the technical character of audiotape had resulted in highly dynamic sound reproduction capability, the width of the tape inside the audio cassette and tape running speed could be reduced significantly without sacrificing quality. This narrower tape could be encased in smaller, more compact cassettes, thus enhancing portability. Record/playback machines could also be designed to be smaller for portability, which made them useful in many applications for which bulky reel-to-reel equipment was impractical. Portability was enhanced further by significant developments in reliable low-voltage battery technology.

Third, the enclosed cassette protected the tape from contamination and wear through physical handling. Constant threading of open reel tape led eventually to worn tape, which affected the quality of sound reproduction. Finally, reduced tape speed meant that more sound could be stored on the same length of tape; by flipping the cassette over and playing its reverse side, that length could, in fact, be doubled.

The Philips company initially marketed the audio cassette in Europe, where it gained widespread popularity in the mid-1960's. Its initial application was for monaural voice recording, although stereo cassettes were introduced, again by Philips, in 1966. Later, four-track stereo audio cassettes were introduced, an innovation that represented a striking leap beyond that available on the highest-quality vinyl recordings, which were limited to two tracks.

One of the most popular uses for audio cassettes was to record music from radios and other audio sources for later playback. During the 1970's, the popularity of FM radio—characterized by higher fidelity audio than was available from standard broadcast, or AM stations—resulted in a new emphasis on popular music programming across the radio dial. Many FM stations developed "all music" formats in which entire albums by artists were often played without interruption. That gave listeners an opportunity to record the music for later playback on specially outfitted radios that included cassette recorder/players. These were the same devices that would reemerge during the 1980's as "boom boxes," mini sound systems often played at high volume on street corners for impromptu socializing. At first, the music recording industry complained about this practice, charging that unauthorized recording of music from the radio was tantamount to copyright infringement and therefore illegal. Eventually, the issue died down as the same companies began to recognize this new, untapped market for recorded music.

Soon after achieving success in Europe, Philips began to license other manufacturers to produce cassettes and related technology, which had the effect of expanding that success throughout the world.

The audio cartridge emerged in 1965. This device was similar to the cassette in that tape was fully encased in a plastic container, convenient to use, and capable of providing high-quality stereo sound reproduction. The cartridge represented an innovation in self-contained audio because its tape was in a continuous loop that did not require rewinding. The user simply inserted the cartridge into a machine, at which point it would immediately begin playing. To stop it, the cartridge was simply grasped and pulled from the machine at any point during playback. Two drawbacks were its larger size—almost four times as big as the cassette—and the fact that it was available only in playback format. Also, it was not designed for rewind and fast forward transport capability, and its bulky size made it impractical as a portable device in the same sense that the cassette was portable. The primary success of the cartridge was attributed to the fact that automobile manufacturers began installing cartridge players in new models as an option in the mid-1960's. By 1967, it had become extremely popular in cars, although it survived for a relatively short period, eventually supplanted by the more compact and more versatile audio cassette and the digital compact disc during the 1980's.

Audio cassettes, all based on the original Philips design, were being manufactured by more than sixty companies within only a few years of their introduction. In addition, derivations of that design were being used in many specialized applications, including dictation, storage of computer information, and surveillance. The emergence of videotape resulted in a number of formats for recording and playing back video based on the same principle. Although each is characterized by different widths of tape—three-quarter inch, half inch, and 8 millimeter—each uses the same technique for tape storage and transport. As tape is spooled off one reel and wound onto the other, the space required by the first reel is reduced, and that same space is free to accommodate the increasing amount of tape on the other reel.

The cassette remained a popular means of storing and retrieving information on magnetic tape for more than a quarter of a century. During the early 1990's, digital technologies were beginning to appear that made it possible to store information in revolutionary new ways. Nevertheless, the audio cassette continued to be the most versatile, reliable, portable, and economical means of recording, storing, and playing sound available around the world.

Impact of Event

The cassette represented a new level of convenience for the audiophile, resulting in a significant increase in the use of recording technology in all walks of life. Even small children could operate cassette recorders and players, which led to their use in schools for a variety of instructional tasks and in the home for entertainment. The recording industry realized that audiotape cassettes would allow consumers to listen to recorded music in places where record players were not able to go: in automobiles, at the beach, even while camping. They recognized the potential for explosive growth in the use of audio technology.

They also saw the need for widespread availability of music and other information on cassette tape. The recording industry soon began distributing albums on audio cassette in addition to long-play vinyl discs, and recording sales increased substantially. This new technology put recorded music into automobiles for the first time in standard and eight-track formats, again resulting in a surge in sales for recorded music. Eventually, other forms of information, including language instruction and books-on-tape, became popular commuter fare.

With the invention of the microchip, audiotape players became available in smaller and smaller sizes, making them truly portable. Topping off a history already characterized by widespread acceptance and use, audio cassettes underwent another explosion in popularity during the early 1980's, when the Sony Corporation introduced the Walkman, an extremely compact, almost weightless version of earlier cassette players that could be attached to clothing and used with lightweight earphones virtually anywhere. At the same time, cassettes were suddenly being used with microcomputers for backing up magnetic data files. Home video soon exploded onto the scene, bringing with it new applications for cassettes. As had happened with audiotape, video camera/recorder units, called camcorders, were miniaturized to the point where 8-millimeter videocassettes capable of recording up to ninety minutes of live action and sound were widely available. These cassettes closely resembled the audio cassette first introduced in 1963.

The introduction of the self-contained, self-threading cassette ushered in the era of the cartridge concept of magnetic information storage in computers in the early 1980's. Just as the cassette provided a transport for moving tape, a similar concept was adopted for the storage and retrieval of digital files in microcomputers on small-format floppy disks. Many computer manufacturers designed products to work with cassettes that were inserted into disk drives to record and store computer files. Magnetic media housed in the cassettes was protected from potential damage through human handling in the same way that the first audio cassettes protected magnetic tape. This highly successful application of the cassette concept was extended to 35-millimeter camera technology in the early 1990's with the introduction of still video photography. These cameras, similar in appearance to standard 35-millimeter cameras, employed digital cassettes to store up to thirty-six frames. Because images were captured digitally instead of on film, they could be transmitted over telephone circuits and other electronic media, making them extremely popular with newspaper editors, who could now send or receive photographs almost instantaneously, a remarkable convenience in a deadline-oriented industry.

When the history of recording technology is written, the cassette will certainly hold a lofty place in the list of significant innovations that have made magnetic recording a universally applied technology in the workplace and in the home.

Bibliography

Burstein, Herman. *Questions and Answers About Tape Recording.* Blue Ridge Summit, Pa.: Tab Books, 1974. Attemps to answer for enthusiasts the most asked questions about audio recording.

Consumer Guide Editors. *The Complete Guide to Stereo Equipment.* New York: Simon & Schuster, 1979. A good reference for those desiring an overview of the available recording technology prior to 1980.

Crowhurst, Norman. *ABC's of Tape Recording.* Indianapolis: Sams, 1971. A layperson's guide to successful audio recording in the home.

Dolan, Edward F., Jr. *It Sounds Like Fun: How to Use and Enjoy Your Tape Recorder and Stereo.* New York: Julian Messner, 1981. An introduction to electronic recording equipment; gives a nontechnical treatment of the subject matter; written for the layperson. For those unaccustomed to working with electronic equipment, it is a good overview of the subject. Illustrations, index.

Hellyer, H. W. *How to Choose and Use Tape Recorders.* Plymouth, England: Clarke, Doble & Brendon, 1970. A thoroughly technical treatment of various types of magnetic tape recorders and players. Contains a good chapter on portable tape recorders and a strong history of the evolution of magnetic media for storing sound and other forms of information. Index and photographs.

Lowman, Charles E. *Magnetic Recording.* New York: McGraw-Hill, 1972. An excellent overview of magnetic recording as it has evolved over the years. Of particular interest are sections on applications of magnetic recording technology, including aerospace, science and medicine, underwater seismology, and electrocardiography and electroencephalography. The section on cassettes and cartridges is broken down into several subtreatments, including audio cassettes, digital cassettes and cartridges, and video cassettes.

Overman, Michael. *Understanding Sound, Video, and Film Recording.* Blue Ridge Summit, Pa.: Tab Books, 1978. Contains an excellent history of the evolution of sound recording from the earliest days, long before electronic recording and reproduction. Primary treatment is of magnetic recording and the technologies associated with it. Index.

Sinclair, I. R. *Stereo Cassette Recording.* Rochelle Park, N.J.: Hayden, 1976. A good reference guide for those interested in audio recording.

Zuckerman, Art. *Tape Recording for the Hobbyist.* Indianapolis: Sams, 1977. A guide for home recording of sound on vintage and advanced recording equipment. Includes discussions of the various environmental and technical characteristics of sound recording.

Michael S. Ameigh

Cross-References

Johnson Perfects the Process to Mass-Produce Disc Recordings (1902), p. 138; Fessenden Perfects Radio by Transmitting Music and Voice (1906), p. 361; Ford Produces Automobiles on a Moving Assembly Line (1913), p. 542; Armstrong Perfects FM Radio (1930), p. 939; Shockley, Bardeen, and Brattain Discover the Transistor (1947), p. 1304; UNIVAC 1 Becomes the First Commercial Electronic Computer and the First to Use Magnetic Tape (1951), p. 1396; Sony Develops the Pocket-Sized Transistor Radio (1957), p. 1528; The Floppy Disk Is Introduced for Storing Data Used by Computers (1970), p. 1923; Compact Disc Players Are Introduced (1982), p. 2200; IBM Introduces a Personal Computer with a Standard Hard Disk Drive (1983), p. 2240.

COHEN SHOWS THAT CANTOR'S CONTINUUM HYPOTHESIS IS INDEPENDENT OF THE AXIOMS OF SET THEORY

Category of event: Mathematics
Time: 1963
Locale: Stanford University, California

Cohen developed logical forcing techniques, an outgrowth of the concept of implication, which allowed him to determine the logical independence of assertions from the accepted axioms of set theory

Principal personages:
ARISTOTLE (384-322 B.C.), a Greek philosopher, logician, and scientist
GOTTFRIED WILHELM LEIBNIZ (1646-1716), a mathematician, philosopher, physical scientist, and diplomat who is best known among scientists as one of the founders of calculus
BERNHARD BOLZANO (1781-1848), a Czech philosopher, mathematician, and one of the founders of set theory
GEORG CANTOR (1845-1918), a German mathematician who is considered the father of modern set theory
DAVID HILBERT (1862-1943), a mathematician who left his imprint on nearly every field of mathematics and contributed to the development of modern physics
KURT GÖDEL (1906-1978), an Austrian logician who took the first step in resolving the continuum hypothesis
PAUL J. COHEN (1934-   ), an American mathematician and logician who created new methods in logic, which he used to clarify the continuum hypothesis and allowed other researchers to resolve problems in modern mathematics

Summary of Event

Early Greek thinkers were concerned with questions about mathematical truths. They were concerned about the nature of their arguments, when an argument made sense, and when they could be assured that deductions and implications were really true. Their speculations led Aristotle to set up certain basic rules of logic. His rules still are the basis of modern logic. Logic was taught throughout the Greek sphere of influence, and it applied to all areas of intellectual endeavor. As the classic world came to an end, Boethius (480-525) wrote a number of small tracts that were to serve as textbooks for the early medieval world, and one of these tracts discussed logic. Logic in Western Europe began to develop again during the twelfth century. The greatest logician and scholar at that time was the Breton scholar Peter Abelard (1079-1142). Although he studied philosophical and theological questions, his arguments and methods of reasoning foreshadowed many later developments. In the following centuries, logic was applied to philosophy and theology, problems in natural philosophy—that is, natural science, and mathematics.

During this period, there was renewed speculation about the infinite and truth in mathematics. Gottfried Wilhelm Leibniz took up an earlier line of thought involving the creation of a universal, mechanized logic, capable of resolving "all" mathematical questions. Leibniz was a proponent of mechanizing routine thought processes. His proof that two plus two equals four contained ideas that were forerunners of some of the modern ideas about the nature of numbers. He also used some of these ideas in his invention of a calculating machine.

After the invention of calculus, foundational questions were obscured by the rapid progress made in all areas of mathematics. Nevertheless, as science and mathematics progressed, work turned to the foundations of mathematics and science.

Modern efforts to understand the foundations of mathematics, to determine what was being assumed and what axioms were acceptable, and to achieve mathematical certainty and truth have centered on the theory of sets and logic. The first steps toward the creation of set theory were taken by Bernhard Bolzano at the beginning of the nineteenth century. For political reasons, he lost his professorship, and his work did not make an impact until later. The credit for the creation of set theory as it is known today belongs to Georg Cantor. According to Cantor, a set is a collection of well-defined objects or elements. There are many examples of sets. The totality of students in a given classroom, the cars in a certain parking lot, and so on, are all examples of sets. Sets can be divided naturally into two finite and infinite sets. Finite sets can be counted in the usual way. There are many examples of infinite sets: The natural numbers $(1, 2, 3 \ldots)$, the whole numbers or integers $(0, 1, 2 \ldots, -1, -2 \ldots)$, the rational numbers (that is, the quotients of whole numbers having a nonzero denominator), and the real numbers. It is possible to devise a scheme for determining whether one infinite set has more elements than another infinite set.

In order to "count" the infinite sets, one needs to generalize the idea of counting. Suppose someone is responsible for seating a large number of people at a banquet and wishes to know if there are enough places for them at the table. Counting them would be difficult and subject to error. The simplest thing would be to ask the people to sit down. If there were not enough places, then additional places could be set up until all were seated. If there were too many places, the extra places could be removed to give those seated extra room. If there were exactly the right number, then nothing need be done. If a large number of sheep needed to be transported, a penny for each sheep could be kept. At the end of the drive, one could see if the number of sheep matched up with the number of pennies. Both of these procedures could be done without counting. What is really fundamental in counting is the idea of a one-to-one correspondence. With the sheep, a one-to-one correspondence with pennies and sheep existed. At the banquet, a one-to-one correspondence between people and place settings existed. In the case of a finite set, each element of the set can be brought into one-to-one correspondence with the sequence of natural numbers $(1, 2 \ldots, n)$ for some natural number n. It the set has no elements, it is said to be empty and it has zero elements. A set, M , with, for example, four elements can be brought into one-to-one correspondence with the set (l, 2, 3, 4). To bring out that fact, one can say that the set, M , has cardinality 4 and write card (M) = 4.

Infinite sets are somewhat more difficult. Suppose that A is a subset of M. If A $\neq$ M, one would expect that card (A) < card (M), but that is not necessarily the case. For example, the set of even natural numbers can be brought into one-to-one correspondence with the set of natural numbers by the simple relationship of letting 2n correspond to n. Thus, the cardinality of the evens and the cardinality of the natural numbers are the same. The fact that a set can have the same "number" of elements as some of its subsets is typical of infinite sets. It is remarkable that the natural numbers, the whole numbers, and the rational numbers all have the same cardinality so that in the sense that they can be brought into one-to-one correspondence with each other, they have the same number of elements. Sets having the same cardinality as the natural numbers are said to be countable. The natural question is if there any sets that are uncountable, and the answer is yes. The cardinality of the real numbers, denoted by c, is greater than the cardinality of the natural numbers. Cantor decided to order the cardinal numbers. The first cardinal number gives the number of elements in a countable set. The main question is: What is the next cardinal number? Cantor thought that the next cardinal number gave the number of elements in a continuum, and he made a number of futile attempts to prove this, but without success. His supposition that equality holds has come to be known as the continuum hypothesis.

After its introduction, set theory was applied on a grand scale to the resolution of fundamental problems that had puzzled philosophers for centuries. Gottlob Frege (1846-1925) resolved the question of what a number is. Based on his work, Giuseppe Peano (1858-1932) formalized an axiom system for the natural numbers. Set theory began to permeate all areas of mathematics. Then a number of unpleasant paradoxes arose. These paradoxes went to the heart of what a set is and involved notions such as the set of all sets, or the set of all cardinal numbers, or all sets satisfying some property. These sets, although imaginable, were found to be inherently contradictory. They are related to medieval paradoxes such as: If God is all powerful, can He create a stone which is so heavy that He cannot lift it? These paradoxes stunned researchers at the beginning of the twentieth century and efforts were made immediately to create a mathematical structure in which classical mathematics was "saved," all mathematical questions could be answered and could be free of contradiction. Several proposals were made, but the one that offered the most hope was made by David Hilbert.

Hilbert suggested that work be started from the beginning with a formal system of logic and every concept either defined or recognized as fundamental. Because of his intellectual prowess, his enthusiasm, and the initial successes of his system, his approach was pushed the hardest. In order to develop a fundamental mathematical theory that was free of contradictions and at the same time broad enough to construct all of classical mathematics within its framework, the mathematicians and logicians Ernst Zermelo (1871-1953) and A. Fraenkel (1891-1965) proposed a system of axioms, or a system of assumptions, characterizing how numbers and sets are viewed, which seemed to meet these needs.

Unfortunately, the continuum hypothesis still could not be resolved. Then, Kurt Gödel proved in 1938 that one could assume the validity of the continuum hypothesis, and the addition of this assumption had no effect on the consistency of the Zermelo-Fraenkel system. In 1963, Paul J. Cohen proved that one could assume the negation of the continuum hypothesis and not affect the consistency of the Zermelo-Fraenkel system.

Impact of Event

As a result of this theorem, the cherished dream of mathematical certainty has had to be abandoned. At first, one might think that the answer is to admit that mathematicians simply do not understand the real numbers very well and that another axiom should be found that would imply the validity of the continuum hypothesis or its negation. Yet, Gödel proved that every axiom system will contain undecidable propositions. Moreover, Cohen's method of proof was so powerful that a number of other conjectures have been shown to be independent of the Zermelo-Fraenkel system as well. At first, one might think that the solution to the problem is to use an axiom system other than the Zermelo-Fraenkel system (there are, in fact, other competing axiom systems), or to admit that the knowledge of the real number system is incomplete and to add more axioms would imply the truth or falsity of the continuum hypothesis. Gödel's theorem is much more far-reaching. It says that any axiom system that is powerful enough to allow arithmetic will contain statements that cannot be proven within the axiom system, so a new axiom system will always contain unprovable statements. Moreover, such unprovable statements are not necessarily obscure and uninteresting, but as Cohen's work shows, they can be quite natural. Adding more axioms to the Zermelo-Fraenkel system could allow the resolution of the continuum hypothesis.

At this time, no such generally agreed upon axiom has been proposed. Even the inclusion of additional axioms would not resolve the more basic problem that Cohen's work and its consequences have raised. There will always be natural questions that cannot be resolved within any given axiom system. This means that it is possible to construct quite different kinds of mathematics, all of which contain two plus two equals four as a true statement, but that allows other statements to be true in one system and false in another.

The philosophical implications are much deeper. It is impossible in mathematics to give an absolute criterion of truth. Instead, it is a matter of belief and not proof that some statements are true and others are false. Most working mathematicians accept the validity of the Zermelo-Fraenkel axioms and probably most believe in the validity of the continuum hypothesis and have simply adopted a "wait and see" attitude as far as the final resolution of the continuum problem is concerned. The broader problem, however, will always remain. Complete certainty cannot be achieved in mathematics. Some mathematicians have remarked that the end of the age of innocence has arrived in mathematics.

Bibliography

Cohen. Paul J. *Set Theory and the Continuum Hypothesis.* New York: W. A. Benjamin, 1966. This book represents Cohen's treatment of his forcing techniques and their application to a rigorous resolution of the continuum problem. Extremely technical.

Fraenkel, Abraham A., and Yehoshua, Bar-Hillel. *Foundations of Set Theory.* Amsterdam: North-Holland, 1958. This book contains an approach to modern set theory originated by Zermelo and Fraenkel. Very mathematical, and assumes the motivations for the development are known.

Gödel, Kurt. "What Is Cantor's Continuum Problem?" *American Mathematical Monthly* 54 (1947): 521-525. This is an article written for the interested reader. Endeavors to get across the crux of the problem and still be understandable.

Kamke, Erich. *Theory of Sets.* New York: Dover, 1950. One of the best introductions to set theory available. Emphasizes the intuitive concepts of set theory and tries to convey the basic ideas of the theory. A good place to begin learning about sets.

Kneale, William C., and Martha Kneale. *The Development of Logic.* Oxford, England: Clarendon Press, 1962. This book is an introduction to the history of logic. Half is devoted to modern developments in logic.

Penrose, Roger. *The Emperor's New Mind: Concerning Computers, Minds, and the Laws of Physics.* New York: Oxford University Press, 1989. This book is basically an attack on the idea that computers will one day be able to do anything that the human mind can do. Penrose takes up many of the same topics such as logic, truth, proof, formal mathematical systems, that other mathematicians considered as well. Discusses quantum mechanics, thermodynamics, cosmology, and other topics of current interest. A very stimulating book.

Russell, Bertrand. *Introduction to Mathematical Philosophy.* London: G. Allen & Unwin, 1919. Russell gives a very coherent treatment of Frege's ideas of what a number is, what the basic problems in the foundations of mathematics are, and how they should be approached. Well written and easily understandable book.

Weyl, Hermann. *Philosophy of Mathematics and Natural Science.* Rev. ed. New York: Atheneum, 1963. This book was originally written by Weyl, one of the foremost mathematical physicists of the 1920's, when the foundational crisis in mathematics was acute and its resolution in doubt. Translated when he was an old man and contains his thoughts not only about the foundations of mathematics but also about a number of other fundamental issues facing thinking scientists and mathematicians. Very well written and thought-provoking.

Ronald B. Guenther

Cross-References

Hilbert Develops a Model for Euclidean Geometry in Arithmetic (1898), p. 31; Russell Discovers the "Great Paradox" Concerning the Set of All Sets (1902), p. 184; Zermelo Undertakes the First Comprehensive Axiomatization of Set Theory (1904), p. 233; Gödel Proves Incompleteness-Inconsistency for Formal Systems, Including Arithmetic (1929), p. 900.

SCHMIDT MAKES WHAT CONSTITUTES
THE FIRST RECOGNITION OF A QUASAR

Category of event: Astronomy
Time: 1963
Locale: Pasadena, California

Schmidt recognized that the previously mysterious "quasi-stellar objects" must be very luminous, very distant cosmological objects

Principal personages:

MAARTEN SCHMIDT (1929-   ), an astronomer and student of the composition and structure of galaxies who was the discoverer of the nature of quasars

ALLAN REX SANDAGE (1926-   ), an astronomer at the Mount Wilson and Palomar observatories and expert in the fields of galaxies and stellar evolution

MARGARET BURBIDGE (1919-   ), a professor at the University of California at San Diego who was one of the foremost explorers of quasars and expert on the masses of galaxies

THOMAS A. MATTHEWS (1924-   ), an astronomer who specialized in identification of strong radio sources using photographs taken with the Palomar 508-centimeter telescope

CYRIL HAZARD (1925-   ), a radio astronomer at the Jodrell Bank Radio Observatory who pioneered the determination of accurate positions of radio sources using the 76-meter radio telescope

Summary of Event

Between 1960 and 1963, radio astronomy was faced with a major puzzle: Several remarkable sources of radio waves had been identified in the sky that seemed to have no normal visible counterpart. Whereas most previously studied radio sources were either peculiar galaxies or nearby gas clouds, this new class of source seemed to have no such identity. The objects were different also from normal radio sources in that they were found to have small angular sizes, only a few arc seconds or less across. Known by their numbers in the massive *Third Cambridge Catalog of Radio Sources* (the 3C catalog), the best studied of these were 3C 48, 3C 286, and 3C 196. Diameters were measured for these objects in 1960 at the giant Jodrell Bank Radio telescope in England by Cyril Hazard and his colleagues, who found them to be surprisingly small.

Intrigued by the peculiarities of these objects, Allan Rex Sandage took photographs of the sky at their positions in September, 1960, using the Palomar Observatory's 508-centimeter telescope, then the largest in the world. Sandage and Thomas A. Matthews, an expert at identifying radio sources, studied the photographs, but found nothing that resembled a normal radio galaxy or gas cloud. They noticed, however, that the photograph of the area at the position of 3C 48 included a star with a peculiar feature: A faint wisp of light seemed to be pointing at it, "as if," as Sandage excitedly exclaimed, "God's finger were pointing to the true radio source." At the next opportunity, in October of that year, Sandage obtained a spectrum of this star and measured its colors. (A spectrum is a picture of the light of a star that has been spread out into all its different colors, so that the effects of absorption and emission by gases of various composition can be seen and studied. Astronomers can use stellar spectrums to deduce the compositions and physical conditions of stars.)

Sandage's spectrum of 3C 48 was extremely puzzling. As he explained to the members of the American Astronomical Society at their December, 1960, meeting, the spectrum resembled nothing that had been seen before. Instead of a bright continuum of light of different colors, with various dark lines, the spectrum of 3C 48 had a weak continuum with broad, fuzzy lines superimposed. The most puzzling feature, however, was that none of these lines corresponded with any known elements seen in stars; they were completely unidentifiable.

It was a mystery as to what this strange object could be. Sandage showed that its colors were somewhat similar to some classes of unusual stars, including white dwarf stars (which are collapsed stars near the end of their lives), novas (which are double stars that include one member that is a white dwarf), and irregular variable stars called U Geminorum stars, after the type example in the constellation Gemini. Unfortunately, none of these objects had a spectrum anything similar to that of 3C 48, and astronomers remained unconvinced that the puzzle could be solved by invoking some strange sort of collapsed star. Nevertheless, the colors did indicate that whatever it might be, it was definitely a very hot object, with a temperature on the order of a hundred thousand degrees.

The distance to 3C 48 (and to the other similar objects, which came to be called "quasi-stellar objects" or "quasars" for short) could not be measured, but there was a method to estimate it roughly. T. D. Kinman of the Kitt Peak National Observatory and others around the world showed that the quasars varied in brightness by considerable amounts on a short time scale, often changing in brightness in only a day or so. This could be interpreted to mean that the object, whether stellar or not, must be no larger than one light-day, or else the light travel time would smear out the variations, making them undetectable from Earth. Thus, they must be small objects, not much bigger than the solar system, therefore, most likely a star. This led to distance estimates for 3C 48 of, at most, a few hundred light years, well inside our galaxy and relatively near the sun.

A major breakthrough occurred in 1962, when Hazard and his collaborators used the Parkes Radio Telescope in Australia to make a high-precision measurement of the position of the quasar 3C 273. As seen from Parkes, the Moon happened to pass directly over the position of this object, and therefore a careful measurement of the time of its disappearance and later reappearance gave a very accurate measurement of its location, as the position of the moving Moon was known very accurately.

When they compared their measured position with optical photographs of that part of the sky (in the constellation Virgo), the radio astronomers found that the smaller of the two components that were detected corresponded exactly with the position of a fairly bright star. (The apparent brightness of this "star," which is the brightest quasar in the sky, is approximately six hundred times fainter than the faintest star visible without a telescope. Other quasars have since been found that are ten thousand times fainter yet.)

When this quite positive identification was announced, Maarten Schmidt of the California Institute of Technology decided to use the Palomar telescope to obtain a photograph and a spectrum of the "star." The photograph showed a bright stellar object with a faint wispy structure to one side, "pointing" toward the other object, much like what was found by Sandage next to 3C 48. The spectrum looked much like that of 3C 48, but with the broad emission lines in entirely different places. This remarkable fact might have confounded the situation even more, only Schmidt had a brilliant insight as he examined the spectrum. He realized that the lines would make sense if they were, in fact, normal lines of common elements, but redshifted greatly to longer wavelengths than usual. (A source of light that is moving rapidly away from an observer will have all its light shifted in wavelength to redder, longer wavelengths, by an amount that depends on the velocity.) If he identified four of the lines as being normal lines because of hydrogen gas—the most common element in the universe—then he found that the corresponding velocity of the object away from Earth must be about 48,000 kilometers per second. Under the assumption, since confirmed, that this high velocity is merely the cosmic velocity of expansion of the universe, it was possible to measure reliably the distance to 3C 273, which was nearly 2 billion light-years.

Schmidt's discovery was announced to the scientific world early in 1963, a date that marks the beginning of the solution to the puzzle of the quasi-stellar sources. Soon after Schmidt unscrambled the puzzle of 3C 273, Matthews and Jesse Greenstein identified the lines in Sandage's spectrum of 3C 48 as being the same familiar hydrogen lines, but redshifted much farther, indicating a velocity of recession of about 109,000 kilometers per second. Other quasars were rapidly identified, some with even greater redshifts.

The quasars were seen at last to be wonderful objects with astounding properties. Large numbers of astronomers, led from the beginning by the galaxy expert Margaret Burbidge, explored the many intriguing properties of the hundreds of quasars that were discovered over the sky (now, thousands are known). Over the next two decades, the understanding of the quasars has advanced to the point where it is known now that they are manifestations of conditions in the relatively early stages of the universe, when gravitational interactions and collisions between galaxies were much more common than they are now. Quasars result when two galaxies interact and material falls into the center of one of them, collapsing to a massive black hole that causes a brilliant outburst of light from its environs, brighter than 1 trillion suns. Because their large distances mean that one sees them as they were billions of years ago, the quasars tell astronomers about conditions in the universe then, when it was smaller and when galaxies were closer together. As probes of the early universe, quasars have proved to be interesting and valuable objects.

Impact of Event

Schmidt's discovery of the nature of the quasars as cosmological objects began a long and sometimes frustrating campaign on the part of many of the world's astronomers to understand what quasars can tell astronomers about the universe. It took nearly two decades to gain enough understanding to see that they are the brilliantly overluminous centers of normal galaxies and that the mechanism that explains their nearly incredible amounts of energy must be gravitational collapse; no other physical mechanism could be found that could do it. It is known now that the evidence is convincing that quasars are the nuclei of galaxies that have close companions, and that it is probable that the adjacent galaxy has lost material to the quasar galaxy. This material, mostly hydrogen gas, has fallen into the very center of the object, where it has collapsed to form a very massive black hole. The black hole is not seen, however, the newly captured gas that is falling toward it heats up to extreme temperatures (hundreds of thousands of degrees) and emits huge amounts of light as it screams its way toward oblivion. Such an explanation fits the facts that have been gathered over the years, and there is a general consensus that the most important features of these remarkable objects are now understood.

Quasars are the most distant objects that can be seen in the universe. They represent the youngest objects that can be viewed, as they are seen as they emitted their light billions of years ago when the universe was young. Thus, their properties can tell cosmologists something about the properties of the universe long ago; for example, galaxy collisions and interactions were far more common billions of years ago than now, even more common than simple models would predict. The spacing between galaxies was closer then and scientists now know—basing their information on quasar densities at various redshifts—about the early stages of galaxies and how their physical properties were different at that time from their physical properties now.

In two important ways, Schmidt's discovery of the nature of the quasars in 1963 has led to new and surprising insight in understanding Earth's cosmic environment. The quasars tell what happens when massive objects collapse, forming black holes at the centers of galaxies, and they show how the universe looked billions of years ago.

Bibliography

Burbidge, Geoffrey, and Margaret Burbidge. *Quasi-stellar Objects.* San Francisco: W. H. Freeman, 1967. Published five years after Schmidt's discovery, this comprehensive book outlines the early history and first results of systematic quasar studies. Some of the text is quite technical, but the descriptive and historical parts are relatively readable.
Hodge, Paul. *Galaxies.* Cambridge, Mass.: Harvard University Press, 1986. A book

for the interested lay reader, this volume covers the current understanding of quasar physics, as well as the history of their discovery.

Kahn, F. D., and H. P. Palmer. *Quasars: Their Importance in Astronomy and Physics*. Manchester, England: Manchester University Press, 1967. A book with much detail about the physical properties of quasars and about the implications of their optical and radio properties for the understanding of the physical mechanisms that explain them.

Rowan-Robinson, Michael. *Cosmology*. Oxford, England: Clarendon Press, 1977. A very readable book on cosmology, with all the necessary details to let the reader understand the cosmological importance of quasars. Chapter 2 includes a good explanation of the relationships between normal galaxies, quasars, and active galaxies.

Sciama, D. W. *Modern Cosmology*. Cambridge, England: Cambridge University Press, 1971. Probably the best book on cosmology for the general reader, being well written, authoritative, and interesting. Chapter 5 gives an excellent account of the discovery of quasars and of their use in cosmology.

Weedman, Daniel W. *Quasar Astrophysics*. Cambridge, England: Cambridge University Press, 1986. Weedman's book is fairly technical. A reader with a familiarity with basic astronomical terms and techniques will find that it is a thorough and insightful source of the results about quasars and their physics.

Paul Hodge

Cross-References

Oppenheimer Calculates the Nature of Black Holes (1939), p. 1150; The Jodrell Bank Telescope Is Completed (1957), p. 1539; Wheeler Names the Phenomenon "Black Holes" (1968), p. 1881; The Oldest Known Galaxy Is Discovered (1988), p. 2367.

PENZIAS AND WILSON DISCOVER
COSMIC MICROWAVE BACKGROUND RADIATION

Category of event: Astronomy
Time: 1963-1965
Locale: Holmdel, New Jersey

Penzias and Wilson discovered that the sky is filled with a uniform background radiation, consistent with the view that the universe began with a "big bang"

Principal personages:
> ARNO A. PENZIAS (1933-), a German-born radio astronomer and long-time employee of Bell Laboratories who was a cowinner of the 1978 Nobel Prize in Physics
> ROBERT W. WILSON (1936-), an American radio astronomer, long-time employee of Bell Laboratories, and cowinner of the 1978 Nobel Prize in Physics
> ROBERT H. DICKE (1916-), an experimental physicist at Princeton University who led the group of scientists that provided a theoretical explanation of Penzias and Wilson's observations

Summary of Event

In 1961, Arno A. Penzias had competed his doctoral thesis on the use of masers (microwave amplification by stimulated emission of radiation) to amplify and then measure the radio signal from intergalactic hydrogen. Penzias noted in his Nobel Prize lecture that the equipment-building went better than the observations. Charles Hard Townes, who won the 1964 Nobel Prize in Physics for his work on masers and lasers (light amplification by stimulated emission of radiation), had worked for Bell Labs' some years earlier and suggested that Penzias consider working there. Penzias wanted to use Bell Labs' 6-meter horn-shaped radio antenna to continue the observations he began in his dissertation, but the antenna was being used for communications. While waiting for the horn antenna, he pursued more practical projects at Bell Labs.

Robert W. Wilson was also using masers to amplify weak astronomical radio signals. Wilson participated in the making of a map of the radio signals from the Milky Way. He also wanted to use the horn antenna to do pure research in radio astronomy. Bell Labs enabled Penzias and Wilson to spend half of their time engaged in applied research.

The horn antenna was originally designed in 1960 to collect and amplify the weak radio signals bounced off large balloons high in the earth's atmosphere. Called "Echo," this early telecommunications system was used to send radio signals over very long distances. Telstar, the first telecommunications satellite that amplified incoming signals, marked the end of the usefulness of the Echo system. Penzias and Wilson were anxious to begin using the antenna because the electronics designed for the Echo system were very sensitive to weak signals, the same kind of signals that come from space. Other characteristics unique to the antenna made it the world's most sensitive radio telescope.

In 1963, in preparation for making their delicate observations, Penzias and Wilson began to identify and measure the various sources of "noise" in the antenna. One source of noise was the "thermal noise" of the antenna itself. The electrons in the atoms of the antenna underwent random thermal motion which generated weak radio signals. Radio astronomers speak of the "temperature" of the antenna when referring to the amount of thermal noise produced by the antenna. The higher the temperature, the greater the thermal motion of the electrons; thus, the greater intensity of the noise produced. Penzias and Wilson adopted the standard language of astronomers in speaking of the "temperature" of the antenna when referring to the intensity of the radio signals they measured: The greater the intensity of the radio signals, the greater the "temperature."

E. A. Ohm, one of the engineers on the Echo project, noted in 1961 an "excess" noise of 3 Kelvins. Little notice was taken of this observation, since the amount of discrepancy was small enough not to upset the functioning of the Echo project. Identifying and eliminating such excesses was crucial, however, for the kinds of sensitive astronomical observations Penzias and Wilson intended to make.

They soon ran into a serious problem which, because it refused to disappear, eventually led to Nobel Prizes for Penzias and Wilson in 1978. To calibrate their system, they constructed a "cold load." This device, an artificial source of radio waves cooled by liquid helium, served as reference source for the amount of noise produced by the electrical circuits. By switching from the signal coming from the antenna to that coming from the cold load, the effect of the noise coming from the electronics was eliminated, since the amount of electrical noise was the same in both cases. The problem was that the signal from the antenna was about 3 Kelvins higher than that from the cold load.

Penzias and Wilson spent much time and energy trying to track down the source of the excess noise. They ruled out man-made sources of noise by pointing the antenna at New York City and noticing no change. They ruled out radiation from our galaxy and from extraterrestrial radio sources. They evicted a pair of pigeons that had taken up residence in the antenna. No change in the amount of noise was seen, even after the antenna had been cleansed of pigeon droppings. They put metallic tape over the riveted joints of the antenna, yet noticed no change. By now it was spring, 1965, and more than a year had passed since the first measurement of the excess noise. Two additional sources of noise were ruled out because of the long period of observation. First, any source in the solar system would have exhibited variation as Earth moved in its orbit, yet no variation was seen. Second, if the excess noise came from the remnant of a 1962 above-ground nuclear test, then the noise should have decreased as the radioactivity decreased. No change, however, was seen.

The "answer" to their problem was that there was no instrument error or random noise. What they had measured was in fact a uniform radio signal in the microwave region of the spectrum coming from all directions. They began to realize that a theoretical explanation for their measurements was possible after a telephone call to Bernard Burke at the Massachusetts Institute of Technology in which the unexplained noise was mentioned. Burke said that he recalled hearing of the work of P. J. Peebles, then working with Robert H. Dicke at Princeton. Penzias and Wilson received a preprint of Peebles' paper which calculated that the universe should be filled with a background radiation of about 10 Kelvins (later revised downward). This radiation was thought to be the aftermath of the hot and highly condensed first few minutes in the life of the universe—the so-called big bang. The model developed by Peebles was of an oscillating universe—periodic expansion and contraction.

Wilson was trained by those who believed in the "steady state" model of the universe. In this model, as the universe expanded, new matter is continually created to keep the separation between galaxies the same. In the steady state model, there is no beginning of the universe. Wilson, in particular, was not convinced that Peebles' explanation was the only one possible, while the group led by Dicke at Princeton was enthusiastic about the observations. The two groups agreed to publish their results in two articles in the *Astrophysical Journal*. In their paper, Penzias and Wilson limited themselves to a discussion of their observations. They left a theoretical explanation to the Princeton group.

Impact of Event

Penzias and Wilson's measurement of the cosmic microwave background radiation represented an interesting case study in the history of science. On numerous occasions for at least twenty years before the 1965 measurements, both theoreticians and experimentalists had run across "evidence" for the 3-Kelvin cosmic microwave background radiation. After completing their measurements, Penzias and Wilson learned of the work of George Gamow and others in the late 1940's, which led to a prediction of 5 Kelvins for the background radiation. Astrophysicists in the Soviet Union and England, working independently of Peebles, performed calculations which also indicated about 5 Kelvins for the background radiation. Steven Weinberg, best known for his work on elementary particles, presented three reasons why the experimentalists and theorists were so far apart: There were some serious problems with the assumptions made in the work done by Gamow; most theorists prior to 1965 were under the mistaken impression that a background temperature of 3 Kelvins could not be measured with existing instruments; and most physicists could not take the theory of the early universe seriously, so no search was made for the remnants of the big bang.

Experimentalists also had measured the cosmic background radiation before 1965, but none appreciated the significance of the observations. Probably the most ironic of these measurements was by Dicke himself in the 1940's. His measurement of the maximum background cosmic radiation was a by-product of his research on the absorption of radio signals by the earth's atmosphere. By the 1960's, he had forgotten about his own measurements made twenty years earlier.

Immediately after the publication of their results, Penzias and Wilson's mood was one of cautious optimism; they were not willing to accept immediately the theoretical interpretation put forth for their measurements nor were they completely convinced of the accuracy of their own measurements. One reason for skepticism was that they had measured the temperature at only one wavelength. By mid-1966, other experimentalists had measured the intensity of the microwave background radiation at a variety of other wavelengths and all results were close to 3 Kelvins. Another issue was the uniformity of the observed radiation. The early phase of the big bang that created the radiation now observed was exceedingly uniform, so if the radiation was truly the remnant of the big bang, then measurements of the equivalent temperature made in many different directions must be the same. By the early 1970's, no differences could be found in the equivalent temperature when measured in different directions.

Penzias and Wilson's measurement of the cosmic microwave background radiation has been called one of the most important scientific discoveries of the twentieth century. While it may be true that the importance of the measurements has been overstated by some proponents, the demonstration of the cosmic microwave background radiation, combined with the earlier demonstration by Edwin Powell Hubble that the galaxies are receding, provided very strong evidence for the big bang model of the universe. By the mid-1970's, a new name had been coined for the big bang model—astronomers simply referred to it as the "standard model."

Weinberg has noted that "in the 1950s, the study of the early universe was widely regarded as not the sort of thing to which a respectable scientist would devote his time." It is not that the steady state model or any other model held sway in the astrophysical community, it is merely that there was insufficient experimental evidence or theoretical justification for the notion of the early universe. In the decades after Penzias and Wilson's measurement, the big bang model was fleshed out by the work of many other physicists. The early universe now had become a respectable field in which to work.

Bibliography

Bernstein, Jeremy. *Three Degrees Above Zero: Bell Labs in the Information Age.* New York: Charles Scribner's Sons, 1984. Presents a dual profile of Penzias and Wilson in the last section of the book. Written for a wide audience, this book contains very little technical language. The first three parts discuss Bell Labs' research on computers, solid-state physics, and telephony.

Davies, Paul. *The Edge of Infinity: Where the Universe Came from and How It Will End.* New York: Simon & Schuster, 1981. Presents the accepted ideas of modern physics and cosmology. Requires no detailed background knowledge of either physics or mathematics, though many of the ideas require some mind-bending imagination. Bases most of the exposition on diagrams and pictures.

Gribbin, John. *In Search of the Big Bang: Quantum Physics and Cosmology.* New York: Bantam Books, 1986. Wide ranging, this book is a readable account of the modern view of cosmology. Although Penzias and Wilson only take up a part of chapter 5, the rest of the book puts their work and the big bang theory into perspective.

Silk, Joseph. *The Big Bang.* Rev. ed. New York: W. H. Freeman, 1989. Using moderately technical language (but no mathematics), this book describes the big bang theory of cosmic evolution. Numerous diagrams. Revised and updated from a 1980 edition.

Weinberg, Steven. *The First Three Minutes: A Modern View of the Origin of the Universe.* New York: Basic Books, 1977. Written for the general reader. The chapter "A Historical Diversion" deals with all the missed opportunities involving the discovery of the microwave cosmic background radiation. Discusses Penzias and Wilson in several sections of the book.

Wilson, Robert. "The Cosmic Microwave Background Radiation." In *Les Prix Nobel, 1978.* Stockholm: Almqvist and Wiksell International, 1978. Clear and concise account of how the cosmic microwave background radiation was discovered and the events that happened after that discovery. One of the few Nobel Prize lectures in physics that is written using nontechnical language.

Roger Sensenbaugh

Cross-References

Lemaître Proposes the Big Bang Theory (1927), p. 825; Jansky's Experiments Lead to the Founding of Radio Astronomy (1930), p. 934; Gamow and Associates Develop the Big Bang Theory (1948), p. 1309; Echo, the First Passive Communications Satellite, Is Launched (1960), p. 1677; Telstar, the First Commercial Communications Satellite, Relays Live Transatlantic Television Pictures (1962), p. 1728.

QUARKS ARE POSTULATED BY GELL-MANN AND ZWEIG

Category of event: Physics
Time: 1964
Locale: California Institute of Technology, Pasadena, California; CERN, Zurich, Switzerland

Physicists Gell-Mann and Zweig independently discovered that the disturbingly large number of so-called elementary particles can be effectively organized by assuming that they are composed of quarks

> *Principal personages:*
> MURRAY GELL-MANN (1929-   ), a theoretical particle physicist at the California Institute of Technology, winner of the 1969 Nobel Prize in Physics, and codeveloper of both the "eightfold way" elementary particle classification scheme and the quark hypothesis
> GEORGE ZWEIG (1937-   ), a theoretical particle physicist at CERN, former graduate student of Gell-Mann and Richard P. Feynman, and codeveloper of the quark hypothesis
> ROBERT SERBER (1909-   ), a theoretical particle physicist at Columbia University who was credited with inspiring Gell-Mann to consider the idea of quarks
> YUVAL NE'EMAN (1925-   ), a theoretical particle physicist at the Imperial College of London who was the codeveloper of the "eightfold way" classification scheme for elementary particles

Summary of Event

Quarks were postulated in the early 1960's in an attempt to simplify the field of elementary particle physics by identifying the smallest, and thus truly elementary, building blocks of matter. At the end of the nineteenth century, the most elementary particles were thought to be atoms, out of which the macroscopic world of molecules was composed. During the early decades of the twentieth century, physicists discovered that the atom was not truly elementary but rather was composed of even smaller particles, which became known as protons, electrons, and neutrons. These subatomic particles were believed to be truly elementary and tremendous simplification resulted from the recognition that *all* the elements on the periodic table were constructed from combinations of these three "elementary" particles.

Further developments in physics, however, especially the study of cosmic rays and collisions in particle accelerators, began to reveal many more supposedly elementary particles and the number of such particles climbed from the familiar three in 1930 to more than one hundred by the 1980's. This large number was disconcerting to the physics community and became known as the "particle zoo." Physicists believed that all of these particles could not be elementary.

Quarks were postulated in 1964 as a possible way to restore the lost simplicity to the burgeoning particle zoo. It was suggested that many of the supposedly elementary particles were not elementary at all but were made up of even simpler units which came to be known as quarks. Perhaps the quarks could do for the particle zoo what the proton, electron, and neutron had done for the periodic table, the atomic zoo.

As is often the case in science, this great breakthrough was accomplished simultaneously by two scientists working independently: Murray Gell-Mann of the California Institute of Technology and George Zweig of CERN, a famous center for European nuclear physics located in Zurich, Switzerland. Gell-Mann was led to the idea of quarks, a word that he got from James Joyce's *Finnegans Wake* (1939), by his analysis of mathematical and symmetrical relationships among some of the apparent groupings of the members of the particle zoo. Gell-Mann, together with Yuval Ne'eman, had previously developed a way of organizing many of these particles into groups using a scheme called the "eightfold way." This scheme suggested that what looked like totally different particles was actually merely one particle with different values for its quantum numbers. (Quantum numbers are numbers that specify the values for certain physical properties of a particle, like charge and magnetic moment.) Therefore, what looked like eight separate particles, for example, might actually be only one particle with eight different possible configurations of its quantum numbers. The "eightfold way" could explain this relationship on the basis of the allowed quantum numbers for the particle. At the heart of this deeply mathematical analysis was the discovery that the particles should be organized into groups with specific numbers of members, such as one, three, eight, ten, and so on.

The "eightfold way" had been demonstrated to work effectively in simplifying the particle zoo. It was widely accepted, having been vindicated by its prediction of new particles needed to "fill up" some of the groups, particles which were subsequently discovered. One way to explain the remarkable, but mysterious, success of the "eightfold way" was to postulate that there was a trio of particles underlying the whole system, out of which many of these groups were constructed. When this was suggested to Gell-Mann in 1963 by Robert Serber, a theoretical physicist from Columbia University, he began to work out the details of what is now the widely accepted theory of quarks.

While Gell-Mann was developing the quark theory by analyzing the deep mathematical symmetries among the elementary particles, Zweig was led to the same ideas while trying to explain an experimental result. Zweig noticed that when a certain "elementary" particle known as the pi-meson disintegrated into other particles, it did not choose the most straightforward path to disintegration. (Normally, when such particles disintegrated, much more of the energy of the original particle showed up as kinetic energy, or energy of motion, of the new particles. In other words, the new particles, into which the pi-meson had disintegrated, should have been moving away from the disintegration location faster.) To explain this unexpected path to disintegration, Zweig suggested that the pi-meson was composed of two constituents, whose individual properties (known as the "strangeness") were transmitted separately to the decay components. To make this scheme work theoretically, Zweig found it necessary to postulate that many of the particles were constructed from an underlying triplet of particles which he called "aces." It was determined later that Zweig's aces were the same as Gell-Mann's quarks, and the idea began to spread among the particle physics community, with "quarks" becoming the accepted term for the new fundamental triplet.

Initially, there were three quarks and three associated antiquarks, which Gell-Mann labeled *u*, *d*, and *s*, for "up," "down," and "strange." They had fractional electric charges: *u* had $\frac{2}{3}$, d had $-\frac{1}{3}$, and *s* had $-\frac{1}{3}$. A proton was composed of two up quarks and a down quark, a combination that gives the known electrical charge of +1 to the proton. A neutron was composed of one up and two down quarks, which yield zero total charge.

The nature of the individual quarks, however, was very controversial. Gell-Mann believed that they might be purely mathematical entities that would never be observed in the same sense that particles, like electrons, are observed by the trail of bubbles that they leave in the specially designed chambers used to chart their paths. Zweig, on the other hand, believed that the quarks should be physically observable. Quarks also had fractional charges, which flew in the face of a half century of particle physics that dealt only with integrally charged particles. To resolve this dilemma, experimentalists began searching for individual quarks. They searched in accelerators, in cosmic rays, in chunks of normal matter, even in oysters, but to no avail. Quarks were nowhere to be found, suggesting that Gell-Mann had been correct. In 1968, however, experiments at the new Stanford Linear Accelerator Center (SLAC) showed that electrons bouncing off protons were recoiling in a way that suggested they were hitting something hard and small inside the proton. Further experimental evidence accumulated to the point where the quark hypothesis became widely accepted. Subsequent theoretical developments showed the quark theory to have remarkable explanatory power; additional quarks were postulated and then verified, and new properties of the existing quarks were uncovered. Nevertheless, no quarks had been observed directly, and no fractionally charged particles had been detected, despite much effort. Physicists began to develop a theory to explain this curious phenomenon called "quark confinement."

Quark confinement grew out of the theory of quantum chromodynamics (QCD), developed in the early 1970's by Gell-Mann to explain the mechanisms by which quarks interact with one another. According to QCD, quarks are bound together very tightly by particles called gluons. The strength of the binding is so great that quarks can never be separated from one another. Thus, quarks are fundamental building blocks of larger particles, but they exist only in combination with other quarks and can never be observed independently.

Impact of Event

It is unlikely that the theory of quarks will ever have any practical value, in the sense that a "product" will someday be based on the idea. The significance of the quark idea lies in the central role that it plays in the theories developed by the physics community to explain the various possible interactions in nature.

One of the deepest mysteries in the physics of the twentieth century has been the nature of the nuclear force that holds the positively charged protons so tightly packed in the nucleus. Since the protons are all positively charged, they experience a powerful repulsive force that should force them apart. Yet, there is some other force that holds them together, a "strong" force as it became known. The source of the strong force was a mystery until the development of the quark theory.

The quark theory, called quantum chromodynamics, or QCD, states that the quarks possess a mysterious property, whimsically named "color," which is analogous to the familiar charge that is the source of the electromagnetic force. Particles with color attract one another by exchanging a force carrier called the gluon, which is analogous to the familiar photon, the carrier of the electromagnetic force. QCD explains the strong force as simply the exchange of gluons between quarks in different protons. So, even though the electrical force might try to separate the protons, the stronger color force holds them together.

In addition to providing the long-sought explanation for the strong force, the quark theory provided a foundation for much of elementary particle physics. By showing that many of the esoteric particles that had been showing up in the various experiments were only combinations of quarks, scientists were able to develop much simpler explanations for the observed phenomena. As the explanation of the "eight-fold way," the quark theory showed that the apparent groupings within the particle zoo were based on deep underlying symmetries among the particles in each family and not on coincidental similarities. Without the quark theory, particle physics would have no strong theoretical foundation.

Perhaps the most significant accomplishment of the quark theory will be its role in the development of a unified field theory. This is the name of the theory that will, hopefully, unify all the possible interactions in nature under a single theoretical umbrella. Some unity has been achieved already via the various (and competing) grand unified theories (GUTs) by showing that the electromagnetic, weak, and strong forces are similar in that they all have a "force carrier" called, respectively, the photon, the intermediate bosons, and the gluon. Physicists are searching for the graviton, the postulated carrier of the gravitational force.

Developments uniting cosmology with particle physics show that these forces may have all emerged from a single force during the first few moments of the big bang. If gravity can be merged with one of the GUTs, then scientists will have shown how all the forces are merely four different manifestations of a single original force. The quark theory is an indispensable part of this grand search.

Bibliography

Carrigan, Richard A., and W. Peter Trower, eds. *Particles and Forces: At the Heart of the Matter*. New York: W. H. Freeman, 1990. This book is a collection of articles reprinted from *Scientific American*, many of which are excellent introductions to quarks. In particular, "Elementary Particles and Forces" by Chris Quigg (from *Scientific American*, April, 1985) and "Quarks with Color and Flavor" by Sheldon Glashow (from *Scientific American*, October, 1975) are superb. There are several other relevant articles as well.

_____. *Particle Physics in the Cosmos*. New York: W. H. Freeman, 1989. This book is a collection of articles reprinted from *Scientific American*, some of which discuss the important role that quarks play in theories of cosmology. In particular, "A Unified Theory of Elementary Particles and Forces" by Howard Georgi (from *Scientific American*, April, 1981) and "Gauge Theories of the Forces Between Elementary Particles" by Gerard't Hooft (from *Scientific American*, June, 1980) are excellent.

Crease, Robert P., and Charles C. Mann. *The Second Creation: Makers of the Revolution in Twentieth-Century Physics*. New York: Macmillan, 1986. This book is an extraordinary, massive presentation of particle physics in the twentieth century. The authors interviewed many of the scientists involved and have produced a colorful introduction to the theory that is accessible to the nonscientist. Highly recommended.

Glashow, Sheldon, with Ben Bova. *Interactions: A Journey Through the Mind of a Particle Physicist and the Matter of This World*. New York: Warner Books, 1988. This highly personal account of particle physics is written by a Harvard professor and Nobel laureate. Glashow was instrumental in developing some of the later ideas that led to the present version of the quark theory. The book is humorous, enjoyable to read, and presents the theoretical developments from the perspective of one of its most important contributors.

Ne'eman, Yuval, and Yoram Kirsh. *The Particle Hunters*. New York: Cambridge University Press, 1986. At a slightly more technical level, this book presents another "insider's" view of the discovery of quarks. Very well written, with many figures and diagrams.

Riordan, Michael. *The Hunting of the Quark: A True Story of Modern Physics*. New York: Simon & Schuster, 1987. This book is written by a physicist who was involved in many of the experiments that helped to establish the quark idea. He knows all the major scientists personally and has provided an interesting "insider's" view.

Karl Giberson

Cross-References

Hofstadter Discovers That Protons and Neutrons Each Have a Structure (1951), p. 1384; Friedman, Kendell, and Taylor Discover Quarks (1968), p. 1871; Gell-Mann Formulates the Theory of Quantum Chromodynamics (QCD) (1972), p. 1966; Georgi and Glashow Develop the First Grand Unified Theory (1974), p. 2014.

KEMENY AND KURTZ DEVELOP
THE BASIC COMPUTER LANGUAGE

Category of event: Applied science
Time: 1964-1965
Locale: Dartmouth College, Hanover, New Hampshire

Kemeny and Kurtz designed an interactive computer system and simple programming language that enabled nontechnical people to use a computer

Principal personages:
JOHN G. KEMENY (1926-   ), the chairman of Dartmouth's mathematics department and president of Dartmouth from 1970 to 1981
THOMAS E. KURTZ (1928-   ), the director of the Kiewit Computation Center at Dartmouth, director of True BASIC, Incorporated, since 1983, and chairman of the X3J2 BASIC Standard Committee from 1974 to 1984
WILLIAM H. GATES (1955-   ), a cofounder and later chairman of the board and chief executive officer of Microsoft Corporation who created a version of BASIC for the first commercially available microcomputer

Summary of Event

The first digital computers were developed during World War II to speed the complex calculations required for ballistics, cryptography, and other military applications. Computer technology developed rapidly, and the 1950's and 1960's saw computer systems installed throughout the world. These systems were very large and expensive, requiring many highly trained people for their operation.

The calculations performed by the first computers were determined solely by their electrical circuits. In the 1940's, John von Neumann and others pioneered the idea of computers storing their instructions in a program, so that changes in calculations could be made without rewiring their circuits. The programs were written in machine language, long lists of zeroes and ones corresponding to on and off conditions of circuits. During the 1950's, "assemblers" were introduced that used short names for common sequences of instructions and were, in turn, compiled into the zeroes and ones native to the computer. The late 1950's saw the introduction of high-level languages, notably FORTRAN, COBOL, and ALGOL, which used English words to represent instructions. Unfortunately, these high-level languages were complicated; required some knowledge of the computer equipment; and were designed to be used by scientists, engineers, and other technical experts.

Programs were coded onto a deck of punched cards that were read into the computer. A user's program, along with many others, was copied by the computer onto a reel of magnetic tape. After enough programs had been copied, the tape would be taken to another computer, where each program was processed in turn. This method of processing programs one at a time is called batch mode. Often, the programmer did not know until the next day what the results were, and so the process of correcting errors was extremely slow and tedious.

In the early 1960's, John G. Kemeny was chairman of the department of mathematics at Dartmouth College in Hanover, New Hampshire. During World War II, Kemeny worked in the computing center of the Manhattan Project at Los Alamos, New Mexico, under von Neumann. After the war, Kemeny worked on his doctorate at Princeton University, where he assisted Albert Einstein in unified field theory. In 1955, Kemeny realized that the proliferation of computers in human society created a growing need to teach computing in a liberal educational environment.

In 1962, Thomas E. Kurtz, Dartmouth's computing director, approached Kemeny with the idea of implementing a time-sharing system at Dartmouth College. Time-sharing had begun to develop as an alternative to the drawbacks of batch mode computing. Experimental computers were being built that could process the instructions of several users interactively connected to the system by teletypewriter terminals. Each user could have the illusion of exclusive access, because the computer alternated its processing between terminals as needed. Kurtz had become familiar with time-sharing while doing research at the Massachusetts Institute of Technology, and he thought such a system would make it possible to teach computer skills to liberal arts students.

Together, Kemeny and Kurtz experimented with interactive computing on the college's small computer. The success of their early experiments led them, with help from undergraduate students, to design a completely new computer system they thought could make computing power available to hundreds of students. After the plan was approved, a grant was obtained from the National Science Foundation that made it possible to purchase the equipment and build the system.

The equipment arrived at Dartmouth in February, 1964. It consisted of two General Electric Corporation computers, a disk drive shared by both, card punch and card reader, tape drives, and a printer, along with several teletypewriter terminals. Virtually no technical information came with the computers, so Kemeny and Kurtz were left together with their undergraduate assistants to figure out how to set up and program them.

One computer was used as a "master" to control the flow of information between the terminals and the "slave" computer, which performed the actual calculations. Most of the time at any terminal was occupied by typing commands or printing output. Very little time was needed by the slave computer to perform processing for any single user. The master computer could manage jobs going in and out of the slave unit for calculation without making anyone wait long for a response. Kurtz was assisted by several undergraduates, notably John McGeachie and Mike Bush, in writing the system programs that controlled the two computers. These programs were known as the Dartmouth Time Sharing System, or DTSS.

In order for students to use the new interactive environment of DTSS, a programming language was also needed. The English commands of FORTRAN and AL-GOL were a tremendous improvement on the cryptic instructions of assembly language, but they were both too complicated for beginners. Kemeny convinced Kurtz that they needed a completely new language, simple enough for beginners to learn quickly, yet flexible enough for many different kinds of applications. The language they developed was known as Beginner's All-purpose Symbolic Instruction Code, or BASIC. The original language consisted of fourteen different statements. Each line of a BASIC program was preceded by a number. Line numbers were referenced by control flow statements, such as IF X = 9 THEN GOTO 200. Line numbers were also used as an editing reference. If line 30 of a program contained an error, the programmer could make the necessary correction merely by retyping line 30.

Within a few months Kemeny and Kurtz had their two-pronged environment of DTSS and BASIC ready. On May 1, 1964, Kemeny and a student programmer typed in BASIC programs at two terminals and simultaneously gave the command to run them. The computer system responded with the right answers, and the Dartmouth Time Sharing System and BASIC were operational.

Programming in BASIC was first taught at Dartmouth in the fall of 1964. Students were ready to begin writing programs after two hours of classroom lectures. The following year, Kemeny and Kurtz added a simple program checker to BASIC. A student could invoke the checker to verify a correct program or obtain hints about possible mistakes. By June of 1968, more than 80 percent of the undergraduates at Dartmouth could write a BASIC program. Most of them were not science majors and used their programs in conjunction with courses in the regular curriculum.

General Electric began using DTSS and BASIC on its own computers late in 1964. GE became the first company to sell time-sharing services. General Electric and the National Science Foundation helped Dartmouth to establish a large computing network, linking many colleges and secondary schools. General Electric's association with Dartmouth in the late 1960's and early 1970's led to a wide proliferation of BASIC on time-sharing computer systems.

Kemeny and Kurtz, and later others under their supervision, wrote more powerful versions of BASIC that included support for graphics on video terminals and structured programming. The creators of BASIC, however, always tried to maintain their original design goal of keeping BASIC simple enough for beginners.

Impact of Event

Kemeny and Kurtz encouraged the widespread adoption of BASIC by allowing other institutions to use their time-sharing system and by placing it in the public domain. Over time, they shaped it into a powerful language with numerous features added in response to the diverse needs of its users. What Kemeny and Kurtz had not foreseen was the advent of the microprocessor chip in the early 1970's, which revolutionized computer technology. By 1975, microcomputer kits were being sold to hobbyists for well under a thousand dollars. The earliest of these was the Altair. That same year, a prelaw student named William H. Gates was persuaded by a friend, Paul Allen, to drop out of Harvard University and help create a version of BASIC that would run on the Altair. Gates and Allen formed a company, Microsoft, to sell their BASIC interpreter, which was designed to fit into the tiny memory of the Altair. It was about as simple as the original Dartmouth BASIC but had to depend heavily on the computer hardware.

Microcomputers quickly began to appear as complete, ready-to-run systems from a number of manufacturers. All but a few of these new machines included BASIC from Microsoft. The rapid development of microchip technology brought about generations of microcomputers with ever-growing power and memory size, allowing more powerful BASIC. As features were added, however, designers relied even more on the hardware of their particular computer, sacrificing compatibility with other computers. This resulted in a confusing array of different BASIC "dialects." Not only would a BASIC program written for one manufacturer's computer not run one from another manufacturer but also programs were often not compatible between different models of the same make.

Meanwhile, the creators of BASIC tried to unify its various dialects under a standard. From 1974 to 1984, Kurtz served as chairman of the X3J2 BASIC Standard Committee of the American National Standards Institute (ANSI). He and Kemeny were aghast at the idea of students learning to program on microcomputers with what they regarded as severely limited BASIC interpreters. They endured what they believed was misplaced criticism by computer professionals for the shortcomings of "Street BASIC," a corrupt argot of their original creation. Their response was True BASIC, an implementation for microcomputers that largely conformed to the ANSI standard and was aimed primarily at the academic community. Released in 1985, True BASIC drew praise for its power and performance, along with criticism for its lack of compatibility with other microcomputer BASICs.

Despite these efforts, BASIC instruction at the college level has declined in favor of such other languages as Pascal, Lisp, and C. Many students are already familiar with BASIC by the time they arrive at college. An increasing number of BASIC courses are being offered at the high school and even elementary school level, and most computers purchased for home use still include BASIC, which assures the survival of the language for many years to come.

Bibliography

Kemeny, John G., and Thomas E. Kurtz. *Back to BASIC*. Reading, Mass.: Addison-Wesley, 1985. The authors give a personal account of their early goals and of the development of Dartmouth's time-sharing computer and BASIC in this twenty-year retrospective. They discuss the corruption of their original creation, particularly by developers of BASIC interpreters for early microcomputers. Examples of program statements in BASIC and other languages are given that can be understood by the nonprogrammer. The authors describe the features of ANSI BASIC and True BASIC, but may be understandably biased in their evaluation in relation to other computer languages.

_____. *BASIC Programming.* New York: John Wiley & Sons, 1967. Readers interested in learning more about BASIC or programming in general may be referred to Kemeny and Kurtz's original text on the language. The first portion is devoted to programming and also covers time-sharing systems and debugging. The second portion contains sample programs for applications ranging from elementary mathematics to games.

_____. "Dartmouth Time-Sharing." *Science* 162 (October, 1968): 223-228. This less personal, more technical account of the development of DTSS and BASIC includes a diagram and description of the original computer equipment. The nontechnical reader can easily understand this well-written article.

Kurtz, Thomas. "BASIC Is Back." *Creative Computing* 10 (November, 1984): 226-229. In this short article, Kurtz discusses the development of standards for BASIC and defends ANSI BASIC against its critics.

Moritz, Michael. "A Hard-Core Technoid." *Time* 123 (April 16, 1984): 62-63. This very brief article provides an account of William Gates's early experience with computers and business ventures, his association with Microsoft cofounder Paul Allen, and the history of their company, which grew to be one of the largest and most influential producers of computer software in the world.

Pournelle, Jerry. "Computing at Chaos Manor: True Madness." *Byte* 10 (September, 1985): 366-373. Readers may be interested in this alternative viewpoint from Pournelle, a reviewer of computer equipment and programs. He devotes a portion of his regular monthly column to relating his frustration in trying to run a simple program in True BASIC. He goes on to argue that Microsoft BASIC is the *de facto* standard BASIC for microcomputer users.

Vose, Michael G. "True BASIC." *Byte* 10 (May, 1985): 279-288. This exhaustive review, replete with comparison tables and charts, performance benchmark tests, and sample listings, will probably be of interest only to the reader who is familiar with BASIC. Vose also has a short, boxed article on the last page, "ANSI Standard BASIC," which describes its differences from the prevailing dialects of Microsoft BASIC in a manner understandable to the nontechnical reader.

Charles E. Sutphen

Cross-References

A Secret English Team Develops Colossus (1940's), p. 1155; Eckert and Mauchly Develop the ENIAC (1943), p. 1213; The First Electronic Stored-Program Computer (BINAC) Is Completed (1949), p. 1347; UNIVAC I Becomes the First Commercial Electronic Computer and the First to Use Magnetic Tape (1951), p. 1396; Backus' IBM Team Develops the FORTRAN Computer Language (1954), p. 1475; Hopper Invents the Computer Language COBOL (1959), p. 1593; The Microprocessor "Computer on a Chip" Is Introduced (1971), p. 1938; Apple II Becomes the First Successful Preassembled Personal Computer (1977), p. 2073; The IBM Personal Computer, Using DOS, Is Introduced (1981), p. 2169.

DOELL AND DALRYMPLE DISCOVER
THE MAGNETIC REVERSALS OF EARTH'S POLES

Category of event: Earth science
Time: Summer, 1964-Summer, 1965
Locale: U.S. Geological Survey, Menlo Park, California

Doell and Dalrymple discovered the Jaramillo normal event and established the Matuyama-Brunhes geomagnetic reversal boundary

Principal personages:
>   RICHARD RAYMAN DOELL (1923-   ), an American geophysicist and paleomagnetist who codiscovered the most recent magnetic reversal of the earth's poles
>   BRENT DALRYMPLE (1937-   ), an American radiometrist and paleomagnetist who codiscovered the most recent magnetic reversal of the earth's poles
>   ALLAN V. COX (1926-   ), an American paleomagnetist who was a pioneer in the study of paleomagnetism

Summary of Event

In the early twentieth century, the idea was proposed that the polarity of the earth's magnetic field experienced changes. This was based on studies by geophysicists of remanent magnetization of volcanic rocks and baked earth. In 1906, Bernard Brunhes, a French physicist, found volcanic rocks magnetized in the opposite direction with reference to the earth's present magnetic field. He concluded that the magnetic field had reversed. His conclusion was accepted, but scientists were not interested in this type of research at that time.

Laboratory studies showed that volcanic rocks and baked earth when heated to their Curie temperature (the temperature above which a substance is no longer magnetic) and allowed to cool, acquired a weak and stable remanent magnetization (thermoremanent magnetism develops in igneous rocks when they cool below the Curie temperature), which was paralleled to the earth's present magnetic field. Scientists also found bricks and baked earth in archaeological sites that had their magnetism reversed because of fires made by man. Lava flows also change the magnetism of rocks (referred to as baked earth) that they have covered.

In 1925, R. Chevallier studied lava flows from Mount Etna, which contained remanent magnetizations that correlated with the magnetic field of the earth at the time of their eruption. In 1926, Paul L. Mercanton suggested that if magnetized rocks showed a reversed magnetic field for the earth, then those reversals should be recorded worldwide in other rocks. Motonori Matuyama, in 1929, was the first paleomagnetist to determine the times when the magnetic field had reversed itself by determining the ages of rocks. He found that the youngest rocks with reversed polarity were of early Quaternary period. After this early work on geomagnetic reversals, little was done in this area from 1928 to 1948. This resulted from the fact that science did not have an adequate theory to explain the earth's magnetic field, much less magnetic reversals. The study of magnetic reversals resumed around 1950. This resulted from the theory of how the earth's magnetic field was produced. The mechanism proposed was that of a magnetohydrodynamic dynamo.

The theory developed from the work of Walter M. Elsasser and Sir Edward Bullard. The dynamo idea suggested that Earth's outer core consisted of molten iron and nickel and was similar to the electrical conductors of a dynamo. It was hypothesized that the rotation of the earth produced convection currents in the outer core and that the resulting electric currents created an eternal magnetic field in the earth. The magnetic lines of force that would develop would be similar to those formed as if there was a bar magnet inside the earth. This, however, did not explain how the earth's magnetic field could reverse itself. Scientists have suggested that a period of strong solar-flare activity could cause the magnetic field to die and that after this activity was over the magnetic field would come back, but in a reversed manner. The question has arisen as to whether the magnetism in a rock can go through self-reversal. Laboratory experiments show that this occurs in less than 1 percent of thousands of rock samples tested from around the world. Therefore, if reversal of the magnetic field is the correct explanation for geomagnetic reversals, transitions from reversed to normal polarization, or the opposite, must occur at the same stratigraphic horizon worldwide.

Many geologists and geophysicists have done work in paleomagnetism, but the work of Richard Rayman Doell and Brent Dalrymple provided a complete picture of paleomagnetic reversals of the past 5 million years. Allan V. Cox, Doell, and Dalrymple spent five years (1959-1964) working on continental volcanic rocks from Alaska, Hawaii, Idaho, California, and New Mexico, to determine if the last magnetic reversal from reversed polarity (named the Matuyama reversed epoch) to the present normal polarity (named the Brunhes normal epoch) occurred contemporaneously around the world approximately 1 million years ago. Paleomagnetists had up to this time not found magnetic reversals in the upper Pleistocene. Geologically, 1 million years ago marks the transition from the Pleistocene epoch (the last Ice Age) to the Holocene (or Recent) epoch of time. (Some geologists refer to the Holocene as upper Pleistocene.) Reversals first appeared in the recent geologic record in the middle and lower Pleistocene (1 million to 2 million years ago). By 1964, Cox, Doell, and Dalrymple had found no evidence for contemporaneous reversals to conform the change from the Matuyama reversed epoch to the Brunhes normal epoch. This problem eluded them for another year.

In 1965, while Cox was doing research abroad, Doell and Dalrymple continued their study of volcanic rocks from the Valles Caldera in New Mexico, which is part of the Jemez Mountains located 56 kilometers northwest of Santa Fe. On November 4, 1965, at a meeting of the Geological Society of America in Kansas City, Missouri, Dalrymple presented a paper by him, Doell, and Cox, where preliminary results from their work in New Mexico were reported. The paper was entitled "Recent Developments in the Geomagnetic Polarity Epoch Time-Scale," and it contained the following statement: "There may be another event at about 0.9 million years, although it is yet not confirmed. Because of the short duration of these events, the chances of finding another one are rather small; thus subsequent work may turn up additional events that are as yet unrecognized."

On May 20, 1966, *Science* published a two-page article by Doell and Dalrymple entitled "Geomagnetic Polarity Epochs: A New Polarity Event and the Age of the Brunhes-Matuyama Boundary." Doell and Dalrymple determined the radiometric age using the potassium-argon method and paleomagnetism of nineteen Pleistocene volcanic rock units collected during the summer of 1964 in the Valles Caldera. Six samples had ages that ranged from 0.7 to 1.0 million years. These dates coincided with the age of the Bishop Tuff of California, which had been dated at between 0.87 and 1.2 million years. The new dates were valuable in defining the Matuyama-Brunhes boundary, which was established at 0.7 million years. Their study of the rock samples from New Mexico showed that a magnetic field reversal took place between 0.8 and 0.9 million years ago. This event occurred toward the end of the Matuyama reversed polarity epoch. These rocks showed a normal polarity, and the event has been named the Jaramillo normal event after a creek in the area where the rocks had been collected. The rocks dated between 0.7 and 0.8 million years ago showed a reversed polarity. From 0.7 million years ago to the present, the rocks from New Mexico indicated a normal polarity. The type of brief reversals, as the Jaramillo normal event, occurred earlier in the Matuyama reversed epoch and is known as the Olduvai normal event, which lasted 0.32 million years. During the Gauss normal epoch, which precedes the Matuyama reversed epoch, a brief reversal event called the Mammoth reversed event occurred, which lasted 0.12 million years.

Impact of Event

In 1963, Fred J. Vine, Drummond H. Matthews, and Lawrence W. Morley independently proposed the hypothesis that the rock of the ocean floor showed evidence of magnetic field reversals. These magnetic stripes mirrored each other on opposite sides of midoceanic ridges and were of the same thickness. In February, 1966, the new geomagnetic polarity-reversal time scale that contained the Jaramillo event developed by Doell and Dalrymple was correlated with the magnetic-anomaly profiles across midoceanic ridges. The Vine-Matthews-Morley hypothesis (better known as the Vine-Matthews hypothesis) was confirmed and the theory of seafloor spreading and continental drift became inevitable. About the same time, from a third source of independently derived data, polarity reversals were demonstrated in deep-sea sediment cores. In February, 1966, while Vine visited Neil Opdyke at the Lamont-Doherty Geological Observatory, Opdyke mentioned to Vine that he and his colleagues had discovered a new magnetic anomaly at about 0.9 million years in deep-sea sediment cores from the South Pacific's East Pacific Rise. These scientists had found the same magnetic reversal as Doell and Dalrymple had found on land. Other oceanic cores from various parts of the world also showed the reversal. This confirmed further that the Jaramillo event was a worldwide event.

At one time the question was asked if the poles had wandered (known as polar wandering) throughout geologic time or if the continents had drifted. Paleomagnetism has proved that the magnetic field, despite its reversals, shows having had a common North Pole. Studies of rocks of various geologic ages from North America and Europe have been correlated and show that the paleomagnetism preserved in the rocks points toward a common North Pole. When Europe and North America are rotated back together to a predrift position, the apparent polar wandering curves of both continents come together and point toward a common North Pole.

Paleomagnetism was the keystone piece of the continental drift puzzle. It also added credence to the plate tectonics theory, formally called the continental drift theory. Other scientific data that had been collected and studied also helped confirm the idea of seafloor spreading. A revolution in the earth sciences had been triggered by the work of Doell and Dalrymple.

Bibliography

Continents Adrift: Readings from "Scientific American." Introductions by J. Tuzo Wilson. San Francisco: W. H. Freeman, 1972. Includes fourteen articles from *Scientific American*, in chronological order, written for the general reader. Traces the history of a scientific revolution in the earth sciences. The articles contain many maps, graphs, photographs, charts, and illustrations. A valuable resource for the student of the earth sciences.

Cox, Allan, ed. *Plate Tectonics and Geomagnetic Reversals.* San Francisco: W. H. Freeman, 1973. A collection of articles on research in plate tectonic and geomagnetic reversals selected, edited, and with introductions by Cox. Articles are in chronological order so the reader can follow the events as they unfold. Includes technical but easily understood articles. A valuable resource for the earth science student. Many illustrations and references.

Cox, Allan, G. Brent Dalrymple, and Richard R. Doell. "Reversals of the Earth's Magnetic Field." *Scientific American* 216 (February, 1967): 44-54. An easy-to-read article on the events leading up to the discovery of the Jaramillo event. It reviews the early work done on the reversals of the earth's magnetic field. A valuable resource for the student of the earth sciences. Includes illustrations and a chronology of the earth's magnetic field for the last 4 million years.

Glen, William. *The Road to Jaramillo: Critical Years of the Revolution in Earth Science.* Stanford, Calif.: Stanford University Press, 1982. The layperson's version of *Plate Tectonics and Geomagnetic Reversals.* The story of a cast of international scientists that produced discoveries in the area of plate tectonics that brought about a revolution in the earth sciences. Includes photographs of scientists and illustrations to explain the concepts being introduced.

Menard, H. W. *The Ocean of Truth: A Personal History of Global Tectonics.* Princeton, N.J.: Princeton University Press, 1986. An insider's account by a geologist who was involved with the findings that led to plate tectonics. He examines the controversial history of global tectonics from 1900 to 1968. A valuable resource for the student of the earth sciences. It includes photographs of scientists, drawings, and maps.

Roberto Garza

Cross-References

Elster and Geitel Demonstrate Radioactivity in Rocks, Springs, and Air (1901), p. 93; Boltwood Uses Radioactivity to Obtain the Age of Rocks (1905), p. 285; Oldham and Mohorovičić Determine the Structure of the Earth's Interior (1906), p. 340; Wegener Proposes the Theory of Continental Drift (1912), p. 522; Richter Develops a Scale for Measuring Earthquake Strength (1935), p. 1050; Hess Concludes the Debate on Continental Drift (1960), p. 1650.

THE VERRAZANO BRIDGE OPENS

Category of event: Applied science
Time: November 21, 1964
Locale: Hudson River between Staten Island and Brooklyn, New York

When the Verrazano-Narrows Bridge was opened on November 21, 1964, the Hudson River was spanned by the world's longest suspension bridge

Principal personages:
  OTHMAR H. AMMANN (1879-1966), the designer of many of the world's most important and most beautiful suspension bridges
  ROBERT MOSES (1888-1981), a politician and bureaucrat who was responsible for many of the most important and most controversial public works in New York
  JOHN MURPHY (1903-   ), the superintendent of construction
  JOHN AUGUSTUS ROEBLING (1806-1869), a bridge designer who defined and clarified the concept of the suspension bridge

Summary of Event

The Verrazano-Narrows Bridge stretches 4,176 meters across the Hudson River, connecting Staten Island with Brooklyn. In 1964, it was the longest suspension bridge in the world, with 2,039 meters suspended and 1,298 meters in the main span. Its 69 meters of clearance at the center above mean high water is typically 3 to 3.7 meters less in summer than in winter. The bridge has become an aesthetic and engineering marvel.

Connecting Staten Island efficiently to the more populated areas of New York City fulfilled a dream of three centuries duration. Irregular boat traffic had been the connecting link until the half-hour-long ferry ride began in 1871. As early as 1888, talk of a railroad tunnel had been broached seriously in governmental circles. In 1923, the city of New York began a railroad-automobile tunnel, only to halt digging after six months and $500,000.

Robert Moses, New York's Commissioner of Parks, made the bridge linking Staten Island and Brooklyn a part of a $600-million package along with the Throgs Neck Bridge and a double deck for the George Washington Bridge ($300 million for the Verrazano-Narrows Bridge). Moses' support helped overcome all opposition, even that of including Verrazano as part of the name. Giovanni de Verrazano had established a claim to have some structure in the bay named for him because he had been the first to cruise it in 1524. Opponents did not want a difficult name to spell. Moses' addition of "Narrows" to the name made it more feasible.

Opposition primarily came from neighborhoods in each borough that the bridge would destroy. On Staten Island, three hundred buildings and thirty-five hundred people were affected; but their opposition, while noisy, lacked the vehemence and political appeal present in the Bay Ridge section of Brooklyn (seven thousand people, eight hundred buildings). Moses prevailed over Joseph T. Sharkey, Democratic boss of Brooklyn; the "Save Bay Ridge Association"; strong press opposition; and numerous court fights. On December 31, 1958, plans for the bridge were made final; and construction began on January 16, 1959. Opinions in Brooklyn ran so high that the ground-breaking ceremony took place on Staten Island amid charges that public officials had sold out their neighbors for "progress."

For the next five years, the bridge construction was plagued with controversy. In 1959, Moses' awarding of a $20-million contract to a construction firm that employed his son-in-law prompted much anger, as did the continual noise of construction. On March 29, 1961, two hundred Staten Islanders charged that the noise between 6:00 P.M. and 6:00 A.M. ruined their sleep and violated antinoise ordinances.

After three men fell to their deaths, the bridge workers struck the project, seeking safety nets. On December 6, 1963, after four days on strike, the workers got their nets, which ended up saving three men in the next nine months. The opening ceremony was boycotted by members of the Iron Workers Union because of the failure of any workers who built the bridge to be included in the festivities. Instead, they attended a mass for the three men who died.

Controversy aside, the bridge itself is an elegant example of Othmar H. Ammann's ability to find a technical solution for problems that his aesthetic sensitivity created. Ammann in 1959 was well known as the world's finest bridge engineer, combining great aesthetic judgment with high performance. He achieved a 1:180 ratio of stiffening-member depth to span, with a bridge span even thinner than that for the Golden Gate Bridge (1:168). Verrazano-Narrows incorporated his basic bridge design vision of a light and graceful structure suspended between plain, massive, and monumental towers. In Verrazano-Narrows, Ammann produced a simple, clear-cut form that is austere almost to a fault.

Designing the Verrazano-Narrows Bridge required that Ammann account not only for strength and stress factors and for deflection but also for the curvature of the earth. The two 211-meter-high towers, although exactly perpendicular to the earth's surface, would have to be 3.8 centimeters farther apart at the summits. The towers, containing 188,000 tons of steel would, nevertheless, be restless structures. Precision measuring would always be done at night because, on hot summer days, the sunny side would warp, causing it to be lower than the shady side.

By early spring of 1962, the long and undramatic, yet vital process of erecting the foundations was finished, and the two towers were going up. John Murphy served as the superintendent of construction at this point. The two cassions sunk in the narrows were the largest ever built. Each stood 67 meters long and 39 meters wide and had sixty-six circular dredging holes (each hole was 5.2 meters in diameter). The Staten Island cassion required 47,000 cubic yards of concrete, and before it settled on firm sand 32 meters below the surface, 81,500 cubic yards of muck and sand were lifted up through the dredging holes by clamshell buckets suspended from cranes. The Brooklyn cassion was sunk to 51.8 meters below sea level and required 83,000 cubic yards of concrete, and 143,700 cubic yards had to be dredged up through it. The foundations were concrete blocks the height of ten-story buildings, triangular-shaped and holding within their hollows the ends of the cable strands that stretch across the bridge. It took more than two years to complete the foundations at a twenty-four-hour-a-day pace.

Tower sections were lifted up by floating derricks anchored alongside the piers. When the first three tiers of each tower leg had been locked into place, rising to about 37 meters, floating derricks were replaced by "creepers" (with a lifting capacity of 100-plus tons) that moved up the towers on tracks bolted to the side of the tower. In that fashion, the towers were completed in the winter of 1962.

Spinning began in March, 1963. Four spinning wheels, each 122 centimeters in diameter and weighing several hundred pounds, ran simultaneously across the two catwalks, each more than 1.6 kilometers long. Each wheel was double-grooved, carrying and laying two wires at once and taking twelve minutes to cross the bridge. Clamping took place as the wheels passed overhead. When 428 wires had crossed the bridge, the wires were bound into a strand. Hydraulic jacks squeezed sixty-one strands into a cylindrical shape, a cable. Each cable (the Verrazano-Narrows had four) was 1 meter thick, 2,196 meters long, and contained 57,935 kilometers of pencil-thin wire. From each cable, 262 suspender ropes—some as long as 136 meters—were hung to hold up the deck.

Both decks (Ammann put the lower second deck in place as an added safety feature) were completed in September, 1964. Dedication occurred on November 21, 1964, when Ammann was honored as the greatest living bridge engineer, perhaps even the greatest of all time. The success of any engineering project is measured by the lack of any dramatic history, and other than the social and political controversies, the Verrazano-Narrows Bridge that Ammann designed has had a very undramatic history.

Impact of Event

The Verrazano-Narrows Bridge achieved one objective exactly as its staunchest proponents had claimed that it would—it ended the isolation of New York's smallest borough, Staten Island. As a result, the Staten Island population almost immediately began to increase at a rate of seventeen hundred people per month as compared to a pre-bridge rate of increase of two hundred per year. This rapid increase continued until 1980, after which the increase leveled off to approximately twelve thousand people per year.

A second deck that was completed in November, 1964, with the original construction was originally intended to open to traffic in 1981. Ammann had designed the bridge with practical considerations in mind. Building the second deck in the original package saved $50 million and produced a significantly enhanced safety margin. Typically, completed bridges attract many more vehicles than planners anticipate. Verrazano-Narrows was no exception. In 1965, 34 percent more vehicles used the bridge than anticipated, and in 1967, 24 million vehicles used the bridge,

50 percent more than predicted. As a result, the second deck was quickly readied for use by June 29, 1969, at the relatively low cost of $14 million. Twenty years later, the two decks carried 84 million vehicles.

Such vastly increased traffic between Staten Island and Brooklyn left its toll on the island just as the bridge left its toll upon Brooklyn's Bay Ridge section. The neighborhood never recovered from the uprooting of its residents by the Brooklyn end of the bridge. For Staten Island, the bridge helped to produce the type of modern problems—crowded public facilities, land booms, traffic jams, increased crime, juvenile gangs, and environmental deterioration—that Staten Island had previously avoided. On the other hand, while polls taken from 1968 to 1984 indicated that there was ambivalence in Staten Islanders' attitudes toward the Verrazano-Narrows Bridge and its consequences, a strong majority (65 percent) believed that the benefits outweighed the problems. The sense that the Verrazano-Narrows Bridge represented progress overcame early opposition. Access to cultural amenities, sophisticated health-care facilities, and the savings in time and money were some of the advantages.

Although Verrazano-Narrows is now only the second longest suspension bridge in the world, it remains a beautiful example of a bridge style that James Finley introduced in the early 1800's with wooden towers and suspension chains. Charles Ellet and John Augustus Roebling pioneered the use of iron-wire cables and stone towers and set the standards for both beauty and utility in suspension bridges. Ammann pursued a vision for slender beauty that found expression in a 1:180 ratio of stiffening-member to span, but remained safe because of the tubular framework that ran through the span. He, like other bridge designers, had backed off from earlier efforts to push the margin of safety outward after the collapse of the Tacoma Narrows (Washington) Bridge in November, 1940. (His 1939 bridge, the Bronx-Whitestone, had a ratio of 1:210.)

Ammann died two years after the Verrazano-Narrows Bridge opened, so that project stands as the last, and quite possibly the best, in his long career. He was honored by Switzerland in a 1979 postage stamp showing him and the Verrazano-Narrows Bridge.

Bibliography

Bakkt, Baidar. *Bridge Analysis Simplified*. New York: McGraw-Hill, 1985. Interesting because of the insights into the resolution of the problem of maintaining artistic qualities without sacrificing safety and convenience. For a wide audience.

Billington, David P. *The Tower and the Bridge: The New Art of Structural Engineering*. New York: Basic Books, 1983. Billington has written extensively about engineering and the social context of technology. Places the Verrazano-Narrows Bridge into the evolutionary pattern of bridge designing and bridge construction. Discusses the relationship of aesthetic considerations with structural considerations. The Verrazano-Narrows Bridge is a significant part of such a discussion.

Kassler, Elizabeth B. *The Architecture of Bridges*. New York: Arno Press, 1972.

While not ignoring the engineering and other technical aspects of bridges, focuses upon the architectural features. Particularly strong on the relationship of art to function, of beauty to utility, and of appearances to practicality.

Talese, Gay. *The Bridge*. New York: Harper & Row, 1964. Focuses upon the people who built the bridge and their relationships with other people and the rest of the surrounding environment. Places all the technical aspects from the designing phase to construction techniques into a context established by those who did them. Does so quite well and with the aid of many anecdotes.

Wittfoht, Hans. *Building Bridges: History, Technology, Construction*. Dusseldorf: Betowverlag, 1984. Places the Verrazano-Narrows Bridge into the broad context of great bridges in the world. Notes how the building of such a long span demanded perfection in both design and building techniques.

William F. Steirer, Jr.

Cross-References

Construction Begins on the Panama Canal (1904), p. 249; Construction Begins on the Empire State Building (1930), p. 906; The Completion of Boulder Dam Creates Lake Mead, the World's Largest Reservoir (1936), p. 1075; The St. Lawrence Seaway Is Opened (1959), p. 1608.

THE FIRST SPACE WALK IS CONDUCTED FROM VOSKHOD 2

Category of event: Space and aviation
Time: March 18, 1965
Locale: Earth orbit

In an experiment that nearly resulted in disaster, Leonov made the first space walk, demonstrating that humans could function outside the safe enclosure of a spacecraft

Principal personages:
ALEXEI LEONOV (1934-   ), a cosmonaut since 1960, accomplished athlete and pilot, and pilot of Voskhod 2
PAVEL I. BELYAYEV (1925-1970), a cosmonaut since 1960, first commander of the cosmonaut team, and commander of Voskhod 2

Summary of Event

In the early 1960's, people from the Soviet Union and the United States took their first, tentative steps into space. At the end of the Vostok ("East") and Mercury missions, each country was eager to send humans to the Moon. Before the Soviet Union's Soyuz ("Union") and the United States' Apollo spacecraft were ready, interim missions were undertaken to gain some of the critical experience that would be necessary for lunar and other ambitious flights. The programs filling the gap were Voskhod ("Sunrise") and Gemini.

One of the vital goals for both nations was to have astronauts work outside their spacecraft. Recognizing that this capability would be essential for any of the challenging missions of the future, the Soviet Union assigned Pavel I. Belyayev and Alexei Leonov to train for Voskhod 2. The flight would test a person's ability to survive in space without the protection of his spacecraft from the near vacuum, radiation, extreme temperatures, and micrometeoroids. There was great concern that psychological stress might prevent a human from functioning outside a spacecraft. Leonov's two years of training for this daring journey into an unknown environment was more intensive and more specialized than that of any other cosmonaut who had made a trip into space.

After an intense blizzard, light snow was falling on March 18, 1965, when Belyayev and Leonov lifted off. Shortly after the 10:00 A.M. launch, they reached an orbit ranging from 173.5 to 497.7 kilometers above their home planet, higher than any other human had been.

As soon as the crew confirmed that all systems were functioning properly, they began preparing for the extravehicular activity (EVA, or space walk). Belyayev helped Leonov put on the backpack life-support system that would sustain him during his excursion outside the confines of the spacecraft. Leonov began an hour of breathing pure oxygen in order to purge nitrogen from his tissues. The space suit was designed to operate at 40 percent of sea-level pressure with pure oxygen, because in the vacuum of space it would have blown up like a balloon if it had used normal atmospheric pressure. With the low pressure of the suit, flushing the nitrogen from his blood was essential to avoid the bends, a hazard familiar to scuba divers.

After Belyayev inflated the 2.5-meter air lock mounted on the outside of the spacecraft and equalized the pressure between it and the crew compartment, he opened the hatch to the air lock, and Leonov floated in. Leonov checked the functioning of his life-support system, tested to ensure there were no leaks, adjusted his helmet, and reported back to Belyayev. Satisfied that all was proceeding well, Belyayev closed the hatch and bled the air out of the air lock. Using the air lock allowed them to keep full pressure in the main compartment of the spacecraft, which had not been designed for operation with a vacuum inside.

When Belyayev remotely opened the outer hatch at 11:33 A.M., blinding sunlight flooded the cylindrical chamber. Leonov floated to the opening and attached a movie camera to a bracket outside the air lock. He removed the lens cap and threw it toward Earth, watching it recede until it disappeared. The view beyond, of the Black Sea and the Caucasian Range of his motherland, was overwhelmingly beautiful.

He pushed off from the air lock, still secured to the spacecraft by a 5.35-meter tether. The tether carried voice communications between him and his commander and relayed data on the performance of his life-support system and his respiration, pulse, and other vital functions. Belyayev kept careful watch over all these data while viewing Leonov's orbital ballet on a television monitor.

Leonov was able to do little more than push off from Voskhod 2, go to the limit of his safety tether, and then pull himself back. The first time he floated toward the spacecraft, he feared that he was going to hit it with his helmet and break the visor, but he found it easy to deflect his motion with his hands. Belyayev could hear the clanging of his partner against the exterior of the spacecraft and even could hear Leonov run his gloved hand over the hull.

Leonov's only problem was that the rigidity of the suit caused him to tire quickly. The tendency of the suit to balloon and hold its own shape meant that he had to fight it whenever he moved. Mounted on his thigh was the manipulator for a camera attached to his chest, but he was unable to reach the device because of the suit's stiffness, so he could not photograph his spectacular view.

Despite finding the activity fatiguing, Leonov enjoyed himself tremendously. It was exceedingly clear to him that the much-feared psychological barriers to EVAs were nonexistent, as he somersaulted, floated, and marveled at the rich colors and wonderful variations of Earth, the inky blackness of space dotted with stars, and the brilliant sun. The cosmonaut was having such a delightful time that when he was first ordered to return, he pushed off again for still another excursion to the limits of his tether.

When he did agree to end his space walk, he removed the movie camera from its bracket. Holding it with his right hand, he grasped the rail on the air lock with his left to maneuver himself in. To his astonishment, he could not enter. He struggled tremendously to get his feet in, but he just could not bend enough; the camera that recorded his historic activities kept getting stuck in the 70-centimeter hatch. Drenched in perspiration and with his pulse soaring to 168, he lowered the pressure in his suit, risking the onset of the bends. Still, he was trapped outside his spacecraft. On the verge of heatstroke, he lowered the pressure below the lowest limit considered to be safe. Finally, after about eight minutes of torturous work, he managed to push the camera in and follow it headfirst.

When he got in, he bumped the camera, and it began to float back out. He managed to grab it, turn over, and hold it with his legs while he ensured that nothing would impede the closing of the hatch. From the control panel inside, Belyayev closed the hatch and repressurized the air lock only twenty-four minutes after he opened it.

When the exhausted space walker got back inside his spacecraft, he had to use towels from the first-aid kit to wipe off all the sweat. Leonov then spent more than ninety minutes (enough time to orbit the entire planet) recording his experiences.

For the remainder of the mission, the crew photographed Earth and conducted experiments on the effects of spaceflight on humans. On their sixteenth orbit, as they prepared to return, they discovered a malfunction in the automatic orientation system of the spacecraft. One orbit later, Belyayev skillfully conducted the Soviet Union's first manual reentry. Touchdown was at 12:02 P.M. on March 19 in a fir forest in the Urals, 2,000 kilometers from their target and the ground teams. They spent a cold night hiding in their spacecraft from a pack of wolves, hungry after a long winter. The next day, rescue teams arrived on skis; after putting on warm clothes and eating, the newest heroes in the Soviet Union skied to a waiting helicopter.

Impact of Event

The importance of being able to work outside a spacecraft has proven itself many times in humankind's exploration and utilization of space. The Soviet space stations Salyut ("Salute") 6 and 7 and Mir ("Peace") have required extensive repairs and experiments to be conducted in the harsh space environment. The longevity and successes of these laboratories in space owe much to the ability of cosmonauts to work outside.

The United States' only space station, Skylab, also depended heavily on EVAs. It suffered damage during launch in 1973, leaving it nearly unusable. Without EVAs to repair it and to replace and retrieve film and experiments mounted on its exterior, the wealth of scientific and engineering data returned from Skylab would never have been accumulated. The Apollo missions to the Moon would have been impossible without the ability of the astronauts to work outside their spacecraft in suits independent of the spacecraft's life-support system. Some of the greatest pride of the National Aeronautics and Space Administration's (NASA's) space shuttle program has come from the repair of satellites by space-walking crews.

Large space stations under study (Mir 2 by the Soviet Union and Space Station

Freedom by the United States) will require construction and maintenance by crews able to undertake EVAs on a regular basis. Before Leonov's twelve-minute EVA, it was unknown whether these activities would be possible. Although still considered strenuous and dangerous, EVAs are accepted as indispensable on many missions.

The Soviet Union did not reveal the difficulties Leonov encountered. Rather, accounts of his wonderful experiences and the technological superiority of the Soviet Union were emphasized. Voskhod 2 was launched only five days before the first astronauts flew in NASA's new Gemini program. Many Soviet scientists, cosmonauts, and officials described future orbiting space stations and visits to the Moon and planets. They claimed that these missions would be enabled by Leonov's success and by the technological and ideological superiority of the socialist system. Some officials in the United States conceded that the successes of Voskhod 2 revealed a disturbing lead by the Soviet Union.

Much effort during the United States' Gemini program in 1965 and 1966 was devoted to developing EVA capability, and NASA was surprised to encounter difficulties. On several Gemini flights, space-walking astronauts struggled to complete assignments, and physical exhaustion prevented some tasks from being accomplished. The extreme exertion required overwhelmed their space suits' life-support systems. The astronauts experienced the same problems Leonov had with fogging inside his helmet, overheating, and being drenched with perspiration. Not until the 1970's did details of Leonov's harrowing experience become known to the West.

Twenty-five years after Leonov's brief space walk, Aleksandr Volkov and Jean-Loup Chrétien conducted a six-hour EVA. Back inside the Mir space station, they were so exhausted that they could not tie their shoes or open tea bags. Yet, the ability of men and women to conduct useful work in space continues as a key component in the extension of humanity's presence in space.

Bibliography

Clark, Phillip. *The Soviet Manned Space Program*. New York: Orion Books, 1988. In addition to descriptions of every Soviet manned flight, this book contains useful information on related unmanned missions, thus helping the reader understand the plans, goals, and significance of much of the Soviet space program. Speculations on intended objectives are carefully explained and make fascinating reading. Includes many drawings and photographs.

Furniss, Tim. *Manned Spaceflight Log*. Rev. ed. London: Jane's, 1986. With a description of every manned mission into space through Soyuz T-15 in March, 1986, this book is entertainingly written and should be enjoyed by general audiences. Provides the essential facts from each flight and allows the reader to understand any flight in the context of humankind's efforts to explore and work in space.

Harvey, Brian. *Race into Space: The Soviet Space Programme*. Chichester, England: Ellis Horwood, 1988. A complete description of Soviet manned and unmanned missions, ground facilities, key technical contributors, and the historical and political context in which the events occurred. Careful readers will find many small technical errors, but the breadth of this text makes it a rich source for all audiences.

Johnson, Nicholas L. *Handbook of Soviet Manned Space Flight*. San Diego, Calif.: Univelt, 1980. This book provides a very readable, detailed description of the history of Soviet manned spaceflight. Suitable for college-level readers, it includes many technical descriptions and drawings of the spacecraft and their systems. Includes many references and an extensive bibliography.

Library of Congress. *Soviet Space Programs, 1962-65: Goals and Purposes, Achievements, Plans, and International Implications*. Washington, D.C.: Government Printing Office, 1966. Prepared for the Senate Committee on Aeronautical and Space Sciences, this authoritative source is part of an ongoing series on the history of the Soviet Union's space activities. College-level readers will find a wealth of detail on the missions and fascinating discussions of the political ramifications of the Soviet space activities. Includes references but has no bibliography.

Newkirk, Dennis. *Almanac of Soviet Manned Space Flight*. Houston: Gulf, 1990. For every manned and unmanned mission associated with the Soviet manned space program, provides a description of the flight, plus the dates, crew, orbital altitude, and a line drawing of the spacecraft. Particularly useful as a quick reference. Includes many references but has no bibliography.

Oberg, James E. *Red Star in Orbit*. New York: Random House, 1981. The author presents a history of the Soviet Union's manned exploration of space from the first flight to midway through the Salyut 6 program. Comfortable reading for all audiences, the book includes accounts of spaceflights and some interesting descriptions of Soviet cover-ups in their space program.

Marc D. Rayman

Cross-References

Gagarin Becomes the First Human to Orbit Earth (1961), p. 1693; Shepard Is the First United States Astronaut in Space (1961), p. 1698; Glenn Is the First American to Orbit Earth (1962), p. 1723; The First Humans Land on the Moon (1969), p. 1907; Apollo 12 Retrieves Surveyor 3 Parts from the Lunar Surface (1969), p. 1913; The First Permanently Manned Space Station Is Launched (1986), p. 2316.

THE SEALAB 2 EXPEDITION CONCLUDES

Category of event: Earth science
Time: August-October, 1965
Locale: La Jolla, California

The successful conclusion of the Sealab 2 expedition set the stage for more ambitious human exploration of the oceans

Principal personages:

EDWIN ALBERT LINK (1904-1981), an inventor who became interested in ocean exploration and invented and tested some of the first submersible habitats/decompression chambers

JACQUES-YVES COUSTEAU (1910-   ), a pioneer explorer of the marine environment who was the coinventor of the Aqualung (self-contained underwater breathing apparatus, or SCUBA)

M. SCOTT CARPENTER (1925-   ), a U.S. Navy commander who was one of the original seven astronauts and an aquanaut

Summary of Event

In the late 1950's and early 1960's, it became apparent that the oceans of the world were very important to the well-being of life on Earth. Not only was there a rise in the study of the oceans for scientific reasons (the increased popularity of oceanographic studies, for example) but also, increasingly, the ocean was looked upon as the next frontier to be explored and exploited for its resources. Those resources, both food and minerals, lay locked beneath a layer of water, which made both exploration and exploitation extremely difficult. Prior to this time, exploration of the ocean occurred almost exclusively by remote means. Scientists working from surface ships used nets, dropped from the surface, to scoop up samples of marine animals, marine plants, and surface minerals. Individual divers also descended from surface ships, encased in metal hard-hat, wearing lead-weighted boots and tethered to the ship by breathing hoses. Whereas they were able to make direct observations and take samples, their mobility was limited.

A major advance in direct, human exploration of the oceans occurred when the first self-contained underwater breathing apparatus (SCUBA) was invented and perfected in the mid-1940's by Jacques-Yves Cousteau. The perception that humans were now completely free to explore the oceans led some enthusiasts to envision human colonization of the relatively shallow (less than 200 meters deep) continental shelves surrounding many continents. Coincidentally, the continental shelves were, and continue to be, the most productive areas of the ocean and the focus of most mineral (particularly oil and gas) exploration. Before those dreams could be realized, however, it remained to be seen if the problems and dangers associated with undersea living and working could be overcome. Almost all the anticipated difficulties were related to medical problems associated with extended periods of living and working in the ocean. Ocean water is considerably denser than air. Thus, performing a simple task in the ocean requires more expense of energy, and perhaps more time, than on land. Work schedules in the ocean would have to consider diver exhaustion and provide for adequate rest or more shifts of divers.

Even more dangerous was the realization that a diver, living and working in the ocean for longer than a day, could not return easily to the surface. Breathing air under pressure saturates the body tissues quickly with gases in the air such as nitrogen. Removing those gases from the tissues, however, must be done by slowly decreasing the pressure (decompressing) over many hours (around eighteen hours) so bubbles do not form in the blood vessels. If the pressure is decreased too quickly and bubbles form, they can cause severe pain (the bends), paralysis, and death. In the late 1950's, U.S. Navy medical doctors designed a series of experiments, using animals and volunteer Navy divers, to test the physiological and psychological effects of extended exposure to pressures which simulated deep dives. At the same time, Edwin Albert Link was experimenting with the equipment necessary to house a diver in the ocean *and* return the diver to the surface for decompression. The results of these efforts laid the foundation for the Navy's efforts in saturation diving.

Sealab 1, completed in 1964, proved that the results obtained in the controlled experiments on land could be translated successfully to the ocean. In Sealab 1, four divers spent eleven days living and working 59 meters below the surface near Bermuda. Sealab 2 was the next step in the process of maintaining working communities in the sea. Unlike the ideal conditions of clear, warm water experienced in Sealab 1, Sealab 2 was to be located in the cold, dark waters of the Pacific off the coast of La Jolla, California. The Southern California location provided access not only to ocean conditions that are more typical of the environment but also to the research base provided by proximity to the oceanographic research facilities of the Scripps Institute of Oceanography.

The objectives of the project were to evaluate both the general ability of divers to function and do useful work in a realistic ocean environment, at 61 meters below the surface under saturation diving conditions. Further, observers were interested in the physiological and psychological effects of living for extended periods of time at that depth. The living quarters were spartan and crowded, which only added to an already stressful situation. The first of three teams of divers occupied Sealab 2 at the end of August, 1965. Each team member spent about fifteen days working in and around Sealab. Commander M. Scott Carpenter, the leader of teams 1 and 2, spent thirty days below the surface. The teams were composed of mostly Navy divers with a few civilians with oceanographic backgrounds in each team. All the team members were monitored to obtain medical and psychological data. In addition, all the team members were involved in evaluating underwater equipment (for example, novel breathing equipment and heated diving suits) and tools (for example, tools used in salvage operations). They were required to perform certain group tasks (for example, assembling at a certain location after a signal) and the time required to perform the task was compared with that required on land. Some of the divers collected data on fish behavior and collected samples for fish physiology studies. One group tested the utility of trained dolphins as aids to working divers. Another group tested various methods, including underwater drilling, to obtain geological samples. At the end of each team's dive, they left Sealab and, while still underwater, entered a Personnel Transfer Capsule that maintained the same internal pressure as the divers experienced in Sealab. The team was raised to the surface while in the capsule and immediately transferred to the more spacious decompression chamber on the deck of the support ship. There the divers underwent the slow (approximately thirty-hour) process of decompression (slowly equilibrating their blood gases to earth surface pressure) in order to return safely to normal life on the surface.

The results of the experiments were, in general, positive. While it was well known that tasks performed underwater take longer than the same tasks performed on land, the magnitude of the delay was not known. Also, the psychological effects of having difficulties performing otherwise simple tasks did not seem to be very adverse. Team morale remained high despite the difficulties.

The heated diving suits were successfully tested in the hope that they would relieve the divers from expending so much of their energy simply trying to maintain body heat in the cold waters of the Pacific near California. In addition to cold water sapping the energy from a diver, the energy required to perform tasks in the water is greater than on land. Simply moving your hand or leg through water takes more effort than moving through air because water is a much denser (that is, thicker) fluid than air. Working in the ocean, therefore, requires divers to consume prodigious amounts of food merely to generate heat and overcome the fluid density difference when working.

The results of the biological and geological collecting efforts were more important because they took place rather than for the information they generated. It proved that scientists, not necessarily professional divers, could work and collect data successfully through saturation diving techniques.

Impact of Event

By the end of the Sealab 2 experiments, the Navy was convinced that there were very few impediments to having divers work for extended periods of time in the ocean. Obviously, there would have to be considerable safety measures in place before such an expedition. The experience gained in the Sealab projects, however, proved that the technology and knowledge were ready to support such an effort. Perhaps more important was the inclusion in the dive teams of civilian scientists. Further, there were specific scientific studies performed by team members during their period of saturation. These were important steps in moving saturation diving from the realms of medical experimentation and record-breaking headlines (for example, records for longest and deepest saturation dives) into the realm of a practical tool for scientific investigation of the ocean. It was now possible for scientists studying oceanic processes (for example, fish behavior, sediment movement, coral reef ecology) to spend extended periods of time in close contact with their study area through saturation diving techniques. The scientists who were interested in a saturation diving experience were not restricted from participation because of rigorous requirements. If a scientist had a well-defined scientific need, was reasonably healthy, and was a knowledgeable SCUBA diver, then participation in subsequent saturation diving programs was permitted. As a result of programs building on the Sealab experience, such as the Hydrolab programs in the Bahamas and U.S. Virgin Islands, an increasing number of scientists have been trained in, and experienced, the science of saturation diving. In addition to training a cadre of scientists in the use of saturation diving, the programs have also trained a large number of support personnel, from medical doctors and nurses to marine engineers and mechanics, in routine and emergency shore-based operations. A wealth of experienced divers coming from the saturation diving programs was available when the off-shore oil drilling boom created a demand for divers capable of performing grueling tasks under adverse conditions. In addition, the medical knowledge from the saturation diving programs made it possible for this new service industry to perform tasks safely.

One of the advantages of the development of medical support personnel has come in a subsequent increased use of hyperbaric (high pressure) medicine. Data from the studies performed by the Navy, coupled with the increased exposure of nonmilitary medical personnel to hyperbaric chamber operations through the Sealab and subsequent programs, spilled over into expansion of hyperbaric treatment through mainstream hospitals.

In the end, Sealab was both encouraging and sobering. Encouragement came from the fact that the complex operation was accomplished and most of the objectives were met. Divers can (and do) work productively in the ocean for extended periods of time. The sobering facts, though, are that the technical support required to mount such an expedition is formidable and the ocean is quick to punish mistakes or miscalculations. It became obvious that the underwater communities of the visionaries were still far in the future. Nevertheless, the reality of living and working in the ocean was within reach.

Bibliography

Cousteau, Jacques-Yves. *Man Re-enters the Sea*. New York: World Publishing, 1974. A very well-illustrated account of human adventures in the ocean from the perspective of the inventor of the SCUBA equipment that made it possible. In sections devoted to undersea habitats, Cousteau focuses on his own programs (Conshelf) but puts them into perspective by providing highlights of other programs (notably those of the U.S. Navy). There is a comprehensive index but no suggestions for additional readings.

Earle, Sylvia A., and Al Giddings. *Exploring the Deep Frontier*. Washington, D.C.: National Geographic Society, 1980. A profusely illustrated volume that covers much of the history of human ocean exploration. There are numerous references and illustrations of undersea habitats (for example, Sealabs 1 and 2, Conshelf,

Tektite, Hydrolab). An extensive index, very good graphics, and a list of additional readings makes this book an excellent reference for the general reader.

MacInnis, Joseph B. "Living Under the Sea." *Scientific American* 214 (March, 1966): 24-33. The author provides a good summary of the worldwide efforts (through 1965) to explore ocean dwelling from the pioneering work of Link to Cousteau and Sealab 2. The level of discussion is easily accessible to high school students. The article is well illustrated with photographs and graphics.

Marx, Robert F. *Into the Deep: The History of Man's Underwater Exploration.* New York: Van Nostrand Reinhold, 1978. Another comprehensive history of human attempts to explore the ocean's subsurface environments. The text is not illustrated (there are several pages of photographs in the middle of the text), but it is well written. The last chapter focuses on the history of undersea habitats. There is a brief list of additional readings and an index.

Pauli, D. C., and G. P. Clapper, eds. *Project Sealab Report: An Experimental 45-Day Undersea Saturation Dive at 205 Feet.* Washington, D.C.: Government Printing Office, 1967. The official summary report of the Sealab 2 project produced by the Navy. Besides providing overviews and summaries of conclusions, the individuals responsible for specific studies have authored specific reports. Although there is much technical information, it is presented in a manner that is easy to understand. An excellent way to find out the details of these experiments, in addition to seeing some of the problems encountered.

Ross, Frank, Jr. *Undersea Vehicles and Habitats: The Peaceful Uses of the Ocean.* New York: Thomas Y. Crowell, 1970. A good focused narrative history of diving vehicles and underwater habitats. The text is not very well illustrated, but there is a good list of suggested further readings and an index. There is an interesting last chapter on the likely vehicles and habitats of the twenty-first century.

Richard W. Arnseth

Cross-References

Beebe and Barton Set a Diving Record in a Bathysphere (1934), p. 1018; Cousteau and Gagnan Develop the Aqualung (1943), p. 1219; The *Glomar Challenger* Obtains Thousands of Ocean Floor Samples (1968), p. 1876; Deep-Sea Hydrothermal Vents and New Life-Forms Are Discovered (1977), p. 2058.

VENERA 3 IS THE FIRST SPACECRAFT TO IMPACT ON ANOTHER PLANET

Category of event: Space and aviation
Time: November 16, 1965-March 1, 1966
Locale: Venus

The Soviet planetary probe, Venera 3, was the first man-made object to impact the surface of another planet

Principal personages:
G. N. BABAKIN (1914-1971), the chief designer of interplanetary spacecraft
A. M. ISAYEV (1908-1971), the chief designer of the spacecraft propulsion system
SERGEI P. KOROLEV (1907-1966), the chief designer of the Soviet space program from 1957 to 1966
VASILI P. MISHIN (1917-   ), the chief designer of the Soviet space program from 1966 to 1974

Summary of Event

The Soviet Venus probe, Venera 3, was launched on November 12, 1965, by a three-stage A-2e booster from the Baikonur Cosmodrome, near Tyuratam, Kazakhstan, Soviet Union. The chief designers were G. N. Babakin, A. M. Isayev, Sergei P. Korolev, and Vasili P. Mishin. The probe's 43-meter-tall, 509,840-kilogram thrust booster placed Venera 3 into a temporary Earth parking orbit. Before completing its first revolution of Earth, the craft's "escape stage" reignited and boosted Venera 3 into a heliocentric transfer orbit, which would reach the planet Venus after a flight of 280 million kilometers over 105 days.

The design of the 960-kilogram Venera 3 was based upon a standardized spacecraft bus developed by Soviet engineers for all Soviet unmanned lunar and planetary spacecraft from the mid-1960's through the early 1970's. The overall length of Venera 3 was 3.5 meters. The core of the probe consisted of a 1-meter-diameter pressurized cylindrical compartment containing electronics, batteries, and command and communications equipment. Solar panels mounted on both sides of the spacecraft recharged Venera 3's batteries. Excess heat generated by the probe's electronics was carried by fluid circulation to a hemispherical radiator mounted at the end of each solar panel. A 90-centimeter-diameter planetary landing capsule was mounted at one end of the spacecraft bus. At the opposite end was a KDU-414 single-chamber 1.96-kilonewton-thrust course correction engine. Venera 3 was stabilized by nitrogen gas jets controlled by a system that used the sun and the star Canopus for reference. Long-range communication was maintained through a 2-meter-diameter wire mesh dish high-gain antenna mounted on the side of the spacecraft.

The prime task of the spacecraft's orientation system was to keep the solar panels aimed at the sun by positioning the entire spacecraft in an attitude required to illuminate the panels. For this reason, the spacecraft's attitude was changed to aim the high-gain antenna toward Earth only during scheduled periods of communication with the Soviet deep space tracking antenna in the Crimea. To aim the antenna at Earth, the spacecraft was rolled around the axis of the sun-seeking sensor until the earth-seeking sensor pointed the center of the antenna toward Earth. Another sensor used the star Canopus to orient properly the spacecraft for firings of the course correction rocket.

Navigation over the extreme distances between Earth and Venus were complicated by the fact that for every 0.3-meter error in the booster rocket's final velocity, the probe would miss Venus by an additional 9,600 kilometers. The initial trajectory of the Venera 3 probe would have resulted in a 60,550-kilometer miss of the planet. A 21.66-meter-per-second course correction velocity change was accomplished on December 26, 1965, when the spacecraft was slightly more than 10 million kilometers from Earth. The speed and distance of Venera 3 was determined by measuring the Doppler shift in the probe's radio signals.

To prepare for the course correction maneuver, Soviet space tracking engineers measured the position of Venera 3 using thirteen hundred distance measurements, five thousand speed measurements, and seven thousand measurements of the angle to Earth. The course correction was so accurate that Venera 3 would have hit the planet even if the aiming error had been ten to fifteen times as great. The course correction also had to ensure that the spacecraft arrived at Venus when it was in line of sight with the Soviet tracking station.

Venera 3 was a twin of the Venera 2 launched four days earlier; however, Venera 2 carried a photographic payload, whereas Venera 3 carried a 90-centimeter-diameter, 337-kilogram planetary landing capsule, which was intended to parachute to the surface. The two spacecraft were to pass on opposite sides of Venus and provide complementary data about Venus.

Investigations of deep space during the cruise phase of the Venera 3 mission included measurements of the interplanetary magnetic field, cosmic rays, low-energy charged particles, magnitude and energy spectra of solar plasma, micrometeorites, and long-wavelength cosmic radio emanations at wavelengths up to 15 kilometers.

Venera 3's objectives at Venus included close up radio studies of the planet's surface using long-wave interferometry and determination of the characteristics and water content of the atmosphere and surface. The high temperature and pressure conditions now known to exist on the Venusian surface had not been confirmed at the time of the Venera 3 flight. Some Soviet scientists thought the high surface temperature readings sent back by the previous American Mariner 2 probe to Venus were really upper atmospheric temperatures and hoped that the surface conditions were more moderate. Because of this uncertainty, the descent capsule carried surface phase sensors to determine if it had landed on a solid surface or in an ocean.

In case Venera 3's landing capsule successfully reached the surface of the planet, it carried a 70-millimeter-diameter commemorative sphere with the outline of Earth's continents. Within the sphere was a medal with the coat of arms of the Soviet Union on one side and the planets of the solar system on the other, showing Earth and Venus in the correct position for the time of Venera 3's launch. An inscription read "Union of Soviet Socialist Republics, 1965." At the time of the Venera 3 mission, it was not known that the planet's atmosphere was so hostile that no living organism could survive. To protect the Venusian environment from Earth contamination, the Venera 3 spacecraft was sterilized by various methods depending upon the tolerance of each spacecraft component. If the components were able to withstand it, portions of the spacecraft were subjected to 115- to 200-degrees Celsius dry heat. Sensitive electronics and rubber seals that could not be heated were exposed to gamma-ray doses totaling 2.5 million rad. Other portions of the spacecraft were bathed in a 60 percent solution of ethylene oxide diluted by 40 percent methyl bromide. The latter chemical was used to render the former one nonexplosive and was a sterilant. All liquids in the spacecraft were filtered through medical-type asbestos filters.

Venera 3 arrived at Venus on March 1, 1966, and struck the planet at six hours, fifty-six minutes, and twenty-six seconds, Greenwich mean time, at a point only 450 kilometers from the visible center of the planet. Because the approach to Venus occurred when the planet was between the sun and the earth, Venera 3 entered the atmosphere on the night side of the planet. Up to that point, the Soviets had successfully contacted the probe sixty-three times during its journey to Venus.

Several days after Venera 3 impacted Venus, the Soviets announced that contact with the spacecraft was lost prior to planetary encounter, and the landing capsule was not ejected. Soviet engineers admitted that as the spacecraft approached Venus, its temperature started to climb above anticipated levels. Initially, the Soviets attributed the loss of the spacecraft to unknown characteristics of Venus or its environment. There was also speculation that the atmosphere of Venus itself caused the radio blackout, but most likely the spacecraft overheated and the orientation system failed during the final hours of the mission. Portions of the landing capsule were likely to survive after being torn loose from the spacecraft bus during atmospheric entry. The landing capsule, however, was not designed to withstand the high-pressure Venusian atmosphere and was likely crushed during free fall.

Impact of Event

The Venera 3 spacecraft has the historical distinction of being the first man-made object to reach the surface of another planet. Although the spacecraft failed only hours before reaching the planet and returned no planetary data, Venera 3 and its companion craft, Venera 2, were the first space probes to cross the distance successfully between Earth and Venus. Much data about interplanetary space between Earth and Venus was relayed by the probe, and the scientific return from the flight up to the Venusian planetary encounter was significant.

Aside from the importance of being the first object from Earth to reach another planet, the impact of Venera 3 on the surface of Venus was the culmination of five years of repeated Soviet efforts to reach another planet in the solar system. Through the end of 1965, there had been a total of eleven Soviet launch attempts to reach the planet Venus and another seven unsuccessful attempts to reach Mars.

In 1961, two Venus flight attempts resulted in the single craft, Venera 1, entering a heliocentric orbit that would pass approximately 100,000 kilometers from Venus. Communication with Venera 1 failed when the craft was 7.25 million kilometers from Earth. Three more Venus launch attempts on August 25, September 1, and September 12, 1962, failed when their booster's escape stage failed to reignite in Earth orbit to propel them into a heliocentric orbit.

Repeated planetary flight failures prompted Soviet engineers to launch a diagnostic flight to determine the cause of the malfunctions plaguing Venus probe attempts. This diagnostic flight, launched on November 11, 1963, also failed to leave Earth orbit. Another Venus launch attempt on March 27, 1964, was also trapped in Earth orbit by booster failure. The backup spacecraft for the 1964 Soviet Venus flights, Zond 1, did succeed in leaving Earth orbit on April 2, 1964. Bad luck still dogged the Soviet planetary program as communication with Zond 1 was lost on May 14, 1964, two months before it was to encounter Venus. Three more Venus probe launches were attempted in 1965. Venera 2 entered a trajectory toward Venus on November 12, and its companion craft, Venera 3, left Earth orbit on November 16. A third 1965 Venus attempt on November 23 exploded in Earth orbit.

Although both Venera 3 and Venera 2 arrived at Venus, the failure of both spacecraft to return any planetary data underscored the weak engineering base in the Soviet space program at that time. As a result of this engineering weakness, two major problems plagued Soviet planetary efforts in the 1960's. Planetary launches are completed from a temporary Earth orbit. A design fault in the third "escape" stage of the A-2e booster prevented the reliable feed of weightless fuel to its engine while the stage was in Earth orbit. This fault resulted in a large number of early Soviet lunar and planetary launches being stranded in Earth orbit. A second problem that lay in Soviet planetary spacecraft design can be traced to the lack of Soviet space simulation chambers for testing spacecraft designs in a thermal and vacuum environment. Extensive American use of space simulation chambers revealed mission-threatening flaws before launch. The Soviets, however, lacking extensive simulation equipment, were forced to evaluate spacecraft designs in flight, often with less than successful results.

After the Venera 3 probe arrived at Venus, there was some skepticism among Western observers who questioned whether the spacecraft struck Venus by accident or by design. Eventually, however, the planetary impact was regarded as a momentous display of space navigation and the Soviets were congratulated for their achievement.

Bibliography

Gatland, Kenneth. *Robot Explorers.* London: Blandford Press, 1972. A chronology of Soviet and American lunar and planetary space exploration programs. Contains numerous color illustrations providing insights into the design and functions of American and Soviet lunar and planetary spacecraft. Descriptive narrative provides details and results of all Soviet and American lunar and planetary exploration spacecraft and their missions. Suitable for general audiences.

McDougall, Walter A. . . . *The Heavens and the Earth*. New York: Basic Books, 1985. A political history of the space age. Well researched and heavily footnoted; describes and analyzes the decisions by the leaders of both the United States and the Soviet Union and their effects on the respective space programs. Heavy emphasis on the key political and technological leaders of the time. Relates how the American and Soviet space programs became an integral part of Cold War politics. For wide audiences.

Short, Nicholas M. *Planetary Geology*. Englewood Cliffs, N.J.: Prentice-Hall, 1975. Summarizes the accomplishments and scientific results of both American and Soviet lunar and planetary space programs. Stresses the chemical nature of the Moon and inner planets, their geological similarities and differences, and their origins. College-level reading, illustrated with many diagrams and photographs taken by the space missions discussed.

Smolders, Peter. *Soviets in Space*. New York: Taplinger, 1974. A well-illustrated narrative on all aspects of the Soviet space program. Suitable for the general audience, it concentrates on the successful portions of the Soviet space program as they were reported by the Soviet Union. Contains numerous diagrams and photographs illustrating the technical details of Soviet spacecraft and their missions.

Turnill, Reginald. *Spaceflight Directory*. London: Frederick Warne, 1978. A lavishly illustrated summary of spaceflight activities by all nations. Lists chronologies of major manned and unmanned space missions. Technical narrative describes worldwide space activities by nation and program, providing details of spacecraft, mission summaries, and program results. Suitable for readers at the high school and college level.

U.S. Congress. Senate Committee on Commerce, Science, and Transportation. *Soviet Space Programs: 1976-80*. Part 2. Washington, D.C.: Government Printing Office, 1985. Comprehensive descriptions of all phases of unmanned Soviet space programs. Provides a detailed overview of the technical development of Soviet unmanned space activities, scientific investigations, and results, as well as the political effects of Soviet space activities. For interested readers. The standard reference for data on Soviet space programs.

Wilson, Andrew. *Solar System Log*. London: Jane's Publishing, 1987. A compilation of all manned and unmanned lunar and planetary spaceflights up to mid-1985 by all space-faring nations. A well-illustrated chronology of the history, spacecraft, mission, and discoveries of all deep space exploration missions. Suitable for all readers.

Robert Reeves

Cross-References

Tsiolkovsky Proposes That Liquid Oxygen Be Used for Space Travel (1903), p. 189; Goddard Launches the First Liquid Fuel Propelled Rocket (1926), p. 810; The First Rocket with More than One Stage Is Created (1949), p. 1342; Sputnik 1, the First Artificial Satellite, Is Launched (1957), p. 1545; Luna 2 Becomes the First Man-Made Object to Impact on the Moon (1959), p. 1614; Mariner 2 Becomes the First Spacecraft to Study Venus (1962), p. 1734; Mariner 9 Is the First Known Spacecraft to Orbit Another Planet (1971), p. 1944; Mars 2 Is the First Spacecraft to Impact on Mars (1971), p. 1950; Soviet Venera Spacecraft Transmit the First Pictures from the Surface of Venus (1975), p. 2042.

THE ORBITAL RENDEZVOUS OF
GEMINI 6 AND 7 SUCCEEDS

Category of event: Space and aviation
Time: December, 1965
Locale: Cape Canaveral, Florida

The rendezvous mission of Gemini 6 and 7, along with the subsequent long-duration flight of Gemini 7, perfected techniques that made possible lunar exploration by astronauts

Principal personages:
WALTER ("WALLY") M. SCHIRRA (1923-   ), a Gemini 6 astronaut
THOMAS P. STAFFORD (1930-   ), a Gemini 6 astronaut
FRANK BORMAN (1928-   ), a Gemini 7 astronaut
JAMES A. LOVELL (1928-   ), a Gemini 7 astronaut

Summary of Event

Project Gemini was the intermediate step in America's manned spaceflight program, which had its genesis with Project Mercury and its greatest triumph with the lunar landings of the Apollo program.

In 1961, President John F. Kennedy committed the United States to making a landing by astronauts on the Moon within the decade. At that time, there was considerable debate within the National Aeronautics and Space Administration (NASA) as to how this feat was going to be accomplished. Some scientists favored the development of a huge rocket that would fly directly to the Moon, make a landing, and then return to Earth. Others advocated an alternative method in which smaller spacecraft would rendezvous in Earth orbit before making the journey to the Moon. A variation of the latter method called for the launching of a multistage rocket that would send a spacecraft into lunar orbit. A manned lander would then separate from the orbiting spacecraft and descend to the lunar surface. Upon completion of the mission, the lander would depart from the lunar surface and rendezvous and dock with the lunar orbiter. The orbiter would then ignite its engine and head back to Earth.

Either of the rendezvous methods promised an enormous savings in fuel and rocket weight and development costs. Choosing a rendezvous technique also meant that the lunar mission could be attempted sooner. The only apparent drawback was that no one had ever attempted a rendezvous mission and scientists had no idea how difficult it might be. Perfecting the technique of rendezvous and docking became one of the primary objectives of the Gemini program.

Unlike the Mercury spacecraft, which had a single astronaut-pilot, the spacecraft designed for the Gemini program would carry two astronauts into space. The spacecraft was conical in shape and was about 5.6 meters long and 3 meters in diameter at its base. It was composed of reentry and adaptor modules, which had a combined weight of about 3,150 kilograms. The reentry module was designed to withstand the extreme heat of reentry into Earth's atmosphere from orbit. The cabin, which was to be occupied by the astronauts as well as the reentry control system and the rendezvous and recovery sections, was contained within the reentry module. The adaptor module enabled the spacecraft to be mated to the launch vehicle.

The primary launch vehicle for the Gemini program was the Titan 2 rocket. First developed as an Intercontinental Ballistic Missile (ICBM) for the Air Force, this two-stage vehicle stood 30.9 meters tall and weighed some 148,500 kilograms when fueled. The Titan 2 developed 430,000 pounds of take-off thrust from its two first-stage engines. The second stage developed 100,000 pounds of thrust.

The Titan 2 was selected for the Gemini program because it had more power than America's other ICBM, the Atlas. The countdown for the Titan 2 was also hours shorter than that required for the Atlas, and astronauts needed to enter their spacecraft only ninety minutes before lift-off. The Titan 2 also had a unique safety feature: If anything went wrong in the seconds between ignition and lift-off, the engines would shut down automatically. This feature, along with the insertion of various backup systems, allowed the Titan 2 to become rated for human safety and join the Gemini program.

In addition to rendezvous and docking, there were other objectives for the program. It had to be demonstrated that astronauts and their life-support systems could be sustained over a two-week mission, spacecraft could be guided accurately through the reentry phase of the mission, extravehicular activities (EVA) were possible and safe, and scientific experimentation could be carried out in space.

Gemini 4, the second manned mission in the new program, met three of these objectives. Various medical experiments were conducted as well as radiation detection and weather-related observations, a spacewalk (EVA) was accomplished, and the crew successfully conducted a guided reentry into Earth's atmosphere. The seven-day mission of Gemini 5 accomplished a portion of the final endurance requirement, and Gemini 6 was to be the first attempt at orbital rendezvous.

The plan for conducting orbital rendezvous was to send first a target vehicle into orbit. This target vehicle would be unmanned. After a stable orbit had been achieved, the manned spacecraft then would be sent into orbit. By using the thrusters on the Gemini spacecraft, astronauts would be able to alter the position and orientation of the spacecraft until it caught up with the target vehicle. The Agena-B was used as the target vehicle in the Gemini program. This second stage of the Atlas-Agena configuration was 7.5 meters in length, had a diameter of 1.5 meters, and weighed 765 kilograms.

The launch of the target vehicle for Gemini 6 took place at 10:00 A.M. eastern standard time, on October 25, 1965. At the time of the launch, astronauts Walter ("Wally") M. Schirra and Thomas P. Stafford were already in their Gemini spacecraft, which was set on top of a Titan 2. The countdowns for Gemini 6 and the target vehicle proceeded simultaneously. The Atlas performed well but the Agena failed to orbit because of an instability that caused the vehicle to break up. The Gemini 6 launch was promptly called off.

After much discussion, NASA officials decided to use the Gemini 7 spacecraft as the target vehicle for Gemini 6 rather than wait for another Atlas-Agena. Gemini 7, which had been planned as a fourteen-day mission, was launched into orbit by a Titan 2 rocket at 2:30 P.M. eastern standard time on December 4, 1965. The primary objectives of the flight were to evaluate the effects of a prolonged mission upon the crew, conduct a rendezvous with Gemini 6, and carry out some twenty in-flight experiments.

For the first several days of the flight, astronauts Frank Borman and James A. Lovell conducted various experiments such as the use of a laser for voice communications, made stellar observations, and worked on navigation problems. Meanwhile, at the Kennedy Spaceflight Center, technicians were preparing the hardware and the pad for the launch of Gemini 6.

The launching of Gemini 6 was not without its share of drama. Two seconds after ignition on December 12, both of the Titan's engines shut down. Telemetric data indicated that there had been a lift-off, although the astronauts had felt no physical sense of motion. As commander of the spacecraft, Schirra had to make an instantaneous decision. He could eject the astronauts from the spacecraft, quite possibly injuring both of them and, at best, forcing a long mission delay. His other option was to do nothing and assume that the data were incorrect and there had been no lift-off. If the data were correct and there had been a slight lift-off, the Titan might well fall back on the pad and explode. Schirra chose the latter option, and as it turned out, the correct one. The mission was saved, but would be postponed for a few days.

Gemini 6 was launched at 8:37 A.M. eastern standard time on December 15, eleven days after the launch of Gemini 7. The mission's primary objective was to achieve an orbital rendezvous with Gemini 7. At the time of launch, Gemini 7 was about 2,200 kilometers ahead of Gemini 6. Within about five hours, Gemini 6 was about 1,200 kilometers from Gemini 7.

During Gemini 6's second orbit of Earth, the astronauts made several course correction maneuvers that enabled them to close to within 320 kilometers of Gemini 7. After switching to a computerized rendezvous mode, Gemini 6 continued to close the distance between the two spacecraft. At 2:33 P.M. eastern standard time on December 15, the spacecraft were only 36 meters apart and were in full view of each other. For nearly four complete orbits of Earth, the distance between the two spacecraft varied from 87 meters to as little as one-third of a meter. The astronauts could see each other easily, and the Gemini 6 astronauts noted the eleven-day growth of beard on Borman and Lovell.

The flight of Gemini 6 was planned as a two-day mission; its objective completed, it reentered Earth's atmosphere to splashdown in the Atlantic Ocean at 10:20 A.M. eastern standard time, on December 16. Although there were some minor problems with fuel cells aboard Gemini 7, it was able to complete its fourteen-day mission and return to Earth at 9:05 A.M. eastern standard time on December 18, 1965.

Impact of Event

To accomplish exploration of the Moon by astronauts, NASA had decided upon a technique that became known as the lunar orbital rendezvous mode. This approach was different from other proposed methods in that the command and service modules of the Apollo spacecraft would remain in lunar orbit, while the lunar excursion vehicle (LEM) would undock and descend to the lunar surface. At the conclusion of the mission, the LEM would then depart the surface at the exact calculated moment and catch up with the orbiting Apollo spacecraft. The LEM, then, would dock with the command and service module combination, and the astronauts would leave the LEM and enter the command module. After the LEM was jettisoned, the Apollo spacecraft would begin its flight back to Earth.

The techniques used in the lunar orbital rendezvous mode first had to be tested and perfected. This was the primary mission of the Gemini program. It had to be shown that two spacecraft could rendezvous and dock, and that life-support systems could sustain human life aboard a spacecraft for a mission of long duration.

In order to accomplish rendezvous in the Gemini 6 and 7 mission, Gemini 6 was launched into an orbit essentially coplanar with the target vehicle, Gemini 7. During the first few orbits, the astronauts of Gemini 6 performed several ground-supplied midcourse maneuvers that led to a rendezvous with Gemini 7. Although the Soviets previously claimed that two of their Vostok spacecraft had conducted a rendezvous on August 12, 1962, the Gemini astronauts conducted the first rendezvous of two manned, maneuverable vehicles. The two Soviet spacecraft were in two completely different orbital planes, and their spacecraft could not be maneuvered to close the distance between them.

The successful rendezvous of Gemini 6 and 7 led to the first docking between two spacecraft in the Gemini 8 mission. These flights proved that rendezvous and docking could be perfected and that the lunar orbital rendezvous technique would be feasible.

During the fourteen-day mission of Gemini 7, the astronauts conducted several experiments related to the effect of zero gravity on human physiology. An in-flight exerciser was used to help prevent deterioration of the heart muscle. In addition, the astronauts experimented with the use of pneumatic pressure cuffs. These cuffs were secured around the astronauts' legs and inflated. The resulting stress on the venous system in the astronauts' legs simulated a low-gravity environment.

Other experiments conducted by the Gemini 7 crew measured the effects of space flight on the chemistry of body fluids, the breakdown of bone and muscle tissue, and human equilibrium.

The long-duration flight of Gemini 7 proved that humans could survive in space over long periods of time. In fact, astronauts Borman and Lovell found that they could conduct many of their mission requirements without wearing pressure suits. Their comfort and mobility were greatly enhanced without the suits, and no detriment to crew health was noted.

Bibliography

Borman, Frank, with Robert Serling. *Countdown*. New York: William Morrow, 1988. A very readable autobiography. Several chapters are devoted to astronaut Borman's experiences while a part of the Gemini and Apollo programs.

Glasstone, Samuel. *The Sourcebook on the Space Sciences*. Princeton, N.J.: D. Van Nostrand, 1965. Covers a wide range of topics from historical background of space exploration, orbits, trajectories, and propulsion units to a general description of the sun, the planets, and the universe. The technical level varies with the subject area covered, but for the most part, the reader should have an elementary knowledge of physics, chemistry, and mathematics.

Hacker, Barton C., and James M. Grimwood. *On the Shoulders of Titans*. NASA SP-4203. Washington, D.C.: Government Printing Office, 1977. A well-illustrated, well-documented volume covering the Gemini program from its beginnings. Suitable for general readers.

Malik, P. W., and G. A. Souris. *Project Gemini: A Technical Summary*. NASA CR-1106. Springfield, Va.: Federal Scientific and Technical Information, 1968. A highly technical volume describing the various systems incorporated within the Gemini spacecraft. A brief summary of each mission is included.

Shelton, William. *American Space Exploration: The First Decade*. Boston: Little, Brown, 1967. A nontechnical volume that presents a history of rocketry and space-flight from the early experiments of Robert Goddard through the Gemini program.

David W. Maguire

Cross-References

The First Rocket with More than One Stage Is Created (1949), p. 1342; Shepard Is the First United States Astronaut in Space (1961), p. 1698; Glenn Is the First American to Orbit Earth (1962), p. 1723; The First Humans Land on the Moon (1969), p. 1907.

ARDREY'S *THE TERRITORIAL IMPERATIVE* ARGUES THAT HUMANS ARE NATURALLY TERRITORIAL

Category of event: Anthropology
Time: 1966
Locale: United States

Ardrey claimed that human site attachment reflects deep-seated biological needs, which should be seen in the context of instinctual animal behavior

> *Principal personages:*
> ROBERT ARDREY (1908-1980), an American playwright and popular writer on anthropological subjects who argued that humans are innately aggressive and territorial
> NIKOLAAS TINBERGEN (1907-1988), a Dutch zoologist and ethologist who carried out fundamental research on animal behavior under natural conditions
> KONRAD LORENZ (1903-1989), an Austrian ethologist who maintained that aggression was an instinctive drive that sought consummation
> RAYMOND ARTHUR DART (1893-1988), the South African anatomist who theorized that human aggression was inherited from ancestral predatory apes
> ASHLEY MONTAGU (1905-   ), an American anthropologist and author who was known for his opposition to instinctual, sexist, and racist explanations of human behavior
> EDWARD O. WILSON (1929-   ), a prominent American ethologist and expert on insect behavior
> ROBERT CHAMBERS (1802-1871), a British publisher and author who anticipated Charles Darwin's evolutionary approach
> CHARLES DARWIN (1809-1882), an English naturalist who presented compelling evidence for organic evolution

Summary of Event

In 1966, Robert Ardrey's *The Territorial Imperative: A Personal Inquiry into the Animal Origins of Property and Nations* was published by Atheneum Press. It was the noted American playwright's second major foray into popular anthropological writing and appeared while his first effort, *African Genesis* (1961), was still a bestseller. Like his previous work, Ardrey's *The Territorial Imperative* placed humanity and its institutions within the instinctual context of animal behavior (ethology). This time, however, he focused upon the origins and implications of territoriality rather than the predatory legacy of humankind's hominid ancestors.

The central thesis of *The Territorial Imperative* is quite straightforward: In territorial species such as *Homo sapiens*, the urge to acquire and defend a specific area of space is an ineradicable genetically based drive reflecting a biological need for identity, security, and stimulation. Territory is acquired instinctively, without the intention of attracting mates or assuring sufficient supplies of food. Accrued benefits such as access to sexual partners and natural resources are by-products of, rather than reasons for, the acquisition of territory. Ardrey's reversal of commonly held axioms of courtship behavior and population economics extended to consequences as well as causes: Cooperation, species propagation, and the effective exploitation of available resources do not flow directly from the simple occupation of a territory. Rather, these things result from the instinctual energy released by the possession and defense of that territory.

For Ardrey, acknowledgment of the importance of this inborn drive was indispensable to both an understanding of humanity's evolutionary heritage and the prospects for its continued survival. His emphasis on the relevance of ethological analyses to the human condition identified his work as a sociobiological treatise. He insisted that both on the individual and the group level, people must learn to respect their instinctive constraints and act within them. Otherwise, they will lose the advantages that have allowed natural selection to operate in humanity's favor.

In order to explore the nature and boundaries of those constraints, Ardrey drew upon a wide spectrum of observed animal behavior, ranging from the spacing patterns of slime molds to the tactics of perimeter defense practiced by chacma baboons. His approach was twofold: to survey the major varieties of animal territoriality and to tease out from those patterns the threads that affect human conduct. In approaching that task, Ardrey adopted Nikolaas Tinbergen's definition of an instinct as an ordered nervous mechanism that is responsive to certain internal and external priming and release impulses, reacts to those impulses in coordinated movements, and promotes either individual or group survival by its activity. Ardrey also used the twin concepts of closed and open instinctual systems. According to Ardrey, a closed system provides an invariant response to stimuli, while an open one allows for behavior modification through learning. The first case, which throws instinctual behavior into sharp relief, illuminates the second one, in which the instinctual elements are normally obscured by learned components. Since the more flexible and adaptive open system prevails in higher animals, fresh insight into the activities of humans and other primates can be obtained by observing the behavior of lower animals such as planarian worms. By postulating comparable instinctive elements in lower and higher organisms, Ardrey placed animal behavior on a continuum that allowed the drawing of conclusions by analogy along its whole length.

In large part, *The Territorial Imperative* is a tour along that ethological continuum, with pauses for the extraction of behavior pertinent to the human condition. Thus, an extensively detailed description of the mating behavior of an African antelope, the Ugandan kob, reveals the principle that ritualized aggression on a defended territory reduces injury. That example is then supplemented by accounts of aggression displacement activity along territorial boundaries by roe deer, sticklebacks, and herring gulls. The descriptions of gulls tearing at grass rather than at their neighbors, roebucks attacking trees instead of other roebucks, and male sticklebacks standing on their heads and churning sand alongside their rivals are then linked to related features of the Olympic Games and Soviet-American space competition.

Connections drawn between points along a continuum were used also to illustrate the instinctual bases of labor and attachment to place. A beaver's dedication to the proper maintenance of his lodge, the increased ferocity of crickets near their niches, the return of salmon and seals to specific breeding grounds, and the savage territoriality shown by sexually immature green sunfish were cited as pertinent examples of invariant instinctual systems. Lessons drawn from these closed system reactions were then applied to analogous human responses such as the increased productivity of family farms over state-run agricultural enterprises and Finland's unflinching resistance to invasion by the Soviet Union in the Winter War of 1939-1940.

Sociobiological inferences usually generate controversy. Ardrey's claims, however, that a territory establishes identity, its periphery offers opportunities for stimulation, and its interior represents security become especially provocative when applied to human societies. He identified two types of territorially based social organizations: the noyau (knot) and the biological nation. The noyau, a fragmented society based upon inward antagonisms, furthers individual expression at the expense of group solidarity and safety. Composed of a coterie of small, noisy neighborhoods, its participants gain stimulation from argumentative interaction with adjoining neighbors, identity and security from attachment to a specific site, and status from performance in periphery defense and small group dynamics. The noyau is a viable response to the territorial imperative, although its internal divisions make it susceptible to incursions. Ardrey identified black-headed gulls, satin bowerbirds, and callicebus monkeys as species that form noyaus. He also maintained that Italy's tradition of political disunity and cultural dynamism is a result of its noyau format and asserted that societies normally organized at a higher level can revert to noyau status. The noyau's weaknesses are avoided by the biological nation, the highest evolutionary expression of the territorial instinct. In this case, the group's energies are directed to the defense of a continuous territory, and it remains isolated from other groups through outward antagonisms. Such societies achieve high levels of cooperation and inward harmony and exhibit a remarkable capacity for coordinated defensive action. Introduced into primate behavior by lemurs, the biological nation offers humanity the best available individual and group response to the problems of survival. While considerable individual freedom is lost in the pressure to conform, extraordinary levels of amnity and security are obtained and the instinctual energies released by the territorial imperative are efficiently used. Ardrey cited the United States, Athens in the Hellenic period, the white minority in South Africa, and the Vietnamese as pertinent applications of the biological nation model.

Ardrey's major sociobiological conclusions are easily summarized: Human societies that respect the instinctual undergirdings of territoriality by preserving the principle of private property are more effective than those that do not; regardless of motivations, aggressors attacking biological nations are at a severe disadvantage, for their incursions release powerful instinctual energies in the territorial defenders; and since humans are predators who will intrude, appropriate instinct-based methods of ritualizing and limiting conflict must be developed.

Impact of Event

In part because it was extremely well written and its arguments were presented with rare passion and conviction, *The Territorial Imperative* created a literary sensation. Several other facts, however, contributed to its early success. In the first place, its appearance coincided with the English language publication of Konrad Lorenz's *On Aggression* (1966), which argued that aggressive behavior was an instinctive, pragmatic response to problems of survival. Second, sales of Ardrey's new work were aided by the continued popularity of *African Genesis*, a defense of aggression based on the anthropological speculations of Raymond Arthur Dart, the discoverer of an early hominid, *Australopithecus*. Third, *The Territorial Imperative* supplied a new interpretation for the great wars of the twentieth century and, by extension, a disturbing prognosis for the intensified American involvement in the Vietnamese conflict. Finally, Ardrey's sociobiological thesis reopened the nature-nurture debate in the sharpest possible way—by presenting learned behavior as the handmaiden of the instincts. For several years after its publication, *The Territorial Imperative* was widely cited in books and articles, ranging from political science to psychiatry and became an established artifact in American popular culture.

It soon became clear, however, that Ardrey's conclusions were vulnerable to challenges from several directions. Since he lacked solid scientific credentials and his evidence was often anecdotal in character, he was viewed as an enthusiastic amateur unfamiliar with research methodology. A related criticism was that he distorted the evidence by presenting those facts that supported his assertions while ignoring contrary information. His fundamental premise that valid conclusions could be reached by analogy also came under attack, as it was doubtful whether the bases of animal motivation were fully understood; until that time arrived, comparisons and conclusions were questionable. Since Ardrey aligned himself so thoroughly with nature over nurture, he also attracted ideological criticism—the best known being that of the American anthropologist Ashley Montagu, who accused him of reintroducing the outmoded concept of innate depravity into scientific discourse by claiming that humans are influenced by instincts. Montagu also charged Ardrey with trying to fabricate ancestral capitalistic genes by positing an instinctual basis for territoriality. The various attacks proved convincing: *The Territorial Imperative* was rarely cited by the early 1970's and later works by Ardrey on related themes provoked little interest.

Although *The Territorial Imperative* failed in its bid for scientific respectability, many of the issues it raised gained new vigor with the apperance, in 1975, of Edward Wilson's *Sociobiology: The New Synthesis*. While Wilson, a noted ethologist, established the legitimacy of sociobiological inquiry in a way that Ardrey could not, the reception of his work was influenced by Ardrey's earlier effort. By arousing interest in sociobiological issues, *The Territorial Imperative* prepared the ground for the later reception of analogous views. In a sense, Ardrey's work was to Wilson's what Robert Chambers' *Vestiges of the Natural History of Creation* (1844) was to Charles Darwin's *On the Origin of Species* (1859)—a flawed yet inspired effort that eased the way for a greater successor.

Bibliography

Archer, John. *The Behavioural Biology of Aggression*. Cambridge, England: Cambridge University Press, 1988. This excellent book provides a historical perspective on aggression research and its relation to territoriality. Clearly written and comprehensive, with charts, tables, diagrams, references, and suggestions for further reading. Offers both a subject and author index.

Ardrey, Robert. *African Genesis: A Personal Investigation into the Animal Origins and Nature of Man*. New York: Atheneum Press, 1961. Ardrey's first anthropological work popularized the notion that the behavior patterns of ancestral killer apes remain an essential part of humankind's instinctive heritage. Assertions about humanity's predatory nature reappear as underlying assumptions in *The Territorial Imperative*. Includes illustrations, a bibliography, an index, and a biographical note.

Burnet, Sir Macfarlane. *Dominant Mammal: The Biology of Human Destiny*. New York: St. Martin's Press, 1971. An interesting attempt to incorporate principles of primate behavior into the making of public policy by a corecipient of the 1960 Nobel Prize in Physiology or Medicine. Burnet appreciates Ardrey's sociobiological efforts, although he doubts their validity. Contains charts, tables, a bibliography, and an index.

Hinde, R. A. *Biological Bases of Human Social Behavior*. New York: McGraw-Hill, 1974. Perhaps the last scholarly book to cite Ardrey as an authority on the relationship between human and animal behavior. The numerous reservations and caveats expressed in Hinde's work reflect clearly the uncertain state of sociobiological inquiries and the tentativeness of their conclusions during the early 1970's. Includes numerous illustrations, tables, and diagrams. A bibliography and a subject and name index are provided.

Montagu, Ashley, ed. *Man and Aggression*. 2d ed. New York: Oxford University Press, 1973. A key work in assessing *The Territorial Imperative*. Contains twenty essays specifically aimed at refuting Ardrey's and Lorenz's assertions about the instinctual bases of human behavior. Often a polemical attack on the notion of territoriality and a passionate defense of nurture over nature. Offers maps, tables, diagrams, and bibliographical references.

Ruse, Michael. *Sociobiology: Sense or Nonsense?* 2d ed. Boston: D. Reidel, 1985. An excellent treatment of the topic by a leading figure in the philosophy of science. Ruse deliberately ignores Ardrey's efforts, maintaining that Wilson's sociobiological writings placed the issue on altogether different epistemological foundations. Contains tables, diagrams, charts, a subject index, and an index of names.

Wilson, Edward O. *Sociobiology: The New Synthesis.* Cambridge, Mass.: The Belknap Press of Harvard University Press, 1975. The indispensable work on sociobiology that covers, in extensive scholarly detail, the major issues that Ardrey grappled with in *The Territorial Imperative.* Wilson recognizes the power of Ardrey's passionate conviction but maintains that intensity of belief is no substitute for careful scholarly research. Profusely illustrated and replete with tables, charts, and diagrams. Wilson also provides an extensive bibliography and an index.

Michael J. Fontenot

Cross-References

Zdansky Discovers Peking Man (1923), p. 761; Dart Discovers the First Recognized Australopithecine Fossil (1924), p. 780; Sibley and Ahlquist Discover a Close Human and Chimpanzee Genetic Relationship (1984), p. 2267; Scientists Date a *Homo sapiens* Fossil at Ninety-two Thousand Years (1987), p. 2341.

SIMONS IDENTIFIES A
30-MILLION-YEAR-OLD PRIMATE SKULL

Category of event: Anthropology
Time: January, 1966
Locale: Fayum badlands, about 80 kilometers south of Cairo, Egypt

Simons identified the earliest known primate ancestor of all modern monkeys, apes, and humans

Principal personage:
ELWYN L. SIMONS (1930-   ), an American vertebrate paleontologist and director of the Yale paleontological expedition to the Fayum

Summary of Event

The Oligocene deposits of the Egyptian Fayum, dated between 40 million years ago and 27 million years ago, have been known as rich sources of fossil primates since 1907, when a professional collector sold specimens to the Stuttgart Museum in Germany. The Fayum quarries consist of the remains of former rivers and lakes in what was once an area of low relief. During the Oligocene epoch, the climate in the Fayum was humid and warm, and dense forests lined the watercourses. In these forests lived a rich array of early animals that are the oldest known examples of catarrhine primates. The catarrhines are the infraorder of primates to which the superfamilies cercopithecoidea and hominoidea belong. Old World monkeys make up the cercopithecoidea, while apes and humans are both members of the hominoidea. The hominoidea, in turn, are divided into the families Pongidae, or apes, and Hominidae, or extinct and living humans.

In 1961, nearly fifty years after the first discovery of these deposits, Elwyn L. Simons of the Peabody Museum at Yale University directed the first expedition to investigate the Fayum with the hope of learning more about these possible human ancestors. Excavations continued over the next two decades and were to lead to the best-known fossil primate of the Oligocene.

In the first years of excavation, a scattering of teeth and fragments of lower jaws convinced Simons that a new genus and species of primate had existed during the Oligocene. He named it *Aegyptopithecus zeuxsis.* Simons' original assessment was vindicated in 1966, when a rare and spectacular discovery was made. This was a nearly complete skull of *Aegyptopithecus.* In subsequent years, additional finds became so numerous that a complete reconstruction of the entire animal was possible. Accurate reconstructions of fossil primates are extremely uncommon because most finds usually consist of only teeth and jaws. As a result, *Aegyptopithecus* has become famous.

Aegyptopithecus lived about 30 million years ago. It differs from the earlier and more primitive prosimians of the Eocene epoch by a variety of features of the head and teeth that are shared by all catarrhines. Its canine teeth are larger than its incisors, it has a mobile jaw, and its skull exhibits postorbital closure, a thin bony septum extending from behind the edge of the eyes to the sides of the skull. The brain of *Aegyptopithecus* is proportionally larger than the brains of Eocene prosimians, although it is smaller than that of any ape or monkey. The interior of its brain case shows that, while *Aegyptopithecus* has a smaller frontal lobe than later catarrhines, vision had become increasingly important, and sense of smell had declined. *Aegyptopithecus* has an extremely projecting snout, which, taken together with its very small brain, gives it the appearance of a lemur, a modern prosimian. Overall, the skull of *Aegyptopithecus* is very primitive in comparison with all other catarrhines.

The most important aspect of the *Aegyptopithecus* lower skeleton lies in its forelimbs. Although sharing certain similarities with later hominoidea, the primitive character of *Aegyptopithecus* forelimbs also resembles the forelimbs of the lemur. Unlike most later catarrhines, *Aegyptopithecus* was not an agile arm-swinger, but rather a slow, heavily muscled quadrupedal climber. The size of a fox or a large cat, it weighed about 7 kilograms, making it a large primate for its time. *Aegyptopithecus* probably made its ponderous way through the leafy canopy of the Fayum forests, subsisting on a diet of fruit supplemented by leaves. Simons stated that, despite its many primitive features, *Aegyptopithecus* resembled modern and extinct apes more than it resembled Old World monkeys. He based this decision in particular on the similarity of its teeth with those of living chimpanzees and gorillas, which, like *Aegyptopithecus*, have large interlocking canines and large molars. Simons declared that *Aegyptopithecus* was the ancestor of the family of Miocene apes known as the dryopithecines, which throve in Africa between 27 million years ago and 4 million years ago. The dryopithecines, in turn, may be ancestral to gorillas, chimpanzees, and humans. *Aegyptopithecus* was, therefore, the earliest known hominoid and the likely ancestor of all modern apes and humans. Other scientists have disagreed with Simons' assessment, claiming that *Aegyptopithecus* is an ancestor of both apes and monkeys. At issue is whether *Aegyptopithecus* is similar to later hominoids because it shares certain primitive features, or whether it exhibits features that are unique to later hominoids.

A development in evolutionary theory called cladism assigns taxonomic relatedness solely on the basis of uniquely shared "derived" or specialized traits that will typify the new group. The earliest members of a taxonomic group will show the first appearance of these derived features. For example, bipedalism is the distinctive trait that unites all hominids. The earliest known hominid, *Australopithecus afarensis*, is fully bipedal, although it has apelike forearms and a small and primitive brain. From the point of view of cladism, similarities based on shared primitive traits cannot show the closeness of the relationship between two taxonomic groups. Unlike the older "evolutionary" approach, which assigned value primarily to similarities, cladism rejects the idea that a species can change gradually over time into a new species. Instead, evolution occurs only when two new species separate from a common ancestor. While the "evolutionists" subscribe to the idea that an ancient lineage can evolve slowly over long periods of time, cladists see human evolution as a series of successive speciation events by increasingly modern-looking groups. By the older perspective, *Aegyptopithecus* (particularly in its dentition) appears to be an early hominoid. By the newer approach, it does not.

Applying cladistic theory, some authors, such as John G. Fleagle, have developed the hypothesis that the dental qualities that *Aegyptopithecus* shares with African apes are not the result of common evolutionary changes, but reflect rather a lack of such change among modern apes. Having apelike teeth does not indicate that *Aegyptopithecus* is the earliest known hominoid species. In this, as in other features of the head, Fleagle believes that *Aegyptopithecus* exhibits sufficiently primitive features for it to be an ancestor of both the hominoidea and the cercopithecoidea. All share a number of features not found in *Aegyptopithecus*, including proportionally larger and more complex brains. With respect to its postcranial anatomy, Fleagle notes that the *Aegyptopithecus* elbow could be ancestral to all later catarrhines. The fact that the elbow of *Aegyptopithecus* resembles the hominoid elbow more than the cercopithecoid elbow again results from the fact that many of the features of the modern hominoid elbow are merely extensions of the primitive early catarrhine condition.

Cladists have pointed out that, in many respects, Old World monkeys are equally or more derived from the ancestral catarrhine condition than apes. Living cercopithecoidea are highly specialized in dentition, diet, habitat, posture, and lower skeleton. These scientists believe that living hominoids, including man, may approximate the primitive ancestral catarrhines more than has previously been considered. If they are correct, then it is possible that Old World monkeys are descended from a hominoid ancestor. Simons disagrees with this hypothesis. He believes that Old World monkeys and apes had already split before the time of the Fayum fauna. Furthermore, he believes that the teeth and body of *Aegyptopithecus* resemble hominoids, not cercopithecoids, and that it is highly unlikely that *Aegyptopithecus* could have given rise to Old World monkeys.

Much of the difficulty in placing *Aegyptopithecus* and related forms is caused by the fact that most primate fossils consist of teeth and jaws. In living animals, these elements often do not differ between species as much as do other parts of the body. The absence of such body parts in other fossils makes comparison with *Aegyptopithecus* difficult. Consequently, it is often impossible to identify derived traits or to identify the last common ancestor shared by two fossil types. This paucity of fossil information means that debates about the evolution of the primates is not likely to cease for a long time.

Impact of Event

Adding to the difficulty imposed by the fossil record, according to Fleagle and Richard F. Kay, is that teeth have been of primary importance to paleoanthropologists in determining taxonomic placement of primates. Even when parts of the lower skeleton have been available, they were not seen as significant sources of taxonomic information. Still more important was the unquestioned assumption by scholars that monkeys were ancestral to apes. The result was that the Fayum fauna were classified as intermediate between monkeys and apes rather than prior to both.

It was the discomfort experienced by many scholars in classifying this most unape-like creature with unquestioned apes that led to the reassessment by some of hominoid and cercopithecoid evolution. To cladists, *Aegyptopithecus* is the only known primate having the potential to give rise equally well to apes and to Old World monkeys. It is what might be expected of an extremely primitive catarrhine that could connect the early prosimians of the Eocene epoch to the apes and monkeys of the Miocene epoch. *Aegyptopithecus* may be neither an ape nor a monkey, but a forerunner of both.

The taxonomic position given to *Aegyptopithecus* by cladists is based on morphology. This position fits the evidence from molecular biology. Biomolecular specialists such as Vincent Sarich have insisted for many years that the cercopithecoid-hominoid split occurred between 20 million years ago and 26 million years ago in the early Miocene epoch. If this is so, then temporally, geographically, and anatomically, *Aegyptopithecus* was in the right place at the right time.

Because of the information stemming from the study of *Aegyptopithecus*, it has been necesary to reconsider the relationship between the cercopithecoidea and the hominoidea. Old World monkeys—clearly less closely related to human beings than apes—were also assumed to be older, more primitive, and less evolved than apes. Scholars such as Fleagle believe that this is a false and anthropomorphic concept resulting from the idea that human beings represent the pinnacle of biological evolution. *Aegyptopithecus* has forced a reevaluation of this idea and the humbling possibility that, at least in some respects, humans and apes may be more primitive than humans' distant relatives, the Old World monkeys.

Bibliography

Delson, Eric, ed. *Ancestors: The Hard Evidence.* New York: Alan R. Liss, 1985. Contains good examples of portions of the debate between Simons and his opponents. Section 2 includes articles by Simons, Fleagle and Kay, and David Pilbeam. Pilbeam's article is an evaluation of the controversy. Simon's introductory text (cited below) should be read before attempting these articles. Illustrated, bibliographies.

Fleagle, John G., and Richard F. Kay. "New Interpretations of the Phyletic Position of Oligocene Hominoids." In *New Interpretations of Ape and Human Ancestry*, edited by Russell L. Ciochon and Robert S. Corruccini. New York: Plenum Press, 1983. Although quite technical, this article is indispensable for an understanding of new ideas regarding the evolution of apes and monkeys and the role of cladistic theory. Copious illustrations, bibliography.

Sarich, Vincent. "A Molecular Approach to the Question of Human Origins." In *Primate Evolution and Human Origins*, edited by Russell L. Ciochon and John G.

Fleagle. New York: Aldine de Gruyter, 1987. A reprint of an early statement of the molecular evidence for primate evolution. Addressing his discussion to readers unfamiliar with biomolecular studies, Sarich discusses problems in identifying ancestral species solely through fossils and explains the molecular approach and its potential utility. A useful introduction to molecular dating. Illustrations, bibliography.

Simons, Elwyn L. *Primate Evolution: An Introduction to Man's Place in Nature.* New York: Macmillan, 1972. Although dated, this textbook is still an excellent introduction to primate evolution, particularly with respect to basic principles. It should be read before attempting more technical material. Illustrations, with a list of taxonomic synonyms, a formal classification of living and extinct primates, and a bibliography.

Lucy Jayne Botscharow

Cross-References

Dart Discovers the First Recognized Australopithecine Fossil (1924), p. 780; Leakey Finds a 1.75-Million-Year-Old Hominid (1959), p. 1603; Anthropologists Discover "Lucy," an Early Hominid Skeleton (1974), p. 2037; Sibley and Ahlquist Discover a Close Human and Chimpanzee Genetic Relationship (1984), p. 2267; Hominid Fossils Are Gathered in the Same Place for Concentrated Study (1984), p. 2279.

THE SOVIET LUNA 9 MAKES THE FIRST SUCCESSFUL LUNAR SOFT LANDING

Category of event: Space and aviation
Time: January 31, 1966-February 8, 1966
Locale: Oceanus Procellarum, the Moon

The Soviet spacecraft Luna 9 became the first man-made object to soft-land on another world and return photographs from its surface

Principal personages:
G. N. BABAKIN (1914-1971), the chief designer of interplanetary space-craft
VALENTIN P. GLUSHKO (1906-   ), the chief designer of rocket engines
A. M. ISAYEV (1908-1971), the chief designer of propulsion systems for interplanetary spacecraft
SERGEI P. KOROLEV (1907-1966), the chief designer of the Soviet space program from 1957 to 1966
A. I. LEBEDINSKY, a principal investigator on the Luna 9 science team
MIKHAIL S. RYAZANSKIY (1909-1987), the chief designer of launch vehi-cle guidance systems

Summary of Event

The Soviet lunar landing attempts were initiated in January, 1963, with the un-successful launching of a lunar soft-landing spacecraft. Six more failures would follow over the next three years before Soviet Luna 9 made the first successful soft land-ing on another world. The chief designers were G. N. Babakin, Valentin P. Glushko, A. M. Isayev, Sergei P. Korolev, and Mikhail S. Ryazanskiy. The principal investiga-tor was A. I. Lebedinsky.

Luna 9 was launched at eleven hours, forty-two minutes, Greenwich mean time on January 31, 1966, by a three-stage A-2e booster from the Baikonur Cosmodrome at Tyuratam in Kazakhstan, Soviet Union. The 43-meter-tall, 509,840-kilogram thrust booster placed Luna 9 into a temporary 169- by 219-kilometer Earth parking orbit. Before completing its first orbit, the third stage reignited and propelled Luna 9 into a translunar trajectory.

Because Luna 9 would not enter Earth's shadow during the long cruise to the Moon, the spacecraft was slowly rolled at a rate of 4 degrees per second to distribute evenly the heat from the direct solar radiation.

The 1,583-kilogram, 2.7-meter-long Luna 9 spacecraft consisted of three basic sections. The upper portion was a 58-centimeter-diameter, 100-kilogram spherical landing capsule carrying a television camera and radiation detector. Below this was a 1-meter-diameter cylindrical compartment containing the control and communications equipment. The bottom portion of the spacecraft housed a 45.5-kilonewton-thrust KTDU-5A mid-course correction and retro-rocket engine. Fuel, weighing 800 kilograms, was stored in a 90-centimeter spherical nitric acid tank and a doughnut-shaped aluminum hydrazine tank above the engine.

The spacecraft's initial trajectory would have resulted in a 9,600-kilometer miss of the Moon. On February 1, 1966, while still 233,000 kilometers from its target, Luna 9 performed a course correction with a 71.2-meter-per-second velocity change to ensure a lunar impact.

The Soviet technique for landing a spacecraft on the Moon involved aiming at the western edge of the Moon. This was done so the motion of the moon's orbit would intercept the descending spacecraft along a line with the local lunar vertical. This simple technique limited Soviet landers to an area near 64 degrees west along the lunar equator and eliminated the need for canceling horizontal velocity as well.

On February 3, 1966, while the spacecraft was still 8,300 kilometers from the Moon, Luna 9 assumed a vertical attitude in relation to the Moon in preparation for landing an hour later. At this point, lunar gravity was accelerating the spacecraft toward the Moon at a speed increasing by 1.3 meters each second. After seventy-nine hours of flight and at an altitude of 75 kilometers, a radar altimeter operating at 93 megahertz triggered the ignition of the retro-rocket for a forty-six-second burn. Simultaneously, 300 kilograms of equipment no longer needed was jettisoned to lighten the spacecraft. The retro-rocket slowed the spacecraft from a 2.6-kilometer-per-second descent speed to about 25 meters per second just above the surface. The Pulkovo Observatory in Leningrad filmed the high-speed impact of the discarded Luna 9 equipment as it struck the Moon's surface. As the spacecraft approached the Moon over Oceanus Procellarum, a proximity sensor mounted on an extended arm detected the lunar surface. This signaled shutdown of the rocket motor and ejected the shock resistant landing capsule off to one side away from the area swept by the rocket blast. The capsule was weighted on one side to roll into an upright position.

Landing occurred at eighteen hours, forty-five minutes, and thirty seconds, Greenwich mean time, on February 3, 1966. Touchdown occurred at 7.8 degrees north, 64.22 degrees west in the western area of the Moon known as the Ocean of Storms. The craft landed halfway up the inner slope of a small 25-meter-diameter crater near the large crater Reiner shortly after local sunrise. Immediately after landing, the upper half of the lander's shell split open into four spring-loaded petals that stabilized the capsule in an upright position. Four minutes and ten seconds after landing, four 75-centimeter antenna rods and an 8-centimeter-diameter television apparatus turret popped up from the lander; radio contact was established at 183.538 megahertz.

The lander's television, a simple 1.5-kilogram facsimile system requiring only 2.5 watts of power, quickly began to scan the surrounding lunar details. Panoramic photographs of the local terrain were taken from a height of 60 centimeters and showed the horizon about 1.5 kilometers away. The camera system was designed to be tilted 16 degrees. This tilt allowed the panoramic view to vary from 11 degrees above to 18 degrees below the horizon and allowed close-ups of near objects as well as views toward the horizon. The rotating camera turret used a nodding mirror to scan 360 degrees and took one hundred minutes to complete a panorama. Each panorama was made of eight exposures, each having a resolution of four lines per millimeter on a picture 2.5 centimeters by 2.75 centimeters. The system had a sharpness about twice that of commercial broadcast television, achieving a resolution one-third that of the human eye. This allowed nearby objects as small as 2 millimeters to be imaged.

The first historic panoramic photograph from the lunar surface was transmitted by Luna 9 to Earth between one hour, fifty minutes, and three hours, thirty-seven minutes, Greenwich mean time, on February 4, 1966. A second panorama was transmitted ten hours later, between fourteen hours, zero minutes, and sixteen hours, fifty-four minutes, Greenwich mean time. A third panorama was sent the next day between twenty hours, thirty-seven minutes, and twenty-two hours, fifty-five minutes, Greenwich mean time, February 5, 1966. The elevation of the sun changed from seven to thirteen degrees, then to twenty-seven degrees between the three exposures. This changed the shadow relief between each panorama, allowing further study of lunar surface details. Between the first and second panoramas, the landing capsule shifted slightly as it settled into the lunar soil. This settling changed the tilt of the imaging system from 16.5 to 22.5 degrees and moved the camera's perspective approximately the distance between two human eyes. This fortuitous accident then allowed stereoscopic study of nearby objects.

Luna 9's periods of activity were limited to when the Moon was in line of sight with the Soviet Deep Space Communication Center's antenna at Yevpatoria, in the Crimea. To conserve the lander's batteries, the craft was shut down when it was not in range of the tracking station. When Luna 9 was active on the surface, live signals from the lander were played over Moscow radio and television. The signals sounded like the slow ticking of a grandfather clock through the hiss of radio static.

On February 6, 1966, the Soviets announced that contact with Luna 9 had concluded after a total of eight hours and five minutes of communication with the craft over three days. Nevertheless, two days later, Luna 9 surprised Western observers by transmitting three more poor-quality photographs. Higher than expected battery reserves had allowed the Soviets to exercise the lander one more time before power depletion.

The historic first soft landing on the Moon by Luna 9 was the first direct evidence that manned lunar exploration was possible. Luna 9 showed that the feared, deep layers of soft, unstable, spacecraft-swallowing dust predicted by astronomer Thomas Gold did not exist and that the Moon's surface was capable of supporting a spacecraft.

Impact of Event

The importance of the first soft landing by a spacecraft on another world must be examined not only from a scientific standpoint but also for its place in political history. In the 1960's, the Soviet Union and the United States were in a scientific as well as a political Cold War. The race between the two nations to reach the Moon first was very much a matter of national pride and prestige for the United States and a continuous source of pro-Communist propaganda for the Soviets.

Any mention of Soviet attempts to reach the Moon in the 1960's brings images of Soviet Premier Nikita Khrushchev gloating about the success of his space spectaculars while the early American space efforts floundered. Khrushchev professed a theme that equated Soviet success in space with Socialist superiority on Earth. Although Khrushchev had been removed from power sixteen months before the Luna 9 landing, his space legacy was still a driving force in the competition between the United States and the Soviet Union to reach the Moon first. Indeed, when Luna 9 made its historic landing, Soviet newspapers featured the headline: "The Moon Speaks Russian."

Scientifically, Luna 9's single most important discovery was that the lunar surface was strong enough to support a spacecraft. The successful lunar landing ended a decade-long debate between leading lunar experts about whether the Moon's surface was covered with a fine layer of fluffy dust many meters deep, which would swallow any craft trying to land on it.

The fact that Luna 9 rested firmly on a solid lunar surface was welcome news to planners in the American Apollo manned Moon landing project. The Luna 9 data contributed to the American decision to abandon experimental designs for a six-legged lander and concentrate on the lighter, four-legged design eventually used.

The historic first photographs from the surface of another world became embroiled in international intrigue. The Soviets did not release the lunar photographs immediately. During the Soviet delay, scientists at the Jodrell Bank radio telescope in England intercepted the signals from Luna 9. Technicians discovered that when the Luna's signals were fed into a standard news wire service photograph facsimile machine, pictures of the lunar surface were produced. Not knowing the true scale of the lunar views as transmitted by Luna 9's photographic apparatus, the English versions of the lunar photographs were distorted vertically by a factor of 2.5. This had the effect of making all lunar features appear sharper and more jagged than they really were. This distortion misled some experts into declaring that snowshoelike devices would be needed to walk on the Moon and American equipment would have to be modified prior to a manned landing.

The Soviets were incensed by what they called the English piracy of their Luna 9 photographs. While the unauthorized release of the distorted Luna photographs by the English annoyed the Soviets, it gave worldwide credibility to the Soviet achievement at a time when many doubted that the Soviets had really succeeded in landing on the Moon. After several days, properly scaled Soviet versions of the Luna 9 panoramas were released by Moscow. These views showed the lunar surface to be a rough-textured, volcanic-origin surface, covered with rocks and boulders of various sizes, but smooth enough to be easily transversed by a visiting astronaut.

Luna 9's only other instrument—an SBM-10 radiation detector—showed the average radiation dosage on the lunar surface was 30 millirads per day, a dose safe for human exploration of the Moon. It was deduced further that this radiation was primarily cosmic rays, while some of it was radiation from lunar material induced by cosmic rays.

Bibliography

Gatland, Kenneth. *Robot Explorers*. London: Macmillan, 1972. A chronology of Soviet and American lunar and planetary space exploration programs. Contains numerous color illustrations providing insights into the design and functions of American and Soviet lunar and planetary spacecraft. Descriptive narrative provides details and results of all Soviet and American lunar and planetary exploration spacecraft and their missions. Suitable for general audiences.

McDougall, Walter A. . . . *The Heavens and the Earth*. New York: Basic Books, 1985. A political history of the space age. A well-researched and heavily footnoted historical text that describes and analyzes the decisions by the leaders of both the United States and the Soviet Union and their effects on their respective space programs.

Short, Nicholas M. *Planetary Geology*. Englewood Cliffs, N.J.: Prentice-Hall, 1975. Summarizes the accomplishments and scientific results of both American and Soviet lunar and planetary space programs. Stresses the chemical nature of the Moon and inner planets, their geological similarities and differences, and their origins. College-level reading, illustrated with many diagrams and photographs.

Smolders, Peter. *Soviets in Space*. New York: Taplinger, 1974. A well-illustrated narrative on all aspects of the Soviet space program. Suitable for a general audience; concentrates on the successful portions of the Soviet space program as they were reported by the Soviet Union. Contains numerous diagrams and photographs illustrating the technical details of Soviet spacecraft and their missions.

Stoiko, Michael. *Soviet Rocketry*. New York: Holt, Rinehart and Winston, 1970. An overview of the Soviet space program, tracing the evolution of Soviet rocket development and satellite technology. Speculates on future Soviet space activities. Nontechnical narrative suitable for the beginner.

Turnill, Reginald. *The Observer's Spaceflight Directory*. London: Frederick Warne, 1978. A lavishly illustrated summary of spaceflight activities by all nations. Lists chronologies of major manned and unmanned space missions. Technical narrative describes worldwide space activities by nation and program, providing details of spacecraft, mission summaries, and program results. Suitable for readers at high school and college level.

U.S. Congress. Senate Committee on Commerce, Science, and Transportation. *Soviet Space Programs: 1976-80* Part 2. *Manned Space Programs and Space Life Sciences*. 98th Congress, 2d session. Washington, D.C.: Government Printing Office, 1984. Comprehensive descriptions of all phases of unmanned Soviet space programs. Provides a detailed overview of the technical development of Soviet unmanned space activities, scientific investigations and results, as well as the political effects of Soviet space activities. The standard general reference for data on Soviet space programs.

Wilson, Andrew. *Solar System Log.* London: Jane's Publishing, 1987. A compilation of manned and unmanned lunar and planetary space flights up to mid-1985 by all space-faring nations. A well-illustrated chronology of the history, spacecraft, mission, and discoveries of all deep-space exploration missions. Suitable for all readers.

Robert Reeves

Cross-References

The Jodrell Bank Radio Telescope Is Completed (1957), p. 1539; Sputnik 1, the First Artificial Satellite, Is Launched (1957), p. 1545; Luna 2 Becomes the First Man-Made Object to Impact on the Moon (1959), p. 1614; Luna 3 Provides the First Views of the Far Side of the Moon (1959), p. 1619; The Lunar Orbiter 1 Sends Back Photographs of the Moon's Surface (1966), p. 1825; The First Humans Land on the Moon (1969), p. 1907; Apollo 12 Retrieves Surveyor 3 Parts from the Lunar Surface (1969), p. 1913; Lunokhod 1 Lands on the Moon (1970), p. 1928.

THE LUNAR ORBITER 1 SENDS BACK PHOTOGRAPHS OF THE MOON'S SURFACE

Category of event: Space and aviation
Time: August 10-October 29, 1966
Locale: Earth's moon

Lunar Orbiter 1 was the first picture-taking spacecraft to orbit a body other than Earth

Principal personages:
HOMER E. NEWELL, a NASA administrator
HAROLD MASURSKY (1923-   ), a scientist at the Jet Propulsion Laboratory, California Institute of Technology
LEE R. SCHERER, a director of the Apollo Lunar Exploration, NASA
CLIFFORD H. NELSON, an assistant director at the Langley Research Center, Virginia
ROBERT J. HELBERG, a manager of the Lunar Orbiter program

Summary of Event

On May 25, 1961, President John F. Kennedy made his famous speech in which he stated: "I believe this nation should commit itself to achieving the goal, before this decade is out, of landing a man on the Moon and returning him safely to Earth." In the light of the state of space technology at that time, this was a quite remarkable statement to make, and it would serve as a challenge to the scientists and engineers to make it happen.

Landing an astronaut on the Moon and ensuring a safe return was not going to be an easy task. A whole new technology had to be developed. It must be remembered that the space age was merely four years old at that time and reaching the Moon seemed to be a dream. To make it a reality would require a systematic approach that would progress in stages. The National Aeronautics and Space Administration (NASA) developed a plan that would use a series of unmanned probes to prepare the way for the manned Apollo missions to the Moon. These probes would parallel a program of manned flights that would develop the techniques and hardware necessary to get the crew safely to the Moon and back. Together, these two programs proved to be the best possible approach to a very difficult task.

Firsthand exploration of the Moon began with the Soviet flyby mission of Luna 1 in January, 1959. It was a crude mission by today's standards, but it did return a photograph of the previously unseen far side of the Moon. This mission was closely followed in September, 1959, by another Soviet probe (Luna 2), which hard-landed on the lunar surface. The United States' answer to the Soviet achievements began with the Ranger program. These spacecraft were designed to obtain high-resolution photographs of the Moon right up to the point of impact. Ranger 3 first passed by the Moon in late January, 1962, and it was followed by a hard-lander (Ranger 4) in April, 1962. Prior to this time, scientists had to be content with what Earth-based telescopes could provide. The clarity of the photographs returned by the Ranger spacecraft ushered in a new age in planetary exploration.

The second step in the U.S. program of lunar exploration was the Surveyor series. These spacecraft were designed to soft-land on the Moon and analyze the surface material. Photography was also a high priority. Surveyor 1 safely landed on the Ocean of Storms on June 2, 1966, and transmitted back high-quality photographs and other important scientific data. It provided scientists with thousands of sharp close-up views and answered many questions about the lunar surface material.

In conjunction with Surveyor was the third step in NASA's plan, the Lunar Orbiter project. It was initially assigned to the Jet Propulsion Laboratory (JPL) in Pasadena, California, but their heavy workload with the Ranger and Surveyor programs forced a management change. Surveyor was reassigned to the Langley Research Center in Virginia, and they assumed all the responsibilities for the missions. Key personnel included Homer E. Newell, Harold Masursky, Lee R. Scherer, Clifford H. Nelson, and Robert J. Helberg.

The basic mission for the Lunar Orbiter spacecraft was to photograph the lunar surface in high resolution and to test the capabilities of a spacecraft in lunar orbit. Many of the techniques and procedures later used by the Apollo astronauts were first attempted by the Lunar Orbiters. The principal goal of the Lunar Orbiter program was to obtain the highest-quality photographs for selection of potential landing sites for Apollo. The Lunar Orbiter series employed five separate spacecraft to accomplish its mission. Later, based upon the success of the first three flights, the overall mission objective was expanded. The final two spacecraft would be placed in nearly polar orbits that permitted them to take overlapping photographs of almost the entire near side of the Moon. These high-resolution photographs were used later to make a photograph-map of the Moon.

All the Lunar Orbiter spacecraft were launched from Cape Canaveral, Florida. The launch vehicle was the reliable Atlas-Agena rocket. The time involved from lift-off to lunar orbital insertion required four days. Once in lunar orbit, the spacecraft would be tracked for several days to determine its exact position. Eventually, Lunar Orbiter 1 was positioned in a highly elliptical orbit with an approximate altitude of 56 kilometers at its closest distance and 1,853 kilometers at its most distant point. This orbit allowed for maximum use of its solar panels for electrical energy, and less reliance on the spacecraft's battery. Photography would be maximized when the spacecraft was at its lowest altitude.

As compared to today's spacecraft, Lunar Orbiter was relatively small. It weighed only 385 kilograms and when its solar panels were extended, had dimensions of 5.7 meters by 3.7 meters. Electrical energy was supplied to the various instruments from its solar panels when it was in sunlight, and it relied on its battery when in darkness. Changes in the spacecraft's orbital altitude were made from small nitrogen-gas jets. These were used also to realign the spacecraft's orientation periodically. To function properly, it had to keep one sensor aligned on the sun and the other on the star Canopus.

The photographic subsystem onboard Lunar Orbiter had the capabilities of taking pictures, processing them, and then converting the optical images into electronic signals for transmission back to Earth. The camera system employed both a wide-angle and telephotographic lens. The camera operated each simultaneously, thereby taking both a close-up and wide-angle image of the same feature. This proved to be extremely valuable for determining the relationship between widely separated features. One very basic problem that the Lunar Orbiter's camera subsystem had to overcome was the motion of the spacecraft. Traveling at almost 7,000 kilometers per hour would cause the image to blur. This problem was solved through the use of a sensor that determined the velocity-to-height ratio of the spacecraft. It would then command the film platen to follow the image and thereby compensate for the space-craft's motion. It was a very remarkable device that proved to be most effective and resulted in clear, crisp images.

Film that was processed onboard the spacecraft was never intended to be returned to Earth. Instead, the film was scanned by a device that "read" the density (dark versus light intensity) of the images as a beam of light passed through them. These changes in intensity were then converted to electronic signals that were proportional to the beam's strength. These signals were then transmitted back to Earth and recon-structed into an image much like that of a conventional television set. Then, enlarge-ments and even stereoscopic pairs were made from these images. It was a very effective procedure that produced good results.

The Lunar Orbiter 1 mission was an important step toward landing a human on the Moon. In its basic accomplishments, it proved that a spacecraft could perform complicated maneuvers in orbit and gather valuable data in the process. In addition, it provided a detailed examination of nine potential Apollo landing sites and mapped a large portion of the lunar surface, thus setting the standard for future missions.

Impact of Event

Lunar Orbiter 1 was launched on August 10, 1966, and achieved lunar orbit on August 14, 1966. In total, it spent seventy-six days in orbit and completed 547 revo-lutions of the Moon. After completing its mission, the spacecraft was deliberately crashed into the lunar surface to prevent any possible interference with future space-craft.

During its time in lunar orbit, Lunar Orbiter 1 accomplished all of its primary goals, and more. Wide-area photographic coverage of nine potential Apollo landing sites was made, as well as extensive far side and limited near side photographic coverage. This included detailed examination of the Surveyor landing sites, future Lunar Orbiter photograph targets, and important landmarks for the Apollo astro-nauts to use. Lunar Orbiter 1 became the first spacecraft to photograph Earth from beyond the Moon. The photographs proved to be so successful that a decision was made to modify the missions of the later orbiters. Several of the sites to be examined by Lunar Orbiter 2 were eliminated from consideration, and thereby freed the spacecraft to look for more acceptable sites.

Lunar Orbiter 1 photographs were both exciting and valuable to science. They provided scientists with their first detailed look at another world in space. The images showed an alien environment pocketed by uncountable numbers of craters of every size. For years, Earth-based telescopes revealed their presence, but no one had guessed how important impact cratering had been to the history of the Moon. By photographing on a much smaller scale, Lunar Orbiter 1 images revealed a remarkable amount of detail concerning the nature of impact craters. Earlier Ranger and Surveyor images hinted at the complexity of an impact crater, but it was Lunar Orbiter 1 that detailed the patterns of small craters made from the secondary impacts of ejected debris. Also, the evidence provided by these photographs helped establish the distinction between young and older craters. Where the two coexist, a relationship can be made that suggests a certain weathering process at work.

Studies of the Lunar Orbiter 1's photographs helped establish the three basic types of lunar terrain: level, gently rolling, and rough. The dark lunar maria proved to be the relatively level features, but they did exhibit a higher crater population than previously thought. In contrast to the maria, the highlands are much rougher and are dominated by much larger craters. The highlands also exhibited features that are often associated with mountain-building processes on Earth, but their origin remains uncertain.

Many of the achievements of Lunar Orbiter 1 were technical in nature. It had to achieve its predicted lunar orbit accurately by executing a series of precise orbital maneuvers. To accomplish this, it had to demonstrate the multiple-restart capability of a liquid-propellant rocket system that would operate for extended periods. This had never been done before in space. In addition, Lunar Orbiter 1 demonstrated the ability to command and control its altitude reliably during 374 maneuvers. Without such an ability, precision photography would not have been possible. Finally, by performing all of its mission, Lunar Orbiter 1 broke new ground in understanding the problems encountered in lunar navigation. This, in turn, greatly aided all future missions.

Bibliography

Greeley, Ronald. *Planetary Landscapes.* London: Allen & Unwin, 1985. This book offers the reader both the fundamentals of planetary geology and an in-depth look at specific topics. The chapter discussing the Moon is very comprehensive and utilizes many of the Lunar Orbiter photographs. An extremely well-illustrated book and readable for post-high school levels.

Kopal, Zdeněk. *A New Photographic Atlas of the Moon.* New York: Taplinger, 1971. The introductory chapters provide the reader with a good overview of the Moon's geological history and its surface features. An extensive collection of lunar photographs are used to illustrate the text. Many of these are from the Lunar Orbiter series. This book serves as a very valuable reference for lunar studies.

Kosofsky, L. J., and Farouk El-Baz. *The Moon as Viewed by Lunar Orbiter.* NASA SP-200. Washington, D.C.: Government Printing Office, 1970. This publication presents a good review of the results of the Lunar Orbiter series, and it includes a representation of the photographs taken. Serves as a useful reference work.

Levin, Ellis, D. D. Viele, and Lowell B. Eldrenkamp. "The Lunar Orbiter Missions to the Moon." *Scientific American* 218 (May, 1968): 58-78. This article was published shortly after the completion of the Lunar Orbiter series and serves as a good review of those missions. The authors provide a detailed presentation of the spacecraft's design and purpose. The article contains several of the best images.

Moore, Patrick, and Garry Hunt. *Atlas of the Solar System.* Chicago: Rand McNally, 1983. These authors have provided one of the most comprehensive reviews of the solar system available in one book. It combines knowledge gained from spacecraft investigations with that of ground-based observations. The content is very readable and well illustrated. The chapter on the Moon is extensive and uses several Lunar Orbiter photographs as examples of specific features.

Mutch, Thomas A. *Geology of the Moon.* Rev. ed. Princeton, N.J.: Princeton University Press, 1972. This work represents one of the first attempts to combine pre-Apollo lunar studies with the early results from the manned missions. Lunar features are discussed in great detail, with numerous Lunar Orbiter photographs used as illustrations. The bibliography listed serves as an excellent reference guide for further study.

Trask, N. J., and L. C. Rowan. "Lunar Orbiter Photographs: Some Fundamental Observations." *Science* 158, no. 3808 (1967): 1529-1535. This article represents one of the first reports on the results of Lunar Orbiter to appear in the professional journals. The article is presented in a more technical manner, but it does provide good insight into the importance of the mission. Readable at the college level.

Paul P. Sipiera

Cross-References

Luna 2 Becomes the First Man-Made Object to Impact on the Moon (1959), p. 1614; Luna 3 Provides the First Views of the Far Side of the Moon (1959), p. 1619; Venera 3 Is the First Spacecraft to Impact on Another Planet (1965), p. 1797; The First Humans Land on the Moon (1969), p. 1907; Apollo 12 Retrieves Surveyor 3 Parts from the Lunar Surface (1969), p. 1913; Mariner 9 Is the First Known Spacecraft to Orbit Another Planet (1971), 1944; Viking Spacecraft Send Photographs to Earth from the Surface of Mars (1976), p. 2052.

DAVIS CONSTRUCTS A SOLAR NEUTRINO DETECTOR

Categories of event: Astronomy and physics
Time: 1967
Locale: Homestake Gold Mine in Lead, South Dakota

Davis constructed a giant neutrino detector, which provided the first direct evidence that the sun runs on thermonuclear power, but saw so few neutrinos that standard solar models were questioned

Principal personages:

RAYMOND DAVIS, JR. (1914-   ), an American chemist who constructed the first successful solar neutrino detector

JOHN NORRIS BAHCALL (1934-   ), an American astrophysicist who performed the theoretical calculations of the expected number of neutrinos from the sun

Summary of Event

In 1871, Hermann von Helmholtz suggested that no ordinary chemical reaction could be responsible for the enormous energy output of the sun. By the 1920's, astrophysicists realized that the energy radiated by the sun must come from nuclear fusion, in which protons or nuclei combine to form larger nuclei and release energy. These reactions were assumed to be taking place deep in the interior of the sun, where the pressures and temperatures were high enough to allow fusion to proceed. Conventional astronomical observations could record only the particles and light emitted by the much cooler outer layers of the sun and could not provide evidence for the existence of a thermonuclear furnace in the interior. Of all the particles released in the fusion process, only one type—the neutrino—interacts so infrequently with matter that it can pass through the sun and reach the earth. These neutrinos provide a way to probe the interior of the sun and verify directly the hypothesis of thermonuclear energy generation in stars.

The neutrino was "invented" in 1930 by physicist Wolfgang Pauli to account for the apparent missing energy in the beta decay, or emission of an electron, from radioactive nuclei. He proposed that an unseen neutrino was also emitted in beta decay, and it carried off the "missing" energy. To balance the energy but not be observed in the decay process, Pauli's hypothetical particle had to be uncharged, have little or no mass, and interact only very weakly with ordinary matter. Typical neutrinos would have to be able to pass through millions of miles of ordinary matter with only a low probability of undergoing a single collision. Scientists' detectors, and even the whole earth or sun, were essentially transparent to Pauli's neutrinos.

Because the neutrino is so difficult to detect, it took more than twenty-five years to confirm the existence of the neutrino. In 1956, Clyde Cowan and Frederick Reines, both physicists at the Los Alamos National Laboratory, built the world's largest scintillation counter, a device to detect the small flash of light given off by the interaction of a neutrino in the apparatus. They placed this scintillation counter adjacent to the Savannah River Nuclear Reactor, a high power reactor producing about 1 trillion neutrinos every second. Even with this enormous number of neutrinos, only one neutrino interaction was observed in their detector every twenty minutes, but Cowan and Reines were able to confirm the existence of Pauli's elusive particle.

The task of detecting the solar neutrinos was even more formidable. If an apparatus similar to the Cowan and Reines detector were employed to search for the neutrinos from the sun, only one interaction would be expected every few thousand years.

At about the same time Cowan and Reines performed their experiment, another type of neutrino detector—this one relying on radiochemical principles—was under development by Raymond Davis, Jr., a chemist at the Brookhaven National Laboratory. Davis employed an idea, orginally suggested in 1948 by Bruno Pontecorvo, that when a neutrino interacts with a chlorine-37 nucleus, it produces a nucleus of argon 37. Since argon is a chemically inert gas, it was hoped that the argon produced by neutrinos could be extracted from large volumes of chlorine-rich liquid by passing helium gas through the liquid. The argon 37 produced is itself radioactive, decaying with a half-life of thirty-five days. Thus, once the argon is extracted from the liquid, it can be detected easily by observing its decay.

Davis tested a version of this neutrino detector, containing about 3,785 liters of carbon tetrachloride liquid, near a nuclear reactor at the Brookhaven National Laboratory in 1954 to 1956. In the scientific paper describing these results, Davis suggested this type of neutrino detector could be made large enough to permit detection of the solar neutrinos. As the detector is enlarged, however, the number of events from cosmic-ray interactions goes up, and these events would dominate over the small number of solar neutrino events. To reduce the effect of cosmic rays, Davis decided to bury his apparatus deep underground, using the earth as a shield against the cosmic rays.

A pilot solar neutrino detector experiment was assembled by Davis 701 meters below the surface in a limestone mine at Barberton, Ohio. This detector, which operated from 1960 to 1962, consisted of two 1,893-liter tanks of perchloroethylene. Only three argon decays every eighteen days were found, which was consistent with background radioactivity. This initial experiment failed to detect any solar neutrinos, but Davis used it to demonstrate the detection principle and he indicated that a 378,540-liter detector 1,372 meters underground should have the sensitivity required to see the neutrinos from the sun.

Davis continued his search for solar neutrinos with a much larger detector, a cylindrical tank 6.1 meters in diameter and 15 meters long, containing 378,540 liters of perchloroethylene (containing 520 tons of chlorine). This detector was constructed 1,478 meters underground in the Homestake Gold Mine in Lead, South Dakota. The tank was surrounded by water to shield the detector from neutrons emitted by trace quantities of uranium and thorium in the walls of the mine.

To describe his results, Davis coined a new unit, the "solar neutrino unit" (SNU), with 1 SNU corresponding to the production of a single atom of argon 37 in his apparatus every six days. Astrophysicist John Norris Bahcall had performed detailed calculations of the number of neutrinos expected in Davis' detector. Using the best available astronomical models of the nuclear reactions going on in the sun's interior as well as the physical properties of the neutrinos, Bahcall had calculated a capture rate of 50 SNUs in 1963. The first results from Davis' detector—from a forty-eight-day run in May to June, 1967, and a 110-day run in June to October, 1967—were much lower than expected. Davis was able to place an upper limit of only 3 SNUs on the solar neutrino flux. The discrepancy between the number of neutrinos detected by Davis' apparatus and the number predicted by the theoreticians left open three possibilities: that the experiment itself was flawed, that the physics of the neutrino was different from that expected, or that the conditions in the interior of the sun differed from the accepted model. Davis undertook a series of calibration experiments to determine the efficiency of his detector, and concluded that the experiment was not flawed. Bahcall repeated the theoretical calculations in 1969, using more recent information on nuclear reactions, but he could not reduce the theoretical prediction below 8 SNUs, far higher than the upper limit of 3 SNUs established by Davis.

In 1970, the argon decay detector was improved substantially, increasing the sensitivity of the experiment. Davis' measurements continued almost uninterrupted from 1967 to 1990, giving essentially the same results over the entire period. The long-term average measured more than twenty years is only 2.3 SNUs, well below the most recent theoretical predictions.

Impact of Event

The main significance of the detection of solar neutrinos by Davis was the direct confirmation that the thermonuclear fusion must be occurring at the center of the sun, thus confirming the basic model of energy generation in stars. The low number of solar neutrinos Davis detected, however, has called into question some of the fundamental beliefs of astrophysics. As Bahcall explained: "We know more about the sun than about any other star. . . . The sun is also in what is believed to be the best-understood stage of stellar evolution . . . If we are to have confidence in the many astronomical and cosmological applications of the theory of stellar evolution, it ought at least to give the right answers for the sun."

For almost two decades, the Homestake detector remained the world's only solar neutrino detector, so there was no independent way to verify Davis' results. In July, 1983, however, a group of Japanese scientists commissioned the Kamiokande II detector, which was designed to search for proton decay using Cherenkov light in a large tank of water. They realized their Kamiokande II detector was also sensitive to solar neutrinos, and their measurements have provided confirmation of the low solar neutrino flux reported by Davis.

The problem of the "missing" solar neutrinos has occupied the attention of physicists and astronomers since Davis' initial discovery. Many solutions have been proposed. These solutions can be divided into two broad classes: those that challenge the standard model of the sun's interior and those that challenge the understanding of the behavior of the neutrino. Since the neutrino is very difficult to detect, many of its properties are based on physicists' ideas of how it should behave rather than on direct experimental observation of that behavior. An idea that has gained favor is that there are several different types of neutrinos, only one of which can be detected by the chlorine detectors. In this model, as the neutrinos are traveling from the interior of the sun to the detector on Earth, they oscillate back and forth from one type to another. They have a chance of being seen only if they happen to be of the correct type when they pass through the detector. Other ideas require modifications to the standard solar model. The number of neutrinos produced is very sensitive to the temperature of the sun's interior. Some astrophysicists have suggested that the true solar temperature may be lower than expected. Other astrophysicists have suggested that the composition of the sun may be different from that assumed in the standard model or that the "opacity," or absorption properties, of solar material may be modeled incorrectly. One suggestion is that the nuclear furnace in the sun is not burning as rapidly as in the past and that the sun may be cooling slowly.

Davis' discovery of the low neutrino detection rate at Earth has focused years of attention by many scientists on a better understanding of the how the sun generates its energy and how the neutrino behaves. New and more elaborate solar neutrino detectors have been proposed and built in order to resolve these questions. These future experiments are aimed at understanding the details of the process by which stars, including the sun, shine and the mechanism by which they age and evolve, as well as developing a more complete theory of the physics and behavior of the elusive neutrino.

Bibliography

Bahcall, John N. "Neutrinos from the Sun." *Scientific American* 221 (July, 1969): 28-37. This well-illustrated article by one of the major theoreticians involved in the solar neutrino search provides a detailed description of the apparatus used by Davis as well as an explanation of the processes in the sun that generate the neutrinos and the mechanism used for their detection.

_____. "The Solar-Neutrino Problem." *Scientific American* 260 (May, 1989): 54-61. This well-illustrated article, suitable for general audiences, describes Davis' solar neutrino detector, explains how the nuclear processes in the sun produce neutrinos and how they are detected, and summarizes the results of two decades of measurements by Davis. Bahcall discusses the implications of the missing solar neutrinos and describes the various solutions such as neutrino oscillations, variations in the composition of the interior of the sun, or a lull in solar activity.

Davis, Raymond, Jr., et al. "Solar Neutrinos." *Annual Reviews of Nuclear and Particle Science* 39 (1989): 467-505. Although intended for professionals, this article provides a detailed, nonmathematical account of the design, operation, and results from the Davis experiment from 1967 through 1988.

Ford, Kenneth William. *The World of Elementary Particles.* New York: Blaisdell, 1963. This book, written to explain particle physics to the general reader, describes the properties of the neutrino, explains how they are produced in the sun and other stars, and describes the difficulties of detecting these particles. It contains a particularly good description of Cowan and Reines's 1956 experiment and explains the problems associated with solar neutrino detection experiments.

Koshiba, Masa-Toshi. "Observational Neutrino Astrophysics." *Physics Today* 40 (December, 1987): 38-42. This well-illustrated, nontechnical article describes the results from the Japanese Kamiokande II neutrino detector, compares those results with those of Davis, discusses the implications of the low solar neutrino flux, and describes further solar neutrino experiments planned for the 1990's around the world.

Noyes, Robert W. *The Sun, Our Star.* Cambridge, Mass.: Harvard University Press, 1982. Chapter 3, "Probing the Depths of the Sun," describes the source of fuel for the sun, the Davis experiment, and the mystery of the missing solar neutrinos.

Wentzel, Donat G. *The Restless Sun.* Washington, D.C.: Smithsonian Institution Press, 1989. Chapter 2, "Solar Interior: Neutrinos," focuses on how neutrinos provide an opportunity to "look inside" the sun and probe its energy generation process. It provides a particularly good, nonmathematical discussion of the various hypotheses to explain the low counting rate of Davis' apparatus and of the new generation of gallium detectors to search for lower energy neutrinos.

Wolfenstein, Lincoln, and Eugene W. Beier. "Neutrino Oscillations and Solar Neutrinos." *Physics Today* 42 (July, 1989): 28-36. This article describes the various attempts to measure the number of solar neutrinos arriving at Earth and examines the implications of the low flux measured by Davis for the accepted models of the sun and the neutrino.

George J. Flynn

Cross-References

Pauli Formulates the Exclusion Principle (1925), p. 800; Lyot Builds the Coronagraph for Telescopically Observing the Sun's Outer Atmosphere (1930), p. 911; Fermi Proposes the Neutrino Theory of Beta Decay (1933), p. 992; Cherenkov Discovers the Cherenkov Effect (1934), p. 1003.

FAVALORO DEVELOPS THE CORONARY ARTERY BYPASS OPERATION

Category of event: Medicine
Time: 1967
Locale: Cleveland, Ohio

Favaloro developed the coronary bypass operation, using a vein from the leg, which developed into the most widely used procedure of this type

Principal personages:

RENE FAVALORO (1923-), a heart surgeon at the Cleveland Clinic who introduced the coronary artery bypass operation

DONALD B. EFFLER (1915-), a heart surgeon at the Cleveland Clinic who was a member of the surgical team that performed the first coronary artery bypass operation

F. MASON SONES (1918-), a physician at the Cleveland Clinic who developed an improved technique of X-raying the heart's arteries, which made the coronary artery bypass operation possible

Summary of Event

In the mid-1960's, the leading cause of death in the United States was coronary artery disease, claiming nearly 250 deaths per 100,000 population (American Heart Association). Since a large proportion of these deaths were from coronary artery disease, there was much research being conducted on the heart. Most of the public's attention was focused on heart transplants performed separately by the famous surgeons Dr. Christiaan Barnard and Dr. Michael DeBakey. Yet, other, less dramatic procedures were being developed and studied.

A major problem with coronary artery disease, besides the threat of death, is chest pain or angina. Individuals whose arteries are clogged with fat and cholesterol are frequently unable to deliver enough oxygen to their heart muscles. This may result in angina, which causes enough pain to limit their physical activities. Some of the heart research in the mid-1960's was an attempt to find a surgical procedure that would eliminate angina in heart patients. The various surgical procedures had varying success rates.

In the late 1950's and early 1960's, a team of physicians in Cleveland was studying surgical procedures that would eliminate angina. The team was composed of Dr. Rene Favaloro, Dr. Donald B. Effler, Dr. F. Mason Sones, and Dr. Laurence Groves. They were working on the concept, proposed by Dr. Arthur M. Vineberg from McGill University in Montreal, of implanting an artery from the chest (mammary artery) in the heart. This procedure would provide the heart with another source of blood, resulting in enough oxygen to overcome the angina. Vineberg's surgery was often ineffective because adequate diagnostic information was not available to make an accurate determination of where to implant the new artery.

In order to make Vineberg's proposed operation successful, better diagnostic tools were needed. This was accomplished by the work of Dr. Sones. He developed a diagnostic procedure, called arteriography, whereby a catheter was inserted into an artery in the arm, which he ran into the heart. He then injected a dye into the coronary arteries and photographed it with a high-speed motion-picture camera. This provided an image of the heart, which made it easy to determine where the blockages were in the coronary arteries. Since this procedure identified precisely where the repairs were needed, heart surgery was able to move ahead quickly. The Cleveland Clinic team used Sones's procedure and expanded on the work by William H. Sewell. Dr. Sewell, instead of implanting the naked mammary artery, implanted the artery and its supporting tissue. This modification made the surgery quicker, reduced the damage to the artery, and made it possible to implant the artery in more locations on the heart. The team of physicians from the Cleveland Clinic developed a standard surgical procedure that was used to treat thousands of heart patients successfully.

The surgical procedure developed by the Cleveland Clinic team was effective and appropriate for treating individuals with severe coronary artery disease. Yet, many patients had blockages in a small portion of one or more vessels that would not warrant such dramatic surgery. Therefore, the team of physicians attempted to find more appropriate procedures. Several techniques were attempted. First, the surgeons tried to ream out the deposits found in the narrow portion of the artery. They found, however, that this actually reduced blood flow. Second, they tried slitting the length of the blocked area of the artery and suturing in a strip of tissue that would increase the diameter of the opening. This procedure was also ineffective because it frequently resulted in turbulent blood flow. Finally, the team attempted to reroute the flow of blood around the blockage by suturing in other tissue. This method proved to work well.

The new method of rerouting blood flow was introduced in 1967 by Dr. Favaloro. He and a team of physicians removed the entire blocked portion of the coronary artery. Then, a vein from the upper leg (saphenous vein) was removed from the patient and a portion of it was sutured to the ends of the artery. In summary, this procedure removed part of the vessel that was clogged and replaced it with a clear vessel, thereby restoring blood flow through the artery.

Although this new procedure proposed by Favaloro was a major step forward for open-heart surgery, it had its limitations. The major problem with the procedure was its flexibility to be used in many areas of the heart. The coronary artery anatomy had many arteries located in areas that made it impossible for the surgeon to expose in order to complete the surgery. Therefore, this bypass surgery was limited primarily to the right coronary artery, which supplies blood to the right side and back side of the heart. It was not effective in the other major arteries, such as the left main, left anterior descending, and circumflex. These vessels supply blood to the front, left side, and portions of the back of the heart; this procedure was unable to restore blood flow to these areas.

In order for Favaloro and other heart surgeons to perform coronary artery surgery successfully, several other medical techniques had to be developed. These included arteriography, extracorporeal circulation, and microsurgical techniques. The significance of the arteriography procedure developed by Sones was previously discussed. The other two techniques are discussed below.

Extracorporeal circulation is the process of diverting the patient's blood flow from the heart and into a heart-lung machine. This procedure was developed in 1953 by John H. Gibbon, Jr. In brief, the heart-lung machine is composed of a pump, which circulates the blood during the surgery, and an oxygenator, which sends oxygen into the blood. Since the blood does not flow through the heart, the heart can be temporarily stopped so that the surgeons can isolate the artery and perform the surgery on motionless tissue. Until this equipment and procedure were perfected, coronary artery surgery was not possible.

Another critical development necessary for Favaloro's work was microsurgery. Some of the coronary arteries are less than 1.5 millimeters in diameter. Since these arteries had to be sutured, optical magnification, spring-handled needle holders, and fine sutures were required. The use of these materials made grafting coronary arteries possible. Although Favaloro and his associates successfully performed coronary artery bypass surgery in 1967, the work of many other physicians and researchers was critical to their success.

After performing this surgery on numerous patients, follow-up studies were necessary to determine the surgery's effectiveness. These studies took several years to complete. Only then was the value of coronary artery bypass surgery recognized as an effective procedure for reducing angina in heart patients. Also, during the period these studies were conducted, improvements were made on the techniques of bypass surgery, which rendered the previous research obsolete.

Impact of Event

In 1968, the year after Favaloro developed his coronary artery bypass technique, there was a wide research interest in that type of surgery. Improvements were needed in order to use the technique on other arteries of the heart besides the right coronary artery. The preferred approach was the aortocoronary bypass graft. In this surgery, a portion of the saphenous vein was grafted from the aorta to the coronary artery instead of grafting it from one portion of the coronary artery to another portion of the same artery. Basically, a new source of blood from the aorta was created from the bypass graft rather than rerouting the same source. The fundamental benefit of this approach was that it could be performed on almost any coronary artery.

Three teams of physicians began work on the aortocoronary bypass, besides Favaloro and his team in Cleveland. In San Francisco, a surgical team headed by William J. Kerth performed three single bypass surgeries on the right coronary artery. A team in Dallas, headed by Harold C. Urschel, successfully completed single bypasses to the right coronary artery or the left anterior descending artery in six patients. Finally, a team in Milwaukee, headed by W. Dudley Johnson, demonstrated double bypass grafts (two graphs in one patient) and showed effectiveness in grafts to the right coronary artery, the left anterior descending artery, and the circumflex artery. These successes laid the groundwork for making coronary artery bypass surgery common and effective in the United States.

The growth of aortocoronary bypass surgery was rapid. Surgeons successfully performed the surgery on a wide basis for the first time in 1968. By 1970, many physicians across the country were performing bypass surgery on a regular basis. Its use, however, was slowed and overshadowed initially by the interest in heart transplant surgery developed at the same time. Critics of heart transplants believed that bypass surgery was a much better option because it was a less dramatic surgery with less risk, it did not require a donor, and it did not have the problems with rejection. Ultimately, bypass surgery was found to be much more feasible, and its use spread quickly.

According to the American Heart Association, approximately 332,000 bypass surgeries were performed in the United States in 1987, an increase of 48,000 from 1986. These figures attest the fact that the work by Favaloro and others has had a major impact on the health of United States citizens. The future outlook is also positive. It has been estimated that five million people had coronary artery disease in 1987 (American Heart Association). Of this group, an estimated 1.5 million had heart attacks, and 500,000 died. Of those living, many had angina. Research has developed new surgical procedures and new drugs to help fight coronary artery disease. Yet, coronary artery bypass surgery is still a major form of intervention.

Bibliography

Effler, Donald B. "Surgery for Coronary Disease." *Scientific American* 219 (October, 1967): 36-43. This article was written by one of the members of the research team included Dr. Favaloro. The three main surgeries for coronary artery disease at that time are discussed. It provides a historical perspective leading up to Favaloro's bypass graft surgery in 1967.

Johnson, Stephen L. *The History of Cardiac Surgery, 1896-1955.* Baltimore: The Johns Hopkins University Press, 1970. This book contains a detailed history of open-heart surgery before the development of coronary artery bypass surgery. It provides a good discussion of the many contributions made by individual physicians that made bypass surgery possible. A list of references is also included.

Miller, Donald W., Jr. *The Practice of Coronary Artery Bypass Surgery.* New York: Plenum Medical Book, 1977. Although this textbook is very technical, the first chapter provides a good overview of the history behind the development of bypass surgery. This chapter is easy to understand and includes the earliest research (from the 1910's) that contributed to the development of the surgery. It follows the procedure to its wide acceptance in the 1970's.

Ochsner, John L., and Noel L. Mills. *Coronary Artery Surgery.* Philadelphia: Lea &

Febiger, 1978. This resource is a textbook primarily composed of technical material. Yet, chapter 2 contains the history of surgery developed to relieve angina and is understandable to the nonmedical person. It begins with the surgeries used in 1916 and concludes with aortocoronary bypass surgery in the 1960's. Although technical in nature, it also has excellent diagrams of how the surgeries are performed, which may be of interest to the nonmedical person.

"Surgery." *Time* 91 (January 19, 1968): 50-51. This article summarizes some of the heart transplants that took place in 1967. It provides information about the transplant recipients, donors, and surgeons. The conclusion is devoted to debate about the premature increase in the use of heart transplants. This leads to the discussion of some alternative surgeries, including the bypass graft developed by Favaloro. This article provides good information about the advantages and disadvantages of the heart surgery options of the time.

Bradley R. A. Wilson

Cross-References

Einthoven Develops the Forerunner of the Electrocardiogram (1900's), p. 41; Carrel Develops a Technique for Rejoining Severed Blood Vessels (1902), p. 134; McLean Discovers the Natural Anticoagulant Heparin (1915), p. 610; Gibbon Develops the Heart-Lung Machine (1934), p. 1024; Wilkins Introduces Reserpine for the Treatment of High Blood Pressure (1952), p. 1429; Barnard Performs the First Human Heart Transplant (1967), p. 1866; Gruentzig Uses Percutaneous Transluminal Angioplasty, via a Balloon Catheter, to Unclog Diseased Arteries (1977), p. 2088; DeVries Implants the First Jarvik-7 Artificial Heart (1982), p. 2195.

MANABE AND WETHERALD WARN OF THE GREENHOUSE EFFECT AND GLOBAL WARMING

Category of event: Earth science
Time: 1967
Locale: Princeton, New Jersey

Manabe and Wetherald found that the increase of carbon dioxide in the atmosphere will create a greenhouse effect and global warming

Principal personages:

SYUKURO MANABE (1931-   ), an American climatologist who helped formulate a model of the atmosphere to estimate the effect of increasing atmospheric carbon dioxide

RICHARD WETHERALD (1936-   ), an American climatologist who helped formulate a model for the atmosphere

STEPHEN HENRY SCHNEIDER (1945-   ), an American climatologist who studied the greenhouse effect

SVANTE AUGUST ARRHENIUS (1859-1927), a Swedish physical chemist who suggested that the emission of carbon into the atmosphere might have a serious impact on the earth's temperature through the greenhouse effect

Summary of Event

The earth's climate is a complex and intricate mechanism, and many factors contribute to its behavior. Climatologists look at past climate to try to understand how the mechanism works and how it can be expected to work in the future. In addition, climatologists use computer simulations, or models, to mimic the atmosphere to see how the mechanism will react to different circumstances. Syukuro Manabe and Richard Wetherald were among the first to use model atmospheres to attempt to predict the effect of increased carbon dioxide on the earth's climate.

It was around the beginning of the twentieth century that scientists first suggested that the carbon dioxide released in the burning of fossil fuels might build up in the atmosphere and cause warming of the planet. In 1896, Svante August Arrhenius published a paper, and in 1899, T. C. Chamberlain also wrote a paper about the possible impact of the burning of fossil fuels on the earth's temperature. For many years, however, it was assumed that the climate is such a large and stable system that human activity cannot have any great effect on it, either for good or for harm. Climatologists have since learned that humans can, indeed, affect the climate in ways that are not yet fully understood but that might have important consequences.

Arrhenius and Chamberlain suggested the phenomenon that today is called the "greenhouse effect." In 1861, John Tyndall first recognized that carbon dioxide and water vapor are transparent to light in the visible wavelengths, but not to infrared radiation. Thus, the earth's atmosphere will allow certain wavelengths of radiation from the sun, the visible wavelengths, to reach the ground. This visible light is absorbed and reemitted by the earth at slightly longer wavelengths, as infrared radiation that cannot be seen but can be felt as heat. The infrared radiation cannot pass back out through the atmosphere as easily as it came in because of the presence of carbon dioxide, water vapor, and other greenhouse gases such a fluorocarbons, oxides of nitrogen, sulfur dioxide, methane, and water vapor. These gases absorb the infrared radiation and reemit it toward Earth, where its heat is trapped near the surface of the earth and cannot escape. A certain amount of carbon dioxide is a good thing for life on Earth, but scientists began to wonder if perhaps too much carbon dioxide might not create an increase in temperature with which it would be difficult to cope.

There are many questions associated with the impact of the greenhouse effect on the climate; for example, how much carbon dioxide, once emitted, would stay in the atmosphere; how quickly the atmospheric content of carbon dioxide and other greenhouse gases is increasing; and when one can expect the amount of atmospheric carbon dioxide to double. Climatologists have determined that there are several places for carbon dioxide to end up, including living things, the ocean, and the atmosphere. A rough estimate is that approximately half of the emitted carbon dioxide remains in the atmosphere, but this is, at present, only an approximation. The climatological record has been studied—both recent measurements of carbon dioxide in the air and ancient records such as polar ice samples, which reveal past atmospheric composition—to determine past concentrations and rate of increase of carbon dioxide. The question of how soon a doubling of carbon dioxide can be expected is fraught with complex political and economic issues, such as fossil fuel use worldwide, population growth, and other factors, and is difficult to answer. One estimate is that the preindustrial concentration of three hundred parts per million (0.03 percent) could double sometime between the years 2020 and 2080.

Another question is what the effect is of an increasing carbon dioxide concentration. Scientists in the 1960's began creating models of how the atmosphere works; they inserted an increased concentration of carbon dioxide into these models to see how the model reacted. A model of the atmosphere is essentially a set of equations that describe the behavior of the atmosphere. Initial conditions are established, such as temperature and atmospheric composition, and then the equations are solved to determine the resulting equilibrium state of the atmosphere. This is often reiterated using the resulting climate condition as "initial condition" to extrapolate further about how the climate will continue to behave. When reiteration is done, so-called feedback mechanisms can be explored—that is, ways in which something resulting from the initial change works to induce more change. For example, if an increase in carbon dioxide were to increase the cloud cover, the increased cloud cover would then "feed back" into the calculations to produce other changes in the climate. The many calculations required to use these models are usually done on a computer.

The earliest of these models were very simple compared to the models being used in the 1990's, but these simple models were very useful. For example, the simplicity of these models allows single factors to be isolated and analyzed without the heavy use of computer time required for the more complex models. In the early 1960's, these models began the intricate task of determining the effect of greenhouse gases on the earth's temperature and climate.

In 1964, Manabe and Robert Strickler began working with a model atmosphere with which they studied the effect of atmospheric water vapor on climate. In 1967, Manabe and Wetherald, working at the National Oceanic and Atmospheric Administration's Geophysical Fluid Dynamics Laboratory in Princeton, New Jersey, published a continuation of this study. Manabe and Strickler had studied an atmospheric model that considered distributions of absolute humidity. This made the model simpler to construct and run. Manabe and Wetherald used distributions of relative rather than absolute humidity, which was a refinement of the model in the direction of closer correspondence to the actual atmosphere. F. Möller had arrived at results earlier that indicated an extreme sensitivity of the atmosphere's behavior to carbon dioxide content, but Manabe and Wetherald found that Möller's conclusion was drawn from calculations involving temperature at the earth's surface only, rather than temperatures of the atmosphere as a whole. Consequently, this extreme sensitivity was not likely to be an accurate representation of reality. They did find, however, that their model was more sensitive to changes in atmospheric carbon dioxide than the models using absolute humidity. They concluded from their work that, were the carbon dioxide in the atmosphere to double, the average global temperature would warm by about 2.3 degrees Celsius. The increase in different areas would vary from this average, with the greatest increase to be expected at the poles and the smallest increase at the equator. The differential warming would have effects on air circulation patterns and on climate in general. In setting up their model, they built on the work of scientists who had studied the way in which carbon dioxide absorbs infrared radiation of varying wavelengths and affects the earth's climate. Manabe and Wetherald pioneered the use of a tool—computer modeling—which is very important in the field of climatology.

Impact of Event

Other types of computer models followed. The makers of each model made different assumptions in setting up its equations, and thus the models arrived at different answers to the same question. This was obvious in the late 1960's and early 1970's, when predictions of the results of carbon dioxide doubling ranged from a global average of 0.7 degree Celsius to 9.6 degrees Celsius. In 1975, Stephen Henry Schneider looked at these studies with their varying predictions and attempted to take into account the assumptions made for each model and how those assumptions related to the real world. He was able to find explanations for most of the variations in the predictions and found that the best estimate of temperature increase in the event of atmospheric carbon dioxide doubling was about 1.5 degrees Celsius to 2.4 degrees Celsius.

The computer models grew in sophistication during the late 1960's and early

1970's, until they were developed into the General Circulation Model, or GCM. This is a three-dimensional model of the atmosphere; some of these models incorporate many more of the intricacies of the real-world climate than was possible for earlier, simpler models. GCM simulations of the atmosphere do not, however, incorporate the ocean into their calculations. This is an important omission, because 70 percent of the earth's surface is water, which plays an important part in the climate. Therefore, climatologists created model oceans and linked these model oceans to their GCM models to attain the most realistic results possible. In 1975, the same year as Schneider's study, Manabe and Wetherald published the results of their work with one of the most complete GCM models of the time, which also included a model ocean. This work concluded that a 2-degree Celsius warming could be expected if atmospheric carbon dioxide doubled. This number fell in the middle of Schneider's range of values and became the accepted rule-of-thumb figure.

Sherwood Idso approached the problem in a different way. He used data gathered throughout the United States over a period of time and looked at how Earth's surface temperature has varied in response to various atmospheric conditions to arrive at a "response function" that will make it possible to predict how an increase in carbon dioxide or other greenhouse gases will affect surface temperature. He presented his method and results in 1980 and 1981. His work implies that the increase in surface temperature corresponding to a doubling in atmospheric carbon dioxide will be much smaller.

The experts are still not in total agreement on the magnitude of temperature change that could be caused by increased atmospheric carbon dioxide, nor on the effects in climate this temperature change could have. Because of the many vital implications of this work for all those living on Earth, the subject still arouses controversy in political and economic circles. The problem of potential global warming is one deserving of serious thought and action.

Bibliography

Allen, Oliver E., and the editors of Time-Life Books. *Atmosphere.* Alexandria, Va.: Time-Life Books, 1983. Provides background information about the way the atmosphere functions to produce Earth's climate; some coverage of the greenhouse effect as well as a discussion of other factors that may cause climate changes in the future. Many photographs, some drawings and graphs, and a map illustrating the global patterns of movement in the atmosphere.

Bryson, Reid A., and Thomas J. Murray. *Climates of Hunger: Mankind and the World's Changing Weather.* Madison: University of Wisconsin Press, 1977. Offers a historical perspective on climate change, discussing the impact of past climate changes on the civilizations that lived through them. Discusses human impacts on climate, including the increase in atmospheric carbon dioxide and its possible effects. Includes some graphs and a bibliography.

Gribbin, John. *Future Weather and the Greenhouse Effect.* New York: Delacorte Press/Eleanor Friede, 1982. The second half of this book concentrates on carbon dioxide and other greenhouse gases in the atmosphere. Includes information on the computer models used to predict the effects of increasing concentrations of these gases, as well as on the efforts made to answer other questions about the greenhouse effect, including political and social questions. Intended for the layperson; includes charts, graphs, and a bibliography.

Kellogg, William W., and Robert Schware. *Climate Change and Society: Consequences of Increasing Atmospheric Carbon Dioxide.* Boulder, Colo.: Westview Press, 1981. Written by climatologists who have studied the greenhouse effect. Takes a somewhat technical approach but is still useful to the interested layperson, and it offers valuable and accessible information on both the scientific studies done on the greenhouse effect and the political and economic implications. Includes graphs, tables, and maps; each chapter has a list of references for further reading.

Miller, G. Tyler, Jr. *Living in the Environment.* 2d ed. Belmont, Calif.: Wadsworth, 1979. A textbook, intended for an introductory course in environmental studies; contains a section on climate change that offers an excellent discussion of the greenhouse effect and analysis of the possible ramifications of global warming. Strong on data and citations to scientific findings. Includes graphs, drawings, and tables, as well as topics for discussion and further readings.

Schneider, Stephen H. *Global Warming: Are We Entering the Greenhouse Century?* San Francisco: Sierra Club Books, 1989. Written by a climatologist who has done research on the greenhouse effect; discusses the scientific aspects as well as the economic and social problems of the possibility of global warming. Includes discussion of atmospheric models used to predict climate change. Clarifies some of the issues involved in global warming; presents behind-the-scenes insight into the scientific and political activity. Informative. Contains drawings, graphs, and maps.

Mary Hrovat

Cross-References

Bjerknes Publishes the First Weather Forecast Using Computational Hydrodynamics (1897), p. 21; Elster and Geitel Demonstrate Radioactivity in Rocks, Springs, and Air (1901), p. 93; Fabry Quantifies Ozone in the Upper Atmosphere (1913), p. 579; Callendar Connects Industry with Increased Carbon Dioxide (1938), p. 1118; Carson Publishes *Silent Spring* (1962), p. 1740; Rowland and Molina Theorize That Ozone Depletion Is Caused by Freon (1973), p. 2009; The British Antarctic Survey Confirms the First Known Hole in the Ozone Layer (1985), p. 2285.

MANDELBROT DEVELOPS
NON-EUCLIDEAN FRACTAL MEASURES

Category of event: Mathematics
Time: 1967
Locale: T. J. Watson IBM Research Center, New York

Mandelbrot developed a simple quantitative model of complex spatial processes in the physical, engineering, atmospheric, and earth sciences, which showed scale-invariance

Principal personage:
BENOIT B. MANDELBROT (1922-   ), a Polish-American mathematician who pioneered fractals

Summary of Event

As detailed by Mary Tiles in 1988, circa 1900, the logical and interpretative and metamathematical problems associated with reconciling Euclidean and non-Euclidean geometries, as well as geometrical with newer Cantorian set-theoretical notions of measure and dimension, were first seriously recognized by Émile Borel and Henri-Léon Lebesgue. From 1910 to 1925, French mathematicians P. Fatuo and G. Julia independently investigated several new set-theoretic approaches to the study of complex two- and three-dimensional spatial distributions using the iterative method of rational functions. These ideas were examined further by French mathematician Costantin Carathéodory in 1914, who sought to define a generalized "length" and "area" for non-Euclidean and other nonstandard shapes, without reliance on traditional coordinate axes. As Benoit B. Mandelbrot and others recount, the next basic step in further developing these ideas was taken by German mathematician Felix Hausdorff, noted for his monograph *Grundzuge der Mengenlehre* (*Foundations of Set Theory*, 1962). In 1919, as an extension of his set-theoretic studies, Hausdorff proposed that "D," the dimensional order, could be an arbitrary nonnegative integer or noninteger (fractional) and still define a spatial dimension. Formally speaking, where $h(p) = k(D) p^D$, the h-measure is called D-dimensional.

Mandelbrot states that his first interest in spatial scaling was triggered, between 1951 and 1961, by empirical ~egularities governing word frequencies, and later by time variations of commodity prices on competitive markets. A common theme in Mandelbrot's observations of such phenomena was the fact that many such time series are frequently very discontinuous, as well as being "cyclic," yet nonperiodic, so that straightforward applications of Fourier methods of harmonic analysis were not possible. In 1961, Mandelbrot further examined scaling of statistical noise in electronic and other systems, as well as so-called Brownian or 1/f noise.

The original method of analysis for fractionality was developed previously by the English physicist-mathematician L. F. Richardson in 1961, in his rather unlikely titled publication, "The Problem of Contiguity: An Appendix of Statistics of Deadly Quarrels." In brief, the length of curves of a coastline, river, mountain range, fault, or international boundary is proposed to be measured by walking a map divider along the curve, with divider points set at each particular spacing. The spacing is changed and the measurement repeated. The total measured line length becomes greater at smaller point spacings (sampling intervals) since more fine detail is encountered, taking progressively smaller and smaller wiggles into account that were missed at larger coarser sample spacings. Richardson first determined that, for a variety of natural boundaries, a log-log (power law) plot of total length versus unit length closely approximates a straight line with a single slope.

To Richardson, the power law exponent in question was merely a value with no special significance. Mandelbrot, having come upon Richardson's study after reviewing scaling of economic time series, was the first to suggest that the exponent— even though not an integer—could be interpreted meaningfully as a fractional dimension. The basis for this conclusion was that spatial features of natural coastlines are scale invariant under positive or negative magnification, such that coastline photographs taken from altitudes of 10 meters, 1,000 meters, or 100 kilometers are intrinsically indistinguishable, unless a specific reference scale or legend is introduced. Otherwise expressed, the relation between the total measured length, and the unit measuring length, was quantified as $L(r) = kr^{1-D}$, where L is the total coastline length measured with a ruler of unit length r, and D is the fractional dimension of the data. D can be seen also as a measure of the persistency of fine spatial details measured over changes in spatial scale.

Many subsequent studies in topographic terrain analysis, quantitative geomorphology, engineering materials, and earthquake fracture suggested that self-similar (scale-invariant shape) apparently occurs in many different natural patterns, where additional finer features are superposed on larger scales. Mandelbrot subsequently proposed to use the formal set-theoretic Hausdorff-Bescovitch dimension. Fractional self-similarity thus clearly manifests itself in a power law. Practically speaking, $N(r)$ is plotted against a double-logarithmic scale. To the extent that true (uni)fractionality exists in the data set examined, the graph approaches a straight line with a single slope, whose value is $-D$. This equation also relates the number of set-theoretic spheres N needed to cover geometrically a given set and their radius ϵ. Therefore, the length of a fractional line varies with the size of the measuring rod. Because lineal and areal fractional measure is undefined in the classical sense, the Hausdorff-Bescovitch, or fractional, dimension is not a spatial or a Euclidean dimension, but a more general topological dimension. The fractional dimension D is a real number lying between the topological dimension D_T and the Euclidean dimension D_E. Another basic attribute of fractional measures of coastlines, topographic profiles, cloud shapes, and the like is their nondifferentiability. That is, for the coastline example, although it seems possible to draw tangents to points on the coastline observed from a given height, as one gets closer, more details become visible, and the concept of unique and well-defined tangents becomes meaningless. Nevertheless, the fractional dimension quantifies many characteristics in the spatial variation and irregularity of such a curve.

The term "fractal" was first coined by Mandelbrot in 1975, in the original French-language edition of his monograph, *Les Objets fractals.* "Fractal" derives from the Latin adjectival root *fractus,* the same root as in fraction, fracture, and fragment. Notwithstanding, a fractal is not a physical theory or datum, but a mathematical concept or model. Mandelbrot subsequently reinterpreted a number of what he called pre- or latent-fractal data sets, such as the time series of stream profiles in the states of Virginia and Maryland, or the general multiscale roughness of particular land and undersea mountain ranges. One of the earliest "fractals to be" was the so-called von Koch snowflake, first discussed as a curiosity in an Italian mathematics journal of 1904. Here, a simple line segment is divided into thirds, the middle segment replaced by two equal segments forming part of an equilateral triangle. Next, each of these four segments is replaced by four new segments of length one-third the original length. This procedure (iteratively) repeated yields a well-known six-pointed star snowflake, having similar details over all length scales.

Mandelbrot's first steps toward explicitly developing a systematic theory of fractal geometry were taken at the T. J. Watson IBM Research Center in central New York state. From 1966 to 1975, Mandelbrot worked in conjunction with hydrologists, meteorologists, statistical physicists, geologists, and many others. Further close relations between fractal measure and traditional Fourier (transform) analysis were underscored in 1968 when Mandelbrot developed a power-law form frequency spectrum for hydrologic time series. Perhaps the most successful liaison of fractal geometry with science came from Mandelbrot's studies of spatial patterns in turbulence. In 1963, a physicist first derived a complete set of nonlinear differential equations to approximate thermal convective motion in a fluid. This set of equations was recognized subsequently to be the first exhibiting so-called chaotic behavior, wherein even infinitesimal variations of the initial conditions governing these equations result in major differences in their subsequent mathematical solutions. What Mandelbrot discovered was an important and previously unrecognized feature of many such dynamical systems: their apparent scale-invariance. Here, it was shown that fractal measures can be used frequently to describe not only static geometrical patterns but also more dynamic system properties.

Impact of Event

Other phenomena with diffusion-controlled, or random-walk, behavior include two-phase fluid flow, as when a nonviscous fluid such as water is pumped into a viscous fluid like oil, in a porous parent medium such as rock (this is done routinely to enhance secondary petroleum recovery from oil wells). The water typically breaks into a complex branching pattern, the oil flowing more easily away governed by rock pore geometry. Because the thermo-hydro-dynamic equations rigorously describing viscous fluid flow in porous media are extremely complex to solve in full form, it is necessary to introduce what accurate simplifications possible that are physically realistic. A fractal model has, in many cases, been shown to provide a good representation of fluid dynamics in porous media.

Another, lesser known but significant, example of fractal applications arises in the areas of signal detection in digital signal and image processing, as in radar, acoustics, and seismology. Consider a time series of mixed signal and noise components, where it is sought to detect and characterize a sudden short burst or transient signal. Systematic segmentation of the time series according to amplitude typically reveals the short burst dividing the original data segment into two unperturbed (noise) zones. The borders of these on either side of the central transient signal also contain precursory and codal signal components, although of much smaller amplitude. By continuing this progressive segmentation, eventually an "infinite" sequence of short (unperturbed) time intervals is obtained, dividing an adjunct hierarchy of signal bursts.

Other examples suggest that fractal geometry and dynamics may apply with sufficient accuracy to a wide variety of physical, chemical, and biological phenomena. If this is true, then many currently intractable equations describing heat transfer, as well as wave propagation and scattering through complex rough-surfaced media, may find solutions of sufficient accuracy to match observed data. Yet, as noted by several mathematical geologists, geophysicists, and others, who have investigated power-law and other spatial pattern analyses, there are several practical problems, as well as possible problems in principle, in the more universal and rigorous applications of fractals. As an example, geophysicists made a comprehensive study of natural topographic surfaces, over the spatial bands 100 kilometers to 10^{-6} meters. They found that natural rock surfaces frequently resembled fractional Brownian or fractal surfaces, however, with a fractal dimension D that varied strongly as a function of spatial wavelength. Subsequent extensions studying power spectra of topographic profiles along earthquake fault and marine bathymetric surfaces showed similar "multi" fractal results. One pragmatic difficulty with multifractals lies in consistently determining the spatial wavelength extent of each scale-invariant. Furthermore, in many applications, the loss of directionality (anisotropy) and fine scale (phase) information inherent in fractal measures precludes a correct, complete reconstruction of certain natural phenomena.

Many natural time series exhibit another long problematic characteristic, known as spatio-temporal nonstationarity. A signal or noise pattern is said to be statistically stationary if all its defining characteristics remain unchanged by a translation in space and/or time. The detection, and subsequent modeling, of nonstationarities usually has caused many problems only partially solved by competing methodologies. One is faced in this case with the difficult question of how to estimate accurately the nonconstant "drift" associated with nonstationarity when first estimating empirical autocorrelation or self-similarity functions. Many papers argue that partitioning random functions into random/stationary and deterministic/nonstationary parts is not a well definable nor unique procedure. These and other conditions not only may require more judicious modifications and tests of attempts to model phenomena with fractals but also may link use of fractals to one of several other statistical techniques to treat complex spatial data.

Numerous contributions to several interdisciplinary and topical conferences, as well as collaborative research, has ensured the further consideration and applications of deterministic and stochastic fractal characterizations. A characteristic of Mandelbrot's fractals research program is his continuous careful search for theoretical and empirical results that fit well with the basic fractal concept. As evident from his general audience publications in 1977, 1982, and 1990, Mandelbrot's rather broad aesthetic feeling, and mixing of theory with applications in conveying new ideas, has played an important part in wider recognition and consideration of fractal methods. Mandelbrot's work has opened the way to a wider recognition and use of other, lesser known mathematical notions, such as "fuzzy sets," "generalized regional variables," and the "catastrophe theory." Considered as an episode in the history of science, the existence of a real physical example endowed with certain mathematical properties is in no way a precondition for the discovery or use of the mathematics in question. Nevertheless, in the case of fractals, it was not primarily abstract contemplation or calculation but specific considerations of concrete examples of scaling that led to the "discovery" of fractals and their wider use. Occasions where new ideas and methods enter numerous sciences by way of obscure subbranches of mathematics are rare in the history of the natural sciences. Likewise uncommon is a new discipline (particularly of wide applications scope) whose foundations are established largely without direct support of previously published work. The discovery and further development of the theory and applications of fractals is a curious and continuing example of such historical anomalies.

Bibliography

Dauben, J. W. *Georg Cantor: His Mathematics and Philosophy of the Infinite*. Cambridge, Mass.: Harvard University Press, 1979. Offers invaluable conceptual and methodological background to the set-theoretic history of fractional measure.

Mandelbrot; B. B. *Fractals: Form, Chance, and Dimension*. San Francisco: W. H. Freeman, 1977. The first English-language general-audience monograph on the history and concepts of fractional dimension.

_____. *Fractals and Multifractals: Noise, Turbulence, and Galaxies*. New York: Springer-Verlag, 1990. Mandelbrot's most comprehensive and rigorous treatment of fractals.

Peitgen, Heinz-Otto, and Dietmar Saupe, eds. *The Science of Fractal Images*. New York: Springer-Verlag, 1988. A brief review of key concepts. Outlines computer programs to generate a catalog of fractal graphics.

Scholz, Christopher, and Benoit B. Mandelbrot. *Fractals in Geophysics*. Boston: Kirkäuser, 1989. A collection of papers for and against the utility of fractals in representing multiscale topographic relief.

Stanley, H. Eugue, and Nicole Ostrowsky, eds. *On Growth and Form: Fractal and Non-Fractal Patterns in Physics*. Dordrecht, The Netherlands: Martinus Nijhoff, 1986. The first conference proceedings dedicated to documenting fractal applications in solid-state physics, diffusion, percolation, critical point phenomena, and Brownian motion.

Gerardo G. Tango

Cross-References

Hilbert Develops a Model for Euclidean Geometry in Arithmetic (1898), p. 31; Lebesgue Develops a New Integration Theory (1899), p. 36; Levi Recognizes the Axiom of Choice in Set Theory (1902), p. 143; Zermelo Undertakes the First Comprehensive Axiomatization of Set Theory (1904), p. 233.

BARGHOORN AND COWORKERS FIND AMINO ACIDS IN 3-BILLION-YEAR-OLD ROCKS

Categories of event: Earth science and biology
Time: 1967-1968
Locale: Harvard University, Cambridge, Massachusetts; Moffet Field, California

The discovery of amino acids in rocks up to 3.1 billion years old influenced thinking about chemical evolution and the fundamental nature of biological systems

Principal personages:
ELSO BARGHOORN (1915-1984), an American paleontologist, professor of botany at Amherst College, 1943-1948; professor and curator of paleobotanical collections, Harvard University, 1948-1984; and member of the United States National Academy of Sciences
J. WILLIAM SCHOPF (1941-   ), an American paleontologist, professor of paleontology at the University of California, Los Angeles; director of the Center for the Evolution and Origin of Life; and consultant to NASA on extraterrestrial life
KEITH KVENVOLDEN (1930-   ), an American organic geochemist and geologist, U.S. Geological Survey; consulting associate professor, Stanford University; and specialist in petroleum geochemistry, chemical fossils, and origins of life
STANLEY MILLER (1930-   ), an American chemist and originator of theories and experiments on the nature of chemical evolution

Summary of Event

On November 16, 1967, J. William Schopf and Elso Barghoorn of Harvard University and Keith Kvenvolden of the U.S. Geological Survey presented a paper to the National Academy of Sciences summarizing their search for traces of amino acids in the oldest known sedimentary rocks. These findings were published in the *Proceedings of the National Academy of Sciences* in 1968. This team of scientists, consisting of two paleontologists and one organic geochemist, had analyzed organic material leached from pulverized black cherts from three Precambrian formations: the 1-billion-year-old Australian Bitter Springs formation, the 2-billion-year-old Canadian Gunflint chert, and the 3-billion-year-old Fig Tree chert from South Africa. The latter was the oldest undeformed Precambrian sedimentary rock known at the time.

The Gunflint locality had already yielded abundant evidence of early life in the form of many examples of structurally preserved microorganisms; it was the subject of a classic 1954 paper in the journal *Science* by Barghoorn and Stanley Tyler, which contained the first indisputable reports of early Proterozoic microfossils. Well-preserved microorganisms had been reported in the Bitter Springs formation by Barghoorn and Schopf in 1965. The fossil evidence for life in the Fig Tree chert was not as compelling, but Schopf and Barghoorn were in the process of examining this material and had reported bacterial microfossils visible with electron microscopy in it in *Science* in 1966.

In a sense, chemical fossils are potentially more informative than fossils of whole organisms in reconstructing the evolutionary history of life, especially in its earliest stages. All life on earth today shares a unique carbon-based chemistry. The presence of deoxyribonucleic acid (DNA) and amino acids is virtually a definition of the presence of life, and these chemicals or their breakdown products are one of the things for which scientists routinely search in meteorites and lunar samples. If the presence of DNA or amino acids could be unequivocally demonstrated in the earth's earliest sedimentary rocks, it would be profoundly significant from several perspectives. First, it would provide corroboration that the ambiguous microfossils found in the Fig Tree chert and other extremely ancient (greater than 3 billion years old) Archaean formations were microbial cells and not aggregations of organic matter formed by some nonbiological process. Second, it would be evidence that these earliest cells had a chemical composition and metabolism similar at least in its broad outlines to present-day microorganisms. Third, it might provide direct fossil evidence for stages in evolution prior to the emergence of discrete microbial cells.

The theory that a period of chemical evolution preceded the emergence of the earliest true life-forms was first coherently articulated by the Soviet Aleksandr Ivanovich Oparin in the 1920's and 1930's. In the early 1950's, Harold C. Urey and Stanley Miller expanded this theory for the early evolution of life, postulating a "soup" of organic chemicals that existed in water bodies on the primeval earth. Heat, electrical discharge, and cosmic rays acted upon this "soup" to produce a broad spectrum of organic compounds, including those which characterize living systems. On a global scale, over millions upon millions of years of geologic time, chemical reactions led to increasingly complex molecules, eventually producing a proto-DNA molecule, which was able to make copies of itself and to direct the synthesis of other complex compounds. The ability to synthesize a membrane to enclose the replicating genetic material was a crucial step in the evolution of simple cells. Urey and Miller also stimulated interest in chemical evolution by taking the theory into the laboratory, simulating conditions that were supposed to have existed in the earth's atmosphere. They showed that by subjecting mixtures of methane, ammonia, water, and hydrogen to electrical discharge, they could produce complex organic compounds, including a number of amino acids. The simple precursors were presumably abundant in the earth's early atmosphere.

In theory, sensitive chemical analysis could detect stages in the precellular evolutionary sequence, although the evidence that Barghoorn and colleagues had in hand suggested that the earliest material available to them contained primitive cells. Nevertheless, the chemistry of these early microorganisms, especially those of the 3-billion-year-old Fig Tree formation, was of profound potential significance to students of evolution.

The types and quantities of amino acids present in the samples were determined by pulverizing carefully cleaned samples of hard, virtually impermeable chert and leaching any organic material present with various solvents. The nature of the organic material was determined by gas chromatography. Twenty amino acids were identified in all samples; a twenty-first occurred only in the Bitter Springs formation. Concentrations were extremely low and decreased with increasing geologic age. Most of the organic matter in the samples consisted not of amino acids or other unaltered biological compounds, but of kerogen, an amorphous mixture of organic hydrocarbons. Kerogen is a precursor of petroleum. Its chemical composition is too altered to give much information about the nature of the organisms that produced it, but its biological origin can be inferred from the ratio of carbon isotopes it contains. Its composition can also be used as a measure of the degree to which other organic matter in a sample is likely to have been altered, because kerogen in rocks that have been heated or deformed loses its hydrogen, ultimately becoming graphite.

Barghoorn and coauthors noted that the distribution of concentrations of various amino acids in all three samples corresponded to the distribution of amino acids from living organisms but differed from results obtained from nonbiological synthesis. The absence of amino acids in controls all but eliminated the possibility of field or laboratory contamination of the samples. Because the amino acids occurred with microfossils in formations high in organic matter, the scientists concluded that they had a biological origin contemporaneous with the microfossils, and that this provided both further confirmation of the existence of life as early as 3 to 3.1 billion years ago and evidence that these fundamental chemical building blocks of cells had remained essentially unchanged from the dawn of organized cellular life to the present.

Impact of Event

The discovery of amino acids in ancient Precambrian sediments attracted attention throughout the scientific community because it confirmed predictions about the nature of early evolutionary events that had been postulated on theoretical grounds and by comparisons of living organisms. The validity of the discovery, however, was questioned almost immediately.

An important piece of information that the authors acknowledged to be missing from the 1968 paper was the optical configuration of the amino acids that had been discovered. Amino acids, and many other complex biological molecules, exist in two forms, a dextro-, or right-handed, form, and a levo-, or left-handed, form, which are mirror images of each other. Although identical in chemical composition and in most physical and chemical properties, they are not identical in living systems. Owing, presumably, to some chance event in early evolutionary history, living systems are composed of left-handed organic molecules. Therefore, one would expect that a sample of amino acids of biological origin would consist primarily of levo- forms, whereas one of nonbiological origin would consist of equal parts levo- and dextro-forms. After long exposure to elevated temperature and pressure, however, biologically produced amino acids undergo racemization; that is, they also become mixtures of the two forms.

In 1969, Kvenvolden and coworkers published a short paper in *Nature* on the optical configuration of amino acids in the Fig Tree chert, in which they reported that they had determined that levo-forms predominated. Thus, the case for their biological origin was strengthened, but the authors also raised the question of whether the amino acids were indeed contemporaneous with the formation. If so, it indicated that the quality of chemical preservation in these 3-billion-year-old rocks was better than that in much younger formations that contained well-preserved organic micro- and macrofossils. The care that had been taken in processing, the consistency of results in multiple samples from the same site, and the absence of amino acids in controls argued compellingly against contamination by the workers themselves, but there remained the possibility that the chert itself was not completely impermeable to dissolved chemicals and that the amino acids were the result of more recent biological activity.

In a review entitled "Precambrian Organic Geochemistry," published in 1983, J. M. Hayes and coauthors expressed doubt that any of the complex soluble chemical fossils reported from the Precambrian are as old as the rocks that contain them, citing Kvenvolden's paper on optical configuration and a calculation that predicts that amino acids racemize within a million years at 25 degrees Celsius. They conclude that "the status of chemical fossils in the Precambrian can, thus, be easily summarized: the low concentrations, evident mobilities, and recognized instabilities of many 'Precambrian' chemical fossils makes their interpretation problematic and leads to the conclusion that these materials do not provide compelling evidence regarding any details of early life."

Hayes and others have conducted extensive analyses of kerogen found in ancient Precambrian sediments and have found a correlation between age, evident degree of metamorphism in the rocks themselves, and degree of loss of hydrogen from kerogen. Formations in which kerogen, a stable, insoluble substance, has been heavily altered are unlikely to contain either reliable microfossils or complex chemical fossils.

Since 1968, several sedimentary formations older than the Fig Tree chert have been identified, including the Onverwacht formation, which underlies it, the 3.5-billion-year-old Warrawoona group in Australia, and the 3.8-billion-year-old Isua formation in Greenland. The Warrawoona group contains stromatolites, simple filamentous microfossils that Schopf accepts as being the oldest plausible microbial microfossils known, and extensively dehydrogenated kerogen with a carbon isotope ratio suggesting a biotic origin. Information on the chemical composition of the microorganisms in this formation would be tremendously useful to scientists studying evolution. Had photosynthesis already evolved at this early date, or did these organisms rely on a chemical energy source? How did the basic building blocks of life 3.5 billion years ago compare to those today? Unfortunately, the state of the rocks is such that any complex chemicals contained in them are almost certainly of recent origin, so a fossil answer to these questions seems unlikely.

The Isua formation has been extensively metamorphosed and contains no plausible microfossils or stromatolites. If any kerogen was contained in the formation, it has been completely converted to graphite, whose biological origin is questionable. The rocks thus lack any convincing evidence of life at either the microfossil or chemical level, but it is uncertain whether this is an indication that there was no life on earth 3.8 billion years ago or whether the quality or preservation is too poor to demonstrate it.

The investigation of chemical fossils failed to fulfill its promise as a tool for the study of the earliest phases in the evolution of life on earth, and scientists studying evolution continue to rely on comparative biochemistry of living forms, mathematical models incorporating known physical parameters, and laboratory experiments in their efforts to unravel the story of the emergence of the unique chemical processes that characterize life on earth.

Bibliography

Brooks, J., and G. Shaw. *Origin and Development of Living Systems*. New York: Academic Press, 1973. A comprehensive textbook for students of biology and paleontology that covers the origins of the solar system and the earth, the common patterns of life's biochemistry and metabolism, theories of chemical evolution prior to the emergence of the first true organisms, the Precambrian fossil record, including chemical fossils, and the relevance of organic chemicals in meteorites. Questions the significance of amino acids in the Fig Tree chert, although not as strongly as in the Schopf (1983) reference listed below. Presupposes familiarity with basic paleontology and biochemistry.

Day, William. *Genesis on Planet Earth*. 2d ed. New Haven, Conn.: Yale University Press, 1984. A clear, well-presented account of current theory about the origin and nature of life on earth. The first five chapters consist of a description of the origin of the earth and the early geologic history of life, which includes a historical narrative of key paleontological discoveries; most of the remainder focuses on the chemistry of life processes and possible evolutionary pathways. Includes a discussion of the evidence for organic matter elsewhere in the universe. The discussions of the basic building blocks of life are useful background for understanding what scientists would have liked to have found in Precambrian chemical fossils. Presupposes familiarity with scientific terminology and organic chemistry.

Kvenvolden, K. A., E. Peterson, and G. E. Pollock. "Optical Configuration of Amino Acids in Precambrian Fig Tree Chert." *Nature* 221 (1969): 141-143. Casts serious doubt on the Precambrian origin of the amino acids reported by Barghoorn, Schopf, and Kvenvolden a year earlier.

Schopf, J. William, ed. *The Earth's Earliest Biosphere*. Princeton, N.J.: Princeton University Press, 1983. A collection of papers from a symposium on early life. Chapter 4, "Prebiotic Synthesis and the Origin of Life," by Sherwood Chang, David DesMarais, Ruth Mack, Stanley Miller, and Gary Strathearn, describes current notions about the physical environment of the early earth, from its initial formation to the first fossil evidence for life 3.5 billion years ago. Covers in detail historical development of early earth models and experimental work on genesis of organic compounds under abiotic conditions. Chapter 5, by J. M. Hayes, Isaac Kaplan, and Jim Wedeking, summarizes the literature casting doubt on Precambrian records of complex organic compounds and describes the formation and analysis of kerogen and its use as a geologic marker.

_____. "The Evolution of the Earliest Cells." *Scientific American* 239 (September, 1978): 16, 110-112. Written for the interested layperson. Presents the metabolic differences between prokaryotes and eukaryotes and a scheme for the timing of emergence of various steps in key metabolic pathways, in tabular as well as narrative form. Focuses on the role of oxygen in key metabolic pathways of prokaryotes and eukaryotes and the relevance of this analysis to timing events in the evolution of cells and of the earth's atmosphere.

Schopf, J. William, Keith A. Kvenvolden, and Elso S. Barghoorn. "Amino Acids in Precambrian Sediments: An Essay." *Proceedings of the National Academy of Sciences* 69 (1968): 639-646. A straightforward technical report that describes the research methods in detail, including the issue of modern contamination.

Martha Sherwood-Pike

Cross-References

Hopkins Discovers Tryptophan, an Essential Amino Acid (1900), p. 46; Elster and Geitel Demonstrate Radioactivity in Rocks, Springs, and Air (1901), p. 93; Boltwood Uses Radioactivity to Obtain the Age of Rocks (1905), p. 285; Libby Introduces the Carbon-14 Method of Dating Ancient Objects (1940's), p. 1160; Miller Reports the Synthesis of Amino Acids (1953), p. 1465; Barghoorn and Tyler Discover 2-Billion-Year-Old Microfossils (1954), p. 1481; Scientists Develop a Technique to Date Ancient Obsidian (1960), p. 1645; Nirenberg Invents an Experimental Technique That Cracks the Genetic Code (1961), p. 1687; Miller Discovers a Dinosaur Egg Containing the Oldest Known Embryo (1987), p. 2357.

KORNBERG AND COWORKERS SYNTHESIZE BIOLOGICALLY ACTIVE DNA

Category of event: Biology
Time: August-September, 1967
Locale: Stanford University and California Institute of Technology, California

Kornberg's discovery—that a fully infective viral DNA could be re-created in a test tube—demonstrated that a purified enzyme could produce virtually error-free synthesis of a simple chromosome outside the living cell

Principal personages:
> Arthur Kornberg (1918-   ), an American physician and biochemist who pioneered the search for an enzyme that could catalyze the synthesis of DNA
> Robert L. Sinsheimer (1920-   ), an American biophysicist and authority on the physical and chemical properties of nucleic acids and on the replication of bacterial viruses
> Mehran Goulian (1929-   ), a physician and biochemist who worked with Kornberg on the enzymatic synthesis of DNA

Summary of Event

Until the mid-1940's, it was believed that proteins were the carriers of genetic information, the source of heredity. Proteins, which are composed of many different amino acid units, appeared to be the only biological molecules that had the complexity necessary to encode the enormous amount of genetic information required to reproduce even the simplest organism. Nevertheless, proteins could not be shown to have genetic properties, and by 1944, it was demonstrated conclusively that deoxyribonucleic acid (DNA) is the material that can transmit hereditary information. DNA, isolated from a strain of infective bacteria that cause pneumonia, was able to transform a strain of noninfective bacteria into an infective strain, and the infectivity trait was transmitted to future generations. Subsequently, it was established that DNA is the genetic material in virtually all forms of life, except some viruses in which the genome is based on ribonucleic acid (RNA).

Once DNA was known to be the transmitter of genetic information, scientists sought to discover how it performs its role. DNA is a polymeric molecule composed of four different units, called deoxynucleotides. The units consist of a sugar, a phosphate group, and a base; they differ only in the nature of the base, which is always one of four related compounds: adenine, guanine, cytosine, or thymine. The means by which such a polymer could transmit genetic information was hard to discern. In 1953, James D. Watson and Francis Crick brilliantly deduced the three-dimensional structure of DNA by analysis of X-ray diffraction photographs of DNA fibers. From their analysis of the structure of DNA, Watson and Crick inferred its mechanism of replication. Their work led to an understanding of gene function in molecular terms. Watson and Crick showed that DNA has a very long double-stranded (duplex) helical structure. In the duplex, the sugar and phosphate units of each deoxynucleotide are joined to form the exterior of the helix and the bases are interior. They proposed that the bases are arranged in a defined sequence, analogous to the arrangement of letters of the alphabet into words. The genetic code, the hereditary message, lies in the precise sequence of the bases. DNA has a duplex structure because each base forms a link to a specific base on the opposite strand. The linkage (or pairing) is most specific; adenine is always paired with thymine, and guanine with cytosine. The discovery of this complementary pairing of bases provided a model to explain the two essential functions of a hereditary molecule: It must preserve the genetic code from one generation to another, and it must direct the development of the cell. Watson and Crick proposed that DNA is able to serve as a mold (or template) for its own reproduction because the two strands of DNA polymer can separate. Upon separation, each strand acts as a template for the formation of a new complementary strand. An adenine base in the existing strand gives rise to the complementary thymine base in the new strand, guanine gives rise to cytosine, and so on. In this manner, a new double-stranded DNA is generated that is identical to the parent DNA.

Watson and Crick's theory provided a valuable model for the reproduction of DNA, but it did not explain the biological mechanism by which the process occurs. The biochemical pathway of DNA reproduction and the role of the enzymes required for catalyzing reproduction were discovered by Arthur Kornberg and coworkers. For his success in achieving DNA synthesis in a test tube and for discovering and isolating an enzyme—DNA polymerase—that catalyzed DNA synthesis, Kornberg was a corecipient of the 1959 Nobel Prize in Physiology or Medicine.

To achieve DNA replication in a test tube, Kornberg found that a small amount of preformed DNA must be present, in addition to DNA polymerase enzyme and all four of the deoxynucleotides that occur in DNA. Although the polymerase enzyme was isolated from a strain of coli bacteria called *Escherichia coli* (*E. coli*), the preformed DNA did not have to come from *E. coli*. Preformed DNA isolated from almost any source—from different strains of bacteria, from a virus, or from calf thymus glands—served as a template with the *E. coli* DNA polymerase enzyme.

DNAs isolated from different sources have different base compositions—that is, different proportions of the base pairs adenine plus thymine and guanine plus cytosine. Kornberg discovered that the base composition of the newly made DNA was determined solely by the base composition of the preformed DNA, which had been used as a template in the test-tube synthesis. This result showed that DNA polymerase obeys instructions dictated by the template DNA. It is thus said to be template-directed. DNA polymerase was the first template-directed enzyme discovered.

Although test-tube synthesis was a most significant achievement, important questions about the precise character of the newly made DNA were unanswered. Methods of analyzing the order, or sequence, of the bases in DNA were not available, and hence, it could not be shown directly whether DNA made in the test tube is a very accurate, exact copy of the template of DNA or merely an approximate copy. In addition, some DNAs prepared by DNA polymerase appeared to be branched structures. Given that chromosomes in living cells contain long, linear, unbranched strands of DNA, this branching might indicate that DNA synthesized in a test tube was not equivalent to DNA synthesized in the living cell. (Conversely, branching could be a technical artifact.) In Kornberg's early experiments, he was unable to show whether the DNA synthesized was a new molecule or merely an extension of the preformed DNA. The technical problems were formidable, and the precision with which polymerase enzyme copied DNA chains, consisting of thousands of nucleotides, was unproved.

Kornberg realized that the best way to demonstrate that newly synthesized DNA is an exact copy of the original was to test the new DNA for biological activity in a suitable system. His first attempts to produce biologically active DNA, using bacterial DNA as a template, were unsuccessful. Failure, although disappointing, was not too discouraging because the lack of success could be attributed to technical problems in obtaining an intact, unfragmented DNA for the template. It is almost impossible to isolate an entire bacterial DNA molecule that is extremely long—4 million base pairs in length—without random fragmentation of the DNA and resultant loss in biological activity. In order to avoid the problem of fragmentation, the synthesis of a simpler DNA, a viral genome, was then attempted.

Robert L. Sinsheimer's group of researchers were experts in the biology and biochemistry of a special bacterial virus that promised to be a good candidate for test-tube DNA synthesis. This virus has a circular, single-stranded DNA molecule approximately fifty-five hundred deoxynucleotides long, which folds upon itself and can be isolated intact. In nature, the virus reproduces inside an *E. coli* bacterial cell by producing double-stranded DNA as a replication intermediate. Identical copies of the original single-stranded viral DNA are made from the intermediate inside the cell to produce a new, infective virus. Sinsheimer and coworkers developed tests of viral infectivity that revealed that a change in even one nucleotide among the fifty-five hundred total in the viral DNA could make the virus noninfective. Kornberg reasoned that a demonstration of infectivity in viral DNA produced in a test tube would prove that polymerase-catalyzed synthesis was virtually error-free and equivalent to natural, biological synthesis. The experiment, carried out by Kornberg, colleague Mehran Goulian at Stanford University, and Sinsheimer at the California Institute of Technology, was a complete success. The viral DNAs produced in a test tube by DNA polymerase enzyme, using viral DNA template, were fully infective. This synthesis showed that DNA polymerase could copy not merely a single gene but an entire chromosome (containing eleven genes) of a small virus without error.

Impact of Event

The purification of DNA polymerase and the preparation of biologically active DNA were major discoveries that influenced biological research on DNA for decades. Kornberg's methodology proved invaluable in the discovery of other enzymes that synthesize DNA. These enzymes have been isolated from *E. coli* bacteria and from other bacteria, viruses, and higher organisms.

In the early 1950's, when Kornberg first attempted to reproduce DNA, many scientists doubted that complex biological molecules could be reconstructed successfully outside the living cell. Although much was known about the degradation of complex molecules, little was known of their synthesis. A number of biochemists thought that the synthesis and breakdown of large biomolecules were two-way processes, proceeding by the same reversible pathways. Kornberg recognized that the biochemical route by which DNA is made is separate and distinct from the route by which it is degraded in the cell. His use of *E. coli* bacteria (after initial unsuccessful experiments with animal cells) was also an inspired choice. Kornberg reasoned that *E. coli* cell extracts should be a good source of DNA polymerizing enzymes because *E. coli* cells duplicate, and hence reproduce their DNA, very frequently (every twenty minutes). Although this choice was correct, the enzyme was difficult to isolate. For example, to obtain half a gram of DNA polymerase, 100 kilograms of *E. coli* cells had to be processed.

The test-tube preparation of viral DNA also had significance in the studies of genes and chromosomes. In the mid-1960's, it had not been established that a chromosome contains a continuous strand of DNA. Kornberg and Sinsheimer's synthesis of a viral chromosome proved that it was, indeed, a very long strand of uninterrupted DNA.

Experiments with *E. coli* bacterial mutants in the mid-1970's led to an unexpected finding concerning the role of polymerase enzyme in DNA synthesis. Mutant *E. coli* bacteria were isolated which reproduced at normal rates, although the activity of their DNA polymerase enzyme was much diminished, reduced to 1 to 2 percent of normal. The apparent inconsistency between growth rates and polymerase activity was explained by the discovery that more than one enzyme is required to copy DNA in nature. DNA polymerase (now called DNA polymerase I) is not the main enzyme that reproduces DNA in the cell. Its main role is to "proofread" DNA, removing unwanted bases from growing DNA strands, and to repair damaged DNA. These findings revealed an important principle in biology: A function in nature cannot be ascribed to an enzyme on the basis of test-tube experiments alone; the use of mutants and the study of reactions inside the cell are also necessary.

Kornberg and Sinsheimer's work laid the foundation for subsequent recombinant DNA research and for genetic engineering technology. This technology promises to revolutionize both medicine and agriculture. The enhancement of food production and the generation of new drugs and therapies are only a few of the benefits that may be expected to accrue to humankind.

Bibliography

Friedberg, Errol C. *DNA Repair.* New York: W. H. Freeman, 1985. This textbook is a useful complement to Kornberg's *DNA Replication* (cited below). A valuable source for the research scientist and advanced student, the text provides current information on DNA damage, the effects of DNA damage, and the mechanisms by which an organism can repair its damaged DNA.

Goulian, Mehran, Arthur Kornberg, and Robert L. Sinsheimer. "Enzymatic Synthesis of DNA, XXIV: Synthesis of Infectious Phage φX 174 DNA." *Proceedings of National Academy of Sciences* 58 (1967): 2321-2328. This research article is the primary source for the reader seeking information on details of the means by which Kornberg and coworkers first synthesized biologically active DNA.

Kornberg, Arthur. *DNA Replication*. San Francisco: W. H. Freeman, 1980. This outstanding and highly readable textbook is the prime resource for the research scientist or student interested in the biochemistry of DNA replication and metabolism. DNA replication in prokaryotes (bacteria and viruses) is covered most comprehensively; replication in eukaryotes (higher organisms) is also treated. Although some information is out of date, this text is still an invaluable source.

_____. *1982 Supplement to DNA Replication*. San Francisco: W. H. Freeman, 1982. Should be used in conjunction with Kornberg's *DNA Replication* (cited above). Covers the extensive new discoveries made between 1980 and 1982.

_____. "The Synthesis of DNA." *Scientific American* 219 (April, 1968): 64-78. This article is addressed primarily to the nonspecialist who is interested in science. Provides a concise, popularized account of DNA synthesis. Though some information is out of date, this article is still essentially correct and has not been superseded.

Stryer, Lubert. *Biochemistry*. 3d ed. New York: W. H. Freeman, 1988. Part 1, "Molecular Design of Life," and Part 5, "Genetic Information: Storage, Transmission, and Expression," provide excellent, current information on hereditary mechanisms and the means by which genetic information is expressed inside the cell. Chapters 4 and 26 describe concisely the structure of DNA and its mode of replication. Text is geared toward a student of science who has some knowledge of biochemical terminology. Includes useful references.

Zubay, Geoffrey. *Biochemistry*. 2d ed. New York: Macmillan, 1988. A useful textbook for the advanced student. Chapter 26, "DNA Metabolism," provides current biochemical information on DNA synthesis and breakdown. Other chapters in section 5, "Nucleic Acid and Protein Metabolism," cover related biochemical processes.

Maureen S. May

Cross-References

Avery, MacLeod, and McCarty Determine That DNA Carries Hereditary Information (1943), p. 1203; Ochoa Creates Synthetic RNA (1950's), p. 1363; Watson and Crick Develop the Double-Helix Model for DNA (1951), p. 1406; Cohen and Boyer Develop Recombinant DNA Technology (1973), p. 1987; Berg, Gilbert, and Sanger Develop Techniques for Genetic Engineering (1980), p. 2115; Erlich Develops DNA Fingerprinting from a Single Hair (1988), p. 2362.

BELL DISCOVERS PULSARS, THE KEY
TO NEUTRON STARS

Category of event: Astronomy
Time: November, 1967-February, 1968
Locale: Mullard Radio Astronomy Observatory, the University of Cambridge, England

Bell discovered pulsars, a new class of star that provides the key to understanding supernovas and neutron stars

Principal personages:
>JOCELYN BELL (1943-   ), a graduate student in radio astronomy at the University of Cambridge who discovered a new type of stellar radio source, pulsars
>ANTONY HEWISH (1924-   ), an astronomer who designed the radio telescope Bell used to discover the pulsar sources; cowinner of the 1974 Nobel Prize in Physics

Summary of Event

The history of science illustrates many serendipitous discoveries that eclipse the original destination of the researcher and experiment. Jocelyn Bell's discovery of pulsars is illustrative of this phenomenon.

The path of discovery leads to the Mullard Radio Astronomy Observatory of the University of Cambridge, where in 1965 astronomer Antony Hewish was constructing a new kind of radio telescope. Although the telescope was designed for quasar detection, quasars became the least significant part of the research. By luck, the same observational parameters for quasar detection were very close to those of something they were not looking for: pulsars. (The word "pulsar" comes from "pulsating star.")

Bell, Hewish's graduate student, was the first person to identify a pulsar. In an effort to bring the new telescope on line and work out the bugs, she could not account for an anomaly in the radio data she called "scruff." The source of this unwanted signal noise was annoying, elusive, and invisible. As with any new instrument, Hewish's first thoughts were that the pulses were electrical noise within the instrument or, perhaps, some type of local noise such as ham operators, automobile ignitions, or other electrical interference. Bell was determined to isolate and filter the pulses from the radio signature. Then, curiously, it disappeared. Bell continued searching, checking the telescope for "scruff." In late November of 1967, it reappeared. Hewish thought the signals were freakish because of their shift in position and their fluctuating appearance. An attempt to measure any parallax failed, which suggested that the source was beyond the solar system. Hewish then hypothesized the pulses might be the radio signature of a flare star. To resolve the question, they used a high-speed chart recorder. Since the telescope was not steerable, Bell had to synchronize her observations with the daily, or nightly, sidereal passage of the object overhead.

It was clear that Bell discovered something unusual, but the source was not clear. These signals did not demonstrate the radio signatures of other known sources: stars, galaxies, or solar wind, which suggested something entirely different. Other explanations pointed to some terrestrial man-made interference with the telescope. The question of how to distinguish the two came from a simple but unique phenomenon: the difference in Earth time and star (sidereal) time. Bell observed the pulsating "scruff" over time and realized that it was not in synchronization with Earth time but was sidereal time. This suggested an extraterrestrial origin. It also raised the question of what could create extraterrestrial pulses with such preciseness, with each pulse arriving at intervals of 1.3373011 seconds. Regularity of this precision is rarely found in nature, which raises the question of whether it is natural. Hewish and Bell had to consider the possibility of the LGM phenomenon (Little Green Men) and in good humor identified the source as LGM 1. These regular pulses could be tangible evidence of alien intelligence. They were presented with a fascinating dilemma: what to do with this kind of knowledge. If they announced the discovery without all the evidence and were proved wrong later, it would be a textbook example of how not to conduct a scientific investigation. Yet, if these pulses were evidence of alien intelligence, then it would be a most momentous discovery. Hewish and Bell attacked the problem in the spirit and method of good science.

The LGM hypothesis faded; they renamed the source CP 1919 (for Cambridge pulsar and its sky position) and turned their attention to describing the phenomenon. Hewish maintained the survey over Christmas in 1967 and placed the raw data on Bell's desk. Upon her return, Bell began to analyze the charts and found another source of pulses. Then, sources number three and four appeared. In the next two weeks, Bell was able to confirm that these were, indeed, independent sources. Perhaps the sky was teeming with pulsating sources. Bell reviewed an endless number of charts to determine if there were other sources she might have overlooked. This research resulted in a number of candidates, but nothing as definitive as the first four sources. The nature of the source was still eluding Hewish, Bell, and other astronomers, such as John Pilkington, P. F. Scott, and R. A. Collins, who had joined the search at Mullard Observatory.

They announced their discovery (without resolving the nature of the pulsating source) in *Nature*, February 24, 1968, with the following statement: "A tentative explanation of these unusual sources in terms of the stable oscillations of white dwarf or neutron stars is proposed." In publications later that year, Hewish seemed to favor the white dwarf hypothesis. The editors of *Nature* seem to favor the other option because on the cover of that issue were the words "Possible Neutron Star." At this point, the problem of the nature of the pulsating sources passed to the world community of scientists. The final connection of the pulsar with a rapidly rotating neutron star, rather than a pulsating white dwarf, came with the combined work of Franco Pacini and Thomas Gold in 1968.

Impact of Event

Jocelyn Bell did not anticipate the instant celebrity status the news of the discovery of pulsars brought, especially in the popular press. Bell quietly ended her observations, wrote her dissertation, and accepted a job in another field of research in another part of the country. The story of the pulsars became an appendix in her dissertation.

The announcement by Hewish and Bell triggered a flood of observational and theoretical papers on pulsars. In the following year, the list of pulsar locations grew to more than twenty-four; in 1976, there were more than 150 identified, and the current list is more than four hundred pulsar locations. Pulsars were not discovered sooner because radio astronomers were using centimeter wavelengths to look at the sky, as opposed to Hewish's meter wavelengths and the adding of signals over long periods of time in order to resolve weak signals. This was the reason why the Hewish telescope was successful and Bell was able to resolve the pulses. For this and other outstanding work, Hewish shared the 1974 Nobel Prize in Physics with Sir Martin Ryle. It was the first awarded to astronomers. Hewish's award was based on his role in the detection of pulsars. Interestingly, Bell—the acknowledged discoverer—was not included in the Nobel recognition.

The discovery carried the teasing phrase "possible neutron star," and the timing mechanism that regulated the radio pulses remained a mystery. The 1968 discovery of the Vela pulsar within a supernova remnant established the link between pulsars and neutron stars. This was strengthened by the discovery of a pulsar in the Crab nebula, another supernova remnant. There was a direct relationship between the age of the supernova remnant, diffusion of the nebulosity, and pulse rate with neutron stars as the product of the supernova event. The history of pulsars appears to follow this sequence: First, a star explodes (supernova); then, the core collapses, forming a neutron star. Finally, as the nebulosity expands, the pulses slow in proportion to the rotation of the neutron star. The "scruff" Bell identified on the radio telescope was the radio signature of rotating neutron stars.

The important consequences of the pulsar-neutron star discovery are that they give astronomers an opportunity to examine the behavior of matter under incredible and extreme conditions of pressure and temperature not obtainable in terrestrial laboratories and at densities so great that they involve general relativistic considerations and micro physics. Pulsars stimulated further research on stellar evolution and its products such as white dwarfs, neutron stars, collapsars, frozen stars, and black holes. Observing binary neutron stars gives confirming evidence for Albert Einstein's theory of general relativity, the distortion of space-time near massive objects, and the existence of gravity waves. Further, pulsar-neutron stars represent matter on the verge of total gravitational collapse; their existence implies that what was once a theoretical convenience like Wolfgang Pauli's neutrino particle may be a physical reality. The paradigms of the nature of the universe have changed because Jocelyn Bell persisted in understanding the nature of the "scruff" on her recording chart.

Bibliography

Astronomical Society of the Pacific. *The Discovery of Pulsars.* San Francisco: Author, 1989. An audio tape interview with Hewish and Bell. Available from A.S.P., 390 Ashton Avenue, San Francisco, CA 94112. Perhaps the best primary source. Targeted to the interested reader as an example of how science works.

Greenstein, George. *Frozen Star.* New York: Freundlich Books, 1983. A thorough work on the nature of pulsars, supernovas, and neutron stars. This work is geared for the interested amateur or astronomy student.

_____. "Neutron Stars and the Discovery of Pulsars." *Mercury* 34 (March/April, 1985): 34-39, 66-73. These are very readable articles that capture the spirit and detail of the discovery. A good starting point for the interested reader.

Hewish, A. "Pulsars, After Twenty Years." *Mercury* 38 (January/February, 1989): 12-15. A summary from the Nobel Prize winner on the discovery of pulsars and the knowledge of these strange radio sources. Written for nonspecialists, with illustrations of the telescope and model of a neutron star.

_____, et al. "Observation of a Rapidly Pulsating Radio Source." *Nature* 217 (February 24, 1968): 709-713. This is the primary source for the serious reader. Interesting understatement illustrating the cautious nature of announcing discoveries whose scope is not fully understood.

Richard C. Jones

Cross-References

Jansky's Experiments Lead to the Founding of Radio Astronomy (1930), p. 934; Chandrasekhar Calculates the Upper Limit of a White Dwarf Star's Mass (1931), p. 948; Chadwick Discovers the Neutron (1932), p. 973; Zwicky and Baade Propose Their Theory of Neutron Stars (1934), p. 1008; Oppenheimer Calculates the Nature of Black Holes (1939), p. 1150; Reber Makes the First Radio Maps of the Universe (1942), p. 1193; Ryle Constructs the First Radio Interferometer (1955), p. 1496; Wheeler Names the Phenomenon "Black Holes" (1968), p. 1881.

BARNARD PERFORMS THE FIRST HUMAN HEART TRANSPLANT

Category of event: Medicine
Time: December, 1967
Locale: Groote Schuur Hospital, Cape Town, South Africa

Barnard transplanted the first human heart, initiating a worldwide era of heart transplantation

Principal personages:
> CHRISTIAAN BARNARD (1922-   ), the South African cardiac surgeon who performed the first human-to-human heart transplant
> LOUIS WASHKANSKY (1914-1967), the Cape Town grocer whose incurably diseased heart was replaced in the first human heart transplant
> DENISE DARVALL (1943-1967), the automobile-accident victim whose heart was donated to Washkansky

Summary of Event

In 1967, many surgeons in medical centers throughout the world were on the verge of performing the first human heart transplant. Since 1954, when the first successful kidney transplant was achieved, surgeons had performed innumerable heart transplants on dogs, calves, and lower primates in preparation for the first human attempt. Yet, the unsolved problems of rejection by the immune system of the recipient and the emotional, moral, and legal aspects of removing a yet-living heart from a brain-dead donor were major obstacles. On December 2, 1967, Christiaan Barnard of Groote Schuur Hospital, Cape Town, South Africa, and his thirty-member team overcame those barriers to perform the first human heart transplant. Even though the transplant was considered partially successful because the patient, Louis Washkansky, lived only eighteen days, it was eminently successful in opening a new frontier in modern medicine.

Louis Washkansky had suffered several major heart attacks since his first bout with angina in 1960. In addition to the irreparable destruction of the coronary vessels, which deliver blood to the heart muscle itself, and of both ventricles, which are the lower chambers of the heart, he suffered from diabetes.

In November, 1967, the team worked steadily to prepare for this landmark surgery. Marthinus Botha, the immunologist, was ready to do the tissue matching of a donor heart when it became available, according to the methods developed by Jan van Rood and Paul Terasaki. Arderne Forder, a bacteriologist, studied innumerable swabs from Washkansky's body to determine the presence of potentially dangerous bacteria. Forder was also studying similar swabs from the entire care-giving team. Many antiseptic washings of the patient's entire body were carried out in addition to the preparation of a germ-free room for his recovery. The hospital staff built a temporary mobile cobalt radiation apparatus to use to prevent the heart's rejection by Washkansky's white blood cells; thus, the machine could be brought to the patient.

A review of reports from the United States and Europe on the signs of incipient rejection proved to be more confusing than informative. Therefore, continuous studies were done of Washkansky's blood chemistry, liver, kidneys, and lungs to establish a standard by which to judge between rejection and infection. Peter Rose-Innis, the neurosurgeon, and the emergency room personnel were requested to report a possible donor. This led to a false alarm on November 23 because of the deterioration of a donor heart in the hours before the donor's parents could be reached to obtain consent.

Washkansky's condition continued to worsen daily. On the afternoon of Saturday, December 2, twenty-five-year-old Denise Darvall and her mother, Myrtle, were struck by an automobile while crossing the street. Myrtle Darvall was killed instantly, and the staff at Groote Schuur Hospital knew that Denise's severely fractured skull was beyond repair. By 5:30 P.M., Dr. Rose-Innis had ascertained the cessation of all reflexes, and a flat EEG confirmed her brain's death. Artificial respiration was applied to keep her heart beating. Within the next few hours, Dr. Botha was able to establish her tissues' relative compatibility with Washkansky. Her father, Edward Darvall, gave permission for the donation of her heart.

By 1:30 A.M. of December 3, both operating rooms were in readiness, and Washkansky was anesthetized. In a most critical and difficult step for Barnard and his pioneering team, the respirator was withdrawn from Darvall at 2:10 A.M. Fifteen minutes later, her heart ceased to beat. It was then chilled to prevent deterioration, and heparin was given to prevent blood clotting. The heart was removed by Christiaan Barnard; his brother, Marius Barnard; Terry O'Donovan; Coert Venter; and Cecil Moss, the anesthesiologist.

In the other operating room, when Christiaan Barnard prepared to remove Washkansky's diseased heart, a moment of crisis arose. Hardening of the femoral artery caused difficulty in attaching the heart-lung machine needed to give his organs oxygen while his body would be temporarily without a heart. While the team attempted to remedy this problem, his blood spilled out on the floor. Soon thereafter, the recipient team of Christiaan Barnard; Rodney Hewitson; François Hitchcock; Siebert Bosman; and Joseph Ozinsky, the anesthesiologist, removed Washkansky's heart while bathing Darvall's heart in his blood. Two hours later, the suturing of the last of the new heart's major blood vessels was complete. The next major difficulty now occurred: It took almost an hour and three attempts to get the donor heart to beat in the recipient's chest cavity. Each time, Washkansky had to be attached temporarily to the heart-lung machine. Finally, at 6:24 A.M., the team rejoiced when they saw the first human heart ever transplanted beat strongly in Louis Washkansky.

While antirejection therapy was begun by the injection of massive doses of hydrocortisone, prednisone, and Imuran, the patient was rapidly transported to a sterile room. The hospital superintendent was informed that the first heart transplant had been accomplished. His first announcement to the press on December 3 was followed in the next few days by a deluge of press representatives who constantly tried to enter the sterile areas, climbed trees outside the patient's room, and demanded endless press conferences with the team.

Washkansky, known as a brave, feisty, uncomplaining person, now began a see-saw existence as his new heart fought for his life. His deliberately weakened immune system failed to fight effectively against infection, and it fought to reject the new foreign heart. The long cobalt treatment wore him out, his pulse raced, and his enzyme levels rose. Higher doses of both antirejection drugs and antibiotics were given. He felt much better from December 9 to 14; his oxygen tent was removed, and he was given sterilized newspapers and a radio. His heart and kidney functions normalized, he was allowed visits from adult family members, and he was even allowed to sun himself on the balcony.

The struggle began on December 15. Daily, endless conferences of the thirty-member team could not solve the problem: to determine whether the infection or rejection was the cause of his increasing fever, chest pains, and weakness. Ultimately, it was a massive bacterial pneumonia of both lungs that caused Washkansky's death on December 21. Since the postmortem showed no rejection of the new heart, it seemed that the team had been more vigorous than necessary in their use of antirejection methods. Yet, they were not vigorous enough in their use of therapy against infection, which they were unable to diagnose in time.

Washkansky's death was a crushing blow to Barnard. Yet, he and his team learned that heart transplantation was possible and promptly planned to apply their hard-won knowledge to saving others for whom a new heart was their only hope for continued life.

Impact of Event

It was expected for some time that the first heart transplant would be performed in a major American cardiac center where decades of research and preparation had already occurred. Yet, while these gifted, talented surgeons stood ready, Christiaan Barnard used the knowledge and skill he had acquired from them and, with courage—some say audacity—performed this unique operation. His action had an immediate impact on the medical community. Others, once free of their hesitancy and scruples, performed five transplantations in the next two months, and 170 transplantations were done worldwide in the next three years.

Between 1946 and 1958, Soviet Vladimir Demikhov performed heart transplants on 250 dogs, attaching a second heart within each, thereby proving it was possible to restart a heartbeat by electric shock. During the 1960's, Norman E. Shumway of Stanford, believing human transplants would soon be possible, performed endless experiments to develop the technique. Working apace with Shumway's developments were Richard Lower, Adrian Kantrowitz, and James Hardy. They perfected the use of hypothermia to keep the donor heart from deteriorating. They learned how to attach the atria, or two top chambers, without destroying the nerve centers.

Barnard, during a fellowship at Minneapolis in 1955, learned open-heart surgery from Owen Wangensteen along with C. Walton Lillehei and returned to South Africa with the first heart-lung machine. In 1966, Barnard returned to the United States to study kidney transplantation. Instead, he learned from Lower what he had experienced already while working for ten years with Shumway at Stanford. Barnard then performed his own canine experiments in South Africa.

Undeterred by the failure of Hardy in 1964 when his patient, Boyd Rush, died two hours after a chimpanzee heart was transplanted, Barnard took his giant step on December 2, 1967. Immediately thereafter, on December 6, Kantrowitz performed the first heart transplant on an infant who survived only two hours. Although Washkansky had died after eighteen days, Barnard proceeded with a transplant of Philip Blaiberg on January 2, 1968, who lived 593 days before his heart was rejected by his immune system. A veritable flood of transplants followed: January 6 by Shumway, January 10 by Kantrowitz, and February 16 by P. K. Sen in Bombay. By 1971, Denton A. Cooley and Michael Ellis De Bakey of Texas had performed more than thirty transplantations, while Shumway had performed twenty.

Yet, of the first 170 transplantations performed worldwide, fifty died from rejection of the heart, thirty died of infections, and others died from various other causes. After four attempts, Barnard gave up. Heart transplants all but ceased in the 1970's; the rejection problem needed to be solved by biochemists and immunologists. In 1969, the answer was found by Jean-François Borel with the discovery of cyclosporine, which not only killed any immune cell but also killed the T lymphocytes that multiply in response to foreign tissue. Cyclosporine became widely used after 1983 and caused an enormous resurgence of heart transplantations.

Although many legal, ethical, and emotional issues still arise, and the number of donors is low compared with the number of waiting recipients, there were twenty times as many hearts transplanted in 1989 as in 1980. Christiaan Barnard's dream today is a daily occurrence throughout the world, because he dared to do something and make it a reality.

Bibliography

Barnard, Christiaan, and Curtis Bill Pepper. *Christiaan Barnard: One Life*. New York: Macmillan, 1969. Biography of Christiaan Barnard. Part 7, "The Transplant," contains detailed information in a highly readable style on the actual operation and postoperative care of Washkansky. Parts 4-6 shed light on the years of study and preparation for this epic surgery. Parts 1-3 chronicle Barnard's early years. Contains index.

Blaiberg, Philip. *Looking at My Heart*. New York: Stein & Day, 1968. Written four months after Blaiberg became Barnard's second transplant patient. Since Washkansky died after eighteen days, little is known about Washkansky's reactions to this experience. Blaiberg's book is a straightforward report on what it is like to live with another person's heart.

Frist, William. *Transplant*. New York: Atlantic Monthly Press, 1989. As director of the Heart Transplant Program at Vanderbilt University Medical Center, Dr. Frist has performed more than one hundred transplants. Especially good explanation of how cyclosporine has helped solve the problem of heart rejection. Excellent review of federal legislation regarding transplants.

Gohlke, Mary, with Max Jennings. *I'll Take Tomorrow.* New York: M. Evans, 1985. On March 9, 1981, Mary Gohlke survived the first transplant of heart and both lungs. Interesting narrative of her experience. Shows great advances in transplantation two decades after Barnard's pioneering work.

Gutkind, Lee. *Many Sleepless Nights: The World of Organ Transplantation.* New York: W. W. Norton, 1988. Documents the evolution of transplantation, especially in the United States. Very thorough summary of the state of the art of transplantation. Especially interesting account of the work of Pittsburgh's Presbyterian University Hospital, the world's largest transplant center. Includes index.

Hawthorne, Peter. *The Transplanted Heart.* Skokie, Ill.: Rand McNally, 1968. Fast-paced, interesting account of the first heart transplant written within two months of the event by a South African journalist. Written largely from interviews with the transplant team and other Groote Schuur personnel. Best source of information in conjunction with the Barnard/Pepper book (cited above). Illustrated.

Leinwand, Gerald. *Transplants: Today's Medical Miracles.* New York: Franklin Watts, 1985. Brief overview of transplantation: techniques, difficulties, moral and legal questions. Written for adolescents. Includes bibliography and index.

Thompson, Thomas. *Hearts: Of Surgeons and Transplants, Miracles and Disasters Along the Cardiac Frontier.* New York: McCall, 1971. Describes the heart transplants performed three years after Barnard's. Focuses especially on the work of Cooley and De Bakey in Texas. Most important feature of book is complete chronological list of the 170 heart transplants attempted from Hardy's surgery in 1964 until March 1, 1971. The list includes place, survival time, and eventual cause of death for nonsurvivors.

Thorwald, Jürgen. *The Patients.* Translated by Richard Winston and Clara Winston. New York: Harcourt Brace Jovanovich, 1972. An excellent and surprisingly complete account of the first heart transplant. Particularly interesting when contrasted with his account of Hardy's 1964 attempt on Boyd Rush and Cooley's transplantation on Everett Thomas in May, 1968. Index.

Grace Dominic Matzen

Cross-References

Carrel Develops a Technique for Rejoining Severed Blood Vessels (1902), p. 134; McLean Discovers the Natural Anticoagulant Heparin (1915), p. 610; Gibbon Develops the Heart-Lung Machine (1934), p. 1024; Favaloro Develops the Coronary Artery Bypass Operation (1967), p. 1835; Gruentzig Uses Percutaneous Transluminal Angioplasty, via a Balloon Catheter, to Unclog Diseased Arteries (1977), p. 2088; DeVries Implants the First Jarvik-7 Artificial Heart (1982), p. 2195.

FRIEDMAN, KENDELL, AND TAYLOR DISCOVER QUARKS

Category of event: Physics
Time: 1968
Locale: Stanford, California

Friedman, Kendell, and Taylor discovered quarks, the building blocks of protons and neutrons

Principal personages:

JEROME I. FRIEDMAN (1930-   ), an experimental physicist who performed the experiments that revealed the existence of quarks, for which he would share the 1990 Nobel Prize in Physics

HENRY W. KENDELL (1926-   ), an experimental physicist who worked with Friedman and Taylor to discover quarks; corecipient of the 1990 Nobel Prize in Physics

RICHARD E. TAYLOR (1929-   ), an experimental physicist who worked with Friedman and Kendell in the quark discovery; corecipient of the 1990 Nobel Prize in Physics

MURRAY GELL-MANN (1929-   ), an American physicist who pioneered the discovery and classification of subatomic particles, hypothesized the existence of quarks, formulated the theory of quantum chromodynamics, and won the 1969 Nobel Prize in Physics

JAMES BJORKEN, a physicist who helped develop the complex mathematical analysis of the particle accelerator runs in which the quarks were discovered

Summary of Event

From some of the earliest recorded documents in ancient science, the early philosophers believed that all matter was made up of microscopically small particles inside of which were yet smaller particles. When the particles were finely subdivided, the Greeks postulated that the smallest particles could not be divided further. They are called *atomos* (meaning indivisible), the word from which "atom" is derived.

This thinking was little more than philosophical musing until modern times, since there was no way such a theory could be supported by evidence. In 1808, John Dalton produced some of the first experimental evidence of atomic elements and compounds. His evidence was correct, but his theory was mostly incorrect. Nevertheless, Dalton's work led to later serious investigations into atomic structure. In the late nineteenth century, with the discovery of radioactive materials and X rays, a series of observations by Sir Joseph John Thomson led him to identify the existence of electrons, atomic particles, which was the first evidence that the atom could be further subdivided. In 1910, experiments were devised by Ernest Rutherford, an English physicist, which would demonstrate that the atom had a core called the nucleus, around which the electrons "orbited." By 1920, Rutherford had identified the proton as a nuclear particle, and in 1932, Rutherford's student, James Chadwick, discovered the neutron.

This version of the atom—a particle consisting of three kinds of subparticles—held for decades. Many were convinced that there was no evidence for any other kind of particles smaller than these. This idea was buttressed, in part, by the science of quantum physics, which demonstrated that at the subatomic level, the tiny electron, proton, and neutron could be either wavelike or particle-like, depending on the state and quality of observation. Albert Einstein's theory of relativity stated further that mass was equivalent to energy and, under certain conditions, could be converted to energy as $E = mc^2$.

The subatomic structure was unique. Subatomic particle positions could not be nailed down; they could only be predicted statistically with a certain degree of uncertainty. The interchangeability with energy states and their adherence to quantum and relativistic laws made them difficult to study.

The first particle inside the nucleus was called a pion, which is the binding force between the proton and neutron and was discovered via cosmic-ray tracings. Later, other particles would be discovered using particle accelerators.

By the end of World War II, huge devices called particle accelerators were perfected, which were used to accelerate subatomic particles toward atoms at great speeds. When the particles collided with an atom, the atom would break apart and create subparticles, which could be recorded and analyzed. It was determined that there were literally hundreds of particles. By the early 1950's, theoretical physicists were trying to sort out the newly discovered particles. Classification schemes were set up to categorize all the particles, which were then classified in families.

Not only did such bombardment yield subparticles and families, but also a careful analysis indicated what the subatomic world looked like. Accelerator work by Stanford physicist Robert Hofstadter in the 1950's revealed the shape and size of protons and neutrons to be "fuzzy little balls." The indistinct nature of the points was caused by the resolution available to Hofstadter, or the ability to make out all the details of the protons and neutrons distinctly. Hofstadter was awarded the Nobel Prize in Physics in 1961 for his work. Hofstadter worked at an accelerator at Stanford's High Energy Physics Laboratory. While he worked, a much improved and more powerful accelerator was under design. In 1967, a 32-kilometer-long, 20-billion-electronvolt accelerator was completed at Stanford University and would be called the Stanford Linear Accelerator Center (SLAC).

In 1964, American physicist Murray Gell-Mann had examined the variety and classifications of subatomic forces and particles and had devised a classification scheme for the particles. In his scheme, Gell-Mann postulated that the proton and neutron were actually composed of smaller, discrete particles he called "quarks." He theorized later that quarks were held together by "gluons." Gell-Mann had actually carried out a classification system for the array of subatomic particles and forces that had been harvested from the accelerators. Gell-Mann had no direct evidence of an actual physical entity he was calling a quark, but his classification scheme was highly accurate with respect to the information and mathematical models relating to the enigmatic subnuclear world that was nearly impossible to describe objectively.

One of the first experiments planned at SLAC was one in which electrons would be fired at protons at very high speeds—close to the speed of light. The purpose of this experiment was to see at what angle the electron would scatter off the proton. Although the proposal sounded easy enough, since the electrons would be traveling at speeds close to light speed, the problem became one involving relativistic physics. SLAC physicist James Bjorken began to analyze the complex mathematics. All the previous work had been accomplished using accelerators with much less energy and slower speeds so that conventional physics could be used to determine the results. With the power of the linear accelerator, the problem required relativistic solutions for the first time.

The first set of experiments at SLAC began and ended with predictable results—so predictable, in fact, that the initial group of experimenters departed Stanford. Experimental physicists Jerome I. Friedman, Henry W. Kendell of the Massachusetts Institute of Technology (MIT), and SLAC's Richard E. Taylor were left behind to continue the experiments. The experiments had been predictable because the group was examining two kinds of collisions between the proton and the speeding electron. They knew well beforehand that from the impact there could be only an elastic collision or an inelastic one. The elastic collision meant that the electron would strike the proton and literally bounce off at some angle. The inelastic collision meant that the electron would collide with the proton dead center with such energy that it would break the proton into subparticles.

The early experiments were looking for the angle of the elastic collisions because examining these angles would predict the same shapes Hofstadter had examined. It was the team's hope that since the energy of SLAC was so much higher than what Hofstadter had used, a finer resolution could be obtained. Unfortunately, the results were roughly the same as Hofstadter's.

Bjorken, undaunted, confided in Friedman, Kendell, and Taylor that the messy and extraordinarily complex inelastic scattering results could be interpreted in such a way as to suggest resolution inside the proton. According to Bjorken, if there were hard substructures located inside the proton, they would be deflected after the inelastic scattering took place by an unmistakable signature. The team, armed with Bjorken's tools, proceeded to probe the proton. Using this method in an approach remarkably similar to the approach used by Rutherford in 1910, the proton was found to consist of smaller subparticles, Gell-Mann's theoretical quarks, and held together by gluons.

Impact of Event

The Royal Swedish Academy of Sciences compared the Friedman, Kendell, and Taylor discovery to the discovery of the nucleus by Rutherford both in method and in importance. It was the finest positive resolution on the smallest particle of matter that may ever be available. Said one American physicist, their work is " . . . one of the pivotal contributions to physics in this century."

Gell-Mann's postulation of quarks was completely theoretical—an attempt to make some logical order out of the avalanche of tiny particles that emanate from every subatomic collision. It was not at all certain that anyone would ever refine the resolution of the nucleus beyond the work done by Hofstadter on protons and neutrons. Without the actual physical confirmation by Friedman, Kendell, and Taylor, Gell-Mann's theory would have remained merely a theory, and the ability of experimental physics to confirm its findings would have diminished considerably.

The insight of Bjorken's contribution cannot be underestimated with his remarkable suggestion to evaluate a proton's shape mathematically by working through the signatures of the proton's breakup. It was essentially a back-door analysis of the inelastic scattering that all other experimenters had ignored as either too difficult to analyze or completely impossible altogether. Such creative insight, based on observed results, is the essence of experimental science. The team could have given up easily were it not for Bjorken's extraordinary insight and confidence.

The 3.2-kilometer-long, powerful SLAC tool was used to delve into the very center of an atom and subdivide an object (the proton) no bigger than 10-13 centimeters across and resolve what was found to be inside. Such an accomplishment is unsurpassed in theoretical physics. The SLAC is not as powerful as those that have been built later and is of a unique design. Yet, SLAC was used successfully as an important theoretical tool to discover one of the most significant aspects of the atomic structure.

For centuries, humankind has sought the smallest particles of nature. The philosophers of ancient Greece accurately surmised that matter could be divided only to a point. It appears likely that the smallest size has been discovered. It will probably be the final assault on the atom. It is believed by many that the quark may be the smallest distinguishable subatomic particle. If this is so, then it will be Friedman, Kendell, and Taylor who discovered the true *atomos*.

Bibliography

Crease, Robert P., and Charles C. Mann. *The Second Creation*. New York: Macmillan, 1986. Crease and Mann follow the making of twentieth century physics from its nineteenth century roots to the most enigmatic mysteries of the late 1980's. Their book examines microscopically characters and personalities as well as the issues of physics. Friedman, Kendell, and Taylor's approach is discussed as is SLAC and its historic first experiments in detail.

Hawking, Stephen W. *A Brief History of Time*. New York: Bantam Books, 1988. One of the most prominent physicists of the twentieth century examines the universe from his view of creation to the late 1980's. Hawking examines the far-flung reaches of space and time from black holes to the interior of the atom and discusses the elementary particles of the atomic nucleus, including quarks. For a wide audience. Illustrated.

Pagels, Heinz R. *The Cosmic Code.* New York: Simon & Schuster, 1982. This book describes quantum physics as "the language of nature." Pagels, a physicist, embarks on a literary quest to explain some of the most profoundly difficult topics in quantum physics in a clear manner to the general reader. Pagels succeeds and opens up the interior of the atom for a clear view of what is inside. Illustrated. Nontechnical.

Sutton, Christine. *The Particle Connection.* New York: Simon & Schuster, 1984. Christine Sutton, former physicist turned reporter, discusses the particle accelerator. Describes how the machine is used, the nature of the particle chase at CERN—the European particle accelerator laboratory—as well as work at SLAC. Illustrated. Suitable for a student with a reasonable background in science.

Waldrop, M. Mitchell. "Physics Nobel Honors the Discovery of Quarks." *Science* 250 (October 26, 1990): 508-509. This article describes how the discovery of quarks was accomplished. Evaluates the significance of the discovery with specific reference to the work of Gell-Mann and Rutherford. Details the input of Bjorken and the interface of the MIT team with SLAC. Illustrated.

Dennis Chamberland

Cross-References

Thomson Wins the Nobel Prize for the Discovery of the Electron (1906), p. 356; Bohr Writes a Trilogy on Atomic and Molecular Structure (1912), p. 507; Rutherford Presents His Theory of the Atom (1912), p. 527; Rutherford Discovers the Proton (1914), p. 590; Lawrence Develops the Cyclotron (1931), p. 953; Chadwick Discovers the Neutron (1932), p. 973; Cockcroft and Walton Split the Atom with a Particle Accelerator (1932), p. 978; Hofstadter Discovers That Protons and Neutrons Each Have a Structure (1951), p. 1384; The Liquid Bubble Chamber Is Developed (1953), p. 1470; Quarks Are Postulated by Gell-Mann and Zweig (1964), p. 1767; Gell-Mann Formulates the Theory of Quantum Chromodynamics (QCD) (1972), p. 1966.

THE *GLOMAR CHALLENGER* OBTAINS THOUSANDS OF OCEAN FLOOR SAMPLES

Category of event: Earth science
Time: 1968
Locale: World oceans

As part of the Deep Sea Drilling Project, the Glomar Challenger *was instrumental in retrieving rock samples from the ocean floors, providing the data for a revolution in earth science*

Principal personages:
MAURICE EWING (1906-1974), an American geophysicist who pioneered the use of seismic imaging to discern the subsurface topography of the ocean
BRUCE CHARLES HEEZEN (1924-1977), an American geologist who postulated the connection between the topography of the midoceanic ridge and the new theory of plate tectonics
ALFRED LOTHAR WEGENER (1880-1930), a German geologist who was the early formulator of the theory of continental drift

Summary of Event

The maiden voyage of the *Glomar Challenger* was preceded by a revolution in earth scientists' thinking about how the earth functioned. The roots of the revolution may date back to the 1600's, when Francis Bacon first wrote about his observation that the recently defined shapes of South America and Africa suggested that they may have been linked in the past.

Similar speculations persisted throughout the ensuing years, supported by an increasing body of geological knowledge from those two continents as well as from India, Australia, and Antarctica. As the evidence mounted, it became clear that not only were all these continents once connected but also they had moved, in the case of Antarctica, from tropical latitudes to the polar regions.

The theory of continental drift, championed by Alfred Lothar Wegener, grew out of a collection of seemingly unrelated observations of geology and fossils on the southern continents. The conclusion seemed inescapable, but there was a major weakness in the theory. In one early conceptualization of the model, the continents were compared to icebergs floating in the "ocean" of denser rocks that make up the earth's interior. There was no known mechanism whereby massive continental blocks could be moved around on the face of the earth while plowing through the rocks of the denser interior. Thus, continental drift had to wait for another set of seemingly unrelated discoveries.

In the 1920's, Maurice Ewing was working on his doctorate in physics and covering some of his expenses by working summers for oil exploration teams. He helped explore for oil in the Gulf Coast region of Texas, where prospectors would set off dynamite charges near the surface and record the arrival of the shock waves sent through the ground at listening devices strung out on the ground. Depending on what the sound waves encountered in the subsurface, they either traveled faster or slower than average. By deciphering the various arrival times, a prospector could "see" what structures existed in the subsurface and decide if there was anything interesting or likely to yield oil before embarking on expensive drilling.

During the 1930's, Ewing was asked to apply some of the same techniques (called seismic exploration) to explore the structure of the continental shelf and ocean basins in the Atlantic. Not only did the results show considerable thicknesses of sediments in the deep ocean but also the surveys suggested that the sediments were covering what once was a very mountainous topography. During World War II, it became increasingly important to map the topography of the ocean basins. Increasing use of submarines made it imperative, and improvements in sonar and seismic technologies made it relatively easy.

In the early 1950's, Bruce Charles Heezen and coworkers were compiling the results of many topographic studies into one picture of the ocean basin topography. Many surveys had identified a major mountain chain running down the length of the Atlantic Ocean. Heezen's group, however, noticed that there was a deep valley located in the middle of the mountain chain and it too ran the length of the Atlantic Ocean. The role of the central valley was unclear, but it was identified as a rift valley based on its morphological similarity to the continental East African Rift Valley. At nearly the same time, Heezen's group was asked by transatlantic telephone companies to locate areas of earthquake activity in the Atlantic. The thinking was that if the earthquakes were localized, telephone cables could be laid down to avoid those areas and thereby avoid being snapped in the aftermath of a submarine earthquake. Much to Heezen's surprise, the earthquakes tended to be located in and around the central rift valley.

A number of lines of evidence began to converge such that by the mid-1960's a minority in the earth science community was offering the theory of seafloor spreading and plate tectonics as the answer to the missing-mechanism dilemma of continental drift. In plate tectonics, the earth surface may be visualized as an egg shell with cracks. The areas between the cracks are called plates, which can move over the surface and include both continents and ocean basins. The cracks are the boundaries between plates and areas where the plates either collide with or move away from each other. The driving mechanism is seafloor spreading, wherein some of the cracks separating plates coincide with the rift valleys running the length of submarine mountain chains (for example, Mid-Atlantic Ridge, East Pacific Rise, Indian Ridge). In the rift valley, molten rock from the earth's interior forces its way to the surface (causing earthquakes) where it cools, forms new oceanic crust, and pushes previously existing oceanic crust to either side. The result in the Atlantic is that the ocean basin is getting larger, while North America moves away from Europe, and

South America moves away from Africa (at a rate of about 5 centimeters every year).

Among the implications of this theory were that oceanic crust near the ridges should be very young and get older as one takes samples nearer the continents. In addition, there should be a very thin sediment cover on oceanic crust near the ridge (reflecting the fact that it has not been there long enough to collect much) and thicker near the continents. All these speculations were testable with the ability to obtain sediment and oceanic crust samples, preferably cores, from any location in the ocean.

The compelling arguments of earth scientists convinced the National Science Foundation to support the voyages of the *Glomar Challenger. Challenger* was essentially an oil drilling platform attached to an oceangoing ship. The crew consisted of the ship's crew, who were responsible for operations (from cooking meals to operating the drilling equipment), and a scientific crew, who were to establish and oversee the technical objectives of each cruise. The first cruise in the Atlantic (actually the second leg of a journey that began in the Gulf of Mexico) confirmed the broad outlines of the seafloor spreading hypothesis. Samples of sediments, their associated fossils, and oceanic crust were retrieved and confirmed the basic "aging"-of-oceanic-crust aspect of the hypothesis. The wealth of samples brought back to academic laboratories, however, initiated new studies and spawned a whole new series of questions regarding the details of the historical record preserved in the sediments. In addition, the samples of oceanic crust revealed evidence of reactions between the rocks and hot water (hydrothermal systems similar to hot springs on continents). It became apparent that with each new cruise of the *Challenger,* analyses of the data would indicate the need for more voyages.

Over the next fifteen years, *Glomar Challenger* crisscrossed the oceans, mapping the topography with sophisticated sonar and seismic techniques, collecting core samples, and taking water column samples and measurements. In the early 1980's, *Challenger* was retired and replaced by a larger ship, the *Glomar Explorer.*

Impact of Event

Each of the cruises of the *Glomar Challenger* was, for the earth science community, the equivalent of a moon shot. The samples returned to shore-based laboratories were from a remote and largely unexplored portion of the earth's surface. The technologies needed to retrieve and analyze the samples were continually evolving. In the early days of the project, the samples were so limited and precious that they were doled out in minute quantities to researchers.

As more and more samples were analyzed, subsequent cruises were designed to explore areas of the ocean that would likely provide key pieces of evidence. The skeletons of seafloor spreading and plate tectonics were fleshed out and modified as the results of each cruise were analyzed by the scientific community.

By the time *Challenger* was retired, the general outlines of ocean basin topography were well known to most of the public. Maps of submarine topography, illustrating the "alligator back" look of the Mid-Atlantic Ridge, were frequently published in popular scientific publications. Plate tectonics became the accepted explanation for the functioning of the earth. The theory explained the connection between the submarine topography of the relatively shallow ridges and the greatest depths of the oceans in trenches. Both are plate boundaries but with totally different functions. New ocean crust is formed at ridges and old ocean crust is pushed back into the earth's interior (and remelted) at trenches. Plate tectonics explained localized areas of earthquake and volcanic activity on land. For example, Japan is both volcanically active and subject to earthquakes because it overlies a plate boundary where old oceanic crust is being forced back into the earth. Similarly active areas are found in the Pacific Northwest of the United States (Oregon and Washington) and along the Pacific coast of South America (Ecuador, Peru, and Chile).

The theories of seafloor spreading and plate tectonics were not developed in a straight line. Many lines of evidence needed to be synthesized over many years. Someone recognized that technologies developed for one application (for example, gravity meters, satellite navigation, heat probes, radiometric dating) could be applied to research-driven ocean exploration. When the theories became testable and the necessary technologies were available, they all came together aboard the *Glomar Challenger.*

Bibliography

Briggs, Peter. *200,000,000 Years Beneath the Sea.* New York: Holt, Rinehart and Winston, 1971. An excellent text that traces the details of the early years of the Deep Sea Drilling Project wherein *Challenger* became the workhorse. Briggs provides an anecdotal history rich with the details of early successes and the early frustrations and failures. Especially interesting is Briggs's accounts of how the early results were received by some entrenched interests in the scientific community. There are a few good illustrations, a brief bibliography, and a good subject index. A highly recommended starting point for any interested reader.

Heezen, Bruce C., and Ian D. MacGregor. "The Evolution of the Pacific." *Scientific American* 229 (November, 1973): 102-112. A good summary article of early concepts in plate tectonics as applied to the Pacific Ocean. The data used in this analysis are largely derived from *Challenger* cores. The discussion begins with some historical background but quickly gets into the technical details. The illustrations are helpful, but the lay reader may find the details a bit daunting. The authors call on a wide range of data, including marine chemistry and paleomagnetics, which are handled well but perhaps are beyond many college-level readers. Includes a very brief bibliography.

Hsu, Kenneth J. *The Mediterranean Was a Desert: A Voyage of the Glomar Challenger.* Princeton, N.J.: Princeton University Press, 1983. An updated and more complete version of the story Hsu began in the *Scientific American* article (cited below). Hsu paints a vivid picture of life on board *Challenger* and the trials and tribulations of the chief scientist responsible for bringing this expensive venture into an area to test his hypothesis. Contains a glossary of terms, a brief list of suggested further readings, and a good subject index.

_____. "When the Mediterranean Dried Up." *Scientific American* 227 (December, 1972): 26-36. A very readable account of Hsu's application of the scientific method to evaluate various lines of data and arrive at a testable hypothesis. The test required the use of *Glomar Challenger* to drill into and retrieve sediments from the floor of the Mediterranean Sea. Those sediments provided the evidence Hsu needed to speculate on the period of time when the sea was closed off from the Atlantic and dried up. The details of the hypothesis are still being debated, but this article presents an excellent account of how science is done.

Sclater, John G., and Christopher Tapscott. "The History of the Atlantic." *Scientific American* 240 (June, 1979): 156-174. This article provides an interesting comparison with the earlier cited Heezen article. The understanding of the functioning of plate tectonics is the foundation of both articles and it is interesting to compare the level of explanation possible with the advantage of another decade of data from *Challenger*. Again, the authors call on several lines of data, especially heat flow data, which may be somewhat difficult for some readers to follow. There is a minuscule bibliography that cites technical literature.

Valentine, James W., and Eldridge M. Moores. "Plate Tectonics and the History of Life in the Oceans." *Scientific American* 230 (April, 1974): 80-89. The authors extrapolate from plate tectonics and the fact that the sizes and shapes of the ocean basins have changed, to the effect this might have on ocean circulation patterns and biological evolution. A good example of the way plate tectonics and the data from the *Challenger* voyages required rethinking of the basic understandings in many fields. A good article for the biologically inclined technical reader. Brief bibliography.

Richard W. Arnseth

Cross-References

Wegener Proposes the Theory of Continental Drift (1912), p. 522; The German *Meteor* Expedition Discovers the Midatlantic Ridge (1925), p. 805; Cousteau and Gagnan Develop the Aqualung (1943), p. 1219; Heezen and Ewing Discover the Midoceanic Ridge (1956), p. 1508; Hess Concludes the Debate on Continental Drift (1960), p. 1650; The Sealab 2 Expedition Concludes (1965), p. 1792; Deep-Sea Hydrothermal Vents and New Life-Forms Are Discovered (1977), p. 2058.

WHEELER NAMES THE PHENOMENON "BLACK HOLES"

Categories of event: Physics and astronomy
Time: 1968
Locale: Princeton, New Jersey

In a paper relating to the collapse of massive stars, Wheeler referred to the resulting point mass as a black hole, since no light or radiation could escape its gravity

Principal personages:

JOHN ARCHIBALD WHEELER (1911-   ), an American physicist and professor who studied general relativity and gravity

KARL SCHWARZSCHILD (1873-1916), a German physicist and astronomer who studied the gravitational effects of Einstein's relativity theory

ALBERT EINSTEIN (1879-1955), a German-American physicist whose relativity theory stimulated extensive research and made him the most popular scientist of the twentieth century

J. ROBERT OPPENHEIMER (1904-1967), an American physicist most familiar for his work with the development of the atomic bomb and who published a paper on gravitational collapse

Summary of Event

In the spring of 1968, John Archibald Wheeler published an article that appeared in both *The American Scholar* and *The American Scientist* in which he used the term "black hole" for the first time. He had become convinced that the mechanism used to hypothesize that stellar collapse could proceed only so far before encountering physical barriers was inadequate to prevent total collapse. He proposed that total collapse into a "singularity" (no size, infinite density) would not allow any light to escape, hence the term "black hole."

Wheeler has enjoyed an exceptionally long and productive career in theoretical physics. His skills as a classroom teacher are legendary. He completed a Ph.D. at the age of twenty-two. After a year of study with Niels Bohr in Copenhagen, he taught at the University of North Carolina before moving to Princeton University in 1938. He collaborated with many of the most significant physicists of the twentieth century. In 1929, in association with Bohr, he published the definitive statement of the theory of fission and predicted the undiscovered plutonium 239 as a synthesizable isotope that would be useful in nuclear weapons. He was the leader of a research group that developed the methods for controlling a nuclear reactor by preparing for "poisoning" by fission products that would absorb the bombarding neutrons. His work in nuclear particle physics resulted in the prediction of polyelectrons, composed of clusters of three or more electrons. In 1949 and 1950, he joined Edward Teller and others to develop the hydrogen bomb. He proposed, in 1953, the "collective" model of the atomic nucleus, a many-particled kinematic version of the functioning of the atomic nucleus. He then studied general relativity, which he called geometrodynamics, exploring the relation between field theory and particle physics.

Wheeler found gravitational collapse the most interesting link between particle physics and the theory of gravitation as expressed in general relativity. Since the publication of Karl Schwarzschild's study completed during World War I, months after Albert Einstein published the theory of general relativity, it had been suspected that a sufficiently large mass of dense matter should be unable to avoid collapse. Little, however, was known of the behavior of matter at extremely high pressure. Wheeler investigated matter and radiation mixtures. By 1954, he was evaluating pure gravitational-electromagnetic entities called "geons," which were stable against the loss of photons. Wheeler's geons possessed energy and thus mass, yet there was no place one could say the mass exists in space-time. He thereby gave classical relativity theory a new comprehensiveness and laid the foundation for the study of gravitational waves.

In 1955, Wheeler proposed "wormholes" with electric lines of force that produced a different explanation of electrical charge. He pressed the position that space is not described by any single geometry but by different geometries under differing conditions which resonate with one another. By 1957, he published a paper with a technique for matching two different space-time geometries. That same year, he published the pioneering analysis of the pulsation and stability of black holes. This work culminated in the publication of geometrodynamics in 1962.

Super-space built Wheeler's reputation as an authority in gravitational studies and contributed to his successful proposal of black holes as the appropriate name for collapsed objects. He indicated that space only looks flat from a distance. At close range, however, it is a chaotic froth. He speculated that the physical constants could be reset with different values at each successive collapse and big bang, for he believed that there was sufficient mass in the universe to generate an eventual collapse. He further suggested that life might be unique to this particular cycle.

In late 1915, Schwarzschild had investigated the geometry of space-time near massive objects. For a star of any given mass, there is a radius such that if the star becomes smaller, it separates itself from surrounding space-time. Objects could enter inside this radius, but nothing could exit. Schwarzschild's radius or "event horizon" became part of theoretical astrophysics, but whether real stars collapsed was unknown.

In 1939, J. Robert Oppenheimer, George Michael Volkoff, and Hartland Snyder published a paper in the *Physical Review* demonstrating that a mass about three times that of the sun would continue to collapse beyond a white dwarf or a neutron star to a singularity. All that would persist was its gravitation. Yet, physicists doubted that such a bizarre result could be reality, so they searched for a mechanism that would prevent collapse. By 1967, pulsars had been discovered, those mysterious rapidly rotating and emitting objects. The proposed solution was collapsed rotating objects called neutron stars by Thomas Gold in 1968.

The possible collapse into an object so dense that no radiation escapes was aptly named a black hole. Previously, the black hole was variously identified as a Schwarzschild singularity, a collapsed star, or a frozen star. These names focused upon optical appearances outside the event horizon. For Wheeler, the event horizon became the surface of the black hole and the external geometry the gravitational field of the black hole. Wheeler never indicated that he was giving it a new name. He simply wrote as if that is what it had always been called, and others followed suit. (In the 1970's, black holes captured public attention, assisted by a general fascination with disaster. The black hole represented the ultimate disaster.)

Wheeler continued his studies of black holes and was among the pioneers who established that black holes were very simple objects, having only mass, electric charge, and a rate of spin. Theoretical work centered around two issues: Were there physical conditions in the universe that would lead to black holes, and would they be stable? Others firmly established that there were many large enough stars and that no effective explanation to avoid collapse had been found. Stability was a more difficult issue, for many physicists believed that a black hole would fall apart if there were perturbations in its surface or motions. Others argued that a black hole would not form if the star was not spherical. Wheeler and his associates calculated away these and other difficulties. Black holes began to appear as inevitable, potential sources of great energy in the centers of galaxies. The search was launched to find them, with Wheeler suggesting many ways they could be identified by their gravitational effects and the release of energy as they captured mass before the event horizon was reached.

Impact of Event

John Archibald Wheeler is a major figure in twentieth century particle and gravitational physics. Along with Schwarzschild, Oppenheimer, Roy Kerr, and Stephen W. Hawking, he stands as a pioneer in the understanding and theory of black holes. Among the most significant contributions Wheeler made was breaking down the psychological barrier that exists for scientists and public alike to believe in something that has an esoteric name. By giving the singularity a common name like black hole, Wheeler put it within reach and made acceptance of the unusual theoretical results easier.

Wheeler's timing was also impeccable. While Wheeler and many others, especially Hawking, had been studying singularities for several years immediately after the radio discovery of the pulsars and their explanation in terms of neutron stars, the total collapse into singularities was the next logical step. By giving these objects a catchy name, Wheeler was able to bring them to attention and start the massive outpouring of interest that followed.

Black holes provide clues to the resolution of outstanding difficulties in cosmology. They have been proposed as explanations of the missing mass needed to bring the mass of the universe to a level where the expansion will be slow and eventually reverse into the next phase of collapse. They have been proposed as a source of the massive energy outpouring of the quasars. Further, they appear to hold significant implications for studies in the field of general relativity. Wheeler has pioneered in seeking a theory that would combine quantum physics and general relativity into a theory of quantum gravity, a first step in formulating the long-sought unified field theory in relativity studies. At the present time, relativistic equations break down when confronted with the infinite forces and gravity of a singularity.

The most fruitful consequence of the naming and study of black holes has been the significant research stimulated by the effort to find black holes. While incontrovertible proof is not yet available, Cygnus X-1 and two or three other dynamical doubles where objects on the order of 10 solar masses are invisible are circumstantial candidates for status as black holes. The search to strengthen the evidence continues, and exciting results will continue to develop.

Bibliography

Bartusiak, Marcia. *Thursday's Universe.* New York: Times Books, 1986. Chapter 3 contains an excellent summary of the theory of black holes in understandable language. Wheeler's theoretical work is placed in historical and theoretical context.

Harrison, Edward R. *Cosmology, the Science of the Universe.* Cambridge, England: Cambridge University Press, 1981. A remarkably comprehensive perspective that includes both history and theory of cosmology. The work of Wheeler, while not prominent, is placed wonderfully and colorfully in context. Harrison, another Wheeler collaborator, reflects much of Wheeler's style in his own.

Klauder, John R., ed. *Magic Without Magic: John Archibald Wheeler.* San Francisco: W. H. Freeman, 1971. A collection of essays honoring Wheeler's sixtieth birthday in 1971. The introduction is a fascinating biographical sketch well worth the reading. The essay on pages 475 to 485 treats with almost reverential awe another aspect of Wheeler's career and collaboration.

Misner, Charles W., Kip S. Thorne, and John A. Wheeler. *Gravitation.* San Francisco: W. H. Freeman, 1971. Although technical, it should be scanned to get a feel for how mathematical this subject is, how much can be said, and how complicated the theory is. Pages 619 to 939 contain scattered historical notes including a delightful dialogue on pages 872 to 875 indicating why the black hole is aptly named.

Thorne, Kip S., and Wojciech H. Zurek. "John Archibald Wheeler: A Few Highlights of His Contributions to Physics." *Foundations of Physics* 16 (February, 1986): 79-86. Consists of a collection of significant quotes from Wheeler's published works demonstrating points at which he made contributions. There are illuminating comments by the authors on the meaning of the quotations.

Wheeler, John Archibald. "Our Universe: The Known and the Unknown." *The American Scholar* 37 (Spring, 1968): 248-274. The famous paper in which he named the black hole. An excellent summary of the state of cosmology in 1968 that touched upon a number of controversial issues in a balanced fashion.

Ivan L. Zabilka

Cross-References

Bohr Writes a Trilogy on Atomic and Molecular Structure (1912), p. 507; Einstein Completes His Theory of General Relativity (1915), p. 625; Schwarzschild Develops a Solution to the Equations of General Relativity (1916), p. 630, Oppenheimer Calculates the Nature of Black Holes (1939), p. 1150; Bell Discovers Pulsars, the Key to Neutron Stars (1967), p. 1862.

BUBBLE MEMORY DEVICES ARE CREATED
FOR USE IN COMPUTERS

Category of event: Applied science
Time: 1969
Locale: Murray Hill, New Jersey

Building on discoveries of the properties of certain ferrimagnetic materials under an applied magnetic field, scientists began to explore the use of these substances for the storage of computer information, leading to commercial products in the late 1970's

Principal personage:
ANDREW H. BOBECK (1926-   ), a Bell Telephone Laboratory scientist who, in 1967, first described the properties and potential device applications of magnetic bubbles

Summary of Event

The fanfare over the commercial prospects of magnetic bubbles ignited in the public domain on August 8, 1969, from a report appearing in both *The New York Times* and the *Wall Street Journal*. The early 1970's would see the flames spread (at least in the computer world) with each prognostication of the benefits of this revolution in information storage technology.

By the late 1970's, however, it was apparent even to diehard advocates that magnetic bubble technology, although sound in theory, would need to benefit from further innovation in the laboratory before conquering the world of computer data storage. It became a victim of high production costs coupled with low reliability as well as the dramatic gains in performance and cost-benefit ratios of competing conventional storage technologies. A few flickers of research shone at a diminishing number of industrial research and development laboratories in the 1980's, mostly in Japan.

Although a new disclosure to the public at large that August day in 1969, magnetic bubble technology had held the technical interest of a small group of researchers around the world for many years. The laboratory that probably can claim the greatest research advances with respect to computer applications of magnetic bubbles is Bell Telephone Laboratories (later part of American Telephone and Telegraph). Basic research into the properties of certain ferrimagnetic materials started at Bell Laboratories shortly after the end of World War II. Ferrimagnetic substances are typically magnetic iron oxides. Research into the properties of these and related compounds accelerated after the discovery of ferrimagnetic garnets in 1956 (these are a class of ferrimagnetic oxide materials that have the crystal structure of garnet). Ferrimagnetism is similar to ferromagnetism, the phenomenon that accounts for the strong attraction of one magnetized body for another. The ferrimagnetic materials most suited for bubble memories contain, in addition to iron, the element yttrium or a metal from the rare earth series.

It is an interesting story of fruitful collaboration between scientist and engineer, between pure and applied science, that produced this promising breakthrough in data storage technology. In 1966, Bell Laboratories' scientist Andrew H. Bobeck and his coworkers were the first to realize the data storage potential offered by the strange behavior of thin slices of magnetic iron oxides under an applied magnetic field. The first United States patent for a memory device using magnetic bubbles was filed by Bobeck in the fall of 1966 and issued on August 5, 1969. It is important to recognize the collaborative nature of this work and the contributions of many of Bobeck's colleagues.

The three basic functional elements of a computer are the central processing unit (CPU), input and output (I/O), and memory. Memory is further categorized into two types: primary (typically semiconductor-chip-resident memory used by the computer for essential operations of the system software and for user applications) and secondary (additional memory used for mass storage and archival purposes). Another distinction that can be drawn between primary and secondary memory is volatility. Most implementations of semiconductor memory require a constant power source to retain the stored data. If the power is turned off, all stored data are lost. Memory with this characteristic is called volatile. Disk and tape, typically used for secondary memory, are nonvolatile. Here memory does not rely on electrical currents to sustain its existence, but on the orientation of magnetic domains.

One can visualize by analogy how this will work by taking a group of permanent bar magnets that are labeled with N for north at one end and S for south at the other. If an arrow is painted starting from the north end with the tip at the south end on each magnet, an orientation can then be assigned to a magnetic domain (here one whole bar magnet). Data are "stored" with these bar magnets by arranging them in a row, some pointing up, some pointing down. Different arrangements translate to different data. In the binary world of the computer, all information is represented by two states. A stored data item (known as a "bit," standing for binary digit) is either on or off, up or down, true or false, depending on the physical representation. The on state is commonly labeled with the number 1 and the off state with the number 0. This is the principle behind magnetic disk and tape data storage.

Now imagine a thin slice of a certain type of magnetic material in the shape of a 3-by-5-inch index card. Under a microscope, using a special source of light, one can see through this thin slice in many regions of the surface. Darker, snakelike regions can also be seen, representing domains of an opposite orientation (polarity) to the transparent regions. If a weak external magnetic field is then applied by placing a permanent magnet of the same shape as the card on the underside of the slice, a strange thing happens to the dark serpentine pattern—the long domains shrink and eventually contract into "bubbles," tiny magnetized spots. Viewed from the side of the slice, the bubbles are cylindrically shaped domains having a polarity opposite to that of the material on which they rest. The presence or absence of a bubble indicates a 0 or 1 bit. Data bits are stored by moving the bubbles in the thin film. As long as the field is applied by the permanent magnet substrate, the data will be retained. The bubble is thus a nonvolatile medium for data storage.

Essentially, magnetic bubble memory is the fully electronic analog to disk or tape memory. Conceivably, this device could replace both primary and secondary memory. A computer system needs quick access to data stored in primary memory, and this is provided by bubble memory because it is electronic and not electromechanical, which is the basic mechanism for disk and tape technology. The property of nonvolatility qualifies bubble memory as a secondary or archival storage medium (at least for small to moderate storage needs). As with any engineering solution, there are trade-offs. Bubble memory is not as fast as semiconductor-based memory. One reason is that bubble memory is inherently a serial device in organization. The bubbles are stored on several paths called loops, and a rotating weak magnetic field applied at right angles to the direction of magnetization of the bubbles causes the bubbles (and lack of bubbles, called "holes") to migrate around the loops. An organizational grid of patterns is superimposed on the surface of the substrate upon which the bubbles rest to create storage locations and enable orderly tracking of the bubbles along loops (or tracks) in the medium. Access time will vary with the migration rate and the number of storage locations being addressed.

Impact of Event

Magnetic bubble memory created quite a stir in 1969 with its splashy public introduction. Most of the chip manufacturer research and development laboratories immediately instituted bubble memory development projects. Texas Instruments, Philips, Hitachi, Motorola, Fujitsu, and International Business Machines (IBM) joined the race with Bell Laboratories to mass-produce bubble memory chips. Texas Instruments became the first major chip manufacturer to mass-produce bubble memories in the mid- to late 1970's. By 1990, however, almost all the research into magnetic bubble technology had shifted to Japan. Hitachi and Fujitsu continue to invest heavily in this area.

Mass production proved to be the most difficult task. Although the materials are different, the process to produce magnetic bubble memory chips is similar to that for semiconductor-based chips such as RAM (random access memory). It is for this reason that major semiconductor manufacturers and computer companies initially invested in this technology. Lower fabrication yields and reliability issues plagued early production runs, however, and, although these problems have mostly been solved, gains in the performance characteristics of competing conventional memory have limited the impact that magnetic bubble technology has had on the marketplace. The materials used for magnetic bubble memories are costlier and possess more complicated structures than those used for semiconductor or disk memory.

Speed and cost of materials are not the only bases for comparison. It is possible to perform some elementary logic with the bubbles. Conventional semiconductor-based memory offers storage only. The capability to perform logic with magnetic bubbles propels bubble technology far beyond any other magnetic technology with respect to functional versatility. Although disk and tape technologies offer the same nonvolatility and rewriteability features as magnetic bubble memory, and greater capacity at a lower cost per bit of storage, they come up short with respect to access time, reliability, and convenience of packaging. Semiconductor-based memory offers tremendous speed and a refined integrated circuit fabrication process that yields low-cost, highly reliable packages. Magnetic bubble memories are packaged as chips, similar to the packaging of semiconductor memories or logic gates. This is much more convenient than disk or tape solutions that require drive units. Also, removable magnetic bubble cartridges have been introduced. Furthermore, since there are no moving mechanical parts, bubble memory is inherently more reliable. Simple interfaces to the memory have been developed that compare favorably to the control logic necessary for disk or tape technology.

A small niche market developed in the 1980's. Magnetic bubble memory can be found in intelligent terminals, desktop computers, embedded systems, test equipment, and other, similar microcomputer-based systems. It seems best suited for applications in which a small amount of secondary memory is needed—on the order of a few megabytes (a byte is a group of eight bits; a megabyte is a group of a million bytes). In summary, the short history of magnetic bubble technology can be characterized in terms of ten-year periods, with the 1950's and 1960's as decades of discovery, basic science, and theoretical refinement; the 1970's as a period of industrial investment and experimenting, leading to mass production; and the 1980's as a time of dwindling impact, a retreat to the laboratory for further innovation.

Bibliography

Bobeck, Andrew H., and H. E. D. Scovil. "Magnetic Bubbles." *Scientific American* 224 (June, 1971): 78-90. An excellent introduction to the topic of magnetic bubbles by two of the original investigators. Thorough in its explanations of the physics of magnetic domains underlying this technology and accompanied by many good diagrams and photographs. Any study of the subject should start here.

Chang, Hsu, ed. *Magnetic Bubble Technology: Integrated-Circuit Magnetics for Digital Storage and Processing*. New York: IEEE Press, 1975. Prepared under the sponsorship of the IEEE Magnetics Society; presents an overview of bubble technology (history, devices, applications, physics, and materials), followed by a compilation of reprinted articles from scientific journals or conferences published from 1971 to 1974. Also contains a complete (1950 to 1974) bibliography of published articles on magnetic bubbles and a list of issued United States patents on bubble domain devices from 1960 to 1974.

Eschenfelder, A. H. *Magnetic Bubble Technology*. 2d ed. New York: Springer-Verlag, 1981. Designed as a supplementary text for a semester course in either solid-state physics or materials science. The reader is expected to have had some background in physics and mathematics at the college junior to senior level. Chapter 1 provides a good overview of the field and is accessible to the general reader.

Hodges, David A. "Microelectronic Memories." *Scientific American* 237 (September, 1977): 130-145. Another excellent review of the state of the art (in 1977) in information storage technology. Part of a dedicated issue on the topic of microelectronics, this article offers a complete picture of the multiple alternative primary memory technologies, along with magnetic bubbles. Highly recommended.

Triebel, Walter A., and Alfred E. Chu. *Handbook of Semiconductor and Bubble Memories.* Englewood Cliffs, N.J.: Prentice-Hall, 1982. Intended as a reference work for practicing engineers and technicians. Contains valuable in-depth information not found in other books on microprocessors or digital electronics. Chapter 1 provides an excellent overview of the subject, and chapter 10 is on magnetic bubble memories. Highly recommended.

Paul G. Nyce

Cross-References

UNIVAC I Becomes the First Commercial Electronic Computer and the First to Use Magnetic Tape (1951), p. 1396; Esaki Demonstrates Electron Tunneling in Semiconductors (1957), p. 1551; The Floppy Disk Is Introduced for Storing Data Used by Computers (1970), p. 1923; The Microprocessor "Computer on a Chip" Is Introduced (1971), p. 1938; IBM Introduces a Personal Computer with a Standard Hard Disk Drive (1983), p. 2240; Optical Disks for the Storage of Computer Data Are Introduced (1984), p. 2262.

THE SOYUZ 4 AND 5 SPACECRAFT DOCK IN ORBIT

Category of event: Space and aviation
Time: 1969
Locale: Earth orbit

By pioneering the manual docking and crew transfer of a two-manned spacecraft, the Soyuz 4 and 5 mission revealed a key Soviet policy shift favoring orbital space stations

Principal personages:

VLADIMIR A. SHATALOV (1927-   ), a colonel in the Red Air Force who was the command pilot of Soyuz 4 and commander of the Soyuz 4 and 5 mission

BORIS V. VOLYNOV (1934-   ), a lieutenant colonel in the Red Air Force who served as the command pilot of the Soyuz 5 spacecraft during the Soyuz 4 and 5 mission

YEVGENI V. KHRUNOV (1933-   ), a lieutenant colonel in the Red Air Force who was the engineer pilot for both the Soyuz 4 and Soyuz 5, and transferred from Soyuz 5 to Soyuz 4 during the docking of the two spacecraft

ALEXEI S. YELISEYEV (1934-   ), the technical scientist for both the Soyuz 4 and Soyuz 5 who transferred from Soyuz 5 to Soyuz 4 during their docking exercise

Summary of Event

On January 16, 1969, two manned Soviet spacecraft, Soyuz (Union) 4 and Soyuz 5, docked in orbit. The ships remained connected for four hours and thirty-five minutes, while two cosmonauts emerged from Soyuz 5, performed a limited number of exterior tasks, and entered Soyuz 4. After separation, both vehicles conducted additional experiments before returning safely to Earth. The Soyuz 4 and 5 mission achieved the first docking of two manned ships and the first transfer of crew members to an already-occupied vessel. It also signaled a Soviet policy shift from lunar circumnavigation to orbital space stations.

The mission began at 10:39 A.M. (Moscow time) on January 14, 1969, when Soyuz 4 was launched from the Tyuratam missile complex near Leninsk in the Soviet republic of Kazakhstan. The A-2 launch vehicle, a modified intercontinental ballistic missile, placed the 6.6-metric-ton Soyuz spacecraft into an orbit that was 225 kilometers at its farthest point from Earth's surface (the apogee) and 173 kilometers at its nearest point (the perigee). With Colonel Vladimir A. Shatalov, the command pilot, on board, Soyuz 4 circled the globe every 88.2 minutes, its orbit intersecting the equator at a 51.7 degree angle.

The spacecraft was an upgraded version of a type that had been in manned use since 1967. Soyuz 4 was cylindrical at the rear (where the service and propulsion elements were housed) and rounded forward. Its front end was divided further into bell-shaped command and spherical work compartments connected by an air lock. Its work compartment contained an exit hatch and an active docking mechanism— that is, a metal probe that could be inserted and locked into the matching receptacle of a second spacecraft. The combined length of the compartments was about 5 meters, with a total volume of approximately 9 cubic meters. The ship's electrical system was powered by two sets of solar panels mounted toward the back. The spacecraft was aerodynamically modified to allow some maneuvering at descent and had sufficient lift to reduce the force of gravity to three or four times normal from the eight or nine typical of ballistic reentries. It was also provided with duplicate 400-kilogram-thrust liquid rocket engines and multiple parachutes for soft-landing capability and had an enhanced capacity to land in water.

The Soviet news services reported the launch promptly; by 11:30 A.M., a video recording of the event was shown on Moscow television; live television coverage from Soyuz 4 accompanied by Shatalov's commentary was aired by noon. Observers long accustomed to the operational security surrounding Soviet space activities knew immediately that a politically significant mission was under way. When Shatalov adjusted his orbit to between 207 and 237 kilometers, there was widespread speculation that a rendezvous with a second spacecraft would take place shortly. A television transmission that revealed two empty seats in Shatalov's spacecraft stirred further conjectures that a transfer of personnel from one spacecraft to another might occur also.

The accuracy of those deductions was soon verified. At 9:46 A.M. on January 15, 1969, Soyuz 5 was launched on a matching orbital path with an almost identical apogee, perigee, and orbital period. The second Soyuz spacecraft—a twin of the first except for its recessed, or passive, docking mechanism—carried three crew members: Lieutenant Colonel Boris V. Volynov, the command pilot; Alexei S. Yeliseyev, the technical scientist; and Lieutenant Colonel Yevgeni V. Khrunov, the engineer pilot. As soon as Soyuz 5 went into orbit, both ships' automatic systems began a series of small positional corrections. By Soyuz 5's eighteenth orbit and Soyuz 4's thirty-fourth orbit, the sequence of automated adjustments brought the two spacecraft within 100 meters of each other. Shatalov, the commander of the active vessel and the overall mission commander, then manually aligned his ship with its partner and completed the docking exercise. At 11:20 A.M., on January 16, the two spacecraft were joined mechanically and electrically and were able to act as a single unit. Although the four crew members were unable to pass from one vessel to another through the docking apparatus, an 18-cubic-meter working area consisting of four compartments was established. The Soviet press described it as the world's first experimental space station.

Khrunov and Yeliseyev then put on spacesuits and life packs, depressurized the work compartment of Soyuz 5, and passed through the external hatch. The two cosmonauts remained outside the combined spacecraft for about thirty-five minutes, attached to safety cords and using handrails to move about. Observed by the television cameras installed for the benefit of Moscow viewers, they took photographs of Earth and celestial bodies, checked their spacesuits and regenerating life packs, and mimicked the assembly of components that would be required in a permanent orbital space station. Khrunov and Yeliseyev then entered the depressurized work compartment of Soyuz 4 through its external hatch, repressurized it, and joined Shatalov in the command compartment. The entire transfer operation, including the release and replenishment of air in the two work compartments, took about one hour. Soyuz 4, which had left Earth with one crew member on board, now had three. Soyuz 5, which had lifted off with a crew of three, now had one. At 3:55 P.M., after four hours and thirty-five minutes of docking, the two spacecraft uncoupled and continued their flight paths in tandem.

The remainder of the Soyuz 4 and 5 mission was occupied with rest periods alternating with system checks, medical experiments, and terrestrial and celestial observations. Shortly before 9:00 A.M., on January 17, Shatalov began the descent sequence for Soyuz 4; within the hour, the three cosmonauts landed safely in the Kazakh uplands approximately 40 kilometers northwest of Karaganda. Shatalov described the landing as exceptionally soft and trouble-free. Soyuz 4 returned to Earth on its forty-eighth orbit after a flight time of seventy-one hours and fifteen minutes.

Volynov, left in sole occupation of Soyuz 5, remained in space about twenty-six hours after the descent of Soyuz 4. Throughout the afternoon of January 17, he conducted television interviews, carried out additional medical tests and observations of Earth and heavenly bodies, and adjusted his spacecraft's orbit to 229 kilometers by 201 kilometers. Following a shortened rest period, Volynov then began the reentry process. At 11:00 A.M., on the morning of January 18, he landed safely at the edge of the Kazakh uplands about 200 kilometers southwest of Kustanai. Soyuz 5 ended its mission on its forty-ninth orbit, after a voyage lasting seventy-two hours and fifty-four minutes.

On January 19, 1969, the Soviet press summarized the major characteristics of the Soyuz 4 and 5 mission. These features included the successful completion of detection, maneuvers, rendezvous, and docking of the two spacecraft, creation of an inhabited experimental space station in orbit, transfer of two cosmonauts from one spacecraft to another, checking and testing of spacecraft systems and components, and conducting of scientific observations and experiments. Spokesmen for the Soviet Academy of Sciences laid particular emphasis upon the value of the crew transfer, stating that it had important implications for the supply, maintenance, replacement, or rescue of the crews of future manned orbital stations.

Impact of Event

The success of the Soyuz 4 and 5 mission gave the Soviet cosmonaut program a much-needed morale boost. Soviet-manned space exploration had been in disarray since the death of Colonel Vladimir Milhaylovich Komarov in the Soyuz 1 mission in April, 1967, and the only manned attempt since then (the Soyuz 2 and 3 mission in October, 1968) had been an operational disappointment. The Soyuz 4 and 5 mission promised to inaugurate a new, dynamic phase of the Soviet space program. The uncharacteristic winter launch and the prompt, thorough media coverage indicated that the Soviet leadership had gained complete confidence in the redesigned Soyuz spacecraft and its support mechanisms. The mission was also a significant event in the strenuous Soviet-American space rivalry of the 1960's, for it upstaged a manual docking and crew transfer by Apollo 9 astronauts in March of 1969.

While the Soyuz 4 and 5 mission was an obvious success, the magnitude of its technological achievements was unclear. Some Western analysts asserted that the linkup was not a true orbital space station. They pointed out that its orbit would have decayed in about ten days, that no part of a Soyuz craft could be left behind for future visits, and that linked compartments of a space station should have an internal docking tunnel. Others noted that docking maneuvers were not new: Two unmanned Soyuz spacecraft, Kosmos (Cosmos) 186 and 188, had performed automatic docking in October, 1967; and in April, 1968, another unmanned Soyuz spacecraft, Kosmos 212, docked automatically with an unmanned craft. Furthermore, an American docking of a manned spacecraft with a satellite had been accomplished in March, 1966, by the Gemini 8 mission, and a Gemini 10 crew member had performed a ship-to-ship spacewalk while inspecting a connected Agena satellite. Finally, the experiments and observations conducted by the Soyuz 4 and 5 mission were difficult to evaluate on their own merits, for they were part of a systematic, long-range research program. It was apparent, however, that the four Soviet cosmonauts performed their difficult sequential tasks with great competence and that the manual docking and transfer of crew members between two occupied spacecraft were important and original achievements.

The mission also signaled a long-term shift in the goals of the Soviet space program. Until the Soyuz 4 and 5 docking, Westerners assumed that the Soviet Union was preparing to send cosmonauts around the Moon. Soviet actions seemed to confirm that view: In September, 1968, Zond (Probe) 5, an unmanned Soyuz-like spacecraft, was dispatched on a lunar voyage; and in November, 1968, Zond 6 repeated the exercise with a reentry speed that could be tolerated by cosmonauts. The intent of the Soyuz 4 and 5 mission, however, was unmistakable. The Soviets had decided to concentrate on manned orbital space stations, with their undeniable scientific, military, and industrial attractions, and leave the first manned circumlunar flights to the United States. A well-established and well-funded set of priorities connects the Soyuz 4 and 5 mission to the increasingly significant and technologically sophisticated Salyut (Salute) and Mir (World) space stations of the 1970's and 1980's.

Bibliography

Bond, Peter R. *Heroes in Space: From Gagarin to Challenger.* New York: Basil Blackwell, 1987. An excellent, detailed treatment of the manned space missions of both the United States and the Soviet Union. Bond's work, which covers the Soyuz 4 and 5 mission in detail, is the best general treatment currently available.

This lengthy book contains diagrams, maps, notes, illustrations, an appendix of Soviet and American manned spaceflights, and an index.

Johnson, Nicholas L. *Handbook of Soviet Manned Space Flight*. San Diego: Univelt, 1980. Volume 48 in the American Astronautical Society's science and technology series is an excellent introduction to Soviet manned space missions from their beginnings through 1979. Johnson provides an in-depth treatment of the Soyuz 4 and 5 docking. Contains illustrations, charts, diagrams, notes, appendices listing launches and launch facilities, and an index.

Lewis, John S. *Space Resources: Breaking the Bonds of Earth*. New York: Columbia University Press, 1987. This well-written popular work is a survey of space exploration to 1986, an overview of the technological factors affecting current American and Soviet space policies, and an extended argument in favor of the exploitation of space. It places the Soyuz flights in the context of all space missions. Contains an appendix of human-related launchings and an index.

Oberg, James E. *Red Star in Orbit*. New York: Random House, 1981. An unflattering treatment of the Soviet space program by an American space authority. Coverage of the Soyuz 4 and 5 mission is dismissive in tone. Includes illustrations, short biographies of cosmonauts, a list of Soviet-manned missions, an annotated bibliography and an index. For a wide audience.

Riabchikov, Evgeny. *Russians in Space*. Translated by Gay Daniels. Garden City, N.Y.: Doubleday, 1971. Presents the official viewpoint of the Soviet government regarding space exploration. While unabashedly partisan in orientation and argumentative in tone, it is well written and provides interesting anecdotes of the Soyuz 4 and 5 mission. The work contains some inaccuracies, however, and should be read with care. Some illustrations are included.

Smith, Marcia S. "The Evolving Role of Man in Space." In *The Space Station: An Idea Whose Time Has Come*, edited by Theodore R. Simpson. New York: Institute of Electrical and Electronics Engineers, 1985. An excellent overview of American and Soviet-manned space missions by a noted American authority. Reviews the competitive aspects of the space race without resorting to controversy. Smith emphasizes the development and uses of orbital space stations, thoroughly discussing the evolution of Soyuz spacecraft. Includes illustrations, charts, a bibliography, and an index.

Smolders, Peter L. *Soviets in Space*. New York: Taplinger, 1973. A laudatory treatment of the Soviet space program from its inception to the establishment of the Salyut space station. Somewhat polemical in tone but very detailed; it has a good treatment of the Soyuz 4 and 5 mission. Contains numerous illustrations and diagrams. An index is provided.

Michael J. Fontenot

Cross-References

Tsiolkovsky Proposes That Liquid Oxygen Be Used for Space Travel (1903),

p. 189; Goddard Launches the First Liquid Fuel Propelled Rocket (1926), p. 820; The First Rocket with More than One Stage Is Created (1949), p. 1342; Sputnik 1, the First Artificial Satellite, Is Launched (1957), p. 1545; Luna 2 Becomes the First Man-Made Object to Impact on the Moon (1959), p. 1614; Gagarin Becomes the First Human to Orbit Earth (1961), p. 1693; The First Space Walk Is Conducted from Voskhod 2 (1965), p. 1787; *Columbia*'s Second Flight Proves the Practicality of the Space Shuttle (1981), p. 2180; The First Permanently Manned Space Station is Launched (1986), p. 2316.

THE FIRST JUMBO JET SERVICE IS INTRODUCED

Category of event: Space and aviation
Time: 1969-1970
Locale: United States and Europe

The introduction of the jumbo jet, or wide-bodied aircraft service, especially for long-distance international travel, revolutionized air travel

Principal personages:
WILLIAM M. ALLEN (1900-   ), a top Boeing executive who was responsible for the earliest negotations leading to the development of the Boeing 747 jumbo jet
NAJEEB E. HALABY (1915-   ), a former test pilot and lawyer who, after joining Pan American Airways in 1965, assumed its presidency
JUAN TRIPPE, the Pan American Airways official who was responsible for commissioning the first order for construction of 747 jets for Pan American

Summary of Event

Between the late 1950's and 1970, travel by commercial jet aircraft over long distances had been limited to what the industry refers to as narrow-bodied planes. Such aircraft included the Boeing models 707 (inaugurated in 1959) and 727 (introduced in 1964), McDonnell Douglas' DC-8, and Lockheed's IL-62. Travel in such aircraft was limited not only by available passenger seating space but also by the amount of fuel that could be stored, mainly in storage tanks in the wings. Although long distances were traversed obviously by such airplanes prior to the introduction of the so-called jumbo jets, routes had to be planned with careful attention to refueling possibilities along the way. In terms of transatlantic flights from or to the United States, for example, direct flights originating or ending in noncoastal cities such as St. Louis or Chicago were rare.

William M. Allen was instrumental in negotiating the contracts for the development of the 747. Thus, when Boeing rolled its first 747 off the assembly line in Everett, Washington, on September 30, 1968, and began a vigorous series of tests, a new era in commercial air travel and cargo transport began. The 747's maiden flight on February 9, 1969, marked the beginning of about one thousand hours of testing carried out by five of the first aircraft set for delivery. It was not until December 13, 1969, that actual delivery was made to a commercial airline company—Pan American Airways. By that date, a full production schedule for 1970 was inaugurated, which provided for completion of one 747 every four and one-half working days.

Meanwhile, Boeing's main competitor, the McDonnell Douglas Company, was pressing its manufacturing efforts to bring its own wide-body jumbo jet—the

DC-10—onto the market. Manufacturing operations began on January 9, 1969. By the end of 1969, the first DC-10 was entering the final assembly (but pretesting) stage in Long Beach, California. The third U.S.-produced jumbo jet, the Lockheed L-1011, then being assembled in Burbank and Palmdale, California, was about a year behind the DC-10; plans for its first test flights were set for the end of 1970.

Boeing's 747 and the jumbo jets that were about to be inaugurated by other commercial companies had a number of impressive specifications that placed them in a category by themselves. The following comparisons show differences between the 747 and Boeing's 727, but they may be taken to reflect similar magnitudes of difference in other major air companies' jumbo jet models. The 747's wing span was 59 meters, 20 centimeters, and its overall length was 70 meters, 25 centimeters. By comparison, the 727's measurements were 33 meters (wingspan) and 41 meters, 5 centimeters (length). Internal passenger cabin width for the 747 was 6 meters. The jumbo jet's maximum ramp weight was more than 700,000 pounds gross. The 727 was well under 200,000 pounds.

The 747 was powered by four turbofan jets of 43,500 pounds thrust each, whereas the 727 was propelled by three 14,500-pound thrust turbofan jets. Passenger and/or cargo weight capacity was the major, immediately distinguishing feature in "new era" commercial aviation. The 747 could carry up to 490 passengers (or 220,000 pounds of cargo) at speeds exceeding 1,000 kilometers per hour. Its predecessor, the 727, carried between 131 and 180 passengers (depending on the submodel) or a cargo load of up to 46,600 pounds. The 727's maximum speed of 966 kilometers per hour was comparable to that of the massive new jumbo jet, but the latter's operating range of more than 6,400 kilometers clearly outdistanced the 727's range of 2,736 kilometers.

Whereas Pan American Airways (through the efforts of Najeeb E. Halaby) had the intention of building an operating fleet of some twenty-five Boeing 747 aircraft by the peak tourist season in mid-1970, Trans World Airlines (TWA) had plans for greater diversification in its jumbo jet fleet. TWA had placed orders for fifteen Boeing 747's in 1970 and twenty-two Lockheed L-1011's for delivery in 1971 and 1972.

About one hundred Boeing 747 aircraft were delivered during 1970. The prototype of the DC-10 flew in September, 1970, and that of the Lockheed L-1011 in November, 1970. Orders for the latter two jumbo jets with middle-range seating (about 350 passengers) by 1971 amounted to about four hundred aircraft. Larger-capacity models of the DC-10 and Lockheed L-1011 fully equipped for the long North Atlantic transit route were under production by that time, with deliveries planned for the following year.

Impact of Event

By the start of 1969, the International Air Transport Association (IATA) had met at its headquarters in Montreal, Canada, to discuss how the twenty-six IATA member airlines that had placed orders for the Boeing 747 would integrate jumbo jet service into existing patterns of air routes throughout the world. IATA had to consider, for example, if the airports at the various locations proposed for jumbo jet service were not only big enough, in terms of landing strip length, but also technically adequate. In cases where special adjustments would have to be made, IATA was to undertake the task of facilitating discussions among respective airlines, government air control authorities, and airport management organizations to determine if minimal requirements could and would be met in time for jumbo jet service to begin on schedule.

In its July, 1969, issue, the *International Civil Aviation Organization Bulletin* provided a list of some 106 airports in sixty-one countries or dependent territories around the world that had been identified as tentative "targets" for jumbo jet service by 1973. Of these, the United States headed the list, with seventeen prospective airports, followed by West Germany and Australia (with six and five prospective airports, respectively). Within six months, five more airports in six more countries were added. The January, 1970, listing also noted that scheduled dates for beginning service had been altered for some thirty-five airports.

The airline industry had to consider relative advantages and disadvantages of adding jumbo jets to their flying fleets. Positive and negative factors had to be weighed. In terms of overall reduction in airline costs for per-passenger service per kilometer, it appeared that approximately 13 percent savings over operating costs in the pre-jumbo-jet era could be realized by employing wide-body aircraft on key transit lines. This estimate attempted to take as many increased immediate incidental costs as possible into consideration. By contrast, probable longer-term benefits over existing "standard" aircraft could not be calculated yet. One of these benefits was the assumption that earlier, technically less efficient aircraft models would have to begin paying penalties for their failure to comply with noise level and pollution standards already introduced by legislative action in various countries. This would decrease their profitability over time.

On the other hand, factors were raised by representatives of less developed countries who found themselves on the IATA list of tentative "beneficiaries" of jumbo jet service but who lacked necessary economic resources to undertake the physical work of airport improvement that would be required. At the same time, transformation of technical services that each airport would have to provide for maintenance of jumbo jets implied a transformation of trained personnel—an added expense that some countries might not be able to meet. An overall estimate suggested that only 15 of 120 potentially targeted countries on IATA's jumbo jet service list either already had nearly sufficient physical plants for jumbo jet service or realistic economic possibilities for making necessary improvements in their airport facilities. In 1971, Mr. Ziya Kursunlu, manager of the Yesilkoy International Airport in Istanbul, Turkey, suggested that in order to avoid serious displacement of scarce investment funds needed by developing countries in other areas, such additional costs might be shared, not by the airlines themselves but by the giant companies engaged in manufacturing the jumbo jets that were scheduled to go into service.

Officials responsible for existing air terminals recognized that designation of their cities as part of the planned international jumbo jet network would involve runway extensions and expansion in the sheer number of passengers. Nearly five hundred passengers leaving jumbo carriers seeking to make connections with smaller aircraft might create bottleneck problems that had not existed previously.

Whereas factors of change such as these represented serious investment commitments by city or county airport authorities, the literature that accompanied the beginnings of jumbo jet service included predictions of profits. First, airport concessions could count on added profits stemming from a wide variety of transit passenger expenditures. More significant, however, was the question of future cooperative efforts between air carriers and local organizations responsible for regional tourism in areas that offered attractions not usually visited by travelers coming from very long distances. An example of entrepreneurial associations is the establishment of multimillion-dollar chains of International Hotels, Inc., following the initiative of Juan Trippe, the Pan American official who was closely involved in the acquisition of the company's first jumbo jets. Although touristic development of regional sites of interest could not pay for all costs that would be associated with such projects if they were undertaken by local government initiative, added sources of revenue would help to fill gaps.

Although predictions of a rapidly expanding role for air travel by jumbo jet were realized during the first half of the 1970's, at least two unpredicted factors soon came into play. Both were connected with political problems that erupted immediately before and after the 1973 Arab-Israeli war. First, passenger security—not merely technical safety—considerations rose exponentially in the early 1970's as major air routes suddenly became targets for international terrorism (specifically hijackings). Airport and in-flight antihijacking security measures became an integral part of the international aviation debit sheets. The second unexpected factor was the politicization of international oil market strategies in the wake of the 1973 Arab-Israeli war that led to petroleum price hikes. The passing on of much higher fuel costs to passengers did not stop air travel, but there was a noticeable reduction in the number of travelers able to pay the increased ticket prices that were inevitable.

Airlines possessing jumbo jets were thus forced to revise several strategies that had been taken for granted before the fuel cost crisis. First, if considerably fewer passengers booked flights on routes traveled by jumbo jets, the obvious factor of economies of scale was considerably reduced. This meant reductions in the number of transatlantic flights in order to ensure that the planes would be full enough to pay acceptable levels of profit. Another effect involved decisions to replace jumbo jets that had been used for flights within the United States and European continents with medium-sized aircraft. During the 1980's, this meant that existing fleets of aircraft of Boeing 707 and 727's were utilized more extensively than might have been predicted in the early 1970's. By 1990, Boeing had committed major planning efforts and funds to the development of a new model—the Boeing 777—designed to meet what had become a recognized need for a medium-sized, fuel-efficient, and technologically more sophisticated intercontinental aircraft.

Bibliography

The Boeing Company. *Pedigree of Champions: Boeing Since 1916.* 4th ed. Seattle: Boeing Company, 1977. Provides a panorama of the "stars" of Boeing's civil aviation fleets for more than half a century. Because the 747 jumbo jet was the most recently added major model when Boeing published this documentary edition, it received the most detailed treatment in the volume.

Davies, D. P. *Handling the Big Jets.* 3d ed. London: Civil Aviation Authority, 1973. A practical guidebook discussion of in-flight phenomena associated with large jet aircraft. It is of particular significance for its coverage of experiences that were only then being recorded by pilots and other technically trained personnel responsible for the newly introduced jumbo jets.

Gialloreto, Louis. *Strategic Airline Management: The Global War Begins.* London: Pitman, 1988. Examines the inner workings of the United States and international aviation marketplace, with emphasis on how airline fleets should be designed for maximum competitiveness according to a volatile and demanding market.

Green, William, and Gordon Swanborough. *An Illustrated Guide to the World's Airliners.* New York: Arco, 1982. This compact volume is among the most detailed manuals of civil aviation, containing specific data on airplanes produced by the major Western and Eastern European countries.

Sampson, Anthony. *Empires of the Sky.* New York: Random House, 1984. Part 1 covers the early history of civil aviation, whereas Part 2 discusses the effects of the coming of jumbo jets. These effects include deregulation in the industry, European cartels, and more.

Byron Cannon

Cross-References

The Wright Brothers Launch the First Successful Airplane (1903), p. 203; Blériot Makes the First Airplane Flight Across the English Channel (1909), p. 448; Lindbergh Makes the First Nonstop Solo Flight Across the Atlantic Ocean (1927), p. 841; The First Jet Plane Using Whittle's Engine Is Flown (1941), p. 1187; Rutan and Yeager Pilot the *Voyager* Around the World Without Refueling (1986), p. 2336.

VERY LONG BASELINE INTERFEROMETRY (VLBI) IS DEVELOPED FOR HIGH-RESOLUTION ASTRONOMY AND GEODESY

Category of event: Astronomy
Time: 1969-1974
Locale: United States

As an outgrowth of radio astronomy interferometry, VLBI enabled the first high-resolution observations of distant radio galaxies, as well as new accuracy levels for global navigation

> *Principal personages:*
> SIR MARTIN RYLE (1918-1984), an English radiophysicist and astronomer
> RONALD BRACEWELL (1919-   ), an Australian physicist
> IRWIN SHAPIRO (1929-   ), an American radiophysicist and astronomer

Summary of Event

Radio telescopes, like their optical counterparts, gather electromagnetic energy at a spatial focus in order to measure intensity, frequency, spatial distribution, polarization, and variability of single or multiple radiating sources. As was established early in the post-World War II era, in order to make radio astronomy measurements with spatial resolution comparable to that at optical wavelengths, the radio receiver must be larger by the ratio of radio to optical wavelengths. This results from the fact that the angular resolution of a radio telescope is basically set by the ratio of the wavelength of the dominant radiation received (lambda) to the diameter of the total receiving instrument D.

Precisely establishing the location and characteristics of diffuse radio objects required antennas with well-known detection patterns. To detect and measure accurately net emitted radiator flux, it is at first sight sufficient to employ a sufficiently large single antenna of geometrically simple design in order to have low side-lobes to reduce the risk of image distortion. This approach, however, is almost always precluded on meter radio wavelengths for mechanical as well as environmental and logistic reasons, since mechanically stable radio antennas cannot be constructed to sizes anywhere near 10 kilometers.

The concept of interference fringe visibility, first noted in radar, was applied to radio astronomy for solar measurements in 1946. From this, the notion was developed of combining concurrent radio measurements from a number of interferometer spacings to produce a contour map of the net distribution of radio emissions. It was soon realized that many electronically linked individual antennas, with tens or even hundreds of kilometers separation, can be formed into a single net receiver having a very large total baseline that, in some cases, could rival or exceed the theoretical resolution of the best optical telescopes. These notions were first discussed from a mathematical viewpoint by the Australian physicists L. McCready, J. L. Pawsey, and R. Payne-Scott about 1947, thereby underscoring the close relations between (radio) interferometry and aperture synthesis, and the Fourier transform (that is, the far and near field radio images being Fourier transforms of each other). Subsequent work in the 1950's showed that a radio interferometer could be used to measure directly the Fourier components of the radio brightness or luminosity distribution of radiating objects. Conceptually, an interferometer in radio astronomy includes two or more radio telescope receivers connected by cables in such a way that signals received by each can be combined later at a central point through signal processing to yield an interference pattern. In this context, interference refers to the fact that the signals from the multiple receivers, or receiving arrays, sometimes reinforce and cancel each other depending on their wavelength, in precise analogy to the visual interference.

The largest interelement or baseline separation distance of the antennas fixes the highest resolution possible, whereas the spatial distribution of measurement samples taken over the x,y plane determines the complexity of the structure that can be imaged. As developed by Ronald Bracewell and Sir Martin Ryle between 1947 and 1961, aperture synthesis in radio astronomy is based on the fact that the crosscorrelation, or mathematical similarity of shape of the signals recorded between two receiving elements i and j, is a measurement of total radio visibility. The brightness or luminosity distribution for distant radio sources whose radiation can be assumed to be spatially incoherent can be directly related to the observed interferometer fringe amplitude and phase. According to the Wiener-Khinchin theorem, the intensity measurement by a radio telescope is essentially the two-dimensional Fourier transform of the source radio distribution weighted by the antenna sensitivity pattern. Provided the data have been sufficiently well sampled in accordance with the Nyquist theorem, an image of the intensity of radio emission versus position can be constructed by the inverse Fourier transform.

The basic computations for processing long baseline interferometric radio telescope data are calculations of the crosscorrelation functions between, for example, the two data streams received from each end of a two-element baseline. The basic idea of employing a variable spacing radio interferometer to explore the then totally-unknown field of radio star diameters occurred almost simultaneously in groups at Jodrell Bank, Cambridge, and Sydney, Australia. The results were published in the English journal *Nature* in 1952. Motivated by this methodological approach, as well as by the need better to resolve localize and resolve 1C radio survey objects, Ryle and his coworkers in England, and W. N. Christiansen and B. Y. Mills in Australia, between 1951 and 1953, notably extended interferometry to multielement radio receiving antennas and arrays with movable elements. The mathematical principles were published by Bracewell and others between 1954 and 1960. In one astronomer's view (not held by all radio astronomers), it took more than a decade to move from the bare principles of very large Fourier aperture synthesis to constructing a full-scale working synthetic aperture receiver with a long movable baseline, notably the University of Cambridge's 1.6-kilometer radio telescope in 1960.

By 1960, many apparently double extragalactic radio objects had been found, almost all from measurements made by prototype interferometers employing increased baselines on the order of several tens of kilometers. As soon as adjacent radio telescopes were separated by more than this distance, however, the cables needed to connect them became prohibitively long and distorted interference patterns because of differential delays caused by differences in thermal expansion or contraction (despite the fact that the cables had been deeply buried underground). To overcome this transmission line problem, the signals from distant radio receivers encompassing a long baseline array were sent to a central base via radio links. In such a system, the radio signal received by one radio telescope is converted to a microwave signal. This converted signal is then transmitted from the original receiver to an antenna near the main station, and in turn controls signals from the other receivers. In this way, two or more radio telescopes could be joined despite separations of even a hundred kilometers or more. In 1960, Jodrell Bank successfully operated the first microwave-linked long baseline radio interferometers over distances of up to 85 kilometers. The U.S. Owens Valley movable paraboloid antennas had a larger baseline.

Notwithstanding these improvements, the variable effects of the earth's atmosphere on microwave transmissions on many occasions caused severe problems when baseline distances, or topographic or man-made obstacles, disrupted the transmission path between microwave links. Nevertheless, the availability of sophisticated digital recorders after the mid-1960's led to the conception and implementation of the first successful transcontinental baselines and eventually intercontinental interferometers. In both configurations, all radio telescopes encompassing the array were equipped with accurate recorders and accurately synchronized atomic clocks establishing a common time base. The first very long baseline interferometer (VLBI) was built in 1966 by the U.S. National Radio Astronomy Observatory (NRAO). In March, 1971, the NRAO Mark-II VLBI initiated operations with a much higher data throughput. The first astrophysical results using VLBI systems were published in the *Astronomical Journal* in 1971. In 1973, the so-called Gold-Stack VLBI was formed, by the combination of the 64-meter antenna of the Jet Propulsion Laboratories in Goldstone, California, and the similar Haystack antenna in Cambridge, Massachusetts. Many VLBI experiments were conducted with researchers from the United States and foreign institutes. Baselines stretching over more than 80 percent of the earth's diameter were soon synthesized, operating at the 3.5-centimeter radio wavelength that permits astronomers to measure radio source diameters as small as 0.0003 second of arc.

Impact of Event

The development of VLBI radio telescopes is an example of a more cumulative than localized scientific discovery. One of the problems in making distant extragalactic observations using intercontinental baselines was ensuring accurate time synchronization in view of logistic and political problems (for example, entering the pre-Glasnost Soviet Union with sophisticated black boxes of electronics). Much higher synchronization was obtained from joint monitoring of radio broadcast time signals such as WWV, and later from the LOng-RAnge-Navigation (LORAN C) system. With the emergence of wide-band satellite communication systems, the tape recording system can be replaced, since video signals from each antenna can be transmitted directly to the central processing center via satellite and correlated in real time.

Perhaps the main interest of radio astronomers developing VLBI arrays has been mapping of radio sources associated with distant galaxies. VLBI units provide a wide range of selectable and much finer resolutions, greater flexibility, and greater weak-signal detection capability. Many maps of extragalactic radio sources have been produced since the construction of the 27-movable unit Very Large Array (VLA) in New Mexico in 1977. Detailed mapping of the intensity and magnetic polarization structures associated with filaments or jets from extragalactic objects remains a major research objective. Related efforts have been undertaken for smaller structures associated with quasars. As was earlier believed, there are several classes of stars in our galaxy that also have observable radio emissions. One of the unique capabilities of VLBI systems is the possibility of making very short or snapshot observations. Snapshot mode makes it possible not only to record very short-lived features but also to map hundreds of strong sources in a single day. Even within the solar system, VLBI arrays have provided new data on the complex radiation belts and emissions surrounding Jupiter. VLBI radio astronomers have observed much deeper into the solar atmosphere than was previously possible, measuring, for example, the conditions leading to formation of major solar flares.

The first application of VLBI to very accurate satellite orbit measurements was conducted in 1969. Employing lunar-based radio transmitters, VLBI provided Irwin Shapiro with some of the first highly accurate measurements of the Moon's libration. In addition, ray-bending predictions of the theory of general relativity were confirmed by a similar method. VLBI observables are affected not only by the radio propagation properties of the atmosphere and outer space, timing clocks, and baseline sites but also by Earth's motions such as Earth tides, plate tectonics, and vertical orogenic/lift motions, and by Earth's speed variations in the rate of rotation, nutation, and precession. Important estimates of these geodetic and geophysical parameters can be obtained from analysis of VLBI observations, and since then, this work has continued. Since 1978, ground site velocities in California and elsewhere caused by continental drift have been measured using a mobile VLBI system.

Since the beginnings of radio astronomy in the 1930's with Karl Jansky's small mono-element radio telescope, angular resolution has progressively increased from tens of degrees to submillisecond of arc resolutions using very long baseline interferometry. Further increases in angular resolution, by extending the terrestrial baseline via antennas in space, are further developments in a long chain of improvements, all based in radio interferometry and the notion of movable baselines.

Bibliography

Bracewell, Ronald N. *The Fourier Transform and Its Applications.* 3d rev. ed. New York: McGraw-Hill, 1987. The principles and uses of the Fourier transform in image synthesis are discussed.

Brown, Robert Hanbury, and A. C. B. Lovell. *The Exploration of Space by Radio.* New York: John Wiley & Sons, 1958. A balanced and detailed account. Includes discussions of early English and Australian work.

Dudgeon, Dan E., and Russell M. Mersereau. *Multidimensional Digital Signal Processing.* Englewood Cliffs, N.J.: Prentice-Hall, 1984. Although somewhat advanced, it contains several tutorial sections on correlation, Fourier transforms, and aperture synthesis.

Kellerman, Kenneth L., and A. Richard Thompson. "The Very-Long Baseline Array." *Scientific American* 258 (January, 1988): 54-61. Gives a good general overview of the New Mexico VLA, related instruments, and ongoing observational work.

Mills, B. Y. "Apparent Angular Sizes of Discrete Radio Sources." *Nature* 170 (1952): 1063-1065. The primary reference for the initial radio interferometer having somewhat movable interelement separation.

Thompson, A. R., James M. Moran, and George W. Swenson, Jr. *Interferometry and Synthesis in Radio Astronomy.* New York: Wiley, 1986. The best overall account of movable interferometric aperture synthesis in radio astronomy. Balanced between methods and results.

Verschuur, G. L. *The Invisible Universe: The Story of Radio Astronomy.* Berlin: Springer-Verlag, 1974. A good general introduction focusing on European results in galactic radio astronomy.

Gerardo G. Tango

Cross-References

Einstein Completes His Theory of General Relativity (1915), p. 625; Jansky's Experiments Lead to the Founding of Radio Astronomy (1930), p. 934; Ryle's Radio Telescope Locates the First Known Radio Galaxy (1946), p. 1271; Franklin and Burke Discover Radio Emissions From Jupiter (1955), p. 1492; Ryle Constructs the First Radio Interferometer (1955), p. 1496; The Jodrell Bank Radio Telescope Is Completed (1957), p. 1539; Van Allen Discovers the Earth's Radiation Belts (1958), p. 1572; A Radio Astronomy Team Sends and Receives Radar Signals to and from the Sun (1959), p. 1598; Apollo 12 Retrieves Surveyor 3 Parts from the Lunar Surface (1969), p. 1913.

GREAT EVENTS
FROM
HISTORY II

CHRONOLOGICAL LIST OF EVENTS

VOLUME I

1888-1906 Ramón y Cajal Establishes the Neuron as the Functional
Unit of the Nervous System 1
1890-1901 Behring Discovers the Diphtheria Antitoxin 6
1891-1905 Strowger Invents the Automatic Dial Telephone 11
1897-1905 Abel and Takamine Independently Isolate Adrenaline 16
1897-1904 Bjerknes Publishes the First Weather Forecast Using
Computational Hydrodynamics 21
1898-1902 Teisserenc de Bort Discovers the Stratosphere and the
Troposphere 26
1898-1900 Hilbert Develops a Model for Euclidean Geometry in
Arithmetic 31
1899-1902 Lebesgue Develops a New Integration Theory 36

1900's   Einthoven Develops the Forerunner of the
Electrocardiogram 41
1900   Hopkins Discovers Tryptophan, an Essential Amino Acid 46
1900   Wiechert Invents the Inverted Pendulum Seismograph 51
1900-1901 Landsteiner Discovers Human Blood Groups 56
1900   De Vries and Associates Discover Mendel's Ignored
Studies of Inheritance 61
1900   Evans Discovers the Minoan Civilization on Crete 67
1900-1901 Reed Establishes That Yellow Fever Is Transmitted by
Mosquitoes 73
1900   Zeppelin Constructs the First Dirigible That Flies 78
1900   Planck Announces His Quantum Theory 83
1901   Booth Invents the Vacuum Cleaner 88
1901   Elster and Geitel Demonstrate Radioactivity in Rocks,
Springs, and Air 93
1901   First Synthetic Vat Dye, Indanthrene Blue, Is
Synthesized, The 98
1901   Grijns Proposes That Beriberi Is Caused by a Nutritional
Deficiency 103
1901   Hewitt Invents the Mercury Vapor Lamp 108
1901   Ivanov Develops Artificial Insemination 113
1901   Röntgen Wins the Nobel Prize for the Discovery of X Rays 118
1901-1904 Kipping Discovers Silicones 123
1901   Marconi Receives the First Transatlantic Telegraphic Radio
Transmission 128

1902   Carrel Develops a Technique for Rejoining Severed Blood
            Vessels 134
1902   Johnson Perfects the Process to Mass-Produce Disc
            Recordings 138
1902   Levi Recognizes the Axiom of Choice in Set Theory 143
1902   McClung Plays a Role in the Discovery of the Sex
            Chromosome 148
1902   Sutton States That Chromosomes Are Paired and Could Be
            Carriers of Hereditary Traits 153
1902   Zsigmondy Invents the Ultramicroscope 159
1902-1903   Pavlov Develops the Concept of Reinforcement 163
1902   French Expedition at Susa Discovers the Hammurabi
            Code, The 169
1902   Kennelly and Heaviside Propose the Existence of the
            Ionosphere 174
1902   Bayliss and Starling Discover Secretin and Establish the
            Role of Hormones 179
1902   Russell Discovers the "Great Paradox" Concerning the
            Set of All Sets 184
1903   Tsiolkovsky Proposes That Liquid Oxygen Be Used for
            Space Travel 189
1903-1904   Hale Establishes Mount Wilson Observatory 194
1903   Becquerel Wins the Nobel Prize for the Discovery of
            Natural Radioactivity 199
1903   Wright Brothers Launch the First Successful Airplane,
            The 203
1904   Elster and Geitel Devise the First Practical
            Photoelectric Cell 208
1904   Hartmann Discovers the First Evidence of Interstellar
            Matter 213
1904   Kapteyn Discovers Two Star Streams in the Galaxy 218
1904-1905   Gorgas Develops Effective Methods for Controlling
            Mosquitoes 223
1904-1907   Brouwer Develops Intuitionist Foundations of
            Mathematics 228
1904-1908   Zermelo Undertakes the First Comprehensive
            Axiomatization of Set Theory 233
1904-1912   Brandenberger Invents Cellophane 238
1904   Sherrington Delivers *The Integrative Action of the
            Nervous System* 243
1904   Construction Begins on the Panama Canal 249
1904   Fleming Files a Patent for the First Vacuum Tube 255
1905   Einstein Develops His Theory of the Photoelectric Effect 260

1905   Hertzsprung Notes the Relationship Between Color and
             Luminosity of Stars 265
1905   Punnett's *Mendelism* Contains a Diagram for Showing
             Heredity 270
1905-1906   Crile Performs the First Direct Blood Transfusion 275
1905-1907   Baekeland Invents Bakelite 280
1905-1907   Boltwood Uses Radioactivity to Obtain the Age of Rocks 285
1905   Lowell Predicts the Existence of Pluto 291
1905   Einstein States His Theory of Special Relativity:
             $E = mc^2$ 297
1906   Anschütz-Kaempfe Installs a Gyrocompass onto a German
             Battleship 303
1906   Barkla Discovers the Characteristic X Rays of the
             Elements 309
1906   Bateson and Punnett Observe Gene Linkage 314
1906   Cottrell Invents the Electrostatic Precipitation Process 320
1906   Fréchet Introduces the Concept of Abstract Space 325
1906   Hopkins Suggests That Food Contains Vitamins Essential
             to Life 330
1906   Markov Discovers the Theory of Linked Probabilities 335
1906, 1910   Oldham and Mohorovičić Determine the Structure of
             the Earth's Interior 340
1906-1913   Willstätter Discovers the Composition of Chlorophyll 345
1906   First German U-Boat Submarine Is Launched, The 350
1906   Thomson Wins the Nobel Prize for the Discovery of
             the Electron 356
1906   Fessenden Perfects Radio by Transmitting Music and
             Voice 361
1907   Haldane Develops Stage Decompression for Deep-Sea
             Divers 365
1907   Hertzsprung Describes Giant and Dwarf Stellar Divisions 370
1907   Louis and Auguste Lumière Develop Color Photography 375
1907   Harrison Observes the Development of Nerve Fibers in the
             Laboratory 380
1908   Haber Develops a Process for Extracting Nitrogen
             from the Air 385
1908   Hardy and Weinberg Present a Model of Population
             Genetics 390
1908   Hughes Revolutionizes Oil Well Drilling 396
1908   Steinmetz Warns of Pollution in *The Future of Electricity* 401
1908-1915   Morgan Develops the Gene-Chromosome Theory 407
1908   Geiger and Rutherford Develop the Geiger Counter 412
1908   Hale Discovers Strong Magnetic Fields in Sunspots 417

1908   Ehrlich and Metchnikoff Conduct Pioneering Research
         in Immunology 422
1908   Boule Reconstructs the First Neanderthal Skeleton 428
1909   Johannsen Coins the Terms "Gene," "Genotype," and
         "Phenotype," 433
1909   Study of Mathematical Fields by Steinitz Inaugurates
         Modern Abstract Algebra, The 438
1909   Millikan Conducts His Oil-Drop Experiment 443
1909   Blériot Makes the First Airplane Flight Across the
         English Channel 448

1910   Electric Washing Machine Is Introduced, The 453
1910   Rous Discovers That Some Cancers Are Caused by
         Viruses 459
1910   Russell and Whitehead's *Principia Mathematica* Develops
         the Logistic Movement in Mathematics 465

VOLUME II

1910   Thomson Confirms the Possibility of Isotopes 471
1910   Ehrlich Introduces Salvarsan as a Cure for Syphilis 476
1911   Boas Publishes *The Mind of Primitive Man* 481
1911   Sturtevant Produces the First Chromosome Map 486
1911   Bingham Discovers an Inca City in the Peruvian Jungle 491
1912   Leavitt's Study of Variable Stars Unlocks Galactic
          Distances 496
1912   Slipher Obtains the Spectrum of a Distant Galaxy 502
1912-1913 Bohr Writes a Trilogy on Atomic and Molecular Structure 507
1912-1914 Abel Develops the First Artificial Kidney 512
1912-1915 X-Ray Crystallography Is Developed by the Braggs 517
1912   Wegener Proposes the Theory of Continental Drift 522
1912   Rutherford Presents His Theory of the Atom 527
1912   Hess Discovers Cosmic Rays Through High-Altitude
          Ionizations 532
1913   Edison Introduces the Kinetophone to Show the First
          Talking Pictures 537
1913   Ford Produces Automobiles on a Moving Assembly Line 542
1913   Geothermal Power Is Produced for the First Time 547
1913   Gutenberg Discovers the Earth's Mantle-Outer Core
          Boundary 552
1913   Hertzsprung Uses Cepheid Variables to Calculate the
          Distances to Stars 557

1913   Salomon Develops Mammography 562
1913   Schick Introduces the Schick Test for Diphtheria 567
1913   Burton Introduces Thermal Cracking for Refining
        Petroleum 573
1913   Fabry Quantifies Ozone in the Upper Atmosphere 579
1913   Russell Announces His Theory of Stellar Evolution 585
1914   Rutherford Discovers the Proton 590
1915   First Transcontinental Telephone Call Is Made, The 595
1915   Fokker Aircraft Are the First Airplanes Equipped with
        Machine Guns, The 600
1915   Corning Glass Works Trademarks Pyrex and Offers
        Pyrex Cookware for Commercial Sale 605
1915-1916 McLean Discovers the Natural Anticoagulant Heparin 610
1915   Transatlantic Radiotelephony Is First Demonstrated 615
1915-1917 Langevin Develops Active Sonar for Submarine Detection
        and Fathometry 620
1915   Einstein Completes His Theory of General Relativity 625
1916   Schwarzschild Develops a Solution to the Equations
        of General Relativity 630
1917   Birdseye Develops Freezing as a Way of Preserving
        Foods 635
1917   Insecticide Use Intensifies When Arsenic Proves Effective
        Against the Boll Weevil 640
1917   Hale Oversees the Installation of the Hooker Telescope
        on Mount Wilson 645
1918   Noether Shows the Equivalence of Symmetry and
        Conservation 650
1918   Shapley Proves the Sun Is Distant from the Center
        of Our Galaxy 655
1919   Aston Builds the First Mass Spectrograph and Discovers
        Isotopes 660
1919   Mises Develops the Frequency Theory of Probability 664
1919   Principles of Shortwave Radio Communication Are
        Discovered, The 669
1919-1921 Bjerknes Discovers Fronts in Atmospheric Circulation 675
1919   Frisch Discovers That Bees Communicate Through Body
        Movements 679
1919   Einstein's Theory of Gravitation Is Confirmed over
        Newton's Theory 684

1920's Slipher Presents Evidence of Redshifts in Galactic Spectra 689
1920-1930 Millikan Names Cosmic Rays and Investigates Their
        Absorption 694

1920   Michelson Measures the Diameter of a Star 700
1921   Calmette and Guérin Develop the Tuberculosis
            Vaccine BCG 705
1921   Larson Constructs the First Modern Polygraph 711
1921   Noether Publishes the Theory of Ideals in Rings 716
1921-1923   Banting and Macleod Win the Nobel Prize for the
            Discovery of Insulin 720
1922   McCollum Names Vitamin D and Pioneers Its Use
            Against Rickets 725
1922   Carter Discovers the Tomb of Tutankhamen 730
1923   Andrews Discovers the First Fossilized Dinosaur Eggs 735
1923   De Broglie Introduces the Theory of Wave-Particle
            Duality 741
1923   Compton Discovers the Wavelength Change of Scattered
            X Rays 746
1923   Zworykin Develops an Early Type of Television 751
1923, 1951 Kahn Develops a Modified Syphilis Test and the Universal
            Serologic Test 756
1923   Zdansky Discovers Peking Man 761
1924   Hubble Determines the Distance to the Andromeda
            Nebula 766
1924   Steenbock Discovers That Sunlight Increases
            Vitamin D in Food 771
1924   Svedberg Develops the Ultracentrifuge 775
1924   Dart Discovers the First Recognized Australopithecine
            Fossil 780
1924   Eddington Formulates the Mass-Luminosity
            Law for Stars 785
1924   Hubble Demonstrates That Other Galaxies Are Independent
            Systems 790
1925   Whipple Finds Iron to Be an Important Constituent of
            Red Blood Cells 795
1925   Pauli Formulates the Exclusion Principle 800
1925-1927   German Meteor Expedition Discovers the Midatlantic
            Ridge, The 805
1926   Goddard Launches the First Liquid Fuel Propelled
            Rocket 810
1926   Eddington Publishes The Internal Constitution of the
            Stars 815
1926-1928   Warner Bros. Introduces Talking Motion Pictures 820
1927   Lemaître Proposes the Big Bang Theory 825
1927   Oort Proves the Spiral Structure of the Milky Way 830
1927   Heisenberg Articulates the Uncertainty Principle 835

1927	Lindbergh Makes the First Nonstop Solo Flight Across the Atlantic Ocean	841
1928	Bush Builds the First Differential Analyzer	846
1928	Gamow Explains Radioactive Alpha-Decay with Quantum Tunneling	851
1928-1932	Szent-Györgyi Discovers Vitamin C	857
1928	Papanicolaou Develops the Pap Test for Diagnosing Uterine Cancer	864
1928	Mead Publishes *Coming of Age in Samoa*	869
1928	Fleming Discovers Penicillin in Molds	873
1929	Hubble Confirms the Expanding Universe	878
1929	Schmidt Invents the Corrector for the Schmidt Camera and Telescope	884
1929	Berger Develops the Electroencephalogram (EEG)	890
1929	Drinker and Shaw Develop an Iron Lung Mechanical Respirator	895
1929-1931	Gödel Proves Incompleteness-Inconsistency for Formal Systems, Including Arithmetic	900
1930	Construction Begins on the Empire State Building	906
1930	Lyot Builds the Coronagraph for Telescopically Observing the Sun's Outer Atmosphere	911
1930	Midgley Introduces Dichlorodifluoromethane as a Refrigerant Gas	916
1930	Zinsser Develops an Immunization Against Typhus	921
1930-1931	Pauling Develops His Theory of the Chemical Bond	926
1930-1932	Jansky's Experiments Lead to the Founding of Radio Astronomy	934
1930-1935	Armstrong Perfects FM Radio	939
1930	Tombaugh Discovers Pluto	944
1931-1935	Chandrasekhar Calculates the Upper Limit of a White Dwarf Star's Mass	948

VOLUME III

1931	Lawrence Develops the Cyclotron	953
1931	Ruska Creates the First Electron Microscope	958
1931	Piccard Travels to the Stratosphere by Balloon	963
1932-1935	Domagk Discovers That a Sulfonamide Can Save Lives	968
1932	Chadwick Discovers the Neutron	973
1932	Cockcroft and Walton Split the Atom with a Particle Accelerator	978

1932   Anderson Discovers the Positron 983

1933-1934   Frédéric Joliot and Irène Joliot-Curie Develop the First
           Artificial Radioactive Element 987

1933   Fermi Proposes the Neutrino Theory of Beta Decay 992

1934   Benedict Publishes *Patterns of Culture* 997

1934   Cherenkov Discovers the Cherenkov Effect 1003

1934   Zwicky and Baade Propose Their Theory of Neutron
           Stars 1008

1934-1938   Carlson Invents Xerography 1013

1934   Beebe and Barton Set a Diving Record in a Bathysphere 1018

1934   Gibbon Develops the Heart-Lung Machine 1024

1934-1935   Yukawa Proposes the Existence of Mesons 1030

1935   Chapman Determines the Lunar Atmospheric Tide at
           Moderate Latitudes 1035

1935   Watson-Watt and Associates Develop the First Radar 1040

1935-1936   Turing Invents the Universal Turing Machine 1045

1935   Richter Develops a Scale for Measuring Earthquake
           Strength 1050

1935-1938   Carothers Patents Nylon 1055

1935   Moniz Develops Prefrontal Lobotomy 1060

1936   Lehmann Discovers the Earth's Inner Core 1065

1936   Müller Invents the Field Emission Microscope 1070

1936   Completion of Boulder Dam Creates Lake Mead, the
           World's Largest Reservoir, The 1075

1936   Fluorescent Lighting Is Introduced 1080

1937   Cerletti and Bini Develop Electroconvulsive Therapy for
           Treating Schizophrenia 1086

1937   Theiler Introduces a Vaccine Against Yellow Fever 1091

1937-1938   Weidenreich Reconstructs the Face of Peking Man 1096

1937   Segrè Identifies the First Artificial Element,
           Technetium 1101

1937   Krebs Describes the Citric Acid Cycle 1107

1937   Reber Builds the First Intentional Radio Telescope 1113

1938   Callendar Connects Industry with Increased Atmospheric
           Carbon Dioxide 1118

1938   Hofmann Synthesizes the Potent Psychedelic Drug
           LSD-25 1123

1938   Kapitsa Explains Superfluidity 1129

1938   Hahn Splits an Atom of Uranium 1135

1939   Bourbaki Group Publishes *Éléments de*
           mathématique, The 1140

1939   Müller Discovers That DDT Is a Potent Insecticide 1146

1939   Oppenheimer Calculates the Nature of Black Holes 1150

1940's   Secret English Team Develops Colossus, A 1155
1940's   Libby Introduces the Carbon-14 Method of Dating
          Ancient Objects 1160
1940   First Color Television Broadcast Takes Place, The 1166
1940   Florey and Chain Develop Penicillin as an Antibiotic 1171
1940   Seventeen-Thousand-Year-Old Paintings Are Discovered
          in Lascaux Cave 1176
1941   Seaborg and McMillan Make Element 94, Plutonium 1181
1941   First Jet Plane Using Whittle's Engine Is Flown, The 1187
1942-1947 Reber Makes the First Radio Maps of the Universe 1193
1942   Fermi Creates the First Controlled Nuclear Fission
          Chain Reaction 1198
1943-1944 Avery, MacLeod, and McCarty Determine That DNA
          Carries Hereditary Information 1203
1943-1944 Von Weizsäcker Finalizes His Quantitative Theory of
          Planetary Formation 1208
1943-1946 Eckert and Mauchly Develop the ENIAC 1213
1943   Cousteau and Gagnan Develop the Aqualung 1219
1943-1944 Waksman Discovers the Antibiotic Streptomycin 1224
1943   World's First Nuclear Reactor Is Activated, The 1230
1944   Germans Use the V-1 Flying Bomb and the V-2 Goes
          into Production, The 1235
1944-1949 Hodgkin Solves the Structure of Penicillin 1240
1944   Kuiper Discovers That Titan Has an Atmosphere 1245
1944   Blalock Performs the First "Blue Baby" Operation 1250
1945   Duggar Discovers Aureomycin, the First of the
          Tetracyclines 1255
1945   Artificial Fluoridation of Municipal Water Supplies to
          Prevent Dental Decay Is Introduced 1260
1945   First Atomic Bomb Is Successfully Detonated, The 1265
1946-1952 Ryle's Radio Telescope Locates the First Known
          Radio Galaxy 1271
1946   Schaefer Performs Cloud Seeding by Using Dry Ice 1276
1946   University of California Physicists Develop the
          First Synchrocyclotron 1282
1947   Gabor Develops the Basic Concept of Holography 1288
1947   Lamb and Retherford Discover the Lambshift 1293
1947   Archaeologists Unearth Ancient Scrolls 1298
1947   Shockley, Bardeen, and Brattain Discover the
          Transistor 1304
1948   Gamow and Associates Develop the Big Bang Theory 1309
1948   Jacobsen Introduces a Drug for the Treatment
          of Alcoholism 1314

1948 Steady-State Theory of the Universe Is Advanced by
   Bondi, Gold, and Hoyle, The 1320
1948 Hale Constructs the Largest Telescope of the Time 1325
1948 Land Invents a Camera/Film System That Develops
   Instant Pictures 1331
1949 X Rays from a Synchrotron Are First Used in Medical
   Diagnosis and Treatment 1336
1949 First Rocket with More than One Stage Is Created, The 1342
1949 First Electronic Stored-Program Computer (BINAC) Is
   Completed, The 1347

1950's Wilkins Discovers Reserpine, the First Tranquilizer 1353
1950's Li Isolates the Human Growth Hormone 1358
1950's Ochoa Creates Synthetic RNA 1363
1950 Artificial Sweetener Cyclamate Is Introduced, The 1368
1950 Boyd Defines Human Races by Blood Groups 1373
1950 Oort Postulates the Existence of the Oort Cloud 1379
1951 Hofstadter Discovers That Protons and Neutrons Each
   Have a Structure 1384
1951 Lipmann Discovers Acetyl Coenzyme A 1390
1951 UNIVAC I Becomes the First Commercial Electronic
   Computer and the First to Use Magnetic Tape 1396
1951-1952 Teller and Ulam Develop the First H-Bomb 1401
1951-1953 Watson and Crick Develop the Double-Helix Model
   for DNA 1406
1951-1954 Oort and Associates Construct a Map of the Milky Way 1414
1951 World's First Breeder Reactor Produces Electricity While
   Generating New Fuel, The 1419
1952 Aserinsky Discovers Rapid Eye Movement (REM) in
   Sleep and Dreams 1424

VOLUME IV

1952 Wilkins Introduces Reserpine for the Treatment of High
   Blood Pressure 1429
1952-1956 Müller Develops the Field Ion Microscope 1434
1952 Bevis Describes Amniocentesis as a Method for Disclosing
   Fetal Genetic Traits 1439
1952 Salk Develops a Polio Vaccine 1444
1952 Baade Corrects an Error in the Cepheid Luminosity Scale 1449
1953 De Vaucouleurs Identifies the Local Supercluster
   of Galaxies 1454

1953	Du Vigneaud Synthesizes Oxytocin, the First Peptide Hormone	1459
1953	Miller Reports the Synthesis of Amino Acids	1465
1953-1959	Liquid Bubble Chamber Is Developed, The	1470
1954-1957	Backus' IBM Team Develops the FORTRAN Computer Language	1475
1954	Barghoorn and Tyler Discover 2-Billion-Year-Old Microfossils	1481
1954	Bell Telephone Scientists Develop the Photovoltaic Cell	1487
1955	Franklin and Burke Discover Radio Emissions from Jupiter	1492
1955	Ryle Constructs the First Radio Interferometer	1496
1956	First Transatlantic Telephone Cable Is Put Into Operation, The	1502
1956	Heezen and Ewing Discover the Midoceanic Ridge	1508
1956	Birth Control Pills Are Tested in Puerto Rico	1512
1957	Isaacs and Lindenmann Discover Interferons	1517
1957	Sabin Develops an Oral Polio Vaccine	1522
1957	Sony Develops the Pocket-Sized Transistor Radio	1528
1957	Bardeen, Cooper, and Schrieffer Explain Superconductivity	1533
1957	Jodrell Bank Radio Telescope Is Completed, The	1539
1957	Sputnik 1, the First Artificial Satellite, Is Launched	1545
1957	Esaki Demonstrates Electron Tunneling in Semiconductors	1551
1957	United States Opens the First Commercial Nuclear Power Plant, The	1557
1958	Donald Is the First to Use Ultrasound to Examine Unborn Children	1562
1958	Sanger Wins the Nobel Prize for the Discovery of the Structure of Insulin	1567
1958	Van Allen Discovers the Earth's Radiation Belts	1572
1958	Parker Predicts the Existence of the Solar Wind	1577
1958	United States Launches Its First Orbiting Satellite, Explorer 1, The	1583
1959	Corroded Mechanism Is Recognized as an Ancient Astronomical Computer, A	1588
1959	Hopper Invents the Computer Language COBOL	1593
1959	Radio Astronomy Team Sends and Receives Radar Signals to and from the Sun, A	1598
1959	Leakey Finds a 1.75-Million-Year-Old Fossil Hominid	1603
1959	St. Lawrence Seaway Is Opened, The	1608

1959   Luna 2 Becomes the First Man-Made Object to Impact
            on the Moon 1614
1959   Luna 3 Provides the First Views of the Far Side of
            the Moon 1619

1960's   Anthropologists Claim That Ecuadorian Pottery Shows
            Transpacific Contact in 3000 b.c. 1624
1960's   Plastic IUD Is Introduced for Birth Control, The 1629
1960's   Sperry Discovers That Each Side of the Brain Can
            Function Independently 1635
1960   Mössbauer Effect Is Used in the Detection of
            Gravitational Redshifting, The 1640
1960   Scientists Develop a Technique to Date Ancient
            Obsidian 1645
1960-1962   Hess Concludes the Debate on Continental Drift 1650
1960-1969   Vaccine Is Developed for German Measles, A 1655
1960   Oró Detects the Formation of Adenine from
            Cyanide Solution 1662
1960   Tiros 1 Becomes the First Experimental Weather
            Reconnaissance Satellite 1667
1960   First Laser Is Developed in the United States, The 1672
1960   Echo, the First Passive Communications Satellite, Is
            Launched 1677
1961   Horsfall Announces That Cancer Results from
            Alterations in the DNA of Cells 1682
1961   Nirenberg Invents an Experimental Technique That
            Cracks the Genetic Code 1687
1961   Gagarin Becomes the First Human to Orbit Earth 1693
1961   Shepard Is the First United States Astronaut in Space 1698
1961   Calvin Wins the Nobel Prize for His Work on
            Photosynthesis 1703
1962   Giacconi and Associates Discover the First Known
            X-Ray Source Outside the Solar System 1708
1962   Lasers Are Used in Eye Surgery for the First Time 1714
1962-1967   Renfrew, Dixon, and Cann Reconstruct Ancient Near
            Eastern Trade Routes 1718
1962   Glenn Is the First American to Orbit Earth 1723
1962   Telstar, the First Commercial Communications Satellite,
            Relays Live Transatlantic Television Pictures 1728
1962-1963   Mariner 2 Becomes the First Spacecraft to Study Venus 1734
1962   Carson Publishes Silent Spring 1740
1963   Cassette for Recording and Playing Back Sound Is
            Introduced, The 1746

1963   Cohen Shows That Cantor's Continuum Hypothesis Is
            Independent of the Axioms of Set Theory 1751
1963   Schmidt Makes What Constitutes the First Recognition
            of a Quasar 1757
1963-1965   Penzias and Wilson Discover Cosmic Microwave
            Background Radiation 1762
1964   Quarks Are Postulated by Gell-Mann and Zweig 1767
1964-1965   Kemeny and Kurtz Develop the BASIC Computer
            Language 1772
1964-1965   Doell and Dalrymple Discover the Magnetic Reversals
            of Earth's Poles 1777
1964   Verrazano Bridge Opens, The 1782
1965   First Space Walk Is Conducted from Voskhod 2, The 1787
1965   Sealab 2 Expedition Concludes, The 1792
1965-1966   Venera 3 Is the First Spacecraft to Impact on
            Another Planet 1797
1965   Orbital Rendezvous of Gemini 6 and 7 Succeeds, The 1803
1966   Ardrey's *The Territorial Imperative* Argues That Humans
            Are Naturally Territorial 1808
1966   Simons Identifies a 30-Million-Year-Old Primate Skull 1814
1966   Soviet Luna 9 Makes the First Successful Lunar Soft
            Landing, The 1819
1966   Lunar Orbiter 1 Sends Back Photographs of the Moon's
            Surface, The 1825
1967   Davis Constructs a Solar Neutrino Detector 1830
1967   Favaloro Develops the Coronary Artery Bypass Operation 1835
1967   Manabe and Wetherald Warn of the Greenhouse Effect
            and Global Warming 1840
1967   Mandelbrot Develops Non-Euclidean Fractal Measures 1845
1967-1968   Barghoorn and Coworkers Find Amino Acids in
            3-Billion-Year-Old Rocks 1851
1967   Kornberg and Coworkers Synthesize Biologically
            Active DNA 1857
1967-1968   Bell Discovers Pulsars, the Key to Neutron Stars 1862
1967   Barnard Performs the First Human Heart Transplant 1866
1968   Friedman, Kendell, and Taylor Discover Quarks 1871
1968   *Glomar Challenger* Obtains Thousands of Ocean Floor
            Samples, The 1876
1968   Wheeler Names the Phenomenon "Black Holes," 1881
1969   Bubble Memory Devices Are Created for Use in
            Computers 1886
1969   Soyuz 4 and 5 Spacecraft Dock in Orbit, The 1891
1969-1970   First Jumbo Jet Service Is Introduced, The 1897

1969-1974   Very Long Baseline Interferometry (VLBI) Is Developed
            for High-Resolution Astronomy and Geodesy 1902

VOLUME V

1969   First Humans Land on the Moon, The 1907
1969   Apollo 12 Retrieves Surveyor 3 Parts from the
            Lunar Surface 1913
1969   Barton and Hassel Share the Nobel Prize for Determining the
            Three-Dimensional Shapes of Organic Compounds 1918

1970   Floppy Disk Is Introduced for Storing Data Used by
            Computers, The 1923
1970-1971   Lunokhod 1 Lands on the Moon 1928
1971   Direct Transoceanic Dialing Begins 1934
1971   Microprocessor "Computer on a Chip" Is Introduced, The 1938
1971-1972   Mariner 9 Is the First Known Spacecraft to Orbit
            Another Planet 1944
1971-1972   Mars 2 Is the First Spacecraft to Impact on Mars 1950
1972   Pioneer 10 Is Launched 1956
1972   Hounsfield Introduces a CAT Scanner That Can See
            Clearly into the Body 1961
1972   Gell-Mann Formulates the Theory of Quantum
            Chromodynamics (QCD) 1966
1972   Texas Instruments Introduces the First Commercial
            Pocket Calculator 1971
1972   Janowsky Publishes a Cholinergic-Adrenergic
            Hypothesis of Mania and Depression 1976
1972   United States Government Bans DDT Use to Protect
            the Environment, The 1982
1973   Cohen and Boyer Develop Recombinant DNA
            Technology 1987
1973-1974   Organic Molecules Are Discovered in Comet Kohoutek 1992
1973-1974   Skylab Inaugurates a New Era of Space Research 1997
1973-1975   Mariner 10 Is the First Mission to Use Gravitational
            Pull of One Planet to Help It Reach Another 2003
1973-1974   Rowland and Molina Theorize That Ozone Depletion Is
            Caused by Freon 2009
1974   Georgi and Glashow Develop the First Grand
            Unified Theory 2014
1974   Optical Pulses Shorter than One Trillionth of a Second
            Are Produced 2020

1974   Tunable, Continuous Wave Visible Lasers Are
Developed 2025

1974   J/psi Subatomic Particle Is Discovered, The 2031

1974   Anthropologists Discover "Lucy," an Early Hominid
Skeleton 2037

1975   Soviet Venera Spacecraft Transmit the First Pictures
from the Surface of Venus 2042

1976   Kibble Proposes the Theory of Cosmic Strings 2047

1976   Viking Spacecraft Send Photographs to Earth from the
Surface of Mars 2052

1977   Deep-Sea Hydrothermal Vents and New Life-Forms
Are Discovered 2058

1977   Heeger and MacDiarmid Discover That Iodine-Doped
Polyacetylene Conducts Electricity 2063

1977   Astronomers Discover the Rings of the Planet Uranus 2068

1977   Apple II Becomes the First Successful Preassembled
Personal Computer 2073

1977   First Commercial Test of Fiber-Optic Telecommunications
Is Conducted, The 2078

1977-1989 Voyager 1 and 2 Explore the Planets 2082

1977   Gruentzig Uses Percutaneous Transluminal Angioplasty, via
a Balloon Catheter, to Unclog Diseased Arteries 2088

1978-1981 Rohrer and Binnig Invent the Scanning Tunneling
Microscope 2093

1978   Brown Gives Birth to the First "Test-Tube" Baby 2099

1979   First Ring Around Jupiter Is Discovered, The 2104

1979   Ancient Sanctuary Is Discovered in El Juyo Cave,
Spain, An 2110

1980   Berg, Gilbert, and Sanger Develop Techniques for
Genetic Engineering 2115

1980   Evidence Is Found of a Worldwide Catastrophe at the End
of the Cretaceous Period 2120

1980   Inflationary Theory Solves Long-Standing Problems with
the Big Bang, The 2125

1980   Griess Constructs "the Monster," the Last Sporadic
Group 2130

1980   Von Klitzing Discovers the Quantized Hall Effect 2136

1980   Pluto Is Found to Possess a Thin Atmosphere 2141

1980   Radar Observations Show That Mayan Agricultural
Centers Are Surrounded by Canals 2145

1981   U.S. Centers for Disease Control Recognizes AIDS for the
First Time, The 2149

1981-1982 Human Growth Hormone Gene Transferred to a Mouse
Creates Giant Mice, A 2154

1981 Bell Laboratories Scientists Announce a Liquid-Junction
Solar Cell of 11.5 Percent Efficiency 2159

1981 Cassinelli and Associates Discover R136a, the Most
Massive Star Known 2164

1981 IBM Personal Computer, Using DOS, Is Introduced, The 2169

1981 Clewell Corrects Hydrocephalus by Surgery on a Fetus 2174

1981 *Columbia*'s Second Flight Proves the Practicality of the
Space Shuttle 2180

1982 Baulieu Develops RU-486, a Pill That Induces Abortion 2185

1982 Cech Demonstrates That RNA Can Act as an Enzyme 2190

1982 DeVries Implants the First Jarvik-7 Artificial Heart 2195

1982-1983 Compact Disc Players Are Introduced 2200

1982-1983 Daffos Uses Blood Taken Through the Umbilical Cord
to Diagnose Fetal Disease 2205

1982-1989 Astronomers Discover an Unusual Ring System of Planet
Neptune 2211

1982 Solar One, the Prototype Power Tower, Begins Operation 2216

1982 First Commercial Genetic Engineering Product, Humulin,
Is Marketed by Eli Lilly, The 2221

1983 Artificial Sweetener Aspartame Is Approved for Use in
Carbonated Beverages, The 2226

1983 Rubbia and van der Meer Isolate the Intermediate
Vector Bosons 2230

1983 First Successful Human Embryo Transfer Is
Performed, The 2235

1983 IBM Introduces a Personal Computer with a Standard
Hard Disk Drive 2240

1983 First Tracking and Data-Relay Satellite System Opens
a New Era in Space Communications, The 2245

1983 Murray and Szostak Create the First Artificial
Chromosome 2251

1983 Spacelab 1 Is Launched Aboard the Space Shuttle 2256

1984 Optical Disks for the Storage of Computer Data Are
Introduced 2262

1984 Sibley and Ahlquist Discover a Close Human and
Chimpanzee Genetic Relationship 2267

1984 Willadsen Clones Sheep Using a Simple Technique 2273

1984 Hominid Fossils Are Gathered in the Same Place for
Concentrated Study 2279

1985 British Antarctic Survey Confirms the First Known
Hole in the Ozone Layer, The 2285

1985 Construction of the World's Largest Telescope
  Begins in Hawaii 2291

1985 Jeffreys Discovers the Technique of Genetic
  Fingerprinting 2296

1985 Tevatron Particle Accelerator Begins Operation
  at Fermilab, The 2301

1986-1987 Tully Discovers the Pisces-Cetus Supercluster Complex 2306

1986 Bednorz and Müller Discover a High-Temperature
  Superconductor 2311

1986 First Permanently Manned Space Station Is
  Launched, The 2316

1986 Chernobyl Nuclear Reactor Explodes, The 2321

1986 Genetically Engineered Vaccine for Hepatitis B Is
  Approved for Use, A 2326

1986 Gene That Can Suppress the Cancer Retinoblastoma Is
  Discovered, A 2331

1986 Rutan and Yeager Pilot the *Voyager* Around the World
  Without Refueling 2336

1987-1988 Scientists Date a *Homo sapiens* Fossil at Ninety-two
  Thousand Years 2341

1987-1990 Search Continues for the Gene That Begins Male
  Development, The 2346

1987 Supernova 1987A Corroborates the Theories of Star
  Formation 2351

1987 Miller Discovers a Dinosaur Egg Containing the Oldest
  Known Embryo 2357

1988 Erlich Develops DNA Fingerprinting from a Single Hair 2362

1988 Oldest Known Galaxy Is Discovered, The 2367

1988 Superconducting Supercollider Is Under Construction in
  Texas, The 2372

1990 NASA Launches the Hubble Space Telescope 2377

1991 Medical Researchers Develop and Test Promising
  Drugs for the Treatment of AIDS Patients 2382